MAXWELL'S DEMON
ENTROPY, INFORMATION, COMPUTING

MAXWELL'S DEMON
ENTROPY, INFORMATION, COMPUTING

Edited by

Harvey S Leff
Physics Department,
California State Polytechnic University

and

Andrew F Rex
Physics Department,
University of Puget Sound

Adam Hilger
Bristol

British Library Cataloguing in Publication Data
Maxwell's demon.
1. Thermodynamics. Theories
I. Leff, H. S. II. Rex, A. F.
536.7

ISBN 0-7503-0056-6
ISBN 0-7503-0057-4 pbk

Published under the Adam Hilger imprint by IOP Publishing Ltd
Techno House, Redcliffe Way, Bristol BS1 6NX, England

Printed in Great Britain by J W Arrowsmith Ltd, Bristol

Contents

Preface

Most of us have had the experience (probably while waiting for an overdue flight) of wondering whether a particular scientific conference was worth a week of valuable research time. Yet scientists continue to attend these meetings, because every once in a while something very worthwhile will come out of one. The two of us met at the AAPT Summer meeting at Columbus in 1986. We both gave papers at a session on thermodynamics, and both papers included some mention of Maxwell's demon. That inspired a fruitful correspondence in which we explored our mutual interests in Maxwell's demon, exchanged bibliographies, and began the collaboration that resulted in this book.

We quickly discovered our mutual frustrations in trying to learn more about the demon. It[†] has appeared time and again in a wide range of scientific and technical publications since its invention by James Clerk Maxwell in 1867. Our demon is cat-like; several times it has jumped up and taken on a new character after being left for dead. This made our literature searches quite difficult. We found that there was no single source that explained the many faces of Maxwell's demon in any detail. The subject is treated inadequately (if at all) in the standard thermodynamics and statistical mechanics texts. As college teachers we were simply looking for a good example to illustrate the limitations and statistical character of the second law of thermodynamics. What we found was that Maxwell's demon does that and much, much more. But it is by no means simple.

Our motivation for putting together this collection was to spare other college teachers the difficult literature search we have done, so that they may easily communicate some understanding of the demon to their students. This is a worthy goal for a number of reasons. First and foremost it still serves Maxwell's original intention of demonstrating the statistical nature of the second law. In our experience students who have failed to appreciate the probabilistic arguments used to develop the laws of thermodynamics often show greater understanding of the role of probability and statistics after learning of Maxwell's demon. Those students who like to think for themselves are then forced to wonder whether Maxwell was correct and whether a demon could defeat the laws of thermodynamics to create a perpetual motion machine. It is then necessary to bring quantum theory into the picture to obtain at least partial relief from the conundrum. We are convinced that there is no teaching tool that shows the intimate connection between classical thermodynamics and quantum theory as well as Maxwell's demon. Although some of the more subtle arguments will be best understood by graduate students, many of these ideas would not be wasted on advanced undergraduates. Finally, students with some experience with computers can be shown the results of Landauer and Bennett, in which Maxwell's demon is related to the idea of dissipationless computing. The demon really has something for everyone, and that helps make it a very powerful teaching tool.

It is so powerful, in fact, that we should not limit its use to college and graduate students and their teachers. Because of the connection with computing just mentioned, researchers in computer science and information theory will benefit from the background this reprint book provides. We also believe that this book will provide useful background

---

[†] We assign the demon neuter characteristics, lest those of either gender feel slighted.

and references for scientists and engineers who work in thermodynamics. Biologists and psychologists will be able to appreciate many of the articles, particularly those relating the second law to life and the human mind. Last but certainly not least, there will be a wealth of information for those who study the history and philosophy of science. A subject that has occupied the minds of Maxwell, Thomson, Szilard, and other luminaries can scarcely be ignored by those trying to piece together the history of our discipline.

We have assembled this book in such a way that it should be useful to all of the interested parties just mentioned. Chapter 1 is an overview of the Maxwell's demon phenomenon. It is designed to familiarize the reader with the most important aspects of the demon. Chapter 1 is also intended to serve as a guide to Chapters 2–4, which contain the reprinted articles. In Chapter 2 the connection between the demon and the laws of thermodynamics is explored thoroughly. This leads unavoidably to a consideration of the role of quantum phenomena in thermodynamics, information gathering, and, ultimately, life processes. The papers reprinted in Chapter 3 focus more narrowly on the crucial question of how the demon gathers and stores information. These problems in information gathering and (more important, as it turns out) information erasure provide the basis for understanding the role of Maxwell's demon in the theory of computing (Chapter 4). We have selected these sentinel papers with the idea of exposing the reader to a wide scope of ideas and problems concerning the demon in its various guises. There are sufficient references in Chapters 1–4 to allow those with particular subject interests to proceed with more in depth studies. The chronological bibliography should be of use to the historians and to anyone else interested in better understanding the sequence of ideas as they have developed over the last century and a quarter. Those interested in seeing a fairly complete Maxwell's demon subject bibliography are referred to our American Journal of Physics resource letter[‡].

Although there is necessarily some variation in the level of difficulty of the reprinted articles, most of the material should be accessible to anyone who has had a good upper division course in statistical mechanics and thermodynamics. A few articles (particularly some in Chapter 2) are appropriate for anyone who has had at least an introductory physics course. Clearly this book is not a textbook, but it could be used as the primary resource for an advanced undergraduate, graduate, or faculty seminar.

Where then does Maxwell's demon stand today? What has it accomplished since it was conceived by Maxwell? It has certainly not achieved the demonic goal of circumventing the second law. If anything the second law is stronger for the challenge to it. The words of Eddington[§] serve as a sharp reminder to those who would imagine otherwise:

> The law that entropy always increases—the second law of thermodynamics—holds, I think, the supreme position among the laws of Nature. If someone points out to you that your pet theory of the universe is in disagreement with Maxwell's equations—then so much the worse for Maxwell's equations. If it is found to be contradicted by observation, well, these experimentalists do bungle things sometimes. But if your theory is found to be against the second law of thermodynamics I can give you no hope; there is nothing for it but to collapse in deepest humiliation.

In spite of that failure, the demon has brought us a host of new and exciting ideas unimagined by Maxwell. In that way this is a wonderful example of the scientific enterprise

---

[‡] Leff, H. S. and Rex, A. F., 'Resource Letter MD-1: Maxwell's demon,' *Am. J. Phys.* **58**, 201–209 (1990).

[§] Eddington, A. S., *The Nature of the Physical World* (Macmillan, New York, 1948), p. 74.

working as we believe it should, not toward any particular result but wherever the truth may lead.

We are indebted to James Revill of Adam Hilger and Edward Tenner of Princeton University Press for their strong support of this project. Thoughtful reviews of Chapter 1 by Rolf Landauer, Peter Landsberg, and Oliver Penrose led to significant improvements. We thank Arthur Fine for providing us with bibliographic information and are grateful for the receipt of camera-ready copies of articles from Charles Bennett, Edward Daub, Martin Klein, Rolf Landauer, Elihu Lubkin, Stefan Machlup, Jerome Rothstein, Myron Tribus, Alvin Weinberg, and Wojciech Zurek. One of us (HSL) thanks Paul Zilsel for sparking his curiosity in Maxwell's demon about 20 years ago and Alvin Weinberg for revitalizing that interest in 1982. The other author (AR) thanks Greg Shubert for several inspiring discussions in 1985. Finally, we acknowledge worthwhile communications on Maxwell's demon with many others too numerous to mention here. They have all helped shape this book.

Harvey Leff Pomona, California

Andrew Rex Tacoma, Washington

November, 1989

Acknowledgments and Copyright Information

We are grateful to the copyright holders listed below for granting permission to reprint materials that are the core of this book. Section numbers refer to the contents list.

2.1 'Kinetic theory of the dissipation of energy' by William Thomson. Reprinted by permission from *Nature* **IX**, 441–444 (1874). Read before the Royal Society of Edinburgh in 1874.

2.2 'Maxwell's demon' by E E Daub. Reprinted by permission from *Stud. Hist. Phil. Sci.* **1**, 213–27 (1970).

2.3 'Molecular forces, statistical representation and Maxwell's demon' by P M Heimann, Reprinted by permission from *Stud. Hist. Phil. Sci.* **1**, 189–211 (1970).

2.4 'Maxwell, his demon, and the second law of thermodynamics' by M J Klein. Reprinted by permission from *Am. Sci.* **58**, 84–97 (1970).

2.5 'Life, thermodynamics, and cybernetics' by L Brillouin. Reprinted by permission from *Am. Sci.* **37**, 554–68 (1949).

2.6 'Information, measurement, and quantum mechanics' by J Rothstein. Reprinted by permission from *Science* **114**, 171–175 (1951). Copyright 1951 by the AAAS.

2.7 'How subjective is entropy?' by K Denbigh. Reprinted by permission from *Chem. Brit.* **17**, 168–85 (1981).

2.8 'On the relation between information and energy systems: A family of Maxwell's demons' by A M Weinberg. This review was first published in *Interdisciplinary Sci. Rev.* **7**, 47–52 (1982) and is reproduced here by permission of J. W. Arrowsmith Ltd.

3.1 'On the decrease of entropy in a thermodynamic system by the intervention of intelligent beings,' by L Szilard. English translation by A Rapoport and M Knoller, Reprinted by permission from *Behavioral Science* **9**, 301–10 (1964).

3.2 'Maxwell's demon cannot operate: Information and entropy. I' by L Brillouin. Reprinted by permission from *J. Appl. Phys.* **22**, 334–7 (1951).

3.3 'The well-informed heat engine' by R C Raymond. Reprinted by permission from *Am. J. Phys.* **19**, 109–12 (1951).

3.4 'Well-informed heat engine: efficiency and maximum power' by C Finfgeld and S Machlup. Reprinted by permission from *Am. J. Phys.* **28**, 324–6 (1960).

3.5 'Some comments on entropy and information' by P Rodd. Reprinted by permission from *Am. J. Phys.* **32**, 333–5 (1964).

3.6 'Light and Information' by D Gabor. Reprinted in part (section 5 and Appendix IV) by permission from *Progress in Optics* **1**, 111–53 (1964).

3.7 'Entropy, information and Szilard's paradox' by J M Jauch and J G Báron. Reprinted by permission from *Helv. Phys. Acta* **45**, 220–32 (1972).

3.8 'Information theory and thermodynamics' by O Costa de Beauregard and M Tribus. Reprinted by permission from *Helv. Phys. Acta* **47**, 238–47 (1974).

3.9 'The operation of Maxwell's demon in a low entropy system' by A F Rex. Reprinted by permission from *Am. J. Phys.* **55**, 359–62 (1987).

4.1   'Irreversibility and heat generation in the computing process' by R Landauer. Reprinted by permission from *IBM J. Res. Dev.* **5**, 183–91 (1961). Copyright 1961, International Business Machine Corporation.

4.2   'Logical reversibility of computation' by C H Bennett. Reprinted by permission from *IBM J. Res. Dev.* **17**, 525–32 (1973). Copyright 1973, International Business Machine Corporation.

4.3   'Maxwell's demon and computation' by R Laing. Reprinted by permission from *Phil. Sci.* **41**, 171–8 (1974).

4.4   'The thermodynamics of computation—a review' by C H Bennett. Reprinted by permission from *Int. J. Theor. Phys.* **21**, 905–40 (1982).

4.5   'Maxwell's demon, Szilard's engine and quantum measurements' by W H Zurek, Reprinted by permission from *Frontiers of Nonequilibrium Statistical Physics*, ed G T Moore and M O Scully (Plenum Press, New York, 1984) pp 151–61.

4.6   'Computation: A fundamental physical view' by R Landauer. Reprinted by permission from *Phys. Scr.* **35**, 88–95 (1987).

4.7   'Keeping the entropy of measurement: Szilard revisited' by E Lubkin. Reprinted by permission from *Int. J. Theor. Phys.* **26**, 523–35 (1987).

4.8   'Notes on the history of reversible computation' by C H Bennett. Reprinted by permission from *IBM J. Res. Dev.* **32**, 16–23 (1988). Copyright 1988, International Business Machine Corporation.

The figures appearing in Chapter 1 have been reproduced from the following sources and we gratefully acknowledge the copyright holders.

Figure 1   *Cybernetics A to Z*, Pekelis, V., (Mir Publishers, Moscow, 1974), p. 106. Copyright 1974, Mir Publishers.

Figure 2   *Symbols, Signals and Noise*, Pierce, J. R., (Harper and Row Publishers, Inc., New York, 1961), p. 199.

Figures 3 and 4 From *Order and Chaos*, by Stanley W. Angiest and Loren G. Hepler. © 1967 by Basic Books, Inc. Reprinted by permission of Basic Books, Inc., Publishers, New York.

Figure 5   *Fundamentals of Cybernetics*, Lerner, A. Y., (Plenum Pub. Corp., New York, 1975), p. 257.

Figure 6   *On Maxwell's Demon*, Darling, L. and Hulbert, E. O., *Am. J. Phys.* **23**, 470 (1955).

Figure 7   Illustration from *Entropy for Biologists: An Introduction to Thermodynamics* by Harold J. Morowitz, copyright © 1970 by Harcourt Brace Jovanovich, Inc. Reprinted by permission of the publisher.

Figure 8   *Entropy and Energy levels*, Gasser, R. P. H. and Richards, W. G., (Clarendon Press, Oxford, 1974), pp. 117–118.

Figure 10   Adapted from Feyerabend, P. K., 'On the possibility of a perpetuum mobile of the second kind'. In *Mind, Matter and Method: Essays in Philosophy and Science in Honor of Herbert Feigl*, Feyerabend, P. K. and Maxwell, G., (University of Minnesota Press, Minneapolis, 1966), p. 411.

Figure 11   *Entropy, Information and Szilard's Paradox*, Jauch, J. M. and Baron, J. G., *Helv. Phys. Acta* **45**, 231 (1972).

Figure 12   'Generalized Entropy, Boundary Conditions, and Biology', Rothstein, J. In *The Maximum Entropy Formalism*, Levine, R. J. D. and Tribus, M., (The MIT Press, Cambridge, Mass., 1979), p. 467.

CHAPTER 1

Overview

Maxwell's demon ... *[after J C Maxwell, its hypothecator]:*
*'A hypothetical being of intelligence but molecular order of
size imagined to illustrate limitations of the second law of thermodynamics.' Webster's Third New International Dictionary*

1.1 Introduction

Maxwell's demon lives on. After more than 120 years of uncertain life and at least two pronouncements of death, this fanciful character seems more vibrant than ever. As the dictionary entry above shows, Maxwell's demon is no more than a simple idea. Yet it has challenged some of the best scientific minds, and its extensive literature spans thermodynamics, statistical physics, information theory, cybernetics, the limits of computing, biological sciences and the history and philosophy of science.

Despite this remarkable scope and the demon's longevity, coverage in standard physics, chemistry and biology textbooks typically ranges from cursory to nil. Because its primary literature is scattered throughout research journals, semipopular books, monographs on information theory and a variety of specialty books, Maxwell's demon is somewhat familiar to many but well known only to very few. Two *Scientific American* articles on the demon (Ehrenberg 1967, Bennett 1987) have been helpful, but they only scratch the surface of the existing literature. The main purpose of this reprint collection is to place in one volume: (1) important original papers covering Maxwell's demon, (2) an overview of the demon's life and current status, and (3) an annotated bibliography that provides perspective on the demon plus a rich trail of citations for further study.

The life of Maxwell's demon can be viewed usefully in terms of three major phases. The first phase covers the period from its 'birth' in approximately 1867, through the first 62 years of its relatively quiet existence. The flavour of the early history is reflected in Thomson's classic paper on the dissipation of energy (Article 2.1). The second phase began in 1929 with an important paper by Leo Szilard (Article 3.1). The entry on Szilard in Scribner's *Dictionary of Scientific Biography* cites his '... famous paper of 1929, which established the connection between entropy and information, and foreshadowed modern cybernetic theory.' Notably, Szilard discovered the idea of a 'bit' of information, now central in computer science. His discovery seems to have been independent of earlier identifications of logarithmic forms for information by Nyquist (1924) and Hartley (1928). The term 'bit' (= binary digit) was suggested approximately 15 years after Szilard's work by John Tukey. The history of the demon during the first two phases is described by Daub (Article 2.2), Heimann (Article 2.3) and Klein (Article 2.4).

After a hiatus of about 20 years, Leon Brillouin (Article 2.5) became involved in the Maxwell's demon puzzle through his interest in finding a scientific framework in which to explain intelligent life. Subsequently Brillouin (Article 3.2) and Dennis Gabor (Article 3.6) extended Szilard's work, focusing on the demon's acquisition of information. Rothstein formulated fundamental information-theoretic interpretations of thermodynamics, measurement, and quantum theory (Article 2.6). Both Brillouin and Gabor assumed the use of light signals in the demon's attempt to defeat the second law of thermodynamics. The result was a proclaimed 'exorcism' of Maxwell's demon, based upon the edict that information acquisition is dissipative, making it impossible for a demon to violate the second law of thermodynamics.

In 1951, independently of Brillouin, Raymond published an account (Article 3.3) of a clever variant of Maxwell's demon that did not explicitly entail light signals—a 'well-informed heat engine' using density fluctuations in a gas. Raymond found that 'an outside observer creates in the system a negative information entropy equal to the negative entropy change involved in the operation of the engine.' His work, though less influential than Brillouin's, also made the important connection between information and entropy. Finfgeld and Machlup (Article 3.4) analyzed Raymond's model further, assuming that the necessary demon uses light signals, and also obtained an estimate of its power output.

The impact of Brillouin's and Szilard's work has been far-reaching, inspiring numerous subsequent investigations of Maxwell's demon. Clarifications and extensions of Brillouin's work by Rodd (Article 3.5) and Rex (Article 3.9) are reprinted here. Weinberg broadened the demon's realm to include 'macroscopic' and 'social' demons (Article 2.8). Despite some critical assessments (Articles 2.7, 3.7 and 3.8) of the connections between information and entropy, those linkages and applications to the Maxwell's demon puzzle remain firmly entrenched in the scientific literature and culture.

The third phase of the demon's life began at age 94 in 1961 when Rolf Landauer made the important discovery (Article 4.1) that memory erasure in computers feeds entropy to the environment. Landauer referred to Brillouin's argument that measurement requires a dissipation of order kT, and observed: 'The computing process ... is closely akin to a measurement.' He also noted that: '... the arguments dealing with the measurement process do not define measurement very well, and avoid the very essential question: When is a system A coupled to a system B performing a measurement? The mere fact that two physical systems are coupled does not in itself require dissipation.'

Landauer's work inspired Charles Bennett to investigate logically reversible computation, which led to Bennett's important 1973 demonstration (Article 4.2) that reversible computation, which avoids erasure of information, is possible in principle. The direct link between Landauer's and Bennett's work on computation and Maxwell's demon came in 1982 with Bennett's observation (Article 4.4) that a demon 'remembers' the information it obtains, much as a computer records data in its memory. Bennett argued that erasure of a demon's memory is the fundamental act that saves the second law. This was a surprising, remarkable event in the history of Maxwell's demon. Subsequent analyses of memory erasure for a quantum mechanical Szilard's model by Zurek (Article 4.5) and Lubkin (Article 4.7) support Bennett's finding.

A key point in Bennett's work is that, in general, the use of light signals for information acquisition can be avoided. That is, although such dissipative information gathering is sufficient to save the second law of thermodynamics, it is not necessary. Bennett's argument nullifies Brillouin's 'exorcism', which was so ardently believed by a generation of scientists. The association of the Maxwell's demon puzzle with computation greatly expanded the audience for the demon, and writings by Bennett (Articles 4.4 and 4.8), Landauer (Article 4.6), and Laing (Article 4.3) illustrating that association are reprinted here.

These three phases of the life of Maxwell's demon are described in further detail in Sections 1.2–1.5. Section 1.6 deals with aspects of the demon not treated in the earlier sections. Chapters 2–4 contain reprinted articles covering, respectively: historical and philosophical considerations; information acquisition; and information erasure and computing. This is followed by a chronological bibliography, with selected annotations and quotations that provide a colourful perspective on the substantial impacts of Maxwell's demon. An alphabetical bibliography plus an extensive index is also included.

1.2 The Demon and its Properties

1.2.1 Birth of the Demon

The demon was introduced to a public audience by James Clerk Maxwell in his 1871 book,

Theory of Heat. It came near the book's end in a section called 'Limitation of The Second Law of Thermodynamics'. In one of the most heavily quoted passages in physics, Maxwell wrote:

> Before I conclude, I wish to direct attention to an aspect of the molecular theory which deserves consideration.
>
> One of the best established facts in thermodynamics is that it is impossible in a system enclosed in an envelope which permits neither change of volume nor passage of heat, and in which both the temperature and the pressure are everywhere the same, to produce any inequality of temperature or of pressure without the expenditure of work. This is the second law of thermodynamics, and it is undoubtedly true as long as we can deal with bodies only in mass, and have no power of perceiving or handling the separate molecules of which they are made up. But if we conceive a being whose faculties are so sharpened that he can follow every molecule in its course, such a being, whose attributes are still as essentially finite as our own, would be able to do what is at present impossible to us. For we have seen that the molecules in a vessel full of air at uniform temperature are moving with velocities by no means uniform, though the mean velocity of any great number of them, arbitrarily selected, is almost exactly uniform. Now let us suppose that such a vessel is divided into two portions, A and B, by a division in which there is a small hole, and that a being, who can see the individual molecules, opens and closes this hole, so as to allow only the swifter molecules to pass from A to B, and only the slower ones to pass from B to A. He will thus, without expenditure of work, raise the temperature of B and lower that of A, in contradiction to the second law of thermodynamics.
>
> This is only one of the instances in which conclusions which we have drawn from our experience of bodies consisting of an immense number of molecules may be found not to be applicable to the more delicate observations and experiments which we may suppose made by one who can perceive and handle the individual molecules which we deal with only in large masses.
>
> In dealing with masses of matter, while we do not perceive the individual molecules, we are compelled to adopt what I have described as the statistical method of calculation, and to abandon the strict dynamical method, in which we follow every motion by the calculus.

Maxwell's thought experiment dramatized the fact that the second law is a statistical principle that holds almost all the time for a system composed of many molecules. That is, there is a non-zero probability that anisotropic molecular transfers, similar to those accomplished by the demon, will occur if the hole is simply left open for a while.

Maxwell had introduced this idea in a 1867 letter to Peter Guthrie Tait (Knott 1911) '... to pick a hole' in the second law. There he specified more detail about the sorting strategy intended for the demon:

> Let him first observe the molecules in A and when he sees one coming the square of whose velocity is less than the mean sq. vel. of the molecules in B let him open the hole and let it go into B. Next let him watch for a molecule of B, the square of whose velocity is greater than the mean sq. vel. in A, and when it comes to the hole let him draw the slide and let it go into A, keeping the slide shut for all other molecules.

This allows a molecule to pass from A to B if its kinetic energy is less than the average molecular kinetic energy in B. Passage from B to A is allowed only for molecules whose kinetic energies exceed the average kinetic energy/molecule in A. In the same letter Maxwell emphasized the quality of 'intelligence' possessed by the demon:

> Then the number of molecules in A and B are the same as at first, but the energy in A is increased and that in B diminished, that is, the hot system has got hotter and the cold colder and yet no work has been done, only the intelligence of a very observant and neat-fingered being has been employed.

William Thomson (1874, Article 2.1) subsequently nicknamed Maxwell's imaginary being 'Maxwell's intelligent demon'. He apparently did not envisage the creature as malicious: 'The definition of a demon, according to the use of this word by Maxwell, is an intelligent being endowed with free-will and fine enough tactile and perceptive organization to give him the faculty of observing and influencing individual molecules of matter.' He expounded further on his view of 'the sorting demon of Maxwell' (Thomson 1879):

> The word 'demon', which originally in Greek meant a supernatural being, has never been properly used to signify a real or ideal personification of malignity.
>   Clerk Maxwell's 'demon' is a creature of imagination having certain perfectly well defined powers of action, purely mechanical in their character, invented to help us to understand the 'Dissipation of Energy' in nature.
>   He is a being with no preternatural qualities and differs from real living animals only in extreme smallness and agility. ... He cannot create or annul energy; but just as a living animal does, he can store up limited quantities of energy , and reproduce them at will. By operating selectively on individual atoms he can reverse the natural dissipation of energy, can cause one-half of a closed jar of air, or of a bar of iron, to become glowingly hot and the other ice cold; can direct the energy of the moving molecules of a basin of water to throw the water up to a height and leave it there proportionately cooled. . . ; can 'sort' the molecules in a solution of salt or in a mixture of two gases, so as to reverse the natural process of diffusion, and produce concentration of the solution in one portion of the water, leaving pure water in the remainder of the space occupied; or, in the other case separate the gases into different parts of the containing vessel.
>   'Dissipation of Energy' follows in nature from the fortuitous concourse of atoms. The lost motivity is essentially not restorable otherwise than by an agency dealing with individual atoms; and the mode of dealing with the atoms to restore motivity is essentially a process of assortment, sending this way all of one kind or class, that way all of another kind or class.

Following Thomson's introduction of the term 'demon', Maxwell clarified his view of the demon (quoted in Knott 1911) in an undated letter to Tait:

> Concerning Demons.
>   1. Who gave them this name? Thomson.
>   2. What were they by nature? Very small BUT lively beings incapable of doing work but able to open and shut valves which move without friction or inertia.
>   3. What was their chief end? To show that the 2nd Law of Thermodynamics has only a statistical certainty.

4. Is the production of an inequality of temperature their only occupation? No, for less intelligent demons can produce a difference in pressure as
well as temperature by merely allowing all particles going in one direction
while stopping all those going the other way. This reduces the demon to a
valve. As such value him. Call him no more a demon but a valve like that
of the hydraulic ram, suppose.

In light of Maxwell's intentions, it is interesting to examine the accuracy of dictionary
definitions. The *Webster's Third New International Dictionary* definition quoted at the
beginning of this chapter, though brief, properly cites Maxwell's intention to 'illustrate
limitations of the second law of thermodynamics.'

In contrast, *The Random House Dictionary of the English Language* (Second Edition
1988) contains the definition:

A hypothetical agent or device of arbitrarily small mass that is considered
to admit or block selectively the passage of individual molecules from one
compartment to another according to their speed, constituting a violation
of the second law of thermodynamics.

And the second edition (1989) of *The Oxford English Dictionary* describes it in the
entry for James Clerk Maxwell:

... a being imagined by Maxwell as allowing only fast-moving molecules to
pass through a hole in one direction and only slow-moving ones in the other
direction, so that if the hole is in a partition dividing a gas-filled vessel into
two parts one side becomes warmer and the other cooler, in contradiction
to the second law of thermodynamics.

Despite the emphasis on violating rather than illustrating limitations of the second
law in these two definitions, there is no indication that Maxwell intended his hypothetical
character to be a serious challenge to that law. Nevertheless, the latter two definitions reflect
the interpretation by many subsequent researchers that Maxwell's demon was a puzzle that
must be solved: If such a demon cannot defeat the second law, then why not? And if it *can*
defeat the second law, then how does that affect that law's status?

Maxwell did not relate his mental construction to entropy. In fact, he evidently mis-
understood the Clausius definition of entropy and went out of his way to adopt a *different*
definition in early editions of his *Theory of Heat*. He wrote: 'Clausius has called the remainder of the energy, which cannot be converted into work, the Entropy of the system.
We shall find it more convenient to adopt the suggestion of Professor Tait, and give the
name of Entropy to the part which can be converted into mechanical work.' He then argued
that entropy *decreases* during spontaneous processes. Later Maxwell recanted: 'In former
editions of this book the meaning of the term Entropy, as introduced by Clausius, was
erroneously stated to be that part of the energy which cannot be converted into work. The
book then proceeded to use the term as equivalent to the available energy; thus introducing
great confusion into the language of thermodynamics.'

Maxwell's discomfort and confusion with entropy is ironic, for his demon has had a
profound effect on the way entropy is viewed. In particular, Maxwell's demon led to an
important linkage between entropy and information. Unfortunately, Maxwell did not live
long enough to see this outgrowth of his thought experiment. It is also noteworthy that
his originally adopted definition of entropy gave rise to a function that decreases during

spontaneous processes. Many years later, Brillouin found it useful for interpretive purposes to define a function, negentropy (= −entropy), with this property (see Section 1.4 for more on negentropy).

1.2.2 Temperature and Pressure Demons

Maxwell's specification of the demon was brief enough to leave considerable room for interpretation. As envisioned, his creature was a temperature-demon that acts within a thermally isolated system of which it is an integral part. Its task was to generate a temperature difference without performing work on the gas. In effect this is the equivalent of producing heat flow from a lower to a higher temperature with no other effect, in conflict with the Clausius form of the second law.

In his later clarification (recall 'Concerning demons' in Section 1.2.1), Maxwell recognized that 'less intelligent' demons could generate differences in pressure. The first detailed investigation of a pressure-demon was by Leo Szilard in 1929 (Article 3.1). Szilard's work is discussed further in Section 1.3. A pressure-demon operates in a system linked to a constant-temperature reservoir, with the sole net effect of converting energy transferred as heat from that reservoir to work on an external object, in conflict with the Kelvin–Planck form of the second law. The 'Maxwell's demon puzzle' is to show why neither a temperature- nor pressure-demon can operate outside the limits imposed by the second law of thermodynamics.

1.2.3 Depictions of the Demon

Maxwell described his proposed being as 'small'. The dictionary definitions above suggest 'molecular' or 'arbitrarily small' size. Various authors have included cartoon depictions of Maxwell's demon with their writings. Figures 1–8 illustrate some of the ways the demon has been portrayed. Figure 1 (Pekelis 1974) is in accord with Maxwell's view that the demon is nothing more than a valve, but does not show any control mechanism. Figures 2 (Pierce 1961) and 3 (Angrist and Hepler 1967) show characters operating trap doors manually from within one of the chambers, but without any obvious means of detecting molecules. Figure 4 (Angrist and Hepler 1967) shows the demon wearing a helmet with a built-in light source. Figure 5 (Lerner 1975) shows a satanic character with a flashlight, operating a shutter from inside one of the chambers.

Figure 6 (Darling and Hulburt, 1955) shows the demon *outside* the two chambers. Figure 7 (Morowitz 1970) depicts a pressure demon controlling a shutter between two chambers that are in contact with a constant-temperature heat bath. Figure 8 (Gasser and Richards 1974) shows yet another view of an external demon, here operating a valve, allowing one species of a two-component gas (hot and cold) through a partition separating the gas from an initially evacuated chamber. Only fast molecules are allowed through, resulting in a cold gas in one chamber and a hot gas in the other.

These cartoons depict the demon as being relatively large compared to the shutter, sometimes with a light source to detect molecules, and sometimes located outside the system. Placing a temperature-demon outside the gas is questionable because of the need for thermal isolation. Depictions with a light source are not surprising in view of Maxwell's specification of a 'being who can see the individual molecules.' Because his intent was to

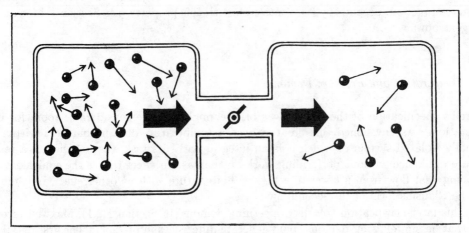

Figure 1

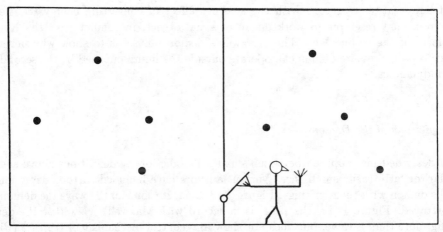

Figure 2

dramatize the statistical nature of the second law rather than to exorcise the demon, Maxwell had no reason to address the question of whether a demon could detect molecules by any means other than vision.

1.2.4 Means of Detection

Leon Brillouin (Article 3.2), closely following the work of Pierre Demers (1944, 1945), took Maxwell's specification of 'seeing' molecules seriously and assumed the use of light signals. Dennis Gabor (Article 3.6) did the same, apparently independently. Others have considered detecting molecules via their magnetic moments (Bennett, Article 4.4), Doppler-shifted radiation (Denur 1981, Chardin 1984, Motz 1983), van der Waals forces, and even via purely mechanical means (Bennett 1987). The prevailing modern view is that one must not prejudice the demon's operation by assuming the use of light signals, for that is too restrictive. The fundamental question is whether measurement in general is necessarily irreversible.

Figure 3

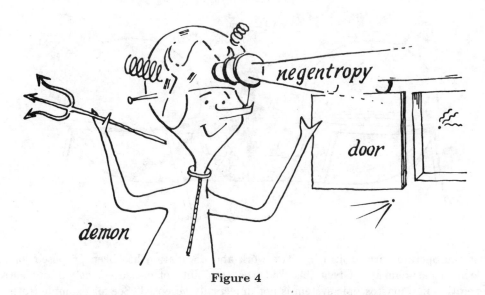

Figure 4

The clever mechanical detector proposed by Bennett in the context of Szilard's 1929 model suggests that, in principle, the presence of a molecule can be detected with arbitrarily little work and dissipation. Bennett's scheme is compelling, but is limited to a one-molecule gas. The general question of whether measurement in a many-particle gas must be irreversible lacks a correspondingly compelling answer. Maxwell's original temperature-demon must distinguish between molecular velocities among numerous molecules, a more complex task than detecting the presence of a single molecule. To our knowledge no specific device

Figure 5

Maxwell's demon at work

Figure 6

that can operate with arbitrarily little work and dissipation has been proposed for such velocity measurements. Given this void, the possibility of measurement without entropy generation in a macroscopic system is not universally accepted. See for example Rothstein (1988); Porod *et al* (1984) and responses thereto.

1.2.5 Thermal Equilibrium and Fluctuations

The demon must be in thermal equilibrium with the gas in which it resides, or irreversible heat transfer between gas and demon would occur, clouding the basic puzzle. As

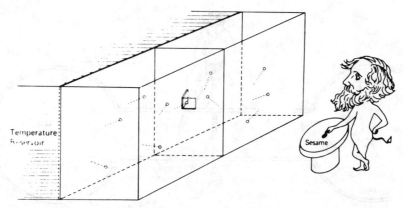

A Maxwell demon controlling a door between two chambers
each initially at temperature T_1 and pressure P_1

Figure 7

a temperature-demon generates a temperature gradient within a gas, its own temperature
presumably changes with its host gas. The heat capacity of a 'small' demon is presumably
much less than that of the gas, and its temperature can vary with that of the gas via negligibly small energy exchanges. Except for the receipt of light signals, energy exchanges with
the demon are usually neglected.

A demon that continually receives energy input via light signals (or other means)
must eventually experience a temperature rise unless it transfers heat to its surroundings.
Additionally, if a torch is used to generate light signals, photons that miss the demon
will heat up the gas and/or container walls. Such phenomena threaten the assumption
of constant-temperature operation, and most treatments of Maxwell's temperature-demon
ignore these details. Of course such photons could heat one chamber directly, with no need
for a demon—a phenomenon for which there is obviously no challenge to the second law.

Located within a gas, a Maxwell's demon is continually bombarded by gas molecules
and by photons from the blackbody radiation field within the container. It can be jostled
around by this bombardment, impeding the accuracy of its measuring activities. Long ago
it was pointed out (Smoluchowski 1912, 1914) that thermal fluctuations would prevent an
automatic device from operating successfully as a Maxwell's demon. A modern discussion
of Smoluchowski's ideas was given by Richard Feynman (1963), who compared Maxwell's
demon with a ratchet and pawl and an electrical rectifier, neither of which can systematically
transform internal energy from a single reservoir to work. He wrote: 'If we assume that the
specific heat of the demon is not infinite, it must heat up. It has but a finite number of
internal gears and wheels, so it cannot get rid of the extra heat that it gets from observing
the molecules. Soon it is shaking from Brownian motion so much that it cannot tell whether
it is coming or going, much less whether the molecules are coming or going, so it does not
work.'

If a demon heats up, periodic dumping of energy to an external reservoir is needed to
keep its temperature approximately equal to the temperature of the gas in which it resides.
For a temperature-demon this violates assumed thermal isolation, and the 'system' must
be expanded to be demon, gas and external reservoir. Of course, feeding entropy to the
reservoir helps to keep the second law intact.

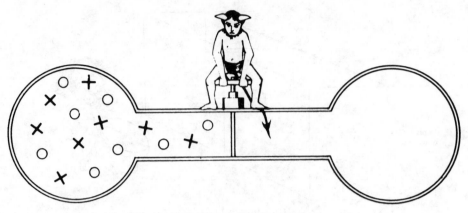

Maxwell's Demon

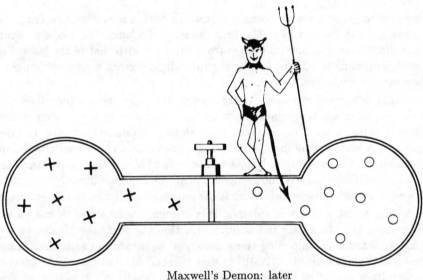

Maxwell's Demon: later
Figure 8

Smoluchowski's observation regarding thermal fluctuations suggested that Maxwell's demon ought to be buried and forgotten. But that did not happen, apparently because Smoluchowski left open the possibility that somehow, a perpetual motion machine operated by an *intelligent* being might be achievable. It was the fascinating idea of using intelligence that captured Leo Szilard's interest.

1.2.6 Intelligence

The demon must have sufficient 'intelligence' to discern fast from slow molecules, right-moving from left-moving molecules, or (in Szilard's model) simply the presence or non-presence of a molecule. In normal parlance intelligence is considered to include, among other things, ability to learn, reason and understand relationships. But none of these seems to be required by Maxwell's demon. One feature associated with intelligence that *is* needed by a demon is memory: it must 'remember' what it measures, even if only briefly. Indeed without somehow recording a result, one can argue that a measurement has not been completed.

Despite his title 'The decrease of entropy by intelligent beings' of his classic 1929 paper, Leo Szilard wrote that physics is not capable of properly accounting for the biological phenomena associated with human intervention. Szilard asserted that 'As long as we allow intelligent beings to perform the intervention, a direct test (of the second law) is not possible. But we can try to describe simple nonliving devices that effect such coupling, and see if indeed entropy is generated and in what quantity.' In 1929, prior to the development of solid state electronics, that was a fanciful thought.

If the demon were an automaton, it would perform pre-programmed functions upon receipt of certain well-defined signals. Evidently a Maxwell's demon need not be any more intelligent than an electronic computing machine connected to some type of transducer that detects molecular phenomena and puts out electrical signals signifying detection. Certainly it need not possess human intelligence. The concept of Maxwell's demon as a computer automaton was explored by Laing (1974, Article 4.3) who, unfortunately, was unaware of Landauer's important 1961 finding (Article 4.1) that memory erasure in computers feeds entropy to the environment.

In recent years some researchers have investigated the feasibility of quantum mechanical computers that operate via changes in the states of individual atoms. Feynman (1986) wrote '... we are going to be even more ridiculous later and consider bits written on one atom instead of the present 10^{11} atoms. Such nonsense is very entertaining to professors like me. I hope you will find it interesting and entertaining also ... it seems that the laws of physics present no barrier to reducing the size of computers until bits are the size of atoms, and quantum behavior holds dominant sway.' This suggests the possibility of Maxwell's demon being a quantum automaton of microscopic size, if such a microscopic demon could avoid devastation from fluctuations.

1.2.7 Interplay Between the First and Second Laws

Before continuing with the demon's history, it is helpful to examine implications of the first and second laws of thermodynamics on its actions. Consider first a temperature-demon that sorts molecules, lowering the entropy of a gas without altering its energy. The term 'demon' here includes any peripheral equipment used to effect sorting. What do the first and second laws of thermodynamics imply? Because the demon–gas system is energetically isolated, the second law requires the demon's entropy to increase at least as much as the gas entropy decreases during sorting. The first law implies that a temperature-demon's energy is unchanged by sorting because the gas and gas–demon system energies are both fixed. Thus, the demon's entropy must increase at fixed energy.

Can the demon be returned to its initial state without disturbing the gas? Such 're-setting' of the demon is desirable for two reasons. First, if the demon is to operate repeatedly, its entropy cannot be allowed to increase indefinitely or it will ultimately become too 'disordered' and unable to operate (see Section 1.2.5). Second, resetting simplifies the thermodynamic analysis, which can focus on the gas and its environment, without regard for the demon's details. Resetting the demon requires an exchange of energy with other objects. For example, the demon's excess entropy might be dumped by heat transfer to a reservoir, with an external work source subsequently increasing the demon's energy at constant entropy, returning it to its initial state.

Evidently the first and second laws assure that: (1) a temperature-demon cannot sort molecules without increasing its entropy, (2) the demon cannot return to its initial state without external energy exchanges, and (3) the combination of sorting and resetting generates an energy transfer from an energy source to a reservoir.

Next consider a pressure-demon, operating a cyclic process in a constant-temperature ideal gas. Contact with a thermal reservoir assures that the temperature will be constant. Initially the gas pressures and densities are equal on each side of a central partition. The cyclic process is defined as follows:

(a) The demon reduces the gas entropy at fixed temperature and energy by letting molecules through the partition in one direction only. This sorting process generates pressure and density differences across the partition.

(b) The gas returns to its initial state by doing isothermal, reversible work on an external load. Specifically, the partition becomes a frictionless piston coupled to a load, moving slowly to a position of mechanical equilibrium (away from the container's centre) with zero pressure and density gradients across the piston. The piston is then withdrawn and reinserted at the container's centre.

(c) The demon is returned to its initial state.

What do the laws of thermodynamics imply? The process sequence (a)–(c) results in a load with increased energy. The first law of thermodynamics requires that this energy come from some well-defined source. It cannot be supplied by the reservoir or the entropy of the universe would decrease in the cyclic process, in violation of the second law. Apparently, resetting the demon in (c) requires the use of a work source which, in effect, supplies the energy to the load. It is helpful to look at the thermodynamic details of steps (a)–(c).

The second law implies that the demon's entropy increases in (a) to 'pay' for the entropy decrease of the gas. That is, sorting must increase the pressure-demon's entropy. In (b) work W is done by the gas on the load, inducing heat transfer $Q = W$ from reservoir to gas. The load's energy increases with its entropy unchanged, and the gas is returned to its initial state. Withdrawing and replacing the piston has zero thermodynamic effect. In step (b) the work on the load is compensated by the diminished energy (and entropy) of the reservoir. The demon's entropy increase offsets the reservoir's entropy decrease to maintain the second law's integrity. Now suppose that in (c) the demon is reset, returning to its initial state by energy exchanges with the reservoir and a reversible work source, with work E done on the demon. The demon's entropy decrease here must be compensated by an entropy increase in the reservoir. We conclude that resetting the demon results in heat transfer to the reservoir.

Overall, in (a)–(c) the entropy change of the universe equals that of the reservoir. The second law guarantees this is non-negative; i.e., the reservoir cannot lose energy. The cyclic process results in an increased load energy and a reservoir internal energy that is no lower than its initial value. The first law implies that the work source loses sufficient internal energy to generate the above gains; in particular, the source does positive work in (c). The relevant energy transfers during the cycle are: work $W > 0$ by gas on load, work $E > 0$ by work source on demon, and energy $E - W \geq 0$ added to the reservoir. The entropy change of the universe is $(E - W)/T \geq 0$, where T is the reservoir temperature.

Maxwell apparently envisioned a being who could run on arbitrarily little energy, an assumption that is implicit in most treatments of Maxwell's demon. Thomson assumed demons could store limited quantities of energy for later use, implying a need for refuelling.

Our analysis here illustrates that if the first and second laws of thermodynamics are satisfied, the refuelling (i.e. resetting) energy to a Maxwell's pressure-demon is transferred to the load as the gas and demon traverse their cycles. This suggests that resetting a demon is of fundamental importance, a view that is strengthened considerably in Section 1.5.

1.3 Szilard's Model: Entropy and Information Acquisition

In 1929, 62 years after Maxwell's demon was conceived, Leo Szilard introduced his famous model in which an 'intelligent' being operates a heat engine with a one-molecule working fluid (Article 3.1). We briefly outline that model. Initially the entire volume V of a cylinder is available to the fluid, as shown in figure 9(a). Step 1 consists of placing a partition into the cylinder, dividing it into two equal chambers. In Step 2 a Maxwell's demon determines which side of a partition the one-molecule fluid is on (for the sake of illustration, figure 9(b) shows the molecule captured on the right side), and records this result. In Step 3 the partition is replaced by a piston, and the recorded result is used to couple the piston to a load upon which work W is then done (figure 9(c) and 9(d)). Strictly speaking, the load should be varied continuously to match the average force on the piston by the fluid, enabling a quasistatic, reversible work process. The gas pressure moves the piston to one end of the container, returning the gas volume to its initial value, V (figure 9). In the process the one-molecule gas has energy $Q = W$ delivered to it via heat transfer from a constant-temperature heat bath.

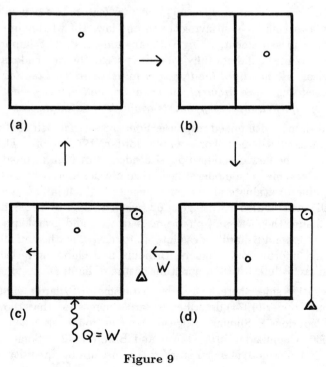

Figure 9

After Step 3 the gas has the same volume and temperature it had initially. The heat bath, which has transferred energy to the gas, has a lower entropy than it had initially. It appears that without some other effect, the second law of thermodynamics has been violated during the cyclic process. Szilard observed: 'One may reasonably assume that a measurement procedure is fundamentally associated with a certain definite average entropy production, and that this restores concordance with the second law. The amount of entropy generated by the measurement may, of course, always be greater than this fundamental amount, but not smaller.' He further identified the 'fundamental amount' to be $k \ln 2$. His observation was the beginning of information theory.

The ingenuity of Szilard's engine is striking. His tractable model allows thermodynamic analysis and interpretation, but at the same time entails a binary decision process. Thus, long before the existence of modern information ideas and the computer age, Szilard had the foresight to focus attention on the 'information' associated with a binary process. In doing so he discovered what is now called the binary digit—or 'bit'—of information. Szilard's observation that an inanimate device could effect the required tasks— obviating the need to analyze the thermodynamics of complex biological systems—was a precursor to cybernetics.

Szilard examined two other models involving memory in his 1929 paper. Unfortunately, his arguments are sometimes difficult to follow, and it is unclear whether the thermodynamic cost is from measurement, remembering, or forgetting. In the course of his analyses, Szilard observed: 'Having already recognized that the only important factor (of intervention) is a certain characteristic type of coupling, a "measurement", we need not construct any complicated models which imitate the intervention of living beings in detail. We can be satisfied with the construction of this particular type of coupling which is accompanied by memory.' His concluding sentence is, 'We have examined the "biological phenomena" of a nonliving device and have seen that it generates exactly that quantity of entropy which is required by thermodynamics.'

Thus, Szilard regarded memory as an important feature in a demon's operation, but he did not identify its specific role in saving the second law. His writing implies the production of entropy during measurement, along with an undefined, but important, effect of the memory process. While he did not fully solve the puzzle, the tremendous import of Szilard's 1929 paper is clear: *He identified the three central issues related to Maxwell's demon as we understand them today—measurement, information, and memory—and he established the underpinnings of information theory and its connections with physics.*

Szilard's work met with mixed response. Some researchers felt that it put the final nail in the coffin of Maxwell's demon. For example, Jordan (1949) wrote, 'This ... stands rather isolated apart from the flow of modern physical ideas; but I am inclined to regard it as one of the greatest achievements of modern theoretical physics, and believe that we are still very far from being able to evaluate all its consequences.' Much later Peter Landsberg (1982) wrote, 'Maxwell's demon died at the age of 62 (when a paper by Leo Szilard appeared), but it continues to haunt the castles of physics as a restless and lovable poltergeist.' Brillouin was stimulated to extend Szilard's ideas into an extensive mathematical theory connecting measurement and information. Demers, Brillouin and Gabor were led to the conclusion that the second law is linked to the quantum nature of light.

On the negative side, there have been criticisms of Szilard's efforts to link entropy and information. Popper (1974) described Szilard's suggestion that knowledge and entropy are related as 'spurious'. Similar criticisms may be found elsewhere (see Popper 1957, Feyerabend 1966, Chambadal 1971, Jauch and Báron 1972). Some objections emanate from the view that thermodynamical entropy is a measurable quantity (within an additive constant) that is independent of an observer's knowledge, and any other definition of entropy that is observer-dependent is unacceptable.

Rothstein (1957) clarified this point as follows: 'Demons do not lower entropy; the information they act on defines a lower entropy state of the system than one not subject to the restrictions in which the information consists.' Later, Rothstein (1971) elaborated further on this point: 'Physical information and its associated entropy reduction, *localized in the system to which the information refers*, can be expressed via specifications or constraints taken as part of the description of a system, or can be obtained from measurement. Measuring a system and thus *finding* it to be in some state is formally equivalent ... to *preparing* it to be in that state, *specifying* it to be in that state, or *constraining* it in a manner so that it can be in no other state (the state in question can, of course, be mixed).' The intimate connections between entropy, a *system* property, and information, a property of the *observer*, are discussed also by Morowitz (1970).

Along similar lines, Jaynes (1979) wrote, 'The entropy of a thermodynamic system is a measure of the degree of ignorance of a person *whose sole knowledge about its microstate consists of the values of the macroscopic quantities X_i which define its thermodynamic state.* This is a completely 'objective' quantity, in the sense that it is a function only of the X_i, and does not depend on anybody's personality. There is then no reason why it cannot be measured in the laboratory.'

Jaynes (1965) also observed that a given physical system corresponds to many different thermodynamic systems. Entropy is not a property simply of the system, but of the experiments chosen for it. One normally controls a set of variables, and measures entropy for that set. A solid with N atoms has approximately $6N$ degrees of freedom, of which only a few (e.g., temperature, pressure, magnetic field) are usually specified to get the entropy. By expanding that set (say, to include components of the strain tensor), we could get a sequence of entropy values, each of which corresponds to a different set of constraints. Extension of this process ultimately gets one outside the normal domain of thermodynamics, for which the number of degrees of freedom greatly exceeds the number of thermodynamic variables.

A one-molecule system never satisfies this requirement, and the use of the entropy concept—or any other thermodynamic concept—must be clarified. One possible clarification envisions an ensemble of similar systems, the average behaviour of which is related to a 'typical' single system. In ordinary statistical mechanics of macroscopic systems, the system of interest is typically in contact with a constant-temperature reservoir. Energy exchanges between system and reservoir go on continually, and observations over a long time period can in principle detect fluctuations about a well-defined, time-averaged energy. The ensemble description replaces the single system, viewed over an extended time by a collection of many similar systems, all viewed at a chosen time. The validity of the ensemble approach is commonly linked to the ergodic theorem, assuring the equality of time and ensemble averages.

In the present context one may consider taking a large number of one-molecule gases through Szilard's cycle. Using statistical mechanics, entropy and average pressure may be defined as meaningful thermodynamic properties of the ensemble. One must choose 'appropriate' variables of the system over which to take statistical averages. In the Szilard cycle left (L) and right (R) side indexes are appropriate. In a sense these are measurable 'macroscopic' variables. Being outside the normal domain of thermodynamics, the Szilard model can be criticized as having no thermodynamic significance. An alternative viewpoint, which we take here, is that it gives an opportunity for extending thermodynamic concepts into interesting new territory with some help from information theory. Jordan (1949) described this well: '... the tendency of Szilard's views is to acknowledge also a microphysical applicability of thermodynamics.' We discuss this further in Section 1.5.

In summary, Szilard's contributions have influenced the way we think about entropy. Through Szilard's ideas Maxwell's demon led to the concept of a 'bit' of information and to key concepts in information theory, cybernetics and computing. In a remarkable and fitting reciprocation, modern-day theories of computing have led to a new understanding of the Maxwell's demon puzzle. A new, fundamentally different resolution of that conundrum involves erasure of the demon's memory, a point that Szilard just narrowly missed in 1929. We return to this in Section 1.5.

1.4 Information Acquisition via Light Signals: A Temporary Resolution

Leon Brillouin and (independently) Dennis Gabor followed up on the measurement aspect about 20 years later using the quantum nature of light. Because quantum theory was still not invented during his lifetime, Maxwell could not have foreseen that his demon would provide a path to the quantum domain. But a small demon exists in a sea of gas molecules and photons. The photons, quanta of the blackbody electromagnetic radiation within the vessel, have a well- defined energy distribution dictated by quantum theory. In the mid 1940s, Pierre Demers recognized that because of this, a high-temperature torch is needed to provide signals that are distinguishable from the existing blackbody radiation. Brillouin, who was influenced by Demers' studies, adopted this assumption.

Consider the non-uniform wavelength distribution of blackbody radiation. For a gas temperature T, Wien's law gives the wavelength of maximum spectral density, $\lambda_{\mathrm{m}}(T) \approx 2900/T \, \mu\mathrm{m}$. Assuming an ambient temperature $T = 290\mathrm{K}$, the wavelength region in the vicinity of $\lambda_{\mathrm{m}}(290) \approx 10 \, \mu\mathrm{m}$ can be avoided by having the torch emit substantial radiation power with $\lambda \ll \lambda_{\mathrm{m}}$. A torch with flame temperature 1500K has $\lambda_{\mathrm{m}}(1500) \approx 2 \, \mu\mathrm{m}$, and an incandescent light bulb with filament temperature 3000K has $\lambda_{\mathrm{m}}(3000) \approx 0.1 \, \mu\mathrm{m}$. Whether a torch's radiation is distinguishable from ambient blackbody radiation depends on the power incident to the demon's eyes in the low wavelength region *with and without* the torch. The radiating area of the torch and geometrical considerations can be important, but the details of this complicated problem do not appear to have been pursued in the literature. It is clear that a torch giving distinguishable signals can be chosen: humans regularly use high-temperature incandescent lamps.

Could a low-temperature radiator, say, with $T = 100\mathrm{K}$ and $\lambda_{\mathrm{m}} = 29 \, \mu\mathrm{m}$ be used? This is less satisfactory for two reasons. First, the total power radiated is proportional to $A_{\mathrm{s}}T^4$, where A_{s} is the radiating area—and a low-temperature torch must have a much larger radiating surface to emit the same total power as a high temperature source. The radiating surface of a 100K radiator must be 810 000 times larger than that for a 3000K lamp with the same total power output. Second, higher wavelength radiation is accompanied by more pronounced diffraction effects than low wavelength light, decreasing the demon's ability to resolve signals.

Brillouin assumed a high-temperature torch and melded the developing field of information theory with the Maxwell's demon puzzle. The first assumption, together with judicious use of the quantum nature of radiation, enabled an explicit demonstration that information gathering via light signals is accompanied with an entropy increase. This increase is sufficient to save the second law.

The mathematical theory of information had been solidified by Claude Shannon (Shannon and Weaver, 1949) in connection with communication processes. Shannon introduced a mathematical function, which he called *information entropy*, to analyze the information carrying capacity of communication channels. Although Shannon's function bears a striking mathematical resemblance to the canonical ensemble entropy of statistical mechanics, Shannon's stimulus, method of attack and interpretation were very different. Brillouin boldly postulated a direct connection between information entropy and thermodynamic entropy.

Suppose a physical system can be in any of P_0 states with equal likelihood, and we do not know which state is actually occupied. Brillouin assigned information $I_0 = 0$ to signify total ignorance. If by measurement we eliminate some of the states as possibilities, reducing the number to $P_1 < P_0$, the information so gathered is defined as $I_1 \equiv K' \ln(P_0/P_1) > 0$. K' is an undesignated positive constant. Had the number of states increased, I_1 would be negative; i.e., we would have lost information. These ideas are described in more detail in Article 3.2.

Five years after his path breaking article, Brillouin published *Science and Information Theory*, which solidified his ideas on the subject. There he distinguished between two kinds of information, 'free' and 'bound', in order to handle information that did not have thermodynamic significance. Free information (I_f) was regarded as abstract and without physical significance. Bound information (I_b) was defined in terms of the possible states of a physical system. Brillouin gave as an example of free information the knowledge possessed by an individual. That knowledge is transformed into bound information when it is transmitted from one individual to another via physical signals.

According to Brillouin it is the *physical* character of signals that makes the information they carry 'bound'. In the communication process, the information might get distorted or partially lost; i.e., I_b can decrease. When the resulting bound information is received by another individual, it is again considered to be free information. Brillouin linked changes in bound information to changes in entropy of a physical system via the hypothesis:

$$I_{b1} - I_{b0} = k(\ln P_0 - \ln P_1) = S_0 - S_1 > 0$$

where the initially arbitrary constant K' has been chosen to be Boltzmann's constant, k; and S_0 and S_1 are the initial and final entropy values for the physical system. Choosing $K' = k$ makes information entropy and physical entropy comparable in the sense that they have the same units.

Brillouin's hypothesis implies that gaining bound information about a physical system decreases its physical entropy. He then made two further important steps. First, he defined 'negentropy' $\equiv N \equiv -(\text{entropy})$; then negentropy change $\equiv \Delta N \equiv -(\text{entropy change})$ $\equiv -\Delta S$. Second, he applied his negentropy principle of information to an isolated physical system. Suppose this system's entropy is $S_1 = S_0 - I_{b1}$, as above. The second law of thermodynamics is then written:

$$\Delta S_1 = \Delta(S_0 - I_{b1}) = \Delta S_0 - \Delta I_{b1} = -\Delta N_0 - \Delta I_{b1} \geq 0$$

or simply

$$\Delta(N_0 + I_{b1}) \leq 0.$$

With the latter result Brillouin gave a new interpretation of the second law of thermodynamics: The quantity (negentropy + information) can never increase, and in a reversible transformation, the sum remains fixed. He applied these ideas to 'exorcise' Maxwell's demon.

As might have been anticipated, Brillouin's proposal to generalize and reinterpret the second law got considerable attention, splitting the scientific community into groups of believers and non-believers. If the subsequent literature accurately reflects level of belief, the believers are more numerous, for Brillouin's method is widely quoted (see for example: Barrow 1986, Bell 1968, Ehrenberg 1967, Dugdale 1966, Rex 1987, Waldram 1985, Zemansky 1981, Yu 1976, Rodd 1964). Unqualified acceptance is evident in a paragraph labeled, 'Obituary: Maxwell's Demon (1871–c.1949)', in Henry Bent's *The Second Law* (1965).

Though smaller in numbers, non-believers levelled thoughtful criticisms of the subjectivism implied by Brillouin's theory. (In contrast, recall arguments illustrating and supporting *objectivity* of entropy within the informational approach in Section 1.3.) Among the most vociferous critics of Brillouin's theory is Kenneth Denbigh, who totally rejects the view that entropy is subjective. He emphasizes (Article 2.7) that Brillouin's exorcism of Maxwell's demon can be accomplished solely using thermodynamic principles, without need for information theory or negentropy. Denbigh's dismay with subjectivism led to a book on the subject (Denbigh and Denbigh 1985). Karl Popper has levelled harsh criticisms at attempts to link information and thermodynamics (Popper 1957, 1974, 1982). Much of this is focused on Szilard's 1929 paper, which began the process of associating information and entropy (see Section 1.3).

Rudolph Carnap (1977) wrote, 'Although the general identification of entropy (as a physical concept) with the negative amount of information cannot be maintained, there are certainly important relations between these two concepts.' He praised Szilard's work analyzing the paradox of Maxwell's demon as showing an important connection between entropy and information. He summarized Brillouin's ideas, which: 'are certainly interesting and clarify the situation with respect to Maxwell's paradox in the direction first suggested by Szilard.' Despite this commendation Carnap also took issue with Brillouin's identification of negentropy with information: 'However, when Brillouin proceeds to identify negentropy with amount of information, I cannot follow him any longer... He does not seem to be aware that the definition of S which he uses (and which he ascribes to Boltzmann and Planck) makes S a logical rather than a physical concept.' We return to connections between logical and physical concepts in the next section.

In work complementary to Brillouin's, Gabor analyzed the use of light signals to operate the Szilard engine. Although that work was not published until 1964, it was actually reported in lectures Gabor presented the same month that Brillouin's paper was published. The point of Gabor's treatment was to illustrate that a Maxwell's demon *could* in principle violate the second law if the light used satisfies *classical* laws. Using a cleverly designed system consisting of an incandescent lamp, mirrors and photodetector, Gabor found that if the light intensity can be made arbitrarily large relative to the background blackbody radiation, then the second law is vulnerable. He argued however that this is prohibited by quantum theory because 'Very weak beams of light cannot be concentrated.' His arguments are reprinted in Article 3.6.

Resolution of the Maxwell's demon puzzle by information acquisition was an important phase of the demon's life. It is interesting that the focus on information acquisition seemed to eliminate all interest in the memory aspects that Szilard emphasized. This is nowhere more clear than in Brillouin's decision to define two types of information, one of which ('free' information, I_f) was designed explicitly to deal with 'knowledge', and the other ('bound' information, I_b) was linked to entropy changes. In effect this inhibited considerations of the physical aspects of memory. Ironically, it is these physical effects of memory that subsequently led to an overthrow of the resolutions proposed by Brillouin and Gabor!

1.5 Computers and Erasure of Information: A New Resolution

1.5.1 Memory Erasure and Logical Irreversibility

Recall that after Step 3 in the Szilard model discussed in Section 1.4, the demon retains the memory of its finding, plus any other effects of the measurement process. We assume the demon has experienced zero temperature change and negligible, if any, 'other' effects of the measurement. In order to make the process within the gas–demon system cyclic, the memory evidently must be erased. The thermodynamic consequences of this process become of fundamental interest.

In 1961 Rolf Landauer (Article 4.1), introduced the concept of 'logical irreversibility' in connection with information-discarding processes in computers. Memory erasure, which takes a computer memory from an (arbitrary) existing state A, to a unique, standard reference state R discards information in a logically irreversible way. Logical irreversibility means that the prescription 'Map the existing state A to the state R' has no unique inverse because state A can be any of many possible states in the computer's memory. Put differently, starting from state R, one cannot get to the state A without using further information—e.g., the computer program and the initial data that led to state A in the first place.

Landauer argued that to each logical state there must correspond a physical state. Logical irreversibility carries the implication of a reduction of physical degrees of freedom, resulting in 'dissipation'. This is a subtle concept. We show shortly that logical irreversibility does not necessarily imply physical irreversibility in the thermodynamic sense. Rather, it can manifest itself in terms of a (thermodynamically reversible) conversion of work to heat; i.e., the work of erasure resulting in heat transfer to the environment. Landauer also showed that computation steps that do not discard information, e.g., writing and reading, can be done reversibly in principle.

In 1973 Charles Bennett (Article 4.2) extended Landauer's work, arguing that a computing automaton can be made logically reversible at every step. This allows an in-principle thermodynamically reversible computer that saves all intermediate results, avoiding irreversible erasure, prints out the desired output, and reversibly disposes of all undesired intermediate results by retracing the program's steps in reverse order, restoring the machine to its original condition.

In 1982 Bennett (Article 4.4) argued that a demon's memory may be viewed as a two-state system that is set in a standard state prior to measurement. The measurement process increases the available phase space of the memory from one state to two (in an ensemble of systems in which measurement can lead to either state). Memory erasure returns it to the standard state, compressing a two-state phase space to a single state. This is a logically irreversible act that is accompanied by an entropy transfer to the reservoir. Bennett showed that if all steps in the Szilard model are carried out slowly, the resulting entropy increase of the reservoir compensates for the entropy decrease of the demon's memory and saves the second law. Strictly speaking this cyclic process is thermodynamically reversible: the gas, demon and reservoir are all returned to their initial states.

It should be mentioned that in his 1970 book *Foundations of Statistical Mechanics*, Oliver Penrose recognized the importance of 'setting' operations that bring all members of an ensemble to the same observational state. Applied to Szilard's heat engine, this is nothing more than memory erasure. Penrose wrote:

> The large number of distinct observational states that the Maxwell demon must have in order to make significant entropy reductions possible may be thought of as a large memory capacity in which the demon stores the information about the system which he acquires as he works reducing its entropy. As soon as the demon's memory is completely filled, however, ... he can achieve no further reduction of the Boltzmann entropy. He gains nothing for example, by deliberately forgetting or erasing some of his stored information in order to make more memory capacity available; for the erasure being a setting process, itself increases the entropy by an amount at least as great as the entropy decrease made possible by the newly available memory capacity.

Penrose did not go as far as Bennett, who argued that measurement can be done with arbitrarily little dissipation and that erasure is the *fundamental* act that saves Maxwell's demon. Published within a rather abstract, advanced treatment of statistical mechanics, Penrose's modest but important treatment of memory erasure went largely unnoticed among Maxwell's demon enthusiasts.

1.5.2 Logical versus Thermodynamic Irreversibility

Because the concept of memory erasure has generated considerable debate, further clarification is appropriate. Motivated by the Szilard model, suppose we choose our memory device to be a box of volume V, partitioned down its middle, and containing a single molecule. The molecule is either in the left (L) side or the right (R) side, and the container walls are maintained at temperature T. In effect the molecule is in a double potential well whose middle barrier potential is infinite. Let the standard, reference state in this example be L, and consider an ensemble (see Section 1.3) of demon memories in which some of the ensemble members can occupy state L and others occupy state R.

Erasure and resetting takes each memory from its existing state and brings it to the standard state L. A crucial observation is this: *It is not possible to use a specific erasure process for an L state and a different one for the R state.* Why? Because that would necessitate first determining the state of each memory. After erasure, the knowledge from that determination would remain; i.e., erasure would not really have been accomplished.

An acceptable erasure/resetting process must work equally well for either initial memory state (L or R). For example, this can be accomplished by the following two-step algorithm applied to each ensemble member:

(i) To effect erasure, remove the central partition from each ensemble member.

(ii) To effect resetting, slowly compress each gas isothermally to the left half of the box.

The diffusion process in the erasure step, (i), eradicates the initial memory state. Despite the fact that this process is *logically irreversible*, it is *thermodynamically reversible* for the special case where the ensemble has half its members in state L and half in state R. This is evident from the fact that partition replacement leads to the initial thermodynamic state. Isothermal compression in (ii) means that the walls of the box are maintained at temperature T. Each gas molecule's energy, on average, is determined by the wall temperature, and the work of compression on each memory results in a transfer of energy to the constant-temperature reservoir. For the ensemble, the average work W must equal the average heat transfer Q. Thermodynamically, work has been 'converted' to heat, and entropy $\Delta S_{\text{res}} = Q/T = W/T = k \ln 2$ has been delivered to the reservoir. This example illustrates how the act of blurring the distinction between L and R can be linked to the delivery of entropy to the reservoir.

How has the ensemble entropy of the memory changed during the erasure process? Under our assumptions, the initial *ensemble* entropy per memory associated with the equally likely left and right states is $S_{\text{LR}}(\text{initial}) = k \ln 2$. After erasure and resetting, each ensemble member is in state L, and $S_{\text{LR}}(\text{final}) = 0$. Therefore, $\Delta S_{\text{LR}} = -k \ln 2 = -\Delta S_{\text{res}}$. In this sense the process is *thermodynamically reversible*; i.e., the entropy change of the universe is zero. This counterintuitive result is a direct consequence of the assumed uniform initial distribution of ensemble members among L and R states. During erasure, work from an external source has been used to effect heat transfer to the reservoir, but without altering the entropy of the universe.

Further understanding of the erasure/resetting procedure's thermodynamically reversible character for a uniform initial distribution of L and R states can be gained by reversing the steps of that procedure. Starting with all ensemble memories in state L ($S_{\text{LR}} = 0$), let each gas in the ensemble slowly expand isothermally to the full volume V. The performance of average work $W = kT \ln 2$ by a gas on its work source (now a work recipient) induces heat transfer $Q = W$ from the reservoir to the gas. The average gas entropy increases by $\Delta S_{\text{LR}} = k \ln 2 = -\Delta S_{\text{res}}$. Subsequent placement of the partition has zero entropic effect, because (approximately) half the ensemble members are likely to end up in each of the two states. The fact that some specific systems that were initially L become R, and *vice versa*, illustrates that the process is *logically irreversible*. However, it is *thermodynamically reversible* in the sense that carrying out the steps in reversed order: (*a*) re-establishes the initial distribution of L and R states among ensemble members; (*b*) returns energy Q, transferred from gas to reservoir during resetting, back to the gas; (*c*) returns energy $W = Q$ used to effect erasure/resetting back to the external work source; and (*d*) leaves the entropy of the universe unaltered.

We emphasize that memory erasure and resetting is always *logically irreversible*, but it is *thermodynamically reversible* only when the initial memory ensemble is distributed uniformly among L and R states. To see how erasure can be *thermodynamically irreversible*, consider the case where all ensemble memories are initially in state L. In the above two-step erasure/resetting procedure, partition removal in step (i) is thermodynamically irreversible, with the entropy change of the universe equaling $\Delta S_{\text{LR}} = k \ln 2$. During the subsequent compression of each ensemble member in step (ii), external work W results in heat transfer $Q = W$ to the reservoir. The initial and final ensemble entropy values of the gas are both zero, and the average entropy change of the universe equals that of the reservoir, namely, $k \ln 2$, which is attributable to irreversible partition removal. Similar reasoning shows that erasure/setting is both thermodynamically and logically irreversible whenever the initial ensemble of memories is not distributed equally among L and R states.

One might argue that prior to an erasure procedure, the memory of a single memory device (rather than an ensemble of memory devices) is in a fixed state and its entropy S_{LR} must be zero. With this view, erasure brings the memory to another single state with zero entropy, and the entropy change of the memory is zero. The only entropy change is the positive one in the reservoir, and the process must be viewed as *thermodynamically irreversible.* Whether this or the previous interpretation is used, the crucial point is that memory erasure saves the second law, and discarding information results in heat transfer to the environment.

The foregoing analysis suggests that the entropy of a collection of Szilard gases does not change when partitions are installed or removed. Without partitions installed, and without the use of special measurements, we expect half the boxes in our ensemble to have their molecules on the left and half on the right at any chosen time, giving an ensemble entropy $S_{LR} = k \ln 2$. This is unchanged by placement of a partition in each box and is unchanged again upon partition removal. Thus, for both replacement and removal of partitions, the change in the ensemble entropy of the gas is zero. John von Neumann (1955; originally published in German, 1932) recognized this in his *Mathematical Foundations of Quantum Mechanics*, writing:

> ... if the molecule is in the volume V, but it is known whether it is in the right side or left side ... then it suffices to insert a partition in the middle and allow this to be pushed ... to the left or right end of the container. ... In this case, the mechanical work $kT \ln 2$ is performed, i.e., this energy is taken from the heat reservoir. Consequently, at the end of the process, the molecule is again in the volume V, but we no longer know whether it is on the left or right ... Hence there is a compensating entropy decrease of $k \ln 2$ (in the reservoir). That is, we have exchanged our knowledge for the entropy decrease $k \ln 2$. Or, the entropy is the same in the volume V as in the volume $V/2$, provided that we know in the first mentioned case, in which half of the container the molecule is to be found. Therefore, if we knew all the properties of the molecule before diffusion (position and momentum), we could calculate for each moment after the diffusion whether it is on the right or left side, i.e., the entropy has not decreased. If, however, the only information at our disposal was the macroscopic one that the volume was initially $V/2$, then the entropy does increase upon diffusion.

It is notable that von Neumann associated entropy decrease with the demon's knowledge. Had he addressed the process of discarding information needed to bring the demon back to its initial state, he might have discovered the Bennett/Landauer resolution of the puzzle fifty years earlier.

The idea that partition placement and removal does not change the one-molecule gas entropy is supported and clarified by a quantum mechanical analysis of entropy changes for the gas (and memory) given by Zurek (1984, Article 4.5). His work was evidently inspired by a criticism of the Szilard model by Jauch and Báron (1972, Article 3.7), who argued that the Szilard model is outside the realm of statistical physics, and should be dismissed altogether! That opinion was subsequently rebuked by Costa de Beauregard and Tribus (1974, Article 3.8). Zurek viewed partition insertion in terms of the introduction of a thin potential barrier of increasing strength V_0. When $V_0 = 0$ there is no barrier, and when V_0 is made sufficiently large, the barrier is effectively impenetrable. As V_0 is increased, the wave function of the molecule distorts, and in the limit $V_0 \to \infty$, allowable wave functions are, as they must be, symmetric about the partition. Zurek's quantum mechanical treatment shows the entropy to be unchanged by partition insertion.

Zurek gives a detailed description of memory erasure in his paper. Another, independent quantum theoretic treatment of memory erasure was given by Lubkin (1987, Article 4.7). Zurek's treatment and the above discussion assume that memory erasure results in the memory being taken to a standard state. In contrast Lubkin assumes erasure to be thermal randomization, obtained by plunging the memory into a reservoir. Both Zurek and Lubkin find that erasure results in an entropy increase of the environment.

1.5.3 Role of Measurement in Szilard's Model

Some authors have argued that in Szilard's engine no measurement is needed prior to coupling the piston to the external load. They believed that clever design of the engine would enable the proper coupling to be made automatically. For example, Chambadal (1971) argued as follows:

> As far as the location of the molecule is concerned, that is determined after its first collision with the piston, since the latter experiences a very small displacement in one direction or the other. We may suppose that the work supplied by the molecule can be absorbed by two gears situated in the two parts of the cylinder. After the piston has experienced the first impact we connect it, according to the direction of its motion, to one or another of these gears which will thereafter absorb the work supplied by the movement of the molecule. This coupling of the piston to the parts which it drives can also be achieved automatically.
>
> But, in fact, it is not even necessary to solve the problem of the location of the molecule. Indeed we can, without altering the principle of the apparatus at all, visualize it in the following way. When the piston is placed in the cylinder, we fix two shafts on its axis, one on either side. These shafts make contact with the piston, but are not connected to it. Consequently, whatever the position of the molecule, the piston, moving in either direction, pushes one of the two shafts and so engages the gears which make use of the work produced.

Chambadal concluded that neither entropy nor information is involved in this model.

Popper (1974) and Feyerabend (1966) proposed similarly modified Szilard engines that couple the piston via pulleys to equal weights on either side of it. The weights can be lifted by the pulley system but are constrained such that they cannot be lowered (see figure 10). If the engine's molecule is in the left chamber, the piston moves to the right, raising the left weight, leaving the right weight unmoved. If the molecule is in the right chamber, the reverse happens; i.e., the right weight gets raised and the left weight stays fixed. Feyerabend wrote 'The process can be repeated indefinitely ... We have here a "perpetual source of income" of the kind von Smoluchowski did not think to be possible.'

Jauch and Báron (1972) imagined a similar situation (see figure 11), writing: 'Near the mid-plane of the cylinder and on both its sides are electrical contacts in its walls. When activated by the piston's motion along them, they operate mechanisms which attach a weight to the piston in whichever direction it moves. Thus a weight is lifted and the engine performs work, without interference by a conscious observer.'

An ingenious coupling was illustrated by Rothstein (1979). His intent was not to argue against Szilard's work but rather to rebut Popper who had attempted to do so. Rothstein couples the piston to two racks that alternately engage a pinion gear as it moves left or right (see figure 12). When it moves left, one rack rotates the pinion gear counterclockwise while the other rack is disengaged. When the piston moves right, the second rack (diametrically opposed to the first) rotates the pinion gear, again counterclockwise. Thus, regardless

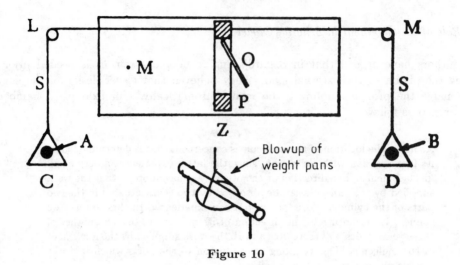

L   M

S   S

· M   O

P

Z

A   B

C   D

Blowup of
weight pans

Figure 10

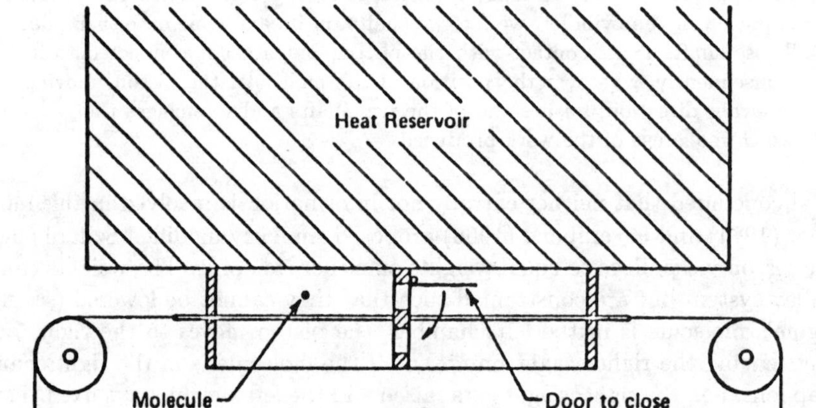

Heat Reservoir

Molecule   Door to close
                                        the hole

"Observer"

Szilard's thought experiment
Figure 11

of whether the molecule is in the left or right chamber, the design of the racks assures counterclockwise motion, suggesting an automatic machine for converting heat from a single reservoir to work.

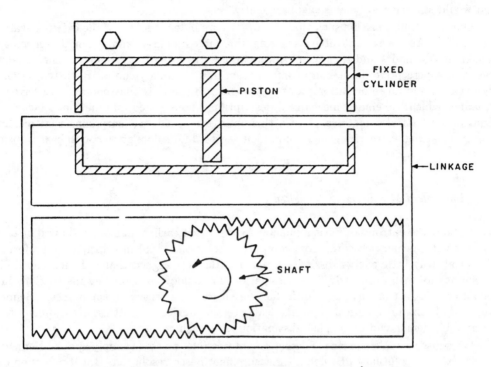

Thought experiment illustrating Popper's refutation of Szilard's assignment of an entropy
equivalent to physical information.
Figure 12

The above examples are clever and do indeed seem to challenge the second law. However, there is more to the story. In figure 10, after the work has been done, one of the weight hangers is raised. The pulley string at the other side is relaxed and limp. In essence, this configuration stores information about the molecule's previous location: *it serves as a memory*. Put differently, the process is not truly cyclic. The memory must be reset enabling commencement of the next cycle. Because resetting of the pulley system was not accounted for, the arguments by Popper and Feyerabend—while rather convincing at first look—must be considered incomplete.

Along the same lines, the Jauch–Báron idea leads to an asymmetric situation (figure 11), with a weight attached on one side only. This is a physical embodiment of a memory that must be reset in order to make the process cyclic. Chambadal's analysis similarly overlooks the need for resetting the apparatus. In Rothstein's example, figure 12, each cycle moves the rack assembly either left or right, where it stays until it is reset. Again this constitutes a memory register that must be zeroed periodically.

In summary, Szilard's engine requires a binary decision process in order to couple the piston and load. This requires information acquisition, memory and subsequent information erasure. Although examples based upon *macroscopic* analogues involving gears and pulleys suggest that resetting can be done at arbitrarily little cost, that is misleading. The reason is that Maxwell's demon entails a memory in which the relevant energy modes are *microscopic*. Erasure must act upon hidden degrees of freedom, without knowledge of their existing states. One cannot simply examine a register and zero it in the least energy-consuming or entropy-producing way. That examination would transfer information to another memory that would still have to be erased subsequently.

Our algorithm must be such that erasure occurs independently of the existing state of the memory. As the example above suggests, this can entail first randomizing the memory's hidden energy modes and then using a work process to bring the memory to the standard state. In a perceptive discussion of information and thermodynamics, Rothstein (1952a) observed: 'From an information viewpoint quantity of heat is thus energy transferred in a manner which has eluded mechanical description, about which information is lacking in terms of mechanical categories.' Given this observation, it is not surprising that memory erasure/resetting via rearrangement of hidden degrees of freedom gives rise to heat transfer.

1.5.4 Entropy of Measurement Revisited

What about the entropy of measurement? As discussed earlier, Landauer showed that, in contrast with memory erasure, most computer operations could in principle be performed with arbitrarily little energy dissipation per bit. Bennett argued that a demon can do its measurements with arbitrarily little dissipation, in analogy with reading instructions in a computer. The act of 'reading' can in fact be viewed as a measurement process. Bennett proposed idealized magnetic and mechanical detection devices to buttress his argument that a Maxwell's demon can accomplish dissipationless measurement.

Were dissipationless means of detection not possible, we could simply append Bennett's erasure-based resolution to Brillouin's measurement-based resolution. But if detection can in fact be done with arbitrarily little dissipation, the Bennett/Landauer viewpoint implies that the exorcism accepted by a generation of researchers and teachers must now be rejected. In retrospect it is clear that assuming the use of light signals is not sufficient to rule out *all* demonic operations. Remarkably, this lack of generality was not recognized by most researchers prior to Bennett's work (for an exception, see Penrose (1970) p. 236). Light signals became widely accepted as *the* way a Maxwell's demon collects information. In *Science and Information Theory*, after showing that detection via light signals saves the Second Law, Brillouin extrapolated his result: 'We have ... discovered a very important physical law ... every physical measurement requires a corresponding entropy increase, and there is a lower limit below which the measurement becomes impossible.'

Why generalization based upon a special case achieved such wide acceptance is puzzling. Landauer (1989) wrote in this regard, 'Brillouin ... and others found dissipative ways of transferring information, and without further justification, assumed that they had discovered a minimally dissipative process. It is one of the great puzzles in the sociology of science why this obviously inadequate argument met with wide and uncritical acceptance. Only in recent years have clearer discussions emerged, and these are not yet widely appreciated.'

Had the use of light signals been questioned earlier, Brillouin's method of attack might have achieved far less credibility. Yet, despite its overly narrow view, Brillouin's work brought Maxwell's demon considerable attention in 1951 and subsequent years. The demon's popularity seemed to grow as its perceived challenge to the second law diminished. Bennett's overthrow in 1982 of Brillouin's exorcism provided further popularity to Maxwell's demon, and more reason to retain it as a tool for understanding.

As mentioned already there is not universal agreement on the thesis that measurement can in principle be accomplished with arbitrarily little dissipation. Rothstein (1952) argued that 'The accuracy of any measurement is limited by how much entropy can be usefully expended in order to perform the measurement.' More recently (Rothstein 1988) he has written:

> Despite several ingenious attempts to achieve reversible computation, including conceptual designs for quantum mechanical computers, we remain convinced that an entropy price for unavoidable selection, measurement, or preparation acts must be paid for every such act in physical communication or computation. ... We are willing to grant that for limited kinds of computation physical systems can be set up in principle whose dynamical equations will generate a succession of states isomorphic to the computation, and, as an idealization, such systems can be reversible. We deny that possibility for a true general purpose computer. Information must be generated and stored until it needs to be consulted. The storage is writing, i.e., a preparation of some subsystem. The consultation is reading, i.e., a measurement on some subsystem. Both kinds of operation are selective and thus demand their entropy costs.

To close this section we point out that the distinction between entropy of data acquisition and entropy of data erasure is not sharp. In Szilard's model, when a demon determines the side (L or R) in which the molecule resides, its own memory state changes from a unique, known reference state to either of two possible states. This generates an entropy increase, in an ensemble sense, that in essence 'pays' entropically for the diminished entropy of the gas. This 'entropy of measurement' is stored by the demon, and ultimately becomes entropy of erasure—which is passed on to the environment when the demon's memory is reset. In a real sense, the entropy of erasure feeds to the environment entropy gained by the demon via information acquisition.

1.6 Other Aspects of Maxwell's Demon

1.6.1 Quantum Conundrums: Szilard and Einstein

Albert Einstein devised a Gedankenexperiment that bears resemblance to Szilard's 1929 model heat engine. Fine (1986) discusses the idea as outlined in a letter from Einstein to Schrödinger in 1935. A ball is located in one of two closed boxes, but it is not known which. We might expect that the probability is 1/2 for either possibility. Einstein was concerned with two concepts, incompleteness and separation. By definition, a complete theory would have unit probability for the ball being in one of the boxes. Otherwise the theory is incomplete. Separation means that if two objects are separated spatially by a sufficient amount, they must become independent of one another. If knowledge about one of the boxes provides information regarding the other, then separation does not hold.

Suppose the ball cannot be destroyed or duplicated, and the two boxes are separated. If observation of box 1 gives a complete answer (YES or NO) as to whether it contains the ball, it is known instantly whether the distant box 2 contains the ball. Thus completeness implies that separation is impossible. On the other hand, if separation holds, then a measurement of one box cannot give a certain answer, for that would lead to an inconsistency. That is, separation implies that completeness is impossible. The conclusion is that separation and completeness are incompatible, a perplexing finding if one believes that both must be valid. The act of observation seems inconsistent with expected physical properties.

A familiar problem of the same ilk arises when a measurement of which box contains the ball is interpreted in terms of 'collapse of the wave function'. That is, if the particle is found in box 1, the wave function collapses to zero in box 2, and it appears that the system's state is intimately connected with the observer's knowledge. Yet we expect the state of the system to be independent of the observer's knowledge.

In the Szilard problem, a possible interpretation is that the entropy decreases by $k \ln 2$ upon determination of which chamber the molecule is in. Once again the state of the observer seems to determine the state of the system. A similar approach envisions the measurement as inducing a phase space increase for the demon's memory, and a corresponding entropy decrease of the gas entropy by the same amount (assuming a non-dissipative measurement). Is this a subjectivist view that 'works' but should be avoided? No, because *any* demon making a measurement of the molecule's location would reach the same conclusion (see Section 1.3). The gas entropy is 'known' to be less to *any* observer who measures the left-right state.

Another interpretation is suggested for an observer outside the gas-demon system. This observer finds that the coupling of the gas to the demon produces a correlation between the two objects so that entropy of gas + demon < (entropy of gas) + (entropy of demon). This outsider cannot discuss the demon and gas independently because they are linked. There is a non-zero mutual entropy just as two interacting molecules have a non-zero potential energy of interaction. The coupling between gas and demon is broken when the gas does work against the piston. Then to the outside observer, the gas has the same entropy it had initially, but the demon's entropy has increased. This increase compensates for the entropy decrease of the reservoir during the isothermal expansion.

Such conundrums are not easy to resolve, or even to accept. They seem to be an integral part of microscopic, probabilistic physics, and often lead to mental discomfort. They extend from quantum mechanics to thermal physics through Maxwell's playful, imaginary demon.

1.6.2 Maxwell's Demon, Efficiency, Power and Time

Although the bulk of the work on Maxwell's demon has centred on its exorcism, one can ask how effective a demon can be *whether or not* it can defeat the second law. The following questions have been posed (Leff 1987a, 1989) in this regard: What rate of energy transfer is attainable by a Maxwell's demon who sorts gas molecules serially, and how much time does it take it to achieve a designated temperature difference, ΔT, across a partition? The assumption of serial processing enables an estimate of minimal effectiveness. By the use of two or more demons operating in parallel, improved performance is possible.

Numerical estimates have been made using the energy–time form of Heisenberg's uncertainty principle and also using classical kinetic theory. For a dilute gas at $300 \, \text{K}$, the uncertainty principle implies that Power $< 1.5 \times 10^{-6} \, \text{W}$. If the gas volume is the size of a large room, and $\Delta T = 2 \, \text{K}$, then the demon's Processing Time $> 10^3$ years. With similar assumptions classical kinetic theory implies much tighter bounds, namely, Power $< 10^{-9} \, \text{W}$ and Processing Time $> 4 \times 10^6$ years. The latter power level, which is comparable to the average dissipation per neuron in a human brain, illustrates the impotence of a lone Maxwell's demon using serial processing.

Once a temperature difference exists between two portions of a gas, it is possible in principle to run a heat engine using this difference. The available energy and efficiency for delivery of this energy as work has been determined (Leff 1987a). The maximum-work efficiency for operating a heat engine between two identical chambers with initial temperatures T_+ and $T_- < T_+$, and equal final temperatures, has the simple form $\eta = 1-(T_-/T_+)^{1/2}$. As expected, this efficiency is lower than that from a Carnot cycle operating between infinite reservoirs at fixed temperatures T_- and T_+. It is noteworthy that the same efficiency expression arises in other contexts, including the reversible Otto and Joule cycles (Leff 1987b), other reversible cycles (Landsberg and Leff 1989), and the irreversible Curzon–Ahlborn cycle (Curzon and Ahlborn 1975) at maximum power.

1.6.3 Physics Outlaw or Physics Teacher?

As we have seen, Maxwell's demon was invented to illustrate the statistical nature of the second law of thermodynamics. It ultimately became viewed as a potential physics outlaw that had to be defeated. Now, over a century later, that process appears to be complete, or at least nearly so. Maxwell's demon is *not* a physics outlaw for the reasons described in the previous sections. However, that does not diminish its tremendous importance. Ehrenberg (1967) captured the spirit of what has kept Maxwell's demon alive in the closing paragraph of his Scientific American review article: 'Let us stop here and be grateful to the good old Maxwellian demon, even if he does not assist in providing power for a submarine. Perhaps he did something much more useful in helping us to understand the ways of nature and our ways of looking at it.'

Indeed, the demon has helped us to understand a variety of important ideas. It seems to have been converted from physics outlaw to physics teacher! Though merely a simple idea, it has provided a vehicle for relating measurement and information to thermodynamics, quantum mechanics and biology. Modern electronic computing seems at first thought to be totally unrelated to Maxwell's demon. Yet, as we have seen, important connections exist, with the demon illuminating the binary decision process and the computer amplifying the importance of information erasure. Remarkably, Maxwell's microscopic demon has even played a role in the development of black hole thermodynamics (Bekenstein 1972, 1980).

Maxwell's demon has not simply survived the advances made in quantum theory, information theory, and computing. It has been fortified by and has provided important insights to each of these fields. Will it play a role in future progress? There are indications that the answer is yes. Bennett (Article 4.4) observed that under certain circumstances algorithmic entropy, defined within the framework of algorithmic information theory, is a microscopic analogue of ordinary statistical entropy.

Zurek (1989a, b) extended the definition of algorithmic entropy to physical systems. He argued that physical entropy must consist of two distinct contributions: (i) a term that represents the randomness of known aspects of the system; and (ii) a term representing the remaining ignorance of the observer about the system's actual state. In his words, 'This recognition of the dual nature of physical entropy allows one to consider "engines" operated by a modern day "Maxwell demon"—a universal Turing machine capable of measuring and processing information—without endangering the validity of the second law.'

Considering its rich history and present research trends, it is likely that Maxwell's demon will continue to live an active life. Though Maxwell's demon is no longer considered an outlaw, we expect it to remain a potent teacher for many years to come!

CHAPTER 2

Historical and Philosophical Considerations

KINETIC THEORY OF THE DISSIPATION OF ENERGY

IN abstract dynamics an instantaneous reversal of the motion of every moving particle of a system causes the system to move backwards, each particle of it along its old path, and at the same speed as before when again in the same position—that is to say, in mathematical language, any solution remains a solution when t is changed into $-t$. In physical dynamics, this simple and perfect reversibility fails on account of forces depending on friction of solids; imperfect fluidity of fluids; imperfect elasticity of solids; inequalities of temperature and consequent conduction of heat produced by stresses in solids and fluids; imperfect magnetic retentiveness; residual electric polarisation of dielectrics; generation of heat by electric currents induced by motion; diffusion of fluids, solution of solids in fluids, and other chemical changes; and absorption of radiant heat and light. Consideration of these agencies in connection with the all-pervading law of the conservation of energy proved for them by Joule, led me twenty-three years ago to the theory of the dissipation of energy, which I communicated first to the Royal Society of Edinburgh in 1852, in a paper entitled " On a Universal Tendency in Nature to the Dissipation of Mechanical Energy.

The essence of Joule's discovery is the subjection of physical phenomena to dynamical law. If, then, the motion of every particle of matter in the universe were precisely reversed at any instant, the course of nature would be simply reversed for ever after. The bursting bubble of foam at the foot of a waterfall would reunite and descend into the water : the thermal motions would reconcentrate their energy and throw the mass up the fall in drops reforming into a close column of ascending water. Heat which had been generated by the friction of solids and dissipated by conduction, and radiation with absorption, would come again to the place of contact and throw the moving body back against the force to which it had previously yielded. Boulders would recover from the mud the materials required to rebuild them into their previous jagged forms, and would become reunited to the mountain peak from which they had formerly broken away. And if also the materialistic hypothesis of life were true, living creatures would grow backwards, with conscious knowledge of the future, but no memory of the past, and would become again unborn. But the real phenomena of life infinitely transcend human science, and speculation regarding consequences of their imagined reversal is utterly unprofitable. Far otherwise, however, is it in respect to the reversal of the motions of matter uninfluenced by life, a very elementary consideration of which leads to the full explanation of the theory of dissipation of energy.

To take one of the simplest cases of the dissipation of energy, the conduction of heat through a solid—consider a bar of metal warmer at one end than the other and left to itself. To avoid all needless complication, of taking loss or gain of heat into account, imagine the bar to be varnished with a substance impermeable to heat. For the sake of definiteness, imagine the bar to be first given with one half of it at one uniform temperature, and the other half of it at another uniform temperature. Instantly a diffusing of heat commences, and the distribution of temperature becomes continuously less and less unequal, tending to perfect uniformity, but never in any finite time attaining perfectly to this ultimate condition. This process of diffusion could be perfectly prevented by an army of Maxwell's " intelligent demons "* stationed at the surface, or interface as we may call it with Prof. James Thomson, separating the hot from the cold part of the bar. To see precisely how this is to be done, consider rather a gas than a solid, because we have much knowledge regarding the molecular motions of a gas, and little or no knowledge of the molecular motions of a solid. Take a jar with the lower half occupied by cold air or gas, and the upper half

* The definition of a "demon," according to the use of this word by Maxwell, is an intelligent being endowed with free will, and fine enough tactile and perceptive organisation to give him the faculty of observing and influencing individual molecules of matter

occupied with air or gas of the same kind, but at a higher temperature, and let the mouth of the jar be closed by an air-tight lid. If the containing vessel were perfectly impermeable to heat, the diffusion of heat would follow the same law in the gas as in the solid, though in the gas the diffusion of heat takes place chiefly by the diffusion of molecules, each taking its energy with it, and only to a small proportion of its whole amount by the interchange of energy between molecule and molecule ; whereas in the solid there is little or no diffusion of substance, and the diffusion of heat takes place entirely, or almost entirely, through the communication of energy from one molecule to another. Fourier's exquisite mathematical analysis expresses perfectly the statistics of the process of diffusion in each case, whether it be "conduction of heat," as Fourier and his followers have called it, or the diffusion of substance in fluid masses (gaseous or liquid) which Fick showed to be subject to Fourier's formulæ. Now, suppose the weapon of the ideal army to be a club, or, as it were, a molecular cricket-bat ; and suppose for convenience the mass of each demon with his weapon to be several times greater than that of a molecule. Every time he strikes a molecule he is to send it away with the same energy as it had immediately before. Each demon is to keep as nearly as possible to a certain station, making only such excursions from it as the execution of his orders requires. He is to experience no forces except such as result from collisions with molecules, and mutual forces between parts of his own mass, including his weapon : thus his voluntary movements cannot influence the position of his centre of gravity, otherwise than by producing collision with molecules.

The whole interface between hot and cold is to be divided into small areas, each allotted to a single demon. The duty of each demon is to guard his allotment, turning molecules back or allowing them to pass through from either side, according to certain definite orders. First, let the orders be to allow no molecules to pass from either side. The effect will be the same as if the interface were stopped by a barrier impermeable to matter and to heat. The pressure of the gas being, by hypothesis, equal in the hot and cold parts, the resultant momentum taken by each demon from any considerable number of molecules will be zero ; and therefore he may so time his strokes that he shall never move to any considerable distance from his station. Now, instead of stopping and turning all the molecules from crossing his allotted area, let each demon permit a hundred molecules chosen arbitrarily to cross it from the hot side ; and the same number of molecules, chosen so as to have the same entire amount of energy and the same resultant momentum, to cross the other way from the cold side. Let this be done over and over again within certain small equal consecutive intervals of time, with care that if the specified balance of energy and momentum is not exactly fulfilled in respect to' each successive hundred molecules crossing each way, the error will be carried forward, and as nearly as may be corrected, in respect to the next hundred. Thus, a certain perfectly regular diffusion of the gas both ways across the interface goes on, while the original different temperatures on the two sides of the interface are maintained without change.

Suppose, now, that in the original condition the temperature and pressure of the gas are each equal throughout the vessel, and let it be required to disequalise the temperature but to leave the pressure the same in any two portions A and B of the whole space. Station the army on the interface as previously described. Let the orders now be that each demon is to stop all molecules from crossing his area in either direction except 100 coming from A, arbitrarily chosen to be let pass into B, and a greater number, having among them less energy but equal momentum, to cross from B to A. Let this be repeated over and over again. The temperature in A will be continually diminished and the number of molecules in it continually increased, until there are not in B enough of molecules with small enough velocities to fulfil the condition with reference to permission to pass from B to A. If after that no molecule be allowed to pass the interface in either direction, the final condition will be very great condensation and very low temperature in A; rarefaction and very high temperature in B; and equal temperature in A and B. The process of disequalisation of temperature and density might be stopped at any time by changing the orders to those previously specified (2), and so permitting a certain degree of diffusion each way across the interface while maintaining a certain uniform difference of temperatures with equality of pressure on the two sides.

If no selective influence, such as that of the ideal "demon," guides individual molecules, the average result of their free motions and collisions must be to equalise the distribution of energy among them in the gross; and after a sufficiently long time from the supposed initial arrangement the difference of energy in any two equal volumes, each containing a very great number of molecules, must bear a very small proportion to the whole amount in either; or, more strictly speaking, the probability of the difference of energy exceeding any stated finite proportion of the whole energy in either is very small. Suppose now the temperature to have become thus very approximately equalised at a certain time from the beginning, and let the motion of every particle become instantaneously reversed. Each molecule will retrace its former path, and at the end of a second interval of time, equal to the former, every molecule will be in the same position, and moving with the same velocity, as at the beginning; so that the given initial unequal distribution of temperature will again be found, with only the difference that each particle is moving in the direction reverse to that of its initial motion. This difference will not prevent an instantaneous subsequent commencement of equalisation, which, with entirely different paths for the individual molecules, will go on in the average according to the same law as that which took place immediately after the system was first left to itself.

By merely looking on crowds of molecules, and reckoning their energy in the gross, we could not discover that in the very special case we have just considered the progress was towards a succession of states in which the distribution of energy deviates more and more from uniformity up to a certain time. The number of molecules being finite, it is clear that small finite deviations from absolute precision in the reversal we have supposed would not obviate the resulting disequalisation of the distribution of energy. But the greater the number of molecules, the shorter will be the time during which the disequalising will continue; and it is only when we regard the number of molecules as practically infinite that we can regard spontaneous disequalisation as practically impossible. And, in point of fact, if any finite number of perfectly elastic molecules, however great, be given in motion in the interior of a perfectly rigid vessel, and be left for a sufficiently long time undisturbed except by mutual impacts and collisions against the sides of the containing vessel, it must happen over and over again that (for example) something more than nine-tenths of the whole energy shall be in one half of the vessel, and less than one-tenth of the whole energy in the other half. But if the number of molecules be very great, this will happen enormously less frequently than that something more than 6-10ths shall be in one half, and something less than 4-10ths in the other. Taking as unit of time the average interval of free motion between consecutive collisions, it is easily seen that the probability of there being something more than any stated percentage of excess above the half of the energy in one half of the vessel during the unit of time, from a stated instant, is smaller the greater the dimensions of the vessel and the greater the stated percentage. It is a strange but nevertheless a true conception of the old well-known law of the conduction of heat to say that it is very improbable that in the course of 1,000 years one half the bar of iron shall of itself become warmer by a degree than the other half; and that the probability of this happening before 1,000,000 years pass is 1,000 times as great as that it will happen in the course of 1,000 years, and that it certainly will happen in the course of some very long time. But let it be re-

membered that we have supposed the bar to be covered with an impermeable varnish. Do away with this impossible ideal, and believe the number of molecules in the universe to be infinite; then we may say one half of the bar will never become warmer than the other, except by the agency of external sources of heat or cold. This one instance suffices to explain the philosophy of the foundation on which the theory of the dissipation of energy rests.

Take however another case in which the probability may be readily calculated. Let a hermetically-sealed glass jar of air contain 2,000,000,000,000 molecules of oxygen, and 8,000,000,000,000 molecules of nitrogen. If examined any time in the infinitely distant future, what is the number of chances against one that all the molecules of oxygen and none of nitrogen shall be found in one stated part of the vessel equal in volume to 1-5th of the whole? The number expressing the answer in the Arabic notation has about 2,173,220,000,000 of places of whole numbers. On the other hand the chance against there being exactly 2-10ths of the whole number of particles of nitrogen, and at the same time exactly 2-10ths of the whole number of particles of oxygen in the first specified part of the vessel is only 4021×10^9 to 1.

[*Appendix.*—*Calculation of Probability respecting Diffusion of Gases.*]

For simplicity I suppose the sphere of action of each molecule to be infinitely small in comparison with its average distance from its nearest neighbour : thus, the sum of the volumes of the spheres of action of all the molecules will be infinitely small in proportion to the whole volume of the containing vessel. For brevity, space external to the sphere of action of every molecule will be called free space : and a molecule will be said to be in free space at any time when its sphere of action is wholly in free space ; that is to say, when its sphere of action does not overlap the sphere of action of any other molecule. Let A, B denote any two particular portions of the whole containing vessel, and let a, b be the volumes of those portions. The chance that at any instant one individual molecule of whichever gas shall be in A is $\dfrac{a}{a+b}$, however many or few other molecules there may be in A at the same time ; because its chances of being in any specified portions of free space are proportional to their volumes ; and, according to our supposition, even if all the other molecules were in A, the volume of free space in it would not be sensibly diminished by their presence. The chance that of n molecules in the whole space there shall be i stated individuals in A, and that the other $n - i$ molecules shall be at the same time in B, is

$$\left(\frac{a}{a+b}\right)^i \left(\frac{b}{a+b}\right)^{n-i}, \text{ or } \frac{a^i b^{n-i}}{(a+b)^n}$$

Hence the probability of the number of molecules in A being exactly i, and in B exactly $n - i$, irrespectively of individuals, is a fraction having for denominator $(a + b)^n$, and for numerator the term involving $a^i b^{n-i}$ in the expansion of this binomial ; that is to say it is—

$$\frac{n(n-1) \, \ldots \, . \, (n-i+1)}{1.2 \, \ldots \, . \, i} \left(\frac{a}{a+b}\right)^i \left(\frac{b}{a+b}\right)^{n-i}$$

If we call this T_i we have

$$T_{i+1} = \frac{n-i}{i+1} \frac{a}{b} T_{i+1}$$

Hence T_i is the greatest term if i is the smallest integer which makes

$$\frac{n-i}{i+1} < \frac{b}{a}$$

this is to say, if i is the smallest integer which exceeds

$$n\frac{a}{a+b} - \frac{b}{a+b}$$

Hence if a and b are commensurable the greatest term is that for which

$$i = n \frac{a}{a+b}$$

To apply these results to the cases considered in the preceding article, put in the first place

$$n = 2 \times 10^{12}$$

this being the number of particles of oxygen; and let $i = n$. Thus, for the probability that all the particles of oxygen shall be in A, we find

$$\left(\frac{a}{a+b}\right)^8 \times 10^{12}$$

Similarly, for the probability that all the particles of nitrogen are in the space B, we find

$$\left(\frac{b}{a+b}\right)^2 \times 10^{12}$$

Hence the probability that all the oxygen is in A and all the nitrogen in B is

$$\left(\frac{a}{a+b}\right)^2 \times 10^{12} \times \left(\frac{b}{a \times b}\right)^8 \times 10^{12}$$

Now by hypothesis

$$\frac{a}{a+b} = \frac{2}{10}$$

and therefore

$$\frac{b}{a+b} = \frac{8}{10}$$

hence the required probability is

$$\frac{2^{26 \times 10^{12}}}{10^{10^{13}}}$$

Call this $\frac{1}{N}$, and let log denote common logarithm. We have $\log N = 10^{13} - 26 \times 10^{12} \times \log. 2 = (10 - 26 \log. 2) \times 10^{12} = 2173220 \times 10^6$. This is equivalent to the result stated in the text above. The logarithm of so great a number, unless given to more than thirteen significant places, cannot indicate more than the number of places of whole numbers in the answer to the proposed question, expressed according to the Arabic notation.

The calculation of T_i when i and $n-i$ are very large numbers is practicable by Stirling's Theorem, according to which we have approximately

$$1.2 \ldots . . i = i^{i+\frac{1}{2}} \epsilon^{-i} \sqrt{2\pi}$$

and therefore

$$\frac{n(n-1) \ldots . (n-i+1)}{1.2 \ldots . i} = \frac{n^n + \frac{1}{2}}{\sqrt{2\pi} i (i+\frac{1}{2})(n-i)^n}$$

Hence for the case

$$i = n \frac{a}{a+b}$$

which, according to the preceding formulæ, gives T_i its greatest value, we have

$$T_i = \frac{1}{\sqrt{2\pi n e f}}$$

where

$$e = \frac{a}{a+b} \text{ and } f = \frac{b}{a+b}$$

Thus, for example, let $n = 2 \times 10^{12}$;

$$e = .2, f = .8$$

we have

$$T_i = \frac{1}{800000\sqrt{\pi}} = \frac{1}{1418000}$$

This expresses the chance of there being 4×10^{11} molecules of oxygen in A, and 16×10^{11} in B. Just half this fraction expresses the probability that the molecules of nitrogen are distributed in exactly the same proportion between A and B, because the number of molecules of nitrogen is four times greater than of oxygen.

If n denote the molecules of one gas, and n' that of the molecules of another, the probability that each shall be distributed between A and B in the exact proportion of the volume is

$$\frac{1}{2\pi e f \sqrt{n\, n'}}$$

The value for the supposed case of oxygen and nitrogen is

$$\frac{1}{2\pi \times .16 \times 4 \times 10^{12}} = \frac{1}{4021 \times 10^9}$$

which is the result stated at the conclusion of the text above.

WILLIAM THOMSON

EDWARD E. DAUB

MAXWELL'S DEMON

IN HIS presentation of the 'two cultures' issue, C. P. Snow relates that he occasionally became so provoked at literary colleagues who scorned the restricted reading habits of scientists that he would challenge them to explain the second law of thermodynamics. The response was invariably a cold negative silence.[1] The test was too hard. Even a scientist would be hard-pressed to explain Carnot engines and refrigerators, reversibility and irreversibility, energy dissipation and entropy increase, Gibbs free energy and the Gibbs rule of phase, all in the span of a cocktail party conversation. How much more difficult, then, for a non-scientist. Even Henry Adams, who sought to find an analogy for his theory of history in the second law of thermodynamics, had great difficulty in understanding the rule of phase.

When Adams sought help with his manuscript 'The Rule of Phase Applied to History', he, too, encountered a cold silence. After months of search he complained to his brother Brooks that he had yet to discover a physicist 'who can be trusted to tell me whether my technical terms are all wrong'.[2] James F. Jameson, editor of the *American Historical Review*, responding to Henry's plea to find him 'a critic . . . a scientific, physico-chemical proof-reader', also met several rebuffs before he found the right man, Professor Henry A. Bumstead of Yale, a former student of Gibbs.[3] Bumstead's twenty-seven pages of detailed commentary must have satisfied Adams's hunger for 'annihilation by a competent hand',[4] as his revised version appeared only posthumously.[5] In it the chastened historian wrote that 'Willard Gibbs helped to change the face of science, but his Phase was not the Phase of History'.[6] Attracted to Gibbs's terminology because of the purely verbal agreement between physical phases and the epochs of Comtean history,[7] Adams erroneously adopted the phase rule as a scientific analogy for the progressive mutations of history.[8] If Maxwell had read Adams's misinterpretation of Gibbs's thought, he might have repeated his quip that the value of metaphysics is inversely proportional to the author's 'confidence in reasoning from the names of things',[9] but he would doubtless have been amused at the antics Adams attributed to his demon in history.

Adams once wrote to his brother Brooks that 'an atom is a man' and that 'Clerk Maxwell's demon who runs the second law of Thermodynamics ought to be made President'.[10] On another occasion he found Maxwell's demon a useful illustration for the behaviour of the German nation. 'Do you know the kinetic theory of gases?' he asked a British friend. 'Of course you do, since Clerk Maxwell was an Oxford man, I suppose. Anyway, Germany is and always has been a remarkably apt illustration of Maxwell's conception of "sorting demons". By bumping against all its neighbours, and being bumped in turn, it gets and gives at last a common motion.'[11] But such an aggressive mobile demon as the German nation was very different from the one Maxwell had conceived, a being who did not jostle atoms but arranged to separate them, not for the sake of generating some common motion but rather to illustrate Maxwell's contention that the second law of thermodynamics was statistical in character.

Maxwell's Tiny Intelligence and the Statistical Second Law

The fundamental basis for the second law of thermodynamics was Clausius's axiom that it is impossible for heat to pass from a colder to a warmer body unless some other change accompanies the process. To show that this law was only statistically true, Maxwell proposed a thought experiment in which a gas at uniform temperature and pressure was separated by a partition, equipped with a frictionless sliding door and operated by a tiny intelligence who could follow the movements of individual molecules. Although the temperature of the gas was uniform, the velocities of the gas molecules need not be, since temperature is the average kinetic energy of the molecules. The velocities should in fact vary, because the molecules would inevitably be exchanging energy in collisions. The demon might therefore circumvent the axiom regarding the behaviour of heat merely by separating the faster molecules from the slower. By permitting only fast molecules to enter one half and only slow molecules to leave it, Maxwell's tiny intelligence could create a temperature difference and a flow of heat from lower to higher temperatures. Maxwell concluded that the second law 'is undoubtedly true as long as we can deal with bodies only in mass, and have no power of perceiving or handling the separate molecules of which they are made up'. In the absence of such knowledge, we are limited to the statistical behaviour of molecules.[12]

Maxwell did not reach this insight immediately upon conceiving the idea of a tiny intelligence regulating the motions of molecules. His thought progressed (as did his characterizations) in the letters to Tait, Thomson and Rayleigh, where he first discussed this quaint creature. Upon introducing him to Tait in 1867 as a 'very observant and neat-fingered being', Maxwell prefaced his description by suggesting to Tait, who was deeply engrossed writing his *Sketch of Thermodynamics* at the time, that in his book Tait might 'pick a hole—say in the second law of $\theta\Delta^{cs}$., that if two things are in contact the hotter cannot take heat from the colder without external agency'. If only we were clever enough, Maxwell suggested, we too might mimic the neat-fingered one.[13] A month later, discussing his newly designated 'pointsman for flying molecules', he teased Thomson with the provocative thought, 'Hence energy need not be always dizzy-pated as in the present wasteful world'.[14]

Not, however, until three years later, when the 'intelligence' had grown to a mature 'doorkeeper . . . exceedingly quick', did Maxwell reach what became his enduring verdict: 'Moral. The 2nd law of thermodynamics has the same degree of truth as the statement that if you throw a tumblerful of water into the sea, you cannot get the same tumblerful of water out again.'[15] Thus was born Maxwell's prophetic insight that the second law of thermodynamics could never be given a mechanical interpretation based on the laws of pure dynamics which follow the motion of every particle. The second law was true only for matter *en masse*, and that truth was only statistical, not universal.

If Maxwell's demon was thus limited to operating a door for the sole purpose of demonstrating the statistical nature of the second law, where did Henry Adams get the idea of a Germanic bouncing demon who could generate a common motion? In his only public reference to the demon, Adams introduced the idea while criticizing the mechanistic view for omitting mind from the universe. Mind would be the only possible source for direction in an otherwise chaotic universe, Adams maintained, noting that 'The sum of motion without direction is zero, as in the motion of a kinetic gas where only Clerk Maxwell's demon of thought could create a value'.[16] This image of a demon who operates amidst molecules to create value from chaos stemmed from Adams's reading of William Thomson's ideas in 'The Sorting Demon of Maxwell'.[17]

Thomson's Demon and the Dissipation of Energy

It was Thomson who baptized and popularized the creature of Maxwell's imagination in an essay in 1874. Maxwell had introduced his brainchild in the span of a few pages in his *Theory of Heat*, describing him simply as a 'being whose faculties are so sharpened that he can follow every molecule in its course',[18] and Thomson went on to christen him the 'intelligent demon'.[19] Whereas Maxwell had stationed his lonely being at the single minute hole in a partitioning wall, there to separate the fleet from the slow, Thomson recruited a whole army of demons to wage war with cricket bats and drive back an onrushing hoard of diffusing molecules.[20] In his second essay, Thomson's description became even more anthropomorphic:

He is a being with no preternatural qualities, and differs from real living animals only in extreme smallness and agility. He can at pleasure stop, or strike, or push, or pull away any atom of matter, and so moderate its natural course of motion. Endowed equally with arms and hands—two hands and ten fingers suffice— he can do as much for atoms as a pianoforte player can do for the keys of the piano—just a little more, he can push or pull each atom in any direction.[21]

Thomson's amazing creature could even subdue the forces of chemical affinity by absorbing kinetic energy from moving molecules and then applying that energy to sever molecular bonds. 'Let him take in a small store of energy by resisting the mutual approach of two compound molecules, letting them press as it were on his two hands and store up energy as in a bent spring; then let him apply the two hands between the oxygen and double hydrogen constituents of a compound molecule of vapour of water, and tear them asunder.'[22] The exploits of Thomson's demon give the impression that his main role was to restore dissipated energy. Is motion lost in viscous friction? Simply sort out the molecules moving in one direction and motion reappears. Is heat lost by conduction? Simply separate the faster and slower moving molecules to restore the temperature gradient. Is chemical energy dissipated as heat? Simply use the kinetic energy of the molecules to tear asunder the chemical bonds.

Such an interpretation of the demon's activity appealed to Thomson, for he had been the first to suggest the rather dire image of a universe ruled by the inexorable second law of thermodynamics. In his 1852 paper on the universal dissipation of mechanical energy, Thomson had observed that mechanical energy is continually being dissipated into heat by friction and heat is continually being dissipated by conduction. In this state of affairs, the Earth and its life are caught in a vicious cycle of energy dissipation and decline unless there is action by some non-mechanical agency.[23] Maxwell's thought-experiment showed, however, that energy dissipation need not be irrevocable from the point of view of an acute and designing mind. ' "Dissipation of Energy" ', Thomson wrote, 'follows in nature from

the fortuitous concourse of atoms. The lost motivity is not restorable otherwise than by an agency dealing with atoms; and the mode of dealing with
the atoms is essentially a process of assortment.'[24]

Such an understanding of the nature of dissipation was not original with
Thomson. Maxwell had drawn the same analogy in far clearer terms,
though without reference to any demonic activity. In discussing the
difference between dissipated and available energy, Maxwell showed that
these concepts were relative to the extent of our knowledge:

It follows . . . that the idea of dissipation of energy depends on the extent of our
knowledge. Available energy is energy which we can direct into any desired
channel. Dissipated energy is energy which we cannot lay hold of and direct at
pleasure, such as the energy of the confused agitation of molecules which we call
heat. Now, confusion, like the correlative term order, is not a property of
material things in themselves, but only in relation to the mind which perceives
them. A memorandum-book does not, provided it is neatly written, appear
confused to an illiterate person, or to the owner who understands it thoroughly,
but to any other person able to read it appears to be inextricably confused.
Similarly the notion of dissipated energy would not occur to a being who could
not turn any of the energies of nature to his own account, or to one who could
trace the motion of every molecule and seize it at the right moment. It is only to
a being in the intermediate stage, who can lay hold of some forms of energy
while others elude his grasp, that energy appears to be passing inevitably from
the available to the dissipated state.[25]

It was thus Maxwell, not Thomson, who assigned the demon the role of
illuminating the nature of dissipated energy and of showing that all
energy remains available for a mind able to 'trace the motion of every
molecule and seize it at the right moment'. No doubt Maxwell first
conceived his tiny intelligence because he was concerned about energy
dissipation.

Why else would Maxwell have suggested to Tait in 1867 that he should
pick a hole in the second law of thermodynamics, namely, 'that if two
things are in contact the hotter cannot take heat from the colder without
external agency'? Why should Maxwell choose this problem and why did
he suggest that if man were clever enough he might mimic Maxwell's
thought-child? Why did Maxwell tease Thomson with the suggestion that
energy need not always be 'dizzypated as in the present wasteful world'?
Since Maxwell did not finally conclude that the second law is statistical
until three years later, he must have had some other reason for beginning
this chain of thought. The reason is to be found in Maxwell's concern
about energy dissipation. It is significant in this connection that Josef

Loschmidt, the scientist on the Continent who most abhorred the image of a decaying universe, also invented a 'demon' to thwart dissipation, even before Maxwell.

Loschmidt's Non-Demon and the Dynamical Interpretation of the Second Law

Ludwig Boltzmann, Loschmidt's colleague in Vienna, gives the following report of Loschmidt's invention in his account of Loschmidt's varied efforts to obviate the dire theoretical consequences of the second law:

On another occasion he imagined a tiny intelligent being who would be able to see the individual gas molecules and, by some sort of contrivance, to separate the slow ones from the fast and thereby, even if all activity [*Geschehen*] in the universe had ceased, to create new temperature differences. As we all know, this idea, which Loschmidt only hinted in a few lines of an article, was later proposed in Maxwell's *Theory of Heat* and was widely discussed.[26]

Boltzmann's memory, however, failed him on two counts. Loschmidt had devoted more than a few lines to the topic, but he had conceived no tiny intelligent creature. Boltzmann was recalling, not Loschmidt's original idea, but the later arguments he had had with Loschmidt concerning Maxwell's creation. In one of these discussions Boltzmann told Loschmidt that no intelligence could exist in a confined room at uniform temperature, at which point Josef Stefan, who had been listening quietly to the dispute, remarked to Loschmidt, 'Now I understand why your experiments in the basement with glass cylinders are such miserable failures'.[27] Loschmidt had been trying to observe gravitational concentration gradients in salt solutions as evidence for refuting the second law and its prediction of final uniformity.

Loschmidt's non-demon appeared in 1869.[28] It represented an attempt to do exactly the kind of thing which Maxwell had suggested to Tait, namely, 'to pick a hole' in the second law of thermodynamics. Loschmidt was also aiming at Clausius's statement that 'It is impossible for heat to pass from a colder to a warmer body without an equivalent compensation'.[29] Although the axiom was admittedly supported by ordinary experience, Loschmidt proposed to show that it was not true for all conceivable cases. Imagine, he said, a large space V with molecules moving about at various velocities, some above and some below the mean velocity c, plus a small adjoining space v that is initially empty. Consider now, he continued, a small surface element of the wall separating the two compartments and the succession of molecules striking it. Given the initial conditions of all the molecules, the order of their collisions with that surface element should be so fixed and determined that the element could be instructed to open and close in a pattern that would admit only the faster molecules into the empty space *v*.

Thus we can obviously conceive of these exchanges as so ordered that only those molecules whose velocities lie above the average value *c* may trespass into *v*, and it would further be possible to allow their number so to increase, that the density of the gas in *v* may become greater than that in *V*. It is therefore not theoretically impossible, without the expenditure of work or other compensation, to bring a gas from a lower to a higher temperature or even to increase its density.[30]

Thus, Loschmidt's conception was both earlier and far less anthropomorphic than Maxwell's doorkeeper.

In some of his later writings, Maxwell moved in Loschmidt's direction. When Maxwell wrote to Rayleigh in 1870, just before the only public appearance of his idea in the *Theory of Heat*, he noted, 'I do not see why even intelligence might not be dispensed with and the thing made self-acting'.[31] In a final undated summary statement entitled 'Concerning Demons', he reduced his creature to a valve:

Is the production of an inequality their only occupation? No, for less intelligent demons can produce a difference of pressure as well as temperature by merely allowing all particles going in one direction while stopping all those going the other way. This reduces the demon to a valve. As such value him. Call him no more a demon but a valve. . . .[32]

But although Maxwell had revised his thinking and moved from a tiny intelligence to a more mechanical device, he still claimed the same important and distinctive role for his thought experiment. What, he asked, is the chief end of my creature? 'To show that the 2nd Law of Thermodynamics has only a statistical certainty.'[33]

Loschmidt drew a very different conclusion from the ability of his non-demon to create temperature differences. Since the absolute validity of Clausius's axiom had been rendered doubtful, he argued, the second law of thermodynamics must be established on other grounds, namely, on those very dynamical foundations[34] which Maxwell's demon had led Maxwell to reject. Thus, despite their common origin in the desire to pick a hole in the second law of thermodynamics, Maxwell's demon and Loschmidt's non-demon performed strikingly different roles. In Maxwell's view, the demon did not undermine Clausius's axiom as a basis for the second law of thermodynamics. Since the axiom was statistically true, the predictions based upon it, namely, the irreversible increase in entropy and the increasing dissipation of energy, were valid conclusions. Since these truths were only statistical, however, Maxwell scorned supposed proofs of the second law based upon dynamical studies that traced the motions of individual atoms.

In his *Theory of Heat* Maxwell had raised the following question: 'It would be interesting to enquire how far those ideas . . . derived from the dynamical method . . . are applicable to our actual knowledge of concrete things, which . . . is of an essentially statistical character'.[35] Although that query stood unchanged throughout the four editions of Maxwell's book, his own conviction became clear in candid comments to Tait with regard to various attempts, notably by Clausius and Boltzmann, to explain the second law of thermodynamics by means of Hamilton's equations in dynamics. In 1873 he jested in lyrical fashion:

But it is rare sport to see those learned Germans contending for the priority in the discovery that the second law of $\theta\Delta^{cs}$ is the Hamiltonsche Princip. . . . The Hamiltonsche Princip the while soars along in a region unvexed by statistical considerations while the German Icari flap their waxen wings in nephelococcygin, amid those cloudy forms which the ignorance and finitude of human science have invested with the incommunicable attributes of the invisible Queen of Heaven.[36]

In 1876, he was pungently clear. No pure dynamical statement, he said, 'would submit to such an indignity'.[37] There in essence lay the true scientific role of Maxwell's doorkeeper, to show the folly of seeking to prove a statistical law as though it expressed the ordered behaviour of traditional dynamic models.

In Loschmidt's thought, a similar devotion to mechanics led to a very different orientation. Since his non-demon disproved the unconditional validity of Clausius's axiom, the appearances, he felt, must be deceptive. The true basis for the second law must lie in traditional dynamical principles. Loschmidt stated his fundamental position most clearly in 1876 when he said: 'Since the second law of the mechanical theory of heat, just like the first, should be a principle of analytical mechanics, then it must be valid, not only under the conditions which occur in nature, but also with complete generality, for systems with any molecular form and under any assumed forces, both intermolecular and external'.[38] He then conceived a variety of models in which columns of atoms in thermal equilibrium would exhibit a temperature gradient and thus contradict the usual thermodynamic axiom proposed by Clausius. Loschmidt concluded that

Clausius's axiom was an inadequate basis for the second law, since these molecular models, which fulfilled all the requisite conditions for proving the second law from Hamilton's principle, did not entail the truth of that axiom.[39]

Loschmidt rejoiced that the threatening implications of the second law for the fate of the universe were finally disproved:

Thereby the terrifying *nimbus* of the second law, by which it was made to appear as a principle annihilating the total life of the universe, would also be destroyed; and mankind could take comfort in the disclosure that humanity was not solely dependent upon coal or the Sun in order to transform heat into work, but would have an inexhaustible supply of transformable heat at hand in all ages.[40]

When Loschmidt pressed his case against Clausius's axiom even further, however, by raising the so-called reversibility paradox, he forced Boltzmann to conclude that no dynamical interpretation of the second law is possible.

Loschmidt's Reversibility Paradox and the Statistical Second Law

The dynamical interpretations of the second law which Loschmidt favoured were restricted to those cases where entropy is conserved in the universe. Such processes are generally called reversible because they are so ideally contrived that the original conditions may always be completely recovered. No entropy increase or dissipation of energy occurs in reversible cycles. Interpretations of the second law based on Clausius's axiom, however, consider another type of process, the irreversible case in which entropy irrevocably increases and energy dissipates. According to Clausius, there were three possible cases corresponding to negative, zero and positive changes in entropy. The negative entropy change was impossible because that would be equivalent to a flow of heat from a cold to a hot body, contrary to Clausius's axiom. Entropy was a quantity, therefore, which could only remain constant or increase, depending on whether the process was reversible or irreversible.[41] Loschmidt's dynamical interpretation would only countenance the reversible case. Boltzmann, however, sought a dynamical interpretation for the irreversible increase in entropy as well, and it was to refute that possibility that Loschmidt created his reversibility paradox.

In order to have a dynamical interpretation of the irreversible case, there would have to be a mathematical function which showed a unilateral change to a maximum, after which it would remain constant, thereby reflecting the irreversible increase of entropy to a maximum at equilibrium. Boltzmann had derived such a function from an analysis of the collisions between molecules. To refute such an idea, only a single counter-example is necessary. One need only demonstrate that there exists at least one distribution of molecular velocities and positions from which the opposite behaviour would proceed. Loschmidt provided just such a thought-experiment. Imagine, he said, a system of particles where all are at rest at the bottom of the container except for one which is at rest some distance above. Let that particle fall and collide with the others, thus initiating motion among them. The ensuing process would lead to increasingly dis-ordered motion until the system reached an apparently static equilibrium, just as the proponents of irreversible entropy change to an equilibrium would predict. But now imagine the instantaneous reversal of every single velocity and the very opposite process becomes inevitable. At first, little change would be evident, but the system would gradually move back towards the initially ordered situation in which all particles were at rest on the bottom and only one rested at a height above them.[42] Boltzmann labelled this Loschmidt's paradox, and a real paradox it became, since Boltzmann managed to reverse all of Loschmidt's conclusions.

The paradox revealed to Boltzmann that his attempt to find a dynamical function of molecular motion which would mirror the behaviour of entropy could only lead to a dead end, for whatever the mathematical function might be, the mere reversal of velocities would also reverse the supposedly unidirectional behaviour of that function. Boltzmann concluded that no purely dynamical proof of the second law would ever be possible and that the irreversible increase of entropy must reflect, not a mechanical law, but states of differing probabilities. Systems move towards equilibrium simply because the number of molecular states which correspond to equilibrium is vastly greater than the number of more ordered states of low entropy. Boltzmann offered an analogy to the Quinterns used in Lotto. Each Quintern has an equal probability of appearing, but a Quintern with a disordered arrangement of numbers is far more likely to appear than one with an ordered arrangement such as 12345. Boltzmann therefore provided the key for quantifying the statistical interpretation of the second law in terms of the relative numbers of molecular states that correspond to equilibrium and non-equilibrium.[43]

Thus, the chief end of Maxwell's creature, 'to show that the 2nd Law of Thermodynamics has only a statistical certainty', became established as a cardinal principle of classical physics by way of Loschmidt's non-demon and his reversibility paradox. Although Maxwell's demon has served to popularize the statistical interpretation of the second law through genera- tions of thermodynamics textbooks, a new thought-experiment involving information theory has now challenged the demon's traditional role. The arguments made there suggest that Maxwell's brainchild must, alas, be laid to rest.

The Price of Information

Consider the case, often discussed in information theory and originally introduced by Szilard in 1929,[44] where but a single molecule is involved. If the second law is merely statistical, then it certainly should fail to meet the test of this simplest of all arrangements. Pierce has described a modified version of Szilard's innovation as follows. Consider a piston equipped with a large trapdoor and with arrangements to allow the piston to lift weights by moving either left or right. Initially the piston is not connected to any weights; it is moved to the centre of the cylinder while the trap door is kept open, thus assuring that no collisions with the lone molecule in the cylinder can occur and that, therefore, no work will be required. Then the trap door is closed and the piston clamped into its central position. The molecule must be entrapped on one of the two sides of the piston, and Maxwell's demon informs us whether it is on the left or the right. With that information in hand, the piston is released and the molecule is made to do work by driving the weightless piston and a suitably suspended weight towards the empty side. The maximum possible work may be readily calculated; it would amount to $W = 0.693\ kT$.[45] In Maxwell's day, the demon would have chalked up another victory, but not now.

'Did we get this mechanical work free?' Pierce succinctly asks. 'Not quite!'

In order to know which pan to put the weight on, we need one bit of information, specifying which side the molecule is on. . . . What is the very least energy needed to transmit one bit of information at the temperature T? . . . exactly $0.693\ kT$ joule, just equal to the most energy the machine can generate. . . . Thus, we use up all the output of the machine in transmitting enough informa- tion to make the machine run![46]

Thus, the reign of Maxwell's brainchild in physics, designed to demon- strate that the second law of thermodynamics has only statistical validity, has come to an end.

The mood of the scientific community had changed. The second law was no longer subject to reproach for the indignities Maxwell and Loschmidt supposed it would inflict on pure dynamics. It was natural, therefore, to extend the province of the law and challenge all imagined contradictions. Szilard was the first to stress that any manipulator of molecules would have to rely on measurement and memory. If one assumed that the demon could perform such operations without causing any changes in the system, one would by that very assumption deny the second law, which requires equivalent compensations for all decreases in entropy.[47] Szilard therefore proposed that whatever negative entropy Maxwell's demon might be able to create should be considered as compensated by an equal entropy increase due to the measurements the demon had to make. In essence, Szilard made Maxwell's doorkeeper mortal—no longer granting this tiny intelligence the ability to 'see' molecules without actually seeing them, *i.e.*, without the sensory exchanges of energy that all other existences require. Szilard took this step for the sake of a grander vision, the dream that the adoption of his principle would lead to the discovery of a more general law of entropy in which there would be a completely universal relation for all measurements.[48] Information theory has brought that vision to reality.

One puzzling question, however, remains. Why did Maxwell not realize that his creature required energy in order to detect molecules? Brillouin has suggested that Maxwell did not have an adequate theory of radiation at his disposal. 'It is not surprising', he said, 'that Maxwell did not think of including radiation in the system in equilibrium at temperature *T*. Black body radiation was hardly known in 1871, and it was thirty years before the thermodynamics of radiation was clearly understood.'[49] It is certainly true that a quantitative expression for radiant energy and the entropy of information would require an adequate theory of black body radiation, but the absence of such a detailed theory does not explain why Maxwell failed to realize that some energy exchanges were required.

If we were able to ask Maxwell, 'Why did you not require your tiny intelligence to use energy in gathering his information?', Maxwell would no doubt reply, 'Of course! Why didn't I think of that?'[50] Why didn't Maxwell think of that? Because his demon was the creature of his theology.

The Demon and Theology

Maxwell's demon is the very image of the Newtonian God who has ultimate dominion over the world and senses the world in divine immediacy. Newton wrote in his General Scholium:

It is allowed by all that the Supreme God exists necessarily, and by the same necessity he exists *always* and *everywhere*. Whence also he is all similar, all eye, all ear, all brain, all arm, all power to perceive, to understand, and to act; but in a manner not at all human, in a manner not at all corporeal, in a manner utterly unknown to us. As a blind man has no idea of colour, so we have no idea of the manner by which the all-wise God perceives and understands all things.[51]

How natural it was for Maxwell, faced with the idea of a universe destined towards dissipation, to conceive a being on the model of God, for whom the universe always remains ordered and under his rule. A memorandum-book, Maxwell said, does not appear confused to its owner though it does to any other reader. Nor would the notion of dissipated energy occur to 'a being who could trace the motion of every molecule and seize it at the right moment'. Maxwell's demon was not mortal because he was made in the image of God. And like God, he could see without seeing and hear without hearing. In short, he could acquire information without any expenditure of energy.

Upon being asked by a clergyman for a viable scientific idea to explain how, in the *Genesis* account, light could be created on the first day although the Sun did not appear until the third day, Maxwell replied that he did not favour reinterpreting the text in terms of prevailing scientific theory. To tie a religious idea to a changeable scientific view, Maxwell said, would only serve to keep that scientific idea in vogue long after it deserved to be dead and buried.[52] Thus Maxwell would certainly sever the demon's ties to theology if he were faced with Szilard's requirements for the cost of information. Witnessing the demise of his creature, he would not long mourn at the grave but rather be grateful for the exciting years his thought-child had enjoyed. Steeped in the knowledge and love of biblical imagery, Maxwell would doubtless take pleasure in the thought that by becoming mortal his doorkeeper had prepared the way for new life in science.[53]

University of Kansas

NOTES

[1] C. P. Snow, *The Two Cultures and the Scientific Revolution* (New York, 1961), 15–16.

[2] H. D. Cater, ed., *Henry Adams and his Friends* (Boston, 1947), 640.

[3] *Ibid.*, 646–7, 650n.

[4] *Ibid.*, 647.

[5] E. Samuels, *Henry Adams: The Major Phase* (Cambridge, 1964), 450: 'Adams minutely revised the essay during the next year or two to meet Bumstead's more specific criticisms. . . . The firm outlines of the script would suggest that all of these changes were made before his stroke in 1912.

No indication remains that he submitted the revised essay to the *North American Review*. Not until 1919, a year after his death, did it appear in Brooks Adams's edition of Henry's "philosophical writings", *The Degradation of the Democratic Dogma. . . .'.

[6] H. Adams, *The Degradation of the Democratic Dogma*, ed. B. Adams (New York, 1919), 267.

[7] W. H. Jordy, *Henry Adams: Scientific Historian* (New Haven, 1952), 166.

[8] *Ibid.*, 169, 170.

[9] Maxwell–Tait Correspondence, Cambridge University Library; letter to Tait, 23 December 1867: 'I have read some metaphysics of various kinds and find it more or less ignorant discussion of mathematical and physical principles, jumbled with a little physiology of the senses. The value of metaphysics is equal to the mathematical and physical knowledge of the author divided by his confidence in reasoning from the names of things.'

[10] Letter to Brooks Adams, 2 May 1903, *op. cit.*, note 2, 545.

[11] H. Adams, *Letters of Henry Adams (1892–1918)*, ed. N. C. Ford (Boston, 1938). Letter to Cecil Spring Rice, 11 November 1897, 135–6.

[12] J. C. Maxwell, *The Theory of Heat*, 2nd edition (London, 1872), 308–9.

[13] Letter from Maxwell to Tait, 11 December 1867, quoted in C. G. Knott, *Life and Scientific Work of Peter Guthrie Tait* (Cambridge, 1911), 213–14.

[14] Letter from Maxwell to William Thomson, 16 January 1868, Edinburgh University Library.

[15] Letter from Maxwell to Strutt, 6 December 1870, quoted in R. J. Strutt, *John William Strutt* (London, 1924), 47.

[16] Adams, *op. cit.*, note 6, 279.

[17] W. Thomson, 'The Sorting Demon of Maxwell', reprinted in *Popular Lectures and Addresses*, Vol. 1 (London, 1889), 137–41.

[18] Maxwell, *op. cit.*, note 12, 308.

[19] W. Thomson, 'Kinetic Theory of the Dissipation of Energy', *Nature*, 9 (1874), 442.

[20] *Ibid.*

[21] Thomson, *op. cit.*, note 17, 137–8.

[22] *Ibid.*, 140.

[23] W. Thomson, 'On a Universal Tendency in Nature to the Dissipation of Mechanical Energy', *Philosophical Magazine*, 4 (1852), 256–60.

[24] Thomson, *op. cit.*, note 17, 139.

[25] J. C. Maxwell, 'Diffusion', *Encyclopedia Britannica*, 9th edition (New York, 1878), vol. 7, 220.

[26] L. Boltzmann, 'Zur Errinerung an Josef Loschmidt', in *Populäre Schriften* (Leipzig, 1905), 231. (I am indebted to R. Dugas, *La théorie physique au sens Boltzmann* (Neuchatel, 1959), 171, note 2, for this reference.)

[27] *Ibid.*

[28] J. Loschmidt, 'Der zweite Satz der mechanischen Wärmetheorie', *Akademie der Wissenschaften, Wien. Mathematisch-Naturwissenschaftliche Klasse, Sitzungsberichte*, **59,** Abth. 2 (1869), 395–418.

[29] *Ibid.*, 399. The editor must have slipped, however, since the text reads 'Die Wärme geht niemals aus einem heisseren in einen kälteren über ohne eine äquivalente Compensation'.

[30] *Ibid.*, 401.

[31] Quoted in Strutt, *op. cit.*, note 15, 47.

[32] Quoted in Knott, *op. cit.*, note 13, 215. Knott seems to have erred in suggesting that this undated letter was penned at about the same time that Maxwell originally proposed his idea to Tait in December 1867.

[33] *Ibid.*

[34] Loschmidt, *op. cit.*, note 28, 401–6.

[35] Maxwell, *op. cit.*, note 12, 309.

[36] Letter from Maxwell to Tait, Tripos, December 1873, Maxwell-Tait Correspondence, Cambridge University Library.

[37] Letter from Maxwell to Tait, 13 October 1876, *ibid*. Martin Klein's recent article, 'Maxwell, his Demon, and the Second Law of Thermodynamics', *American Scientist*, **58** (1970), 84–97, treats these attempts to reduce the second law to dynamics in considerable detail.

[38] J. Loschmidt, 'Ueber den Zustand des Wärmegleichgewichtes eines System von Körpern', *Sitzungsberichte* (see note 28), **73,** Abth. 2 (1876), 128.

[39] *Ibid.*, 128–35.

[40] *Ibid.*, 135.

[41] R. Clausius, 'Ueber eine veränderte Form des zweiten Hauptsatzes der mechanischen Wärmetheorie', *Annalen der Physik*, **93** (1854), 481–506. Clausius did not use the word 'entropy' until 1865. In the original paper he spoke of the sum of transformation values $\int dQ/T = N$ for a cycle, where $N < 0$ was impossible, $N = 0$ was the reversible case, and $N > 0$ was the irreversible cycle.

[42] Loschmidt, *op. cit.*, note 38, 137–9.

[43] L. Boltzmann, 'Bemerkungen über einige Probleme der mechanischen Wärmetheorie' (1877), reprinted in *Wissenschaftliche Abhandlungen von Ludwig Boltzmann*, ed. F. Hasenohrl (Leipzig, 1909), Vol. II, 120.

[44] L. Szilard, 'Ueber die Entropieverminderung in einem thermodynamischen System bei Eingriffen intelligenter Wesen', *Zeitschrift für Physik*, **53** (1929), 840–56.

[45] J. R. Pierce, *Symbols, Signals, and Noise* (New York, 1961), 198–201.

[46] *Ibid.*, 201.

[47] Szilard, *op. cit.*, note 44, 842.

[48] *Ibid.*, 843.

[49] L. Brillouin, *Science and Information Theory* (New York, 1956), 164.

[50] I am indebted to my colleague Richard Cole of the Kansas University Philosophy Department for this thought-experiment.

[51] I. Newton, *Newton's Philosophy of Nature*, ed. H. S. Thayer (New York, 1953), 44.

[52] L. Campbell and W. Garnett, *The Life of James Clerk Maxwell* (London, 1882), 394.

[53] The support of the National Science Foundation is gratefully acknowledged.

P. M. HEIMANN

MOLECULAR FORCES, STATISTICAL REPRESENTATION AND MAXWELL'S DEMON

I

THIS paper is concerned with Maxwell's discussion of the nature of molecular forces and of the use of statistical methods in gas theory, and with some epistemological and methodological aspects of his work on the kinetic theory of gases. His discussion of these problems arose from his two classic papers on gas theory: Maxwell used a statistical distribution function to describe the velocities of gas molecules and—it will be argued—his work on the theory of gases was governed by his interest in the nature of matter. In his first attempt to formulate a theory of gases, in 'Illustrations of the Dynamical Theory of Gases' (1860), he used an elastic-sphere model for the molecules and described collisions between such molecules.[1] He subsequently abandoned this molecular model in his paper 'On the Dynamical Theory of Gases' (1867), where he used a 'centre of force' molecule. In this paper he did not consider collisions, the impact of elastic spheres, but intermolecular encounters, the interactions between 'centres of force'.[2] In his later work on gas theory he further considered the problem of the nature of molecular forces and came to question the principle that the same laws applied to micro- as to macro-phenomena; I will suggest that he implicitly questioned the transference of the laws of dynamics to the motions of individual molecules.

His use of statistical representation to describe the velocities of gas molecules was fundamental to his theory of gases. Maxwell did not consider that this method was a temporary mode of representation which would be replaced by a treatment of the motions of individual molecules, but regarded it rather as a method imposed by the phenomena, that is, by experiments on sensible aggregates of molecules. He nevertheless argued that individual, insensible molecules were not subject to 'chance and change', for their behaviour was 'certain and immutable';[3] the statistical method was not applicable to the motions of individual molecules. Here I shall be concerned with Maxwell's distinction between the treatment of a sensible aggregate of molecules; individual, observable particles; and individual, insensible particles. Maxwell's distinction between individual molecules and an immense number of molecules will be illustrated by consideration of the famous 'demon', which he employed to express the difference between laws applicable at the macro- and micro-levels.

II

The origins of Maxwell's interest in the theory of gases is particularly important because his interest appears to have arisen from a concern with the use of statistical, probabilistic methods and with the problem of collisions between particles, which were fundamental to his discussions of the nature of matter in his papers on gas theory. As will be shown in section III, there can be no doubt that the crucial influence on Maxwell was Clausius's work on the theory of gases (which Maxwell read in 1859) in which arguments involving probabilities were used.[4] But two other factors may well have influenced Maxwell, and though in part both have been suggested before, little evidence has been adduced in their favour. Before examining the relations between the theories of Maxwell and Clausius and the attendant problems of molecular forces, these two factors will be discussed, and it will be emphasized that they were both to relate to features of Clausius's theory.

The first concerns the origins of Maxwell's interest in the method of analysis by probabilities. It has been suggested[5] that Maxwell learned of probabilities from John Herschel's review of Quetelet's *Letters on . . . Probabilities*[6] in the *Edinburgh Review* in July 1850.[7] From his letters[8] it seems likely that Maxwell read the review when it first appeared, and he certainly came upon it again when it was reprinted in Herschel's *Essays* in 1857.[9] A case for his interest in probabilities before he read Clausius's paper—in which such methods were used—is not implausible, and this case can be strengthened.

In his *Outlines of Astronomy* (1849),[10] Herschel referred to John Michell's use of probabilistic arguments in 1767 in connection with the distribution of stars.[11] This use of probabilities, as reported by Herschel, was immediately attacked by Maxwell's Edinburgh professor, J. D. Forbes, in the *Philosophical Magazine*. Forbes made the point that probabilities were inapplicable to the case of stellar distribution: Michell had assumed the probability of the uniform spacing of stars, but Forbes argued that the assumption of the probability of uniform spacing was 'inconsistent with a total absence of Law or Principle',[12] and that probability arguments depended on the assumption of random—or lawless—distribution. Herschel gave an account of the method of probabilities as applied to stellar distribution in his anonymous review of Quetelet, dismissing Forbes's objections.[13] Forbes replied with a long paper in the *Philosophical Magazine*[14] re-emphasizing his logical objections, arguing that to assume that stars were likely to be evenly distributed was 'obviously at variance with the idea of random or lawless distribution',[15] and hence an appeal to the mathematical theory of probabilities was a 'false step'.[16]

The method of probabilities as a method firmly founded on logical principles was defended shortly afterwards by George Boole,[17] who discussed the logical question raised by Forbes. Boole's point was that in the formal relations of logic and arithmetic 'lies the basis of a new and general theory of probabilities', and he was not concerned with the content of propositions which might be considered in terms of the theory of probabilities but with their form, 'the mere logical connexion'.[18] Boole's argument was significant, then, as a defence of the theory of probabilities as a mathematical method. He followed this paper with several others on probabilities, all published in the *Philosophical Magazine*,[19] and the theory that probabilities were founded on logic was fully argued in his *Investigation of the Laws of Thought* (1854). In view of Maxwell's interest in Boole's work[20] and the contribution of Forbes to the debate on probabilities—at the time when Maxwell was his pupil at Edinburgh University—there seems some reason to connect Maxwell's remarks on probabilities in his letters with Herschel's review, and to infer that Maxwell might well have become interested in probabilities before seeing Clausius's theory. In addition, Maxwell might well have noted J. S. Mill's discussion of the logic of probabilities in his *System of Logic* (1843), which Maxwell read in 1854.[21]

The other factor in the origin of Maxwell's interest in gas theory was suggested by William Garnett in the *Life of James Clerk Maxwell*. Garnett argued that Maxwell's work on Saturn's rings led him to gas theory.[22] In his Adams Prize essay 'On the Stability of the Motion of Saturn's Rings', which was completed in 1858,[23] Maxwell showed that the rings were a collection of small particles, and he investigated their gravitational attraction. He did not consider the collisions of the particles but did note that 'when we come to deal with collisions among bodies of unknown number, size, and shape, we can no longer trace the mathematical laws of their motion with any distinctness'.[24] He was thus interested in the problem of particulate collisions shortly before he was to become interested in gas theory. Clausius's theory involved a treatment of such collisions probabilistically, and would clearly have excited his interest under these circumstances, particularly in view of the likelihood of his prior interest in the method of probabilities. Maxwell certainly did associate the problem of the rings of Saturn with problems in gas theory, for in a manuscript dating from the early 1860s on 'The Mathematical Theory of Saturn's Rings', he pointed out that: 'In my former paper I restricted myself to cases in which no collisions take place . . . [But the particles] influence each other far more by collisions and jostling than by the attraction of gravitation. . . . The principle by which problems of this kind can be treated were first discussed by Prof. Clausius . . . [and] by myself.'[25] In other words, the problem which had eluded him before he had worked on the theory of gases could now be solved using methods he had employed in his work on gas theory.

Both these factors, however, have relation to features in Clausius's work, and it was the problems of the nature of matter and molecular forces raised by Clausius that were to be discussed by Maxwell.

III

In 1859 Maxwell read his paper 'Illustrations of the Dynamical Theory of Gases' to the British Association in Aberdeen. His purpose was to investigate the nature of matter by 'determining accurately the mean length of path which a particle describes between two successive collisions'.[26] Maxwell's success in calculating the mean length of path between molecular collisions was a major advance on Clausius's theory of gases, on which his own theory was founded.

Clausius was drawn to the study of gases by his interest in explaining heat in terms of molecular motions,[27] and in two papers[28] he introduced the concept of mean free path and the method of probabilities into gas theory. In his first paper, published in 1857, he used an elastic-sphere model for the molecules and assumed that his numerical values for the velocities of the molecules of gases were mean values, arguing that 'although it is not actually necessary that a molecule should obey the ordinary laws of elasticity . . . the laws of probability . . . indicate that no difference will be produced in the final result if we assume that for each molecule the angle and velocity of reflection are equal to those of incidence'.[29] In this first paper Clausius assumed that intermolecular forces were unimportant, but he was unable to explain the slow diffusion of gas molecules[30] and, in his second paper, which was published in 1858, he introduced a more sophisticated molecular model and the concept of the mean free path.[31] He now attached great importance to the effect of molecular forces, and he argued that (if the forces of chemical affinity were ignored) there were two forces associated with a molecule, for 'when two molecules approach one another an attraction is at first exerted, which begins to be of sensible effect even at some distance, and which increases as the distance diminishes; but that, when the molecules have arrived into the immediate neighbour-hood of one another, a force comes into play which seeks to drive them asunder'.[32] He emphasized that he did not intend to discuss the problem of the cause and nature of the forces: whether they were due to the parti-cles of matter or to an imponderable fluid, or whether the repulsive force began to act before the actual contact of the molecules.[33] The inter-molecular forces were thus attractive at some sensible distances and repulsive at smaller separations.[34]

Clausius went on to define a distance ρ at which the attractive and repulsive forces balanced; if the centres of gravity in an encounter were at distances greater than ρ then they would only interact through recipro-cal attraction, whereas if the distance of encounter was less than ρ the repulsive force would come into play 'and a rebounding of the molecules takes place'.[35] This latter case would be considered as one of impact, and was the only case that Clausius discussed. He argued that a sphere of radius ρ could be described around a molecule, and he called this the '*sphere of action*' of the molecule.[36] The problem he attempted to solve was 'how far, on the average, can the molecule move, before its centre of gravity comes into the sphere of action of another molecule';[37] he called this distance the mean free path of the molecule. He was able to obtain an expression for the ratio of the mean free path to the sphere of action, but not to obtain values for these magnitudes.[38] It was thus only in the second of these papers that the concept of the mean free path was introduced.

As is clear from Maxwell's correspondence,[39] it was reading Clausius's second paper in translation in the *Philosophical Magazine* that led him to an interest in the theory of gases, and he developed Clausius's ideas in his 1860 paper 'Illustrations of the Dynamical Theory of Gases'. In this paper Maxwell used an elastic-sphere model, showing that the molecules moved equally in all directions of space; his physical model followed that of Clausius's first paper on gas theory. Maxwell demonstrated that, though the molecules would have different velocities and the velocities of indi-vidual molecules might change, the average number of molecules with a distribution of velocities within certain limits did not change at equilibrium. These elements of Maxwell's theory correspond to Clausius's first paper, but Clausius had not introduced a statistical treatment of the distribution of the motions of the molecules in either of his papers. Maxwell assumed that all motions were equally probable and that the probability distributions for the velocity components of a molecule in different directions were independent of one another, and from these assumptions he obtained his distribution law.[40] This was an advance on Clausius's treatment, for Maxwell was able to calculate the distribution of velocities among the particles, not merely their mean square velocity. As Maxwell told Stokes, he was able to show that 'the velocities are distributed [among the particles] according to the same formula as the errors are distributed in the theory of least squares'.[41]

On the basis of the elastic-sphere molecule Maxwell was able to calculate the mean free path. It was this feature of Clausius's second paper (1858) which particularly attracted his interest, but he used the elastic-sphere model of Clausius's first paper (1857). Indeed, a prediction which depended on the elastic-sphere model was to prove crucial to the theory of 'Illustrations'; this was, that the viscosity varied as the square root of the temperature.[42]

Maxwell's emphasis in this paper was on investigating the nature of matter. He assumed 'an indefinite number of small, hard and perfectly elastic spheres acting on one another',[43] but for him this was only a temporary hypothesis. He told George Stokes that he intended to 'arrange my propositions about the motions of elastic spheres in a manner independent of the speculations about gases',[44] just as in 1855 he had told William Thomson—with reference to his paper 'On Faraday's Lines of Force'[45]—that 'I have been planning and partly executing a system of propositions about lines of force &c which may be *afterwards* applied to Electricity, Heat, or Magnetism'.[46] Maxwell stated that 'if the properties of such a system of bodies are found to correspond to those of gases, an important physical analogy will be established, which may lead to more accurate knowledge of the properties of matter'.[47] He was by no means committed to the elastic-sphere model of gas molecules, and noted that this led to the same results as the assumption that 'the particles are centres of force, of which the action is insensible except at a certain small distance, when it suddenly appears as a repulsive force of very great intensity'.[48]

Maxwell's first formulation of the theory of gases was criticized by Clausius in 1862.[49] Clausius was able to show that Maxwell's assumption in deriving the velocity distribution function (*viz.*, that all directions of motion in the gas were equally probable) was invalid, for the motion of the molecules was affected by temperature differences. Maxwell tried to meet Clausius's criticisms but was unable to obtain an appropriate distribution function, and did not publish this projected paper.[50] Shortly afterwards, however, his own determination of viscosities showed him that viscosity varied directly with temperature,[51] a result which contradicted his elastic-sphere model. This undoubtedly led him to reconsider his approach to the problem of molecular structure; this in turn enabled him to revise his derivation of the distribution function. It was thus by emphasizing the problem of the nature of matter that Maxwell was able to meet Clausius's arguments.

In his paper on 'The Dynamical Theory of Gases' (published in 1867),[52] Maxwell adopted the 'centre of force' molecule of Clausius's second paper but abandoned the mean free path concept of that paper. In the 'Dynamical Theory of Gases' he considered 'encounters' between molecules rather than 'collisions' (between elastic spheres), as in the earlier paper.[53] He was able to obtain the same expression as before for the distribution function, but he now used statistical methods to analyse the encounters of two molecules, assuming that the velocities of the two molecules, rather than the velocity components of a single molecule (as in the 1860 paper), were statistically independent.[54] He found that if the law of repulsion of his centre of force molecules was an inverse fifth-power law, the viscosity varied directly with the temperature.[55] This was the force law he adopted, and the elastic-sphere model was here abandoned in favour of considering molecules as 'mere points or pure centres of force endowed with inertia'.[56]

His earlier use of an elastic-sphere model was a temporary physical hypothesis, used as a result of his intention, as he put it in his paper 'On Faraday's Lines of Force', of presenting 'the mathematical ideas to the mind in an embodied form . . . not as mere symbols which neither convey the same ideas, nor readily adapt themselves to the phenomena to be explained',[57] but his use of a centre of force molecule here must be understood as a mathematical model, for he went on to point out that he did not specify the nature of the molecules: the molecules could be systems of several centres of force, or could even be small, solid bodies.[58]

IV

This concern with the nature of matter can also be seen in his later discussions of the problem of molecular forces, and again his ideas can be seen to derive from Clausius. In a discussion of the work of van der Waals in 1874, Maxwell pointed out that the deviations from Boyle's law by gases at high pressures were due to 'the mutual action of molecules when engaged in close encounter', and he referred to experiments by Andrews on carbon dioxide at high pressures.[59] He argued that these experiments indicated that

the molecules of gases attract each other at a certain small distance, but when they are brought still nearer they repel each other. This is quite in accordance with Boscovich's theory of atoms as massive centres of force, the force being a function of the distance, and changing from attractive to repulsive, and back again several times, as the distance diminishes.[60]

In his lecture on 'The Dynamical Evidence of the Molecular Constitution of Bodies' the following year, he discussed the problem of attractive and repulsive forces associated with molecules, again prompted by the necessity of accounting for deviations from Boyle's law. He stated that

the action between two particles at any sensible distance is quite insensible. As the two particles approach each other the action first shows itself as an attraction, which reaches a maximum, then diminishes, and at length becomes a repulsion so great that no attainable force can reduce the distance of the particles to zero.[61]

This problem was clearly one which preoccupied him at this time, and in the following year (1876) he gave it an extended analysis in his referee's report on one of Andrews's papers. He pointed out that

the action between the two molecules is not like a collision confined to a definite distance between the encountering molecules, but extends through a certain range. . . . As two molecules approach each other, the action between them is insensible at all sensible distances. At some exceedingly small distance it begins as an attractive force, reaches a maximum at a still smaller distance and then becomes repulsive. In certain cases such as that of two kinds of molecule which can enter into chemical combination but which do not do so combine when simply mixed, we must admit that within the region of repulsion there is a second region of attraction, and if we continue to believe that two bodies cannot be in the same place we must also admit that the force becomes repulsive, and that in a very high degree, when the atoms are as near together as is possible.

These attractive and repulsive forces may be regarded as facts established by experiment, like the fact of gravitation, without assuming either that they are ultimate facts or that they are to be explained in a particular way.[62]

Maxwell went on to refer to 'the sphere about the centre of a molecule with a radius such that if the centre of any other molecule is outside this sphere the action between them will be insensible' as the 'sphere of action of the molecule'.

His whole approach, his use of the phrase 'sphere of action', and his remark that the forces of attraction and repulsion need not be further explained, are clearly reminiscent of Clausius's discussion in his 1858 paper 'On the Mean Lengths of Paths Described by the Separate Molecules of Gaseous Bodies'. Maxwell's discussion of the alternation of attractive and repulsive regions of force, while undoubtedly based on Clausius's theory, is an extension beyond Clausius's argument. While Clausius had merely considered two such regions of force, Maxwell argued that in certain cases there would be two more such regions of force. This notion of regions of attractive and repulsive forces associated with the particles of matter shows marked affinities with a tradition of speculative natural philosophy deriving from Newton's statement in Query 31 of the *Opticks* that the attractive force of the particles 'can reach but to a small distance from them . . . [and] where Attraction ceases, there a repulsive Virtue ought to succeed'.[63] In Maxwell's own time statements of this kind were made by Faraday in his 'Thoughts on Ray-Vibrations'[64] and by James Challis,[65] and Boscovich's theory—which Maxwell explicitly recognized as having affinities with his own views— belongs to this tradition.

However, despite Maxwell's statement on this point, it is the resemblance to Clausius's theory that is particularly significant.[66] Given the nature of the problem with which he was concerned, that of molecular forces in gas theory, Clausius was an obvious source for speculations on this question and, indeed, his representation of these forces displays an important difference from his account of Boscovich's system in his celebrated 'Atom' article, written in the same period as the speculations discussed above. In this article he did not fail to emphasize that in Boscovich's theory the forces between the atoms at mutual distances greater than a certain distance—a thousandth of an inch, according to Maxwell— were attractive inverse-square law forces of sensible magnitude, and the alternation of regions of attractive and repulsive forces occurred only at distances smaller than this.[67] But in his remarks on the forces associated with molecules, Maxwell represented the action as insensible at all sensible distances, for molecular forces were sensible only at the micro-level, and he argued that the action between two molecules only began as a sensible attractive force at 'some exceedingly small distance' between the molecules.[68]

Maxwell's assumption in the manuscript quoted above that 'two bodies cannot be in the same place' was the basis of Boscovich's theory, as he made clear in his 'Atom' article, stating that 'Boscovich himself, in order to obviate the possibility of two atoms ever being in the same place, asserts that the ultimate force is a repulsion which increases without limit as the distance diminishes without limit, so two atoms can never coincide'.[69] The assumption raises an important problem in Maxwell's thought. Maxwell questioned the applicability of this principle to the behaviour of atoms and molecules. In the 'Dynamical Theory of Gases' he stated that 'the doctrines that all matter is extended, and that no two portions of matter can coincide in the same place, being deductions from our experiments with bodies sensible to us, have no application to the theory of molecules',[70] and he argued that the molecules could be centres of force or 'systems of several such centres of force . . . [and] the different centres may either be separated, so as to form a group of points, or they may be actually coincident, so as to form one point'. In the 'Atom' article he used this argument against Boscovich's theory, pointing out that the assumption that two atoms could not coincide 'seems an unwarrantable concession to the vulgar opinion that two bodies cannot co-exist in the same place. This opinion is deduced from our experience of the behaviour of bodies of sensible size, but we have no experimental evidence that two atoms may not sometimes coincide'.[71]

In refusing to ascribe impenetrability to atoms and molecules, Maxwell was implicitly denying Newton's third Rule of Philosophizing, that the 'analogy of Nature' enabled properties perceived in sensible bodies to be 'ascribed universally to all others also',[72] that is, to the insensible particles of matter. Newton regarded this Rule as the 'foundation of all philosophy',[73] and in Maxwell's own time it had been taken as such by James Challis in a long series of papers on the various forces of nature, published in the *Philosophical Magazine* from the late 1850s onwards.[74]

Maxwell was thus distinguishing between the laws applicable to sensible bodies and those applicable to unobservable particles, and this distinction was an important feature of his ideas. In his 1873 essay on 'Science and Free Will' he stated that 'a constituent molecule of a body has properties very different from those of the body to which it belongs',[75] and this problem was given a more extended discussion in a manuscript on the 'Dimensions of Physical Quantities' in which Maxwell further emphasized the distinction between macro- and micro-phenomena. He stated that 'when we come to deal with very small quantities of matter its properties begin to be different from those observed in large masses. . . . The forces which we call molecular begin to show themselves acting in a different manner from those forces which are alone sensible in their action on great masses. There is therefore a real distinction between very small and very large bodies in nature'.[76] There was thus nothing to justify the 'analogy of Nature'. The molecular forces were quite different from those forces acting on sensible masses, and he implicitly questioned the transference of Newton's laws of dynamics to the motions of molecules. There was thus a distinction in nature between the properties of individual molecules and the properties of observable bodies. However, Maxwell also made a distinction between the methods applicable to the treatment of different kinds of observable entities: the 'statistical method' which was used when a number of molecules large enough to be observed experimentally was considered, and the 'dynamical method' which could only be used under circumstances where the motions of individual particles could be followed. The implications of this distinction will be discussed below, but some attention must first be paid to an important terminological question which relates to his use of the expression 'dynamical method'.

V

Maxwell's discussions of the distinctions between macro- and micro-phenomena derived from his concern with the forces involved in molecular interactions in gases, and this concern was reflected in his terminology, for he called his theory a 'dynamical' theory. However, in a letter to William Thomson in 1871 he referred to his theory as the 'kinetic theory of gases',[77] as in modern usage. This terminology is significant and some consideration must be given to the meaning he attached to the terms.

In his 'Introductory Lecture' at King's College, London, in 1860 Maxwell said that 'the science of pure motion is called Cinematics or Kinetics' while 'Dynamics considers the relations between force and motion'. He went on to state that 'the possible motions are brought into a mathematical form by Kinetics, and then these are brought into relation by Dynamics, which is the science of the motion of matter as produced by known forces'.[78] Thus, kinetics and dynamics were not the same here, and his dynamical theory of gases involved consideration of the forces. In 1866, writing to Stokes in connection with the publication of his 'Dynamical Theory of Gases' in the *Philosophical Transactions*, he noted that he took 'Kinetics to be the theory of the motions of systems without regard to the forces in action, [and] Dynamics to be the theory of the motion of bodies as the result of given forces',[79] once again emphasizing that his theory involved the consideration of the forces between the molecules.

However, his terminology changed after 1867, and under the influence of Thomson and Tait's *Treatise on Natural Philosophy* (1867) he distinguished kinematics from kinetics. Thomson and Tait considered 'kinematics' to be a purely geometric science of motion in the abstract and 'dynamics' the science that considered the action of force; 'kinetics' was a branch of dynamics, the study of forces that produced acceleration of relative motion.[80] Maxwell followed Thomson and Tait in using 'kinetics' to include the treatment of forces, though he did not adopt their terminology in all particulars. This can be seen from a manuscript, 'Remarks on the Classification of the Physical Sciences', dating from the early 1870s, in which he spoke of dynamics as treating 'the Motion of Bodies as affected by force', and he considered that kinematics, statics, kinetics and energetics were all 'divisions of dynamics', kinetics being 'the relation between the motions of material bodies and the forces which act on them'.[81] Clearly 'kinetics' had become the science which he had formerly called 'dynamics'. Yet a further divergence from Thomson and Tait, however, can be found in *Matter and Motion* (1877). Here kinematics was the theory of motion treated geometrically, as in Thomson and Tait's *Treatise*, but he went on to say that 'when the mutual action between bodies is taken into account, the science of motion is called Kinetics', adding that 'when special attention is paid to force as the cause of motion, it is called Dynamics',[82] whereas for Thomson and Tait kinetics was a branch of dynamics.

After 1867 he thus associated kinetics with the treatment of the mutual action between bodies rather than with the treatment of motion in its purely geometrical aspect, and this change of terminology governed his usage when he described his theory to Thomson in 1871 as the 'kinetic theory of gases'. After 1870 his use of the term 'dynamical *method*' had particular connotations. In his 1873 lecture on 'Molecules' he distinguished between what he called the 'historical' or 'dynamical' method and the 'statistical' method,[83] and a similar distinction was made in his essay on 'Science and Free Will' dating from the same year.[84] The historical or dynamical method was concerned with the behaviour of entities which could be observed individually, whereas the statistical method was used for the investigation of entities collectively. He made it clear that 'the equations of dynamics completely express the laws of the historical method as applied to matter, but the application of these equations implies a perfect knowledge of all the data'. In cases where the individual particles were unobservable, all the data could not be known and the equations of dynamics could not be applied, and so the statistical method was appropriate. Thus, in the study of gases 'the smallest portion of matter which we can subject to experiment consists of millions of molecules, not one of which ever becomes individually sensible to us', and the statistical method had to be used. [85] Significantly, in writing a paper on diffusion experiments at this time, he included the term 'kinetic theory of gases' in the title, [86] and though he continued to use the term 'dynamical' in connection with the theory of gases he did so only in a general way, for the theory of gases could not be described as subject to the 'dynamical *method*'. [87]

He gave a full description of the difference between the dynamical and statistical methods in a review in *Nature* in 1877, where he made it clear that the strict dynamical method in which 'our analysis enables us to trace every particle throughout its whole course' could not be applied to 'systems consisting of large numbers of bodies'. The statistical method was therefore used, in which 'we fix our attention not on the bodies themselves, but on the *number* belonging at any instant to one particular group'. Anybody entering the group would be regarded as a new body, 'just as the turnstile at an exhibition counts the visitors who enter without respect to what they have done or are going to do, or whether they have passed through the turnstile before'. [88] Thus, in the theory of gases individual molecules were not treated as such, because they were unobservable; only sensible aggregates of molecules were considered, because only a large number of molecules could be observed by experiment.

Maxwell considered that the certainty provided by the two methods was different. In a manuscript he distinguished between the status of the two methods, noting that the dynamical method gave 'absolute' certainty, but that despite the unvarying regularities revealed by the statistical method these regularities 'must be carefully distinguished from that absolute uniformity . . . according to which we suppose that every individual event is determined by its antecedents'. Despite the 'stability of the averages of large numbers of variable events . . . in a particular case a very different event might occur' from that expected from 'the regularity of averages', though 'we are morally certain that such an event will not take place'. [89] This epistemological distinction between absolute and moral certainty— which he clearly derived from his interest in philosophy [90]—was the result of the different methods used.

Now, it has been argued that Maxwell believed the statistical method to be merely a temporary expedient, necessary only until a more complete 'dynamical' theory of the motions of molecules could be provided. [91] It is true that Maxwell supposed that 'when a physical phenomenon can be completely described as a change in the configuration and motion of a material system, the dynamical explanation of that phenomenon is said to be complete . . . [and that we] cannot conceive any further explanation to be either necessary, desirable, or possible',[92] but he did not regard this strict dynamical method as applicable to the theory of gases. As he emphasized in his lecture on 'Molecules', the statistical method was used because 'molecular science teaches us that our experiments can never give us anything more than statistical information', and it is clear that for Maxwell the statistical method was imposed by experiments, which provided information about large numbers of molecules, for individual molecules were insensible.[93] He made it clear, however, that these statistical laws, which were derived from experiments in molecular science and could not 'pretend to absolute precision', applied only to sensible aggregates of molecules, not to individual molecules, for he stated that 'when we pass from the contemplation of our experiments to that of the molecules themselves, we leave the world of chance and change, and enter a region where everything is certain and immutable'.[94]

Thus, in considering the behaviour of large numbers of molecules the statistical method had to be used, but the laws of the statistical method did not apply to individual molecules. His discussion here relates to the problem of the distinction between micro- and macro-phenomena which was analysed in section IV above, for the evidence cited indicates that Maxwell questioned the application of the *dynamical* method to the description of the motions of individual molecules. As he made clear, the dynamical method involved tracing every particle throughout its course by means of the equations of dynamics, but in suggesting that molecular forces acted in a different manner from those between sensible bodies he implicitly questioned the transference of the laws of dynamics to the motions of insensible molecules. In his manuscript on the 'Dimensions of Physical Quantities', which was quoted in section IV, Maxwell carefully distinguished molecular forces from 'those forces which are alone sensible in their action on great masses'; he distinguished forces between macro-particles from intermolecular forces. But whatever the nature of the molecular forces he made it clear that on the molecular level nature was not statistical, for the individual molecules were not subject to the laws of chance. The statistical method was thus to be applied to large numbers of molecules (on which the experiments were performed) but not to individual molecules. However, individual, insensible molecules were not subject to the same laws as individual, sensible particles.

In his lecture on 'Molecules' Maxwell made it clear that the idea that the individual molecules were immutable and not subject to chance was related to his theological ideas. Following John Herschel in his *Preliminary Discourse on the Study of Natural Philosophy* (1830),[95] Maxwell considered that molecules had 'the essential character of a manufactured article', and argued that the exact similarity of each molecule to all others of the same kind 'precludes the idea of its being eternal and self-existent'.[96] The identity of the molecules could be seen from comparison of stellar and terrestrial spectra, which showed that 'no theory of evolution can be formed to account for the similarity of molecules, for evolution necessarily implies continuous change, and the molecule is incapable of growth or decay, of generation or destruction'.[97] The similarity of molecules was an argument for their creation, the molecules remaining to this day as they were created, and 'the ineffaceable characters impressed on them' were 'essential constituents of Him who in the beginning created, not only the heaven and the earth, but the materials of which heaven and earth consist'.[98] No natural process could affect the nature of the immutable molecules, and 'we are therefore unable to ascribe either the existence of the molecules or the identity of their properties to the operation of any causes which we call natural'.[99] The basis of his argument that molecules were immutable, then, was to be found in the belief that their similarity was outside the boundaries of science, for: 'Science is incompetent to reason upon the creation of matter itself out of nothing. We have reached the utmost limit of our thinking faculties when we have admitted that because matter cannot be eternal and self-existent it must have been created.'[100] Maxwell referred to Thomas Chalmers in connection with these remarks,[101] and these arguments were drawn from Chalmers's *Natural Theology* (1836).[102] Maxwell's statement of these ideas in a lecture on the nature of molecules—he was to reaffirm them in his 'Atom' article[103]—is a clear indication of the importance of theological ideas in his scientific thought.

VI

A significant illustration which Maxwell gave of the distinction between individual molecules and an immense number of molecules was that of the 'demon'. This conception, which appeared in print in the *Theory of Heat* (1871),[104] was first formulated in a letter to Tait in 1867. Maxwell supposed that A and B were two vessels divided by a diaphragm, containing molecules in a state of agitation:

Now conceive a finite being who knows the paths and velocities of all the molecules by simple inspection but who can do no work except open and close a hole in the diaphragm by means of a slide without mass.

Let him first observe the molecules in *A* and when he sees one coming the square of whose velocity is less than the mean sq[uare] vel[ocity] of the molecules in *B* let him open the hole and let it go into *B*. Next let him watch for a molecule of *B*, the square of whose velocity is greater than the mean sq[uare] vel[ocity] in *A*, and when it comes to the hole let him draw the slide and let it go into *A*, keeping the slide shut for all other molecules.[105]

Maxwell's argument was that there would be no expenditure of work because 'only the intelligence of a very observant and neat-fingered being has been employed',[106] and the being would raise the temperature of *A* and lower that of *B* 'in contradiction to the second law of thermodynamics'.[107] The purpose of this ingenious illustration was to show that the second law of thermodynamics only applied to a system of large numbers of molecules and could be violated by individual molecules. The second law of thermodynamics thus had only a statistical certainty.[108] Maxwell was providing an illustration of a fundamental feature of nature, that while the second law of thermodynamics could not be applied to individual molecules it remained perfectly valid for the treatment of immense numbers of molecules; it was not a law applicable to micro-phenomena. Maxwell's use of the illustration was directed entirely to this end, and he was not speculating as to whether a being could operate in such a way.[109] In a letter to Tait he objected to William Thomson's use of the term 'demon'[110] to describe his 'finite being' and suggested that Tait 'call him no more a demon but a valve'.[111] In reducing his finite being with 'sharpened' faculties[112]—his mode of expression reflecting his quizzical humour—to a valve, Maxwell indicated that he did not wish to engage in physical speculations as to the mode of action of such a 'demon', and for him the notion merely expressed the distinction between laws applicable at the micro- and at the macro-level. As he emphasized to Tait in this letter, his aim had been 'to show that the 2nd Law of Thermodynamics has only a statistical certainty', and his illustration served this epistemological purpose.

VII

Maxwell's treatment of the problem of molecular forces and his discussion of the 'dynamical method' make it possible to delineate the relations between his work on the kinetic theory of gases and on electricity and magnetism. Thus, the *Treatise on Electricity and Magnetism* (1873) was founded on a theory of particulate action,[113] and his concern in the

Treatise to account for the phenomena by means of 'internal forces' of an unknown nature acting between particles across insensible distances[114]— while he recognized that he had not succeeded in doing so[115]—was an attempt to discuss molecular forces in the way that he had tried in his theory of gases.

His distinction between kinetics and dynamics in gas theory also extends to the *Treatise*, where his usage relates to his distinction in *Matter and Motion*. He called the section in which he considered the Lagrangian formalism of dynamics 'Kinetics',[116] but while he considered Lagrange's method as being 'free from the intrusion of dynamical ideas' his own aim in this section was 'to cultivate our dynamical ideas',[117] using the term 'dynamical ideas' in a general way here. 'Kinetics' was thus the science that 'endeavoured to retranslate the principal equations of the [Lagrangian] method into language which may be intelligible without the use of symbols'.[118] Nevertheless, he made it clear that this 'kinetic' theory was quite different from a 'complete *dynamical*' theory of electromagnetism, stating that: 'In this outline of the fundamental principles of the dynamics of a connected system, we have kept out of view the mechanism by which the parts of the system are connected';[119] for it was in the next chapter, on a 'Dynamical Theory of Electromagnetism',[120] that he developed his ideas on a mechanism to explain the connection between the parts of the system. Here he referred to the attainment of 'a complete dynamical theory of electricity, in which . . . the whole intermediate mechanism and details of the motion, are taken as the objects of study'.[121] Thus here the science of 'Dynamics' involved consideration of the forces by an inter-mediate mechanism.

Nevertheless, despite this programme of dynamical explanation, his remarks on internal forces show that here, too, he was concerned with the problem of the forces between unobservable particles, and he stated that he had 'advanced a step' despite his failure 'in accounting for these internal forces'.[122] He emphasized, however, that the Lagrangian formalism of dynamics used in the *Treatise* made it possible to ignore the nature of the internal forces, for he had assumed the electromagnetic medium to be a moving system, 'the motion being communicated from one part of the system to another by forces, the nature and laws of which we do not yet even attempt to define, because we can eliminate these forces from the equations of motion by the method given by Lagrange for any connected system'.[123]

Both in gas theory and in electricity he was thus concerned to discuss molecular forces. It is important to note that Maxwell regarded each mode of representation, whatever its nature, as a conceptual scheme imposed upon nature. In his address to the mathematical and physical sections of the British Association in 1870 he pointed out that

the molecules have laws of their own, some of which we select as most intelligible to us and most amenable to our calculation. We form a theory from these partial data, and we ascribe any deviation of the actual phenomena from this theory to disturbing causes. At the same time we confess that what we call disturbing causes are simply those parts of the true circumstances which we do not know or have neglected, and we endeavour in future to take account of them. We thus acknowledge that the so-called disturbance is a mere figment of the mind, not a fact of nature, and that in natural action there is no disturbance.[124]

Any mode of representation was thus 'about the net and not about what the net describes'.[125, 126]

University of Cambridge

NOTES

[1] J. Clerk Maxwell, 'Illustrations of the Dynamical Theory of Gases', *Phil. Mag.*, **19** (1860) 19–32; **20** (1860), 21–37. Reprinted in *The Scientific Papers of James Clerk Maxwell*, ed. W. D. Niven, 2 vols. (Cambridge, 1890), vol. 1, 377–409 (hereafter I refer to this work as *Papers*).

[2] Maxwell, 'On the Dynamical Theory of Gases', *Phil. Trans.*, **157** (1867), 49–88; *Papers*, vol. 2, 26–78.

[3] Maxwell, 'Molecules' (1873), in *Papers*, vol. 2, 374.

[4] For my discussion of the influence of Clausius on Maxwell's derivations of his statistical distribution function (in the papers referred to in notes 1 and 2), I have profited from seeing an unpublished article by Elizabeth Garber, 'Clausius and Maxwell's Kinetic Theory of Gases'. Dr Garber also notes Maxwell's concern with the nature of matter in his work on gas theory. For an account of the theories of Clausius and Maxwell, see also Stephen G. Brush, 'The Development of the Kinetic Theory of Gases, III: Clausius', *Annals of Science*, **14** (1958), 185–96; *id.*, 'The Development of the Kinetic Theory of Gases, IV: Maxwell', *ibid.*, 243–55; and *id.*, 'Foundations of Statistical Mechanics, 1845–1915', *Arch. Hist. Exact Sci.*, **4** (1967), 145–83.

[5] C. C. Gillispie, 'Intellectual Factors in the Background of Analysis by Probabilities', in *Scientific Change*, ed. A. C. Crombie (London, 1963), 431–53.

[6] A. Quetelet, *Letters . . . on the Theory of Probabilities as applied to the Moral and Political Sciences*, trans. O. G. Downes (London, 1849).

[7] J. F. W. Herschel, 'Quetelet on Probabilities', *Edinburgh Review*, **92** (1850), 1–57.

[8] See a letter of 1850 to Lewis Campbell, in L. Campbell and W. Garnett, *The Life of James Clerk Maxwell* (London, 1882), 143. Campbell tentatively dated this letter at June 1850, but July seems more probable. Campbell was largely responsible for the biographical section of the work (*ibid.*, vii).

[9] In letters dated 22 December 1857 (to Campbell) and 7 February 1858 (to R. B. Litchfield), Maxwell stated that he had been reading Herschel's *Essays from the Edinburgh and Quarterly Reviews* (London, 1857), in which the review of Quetelet was reprinted (*ibid.*, 365–465). See Campbell and Garnett, *op. cit.*, note 8, 294, 302.

[10] J. F. W. Herschel, *Outlines of Astronomy* (London, 1849), 564f.

[11] John Michell, 'An Inquiry into the probable Parallax and Magnitude of the fixed Stars, from the Quantity of Light which they afford us, and the particular Circumstances of their Situation', *Phil. Trans.*, **57** (1767), 234–64.

[12] J. D. Forbes, 'On the alleged Evidence for a Physical Connexion between Stars forming Binary or Multiple Groups, arising from their Proximity alone', *Phil. Mag.*, **35** (1849), 133.

[13] Herschel, *op. cit.*, note 9, 429.

[14] J. D. Forbes, 'On the alleged evidence for a Physical Connexion between Stars Forming Binary or Multiple Groups, deduced from the Doctrine of Chances', *Phil. Mag.*, **37** (1850), 401–27.

[15] *Ibid.*, 416.

[16] *Ibid.*, 422.

[17] George Boole, 'On the Theory of Probabilities, and in particular on *Michell's* Problem of The Distribution of the Fixed Stars', *Phil. Mag.*, **1** (1851), 521–30.

[18] *Ibid.*, 526, 524.

[19] For example: George Boole, 'On a general method in the Theory of Probabilities', *Phil. Mag.*, **8** (1854), 431–44; *id.*, 'On the Conditions by which the Solutions of Questions in the Theory of Probabilities are limited', *Phil. Mag.*, **8** (1854), 91–8.

[20] Lewis Campbell implied that Maxwell knew Boole's *Mathematical Analysis of Logic* (Cambridge, 1847) at this time. (See Campbell and Garnett, *op. cit.*, note 8, 113.) Maxwell quoted from the last chapter of the *Laws of Thought* in his 1870 address to the mathematical and physical sections of the British Association, *Papers*, vol. 2, 229.

[21] See Maxwell to R. B. Litchfield, 25 March 1854, in Campbell and Garnett, *op. cit.*, note 8, 207.

[22] *Ibid.*, 562. Garnett was responsible for the 'account here given of Maxwell's contributions to science' (*ibid.*, vii).

[23] Maxwell, 'On the Stability of the Motion of Saturn's Rings', *Monthly Notices of the Royal Astronomical Society*, **10** (1859), 297–384; *Papers*, vol. 1, 288–376.

[24] Maxwell, *Papers*, vol. 1, 354.

[25] Manuscript on 'The Mathematical Theory of Saturn's Rings', University Library, Cambridge, Add. MSS 7655. This manuscript clearly dates from after 1860, but given its subject-matter—Saturn's rings—probably not much later than this date. I am grateful to Mr A. E. B. Owen of the University Library, Cambridge, and to the library staff of the Royal Society for help with Maxwell's manuscripts.

[26] Maxwell, *Papers*, vol. 1, 377.

[27] See Edward E. Daub, 'Atomism and Thermodynamics', *Isis*, **58** (1967), 293–303.

[28] R. Clausius, 'On the Kind of Motion which we call Heat', *Phil. Mag.*, **14** (1857), 108–27 (*Ann. Phys.*, **100** (1857), 353–80); 'On the Mean Lengths of Paths described by separate Molecules of gaseous Bodies', *Phil. Mag.*, **17** (1859), 81–91 (*Ann. Phys.*, **105** (1858), 239–58).

[29] Clausius, *Phil. Mag.*, **14** (1857), 120.

[30] Clausius was criticized by C. H. D. Buijs-Ballot, 'Über die Art von Bewegung, welche wir Wärme und Electricität nennen', *Ann. Phys.*, **103** (1858), 240–59.

[31] Clausius, *Phil. Mag.*, **17** (1859), 82.

[32] *Ibid.*, 82f.

[33] *Ibid.*, 83.

[34] These remarks show strong affinities with a Newtonian tradition in the eighteenth and nineteenth centuries. Maxwell expressed similar notions, which will be discussed further below: see note 63 for some references.

[35] Clausius, *op. cit.*, note 31, 83.

[36] *Ibid.*, 84. Clausius's own phrase was 'Wirkungssphäre' (*Ann. Phys.*, **105** (1858), 243).

[37] Clausius, *op. cit.*, note 31, 84.

[38] *Ibid.*, 88f.

[39] See a letter to Stokes of 30 May 1859, in *Memoir and Scientific Correspondence of the late Sir George Gabriel Stokes, Bart.*, ed. J. Larmor, 2 vols. (Cambridge, 1907), vol. 2, 8.

[40] Maxwell, *Papers*, vol. 1, 380f. (*Op. cit.*, note 1.)

[41] Maxwell to Stokes, 30 May 1859, *op. cit.*, note 39, vol. 2, 10. See also *Papers*, vol. 1, 382.

[42] This was a consequence of the independence of viscosity from density, if the molecules were elastic spheres (Maxwell, *Papers*, vol. 1, 390f; vol. 2, 11). Maxwell's prediction that viscosity was independent of density was compatible both with the elastic sphere model of the 1860 paper and with the centre of force model of the 1867 paper.

[43] *Ibid.*, 377.

44 Maxwell to Stokes, 8 October 1859, *op. cit.*, note 39, vol. 2, 11.

45 Maxwell, 'On Faraday's Lines of Force', *Papers*, vol. 1, 155–229.

46 Maxwell to William Thomson, 13 September 1855, in *The Origins of Clerk Maxwell's Electric Ideas as Described in Familiar Letters to William Thomson*, ed. J. Larmor (Cambridge, 1937), 17.

47 Maxwell, *Papers*, vol. 1, 378.

48 *Ibid.*

49 R. Clausius, 'On the Conduction of Heat in Gases', *Phil. Mag.*, 23 (1862), 417–35, 512–34 (*Ann. Phys.*, 115 (1862), 1–56).

50 Manuscript 'On the Conduction of Heat in Gases', U.L.C. Add. MSS 7655. This is one of Maxwell's drafts of 'The Dynamical Theory of Gases' (see note 2).

51 Maxwell, 'On the Viscosity or Internal Friction of Air and other Gases', *Phil. Trans.*, 156 (1866), 249–68; *Papers*, vol. 2, 1–25.

52 Paper cited in note 2. There are a number of drafts of this paper in U.L.C. Add. MSS 7655.

53 Maxwell, *Papers*, vol. 2, 35ff.

54 *Ibid.*, 43ff.

55 *Ibid.*, 41.

56 *Ibid.*, 33.

57 Maxwell, *Papers*, vol. 1, 187.

58 Maxwell, *Papers*, vol. 2, 33.

59 Maxwell, 'Van der Waals on the Continuity of the Gaseous and Liquid States', *Papers*, vol. 2, 409. Maxwell was discussing J. D. van der Waals, *Over de Continuiteit van den Gas en Vloeistoftoestand* (Leiden, 1873). The experiments by Thomas Andrews were reported to the British Association meeting in Belfast in 1874, 'Experiments at High Pressures', *Report of the Forty-fourth Meeting of the British Association for the Advancement of Science; held at Belfast in August 1874* (London, 1875), 'Communications to Sections', 22. See Maxwell to Andrews, November 1874, in P. G. Tait and A. Crum Brown, *Scientific Papers of the Late Thomas Andrews* (London, 1889), liv f.

60 Maxwell, *Papers*, vol. 2, 412. Maxwell was referring to R. J. Boscovich, *Theoria Philosophiae Naturalis* (Venice, 1763). This edition was translated by J. M. Child as *A Theory of Natural Philosophy* (London, 1922).

61 Maxwell, *Papers*, vol. 2, 423.

62 Maxwell, 'Report on Dr Andrews' paper "On the Gaseous State of Matter"', Royal Society, *Referees' Reports*, 7, 434. Andrews's paper, his Bakerian lecture, was published in *Phil. Trans.*, 166 (1876), 421–49. As I point out below, Maxwell questioned the applicability of the principle that 'two bodies cannot be in the same place' to atoms and molecules.

63 Isaac Newton, *Opticks* (Dover reprint of 4th edition, New York, 1952), 395. Other statements of this kind can be found in J. T. Desaguliers, *A Course of Experimental Philosophy*, 3rd edition, 2 vols. (London, 1763), vol. 2, 337; Robert Smith, *A Compleat System of Opticks* (London, 1738), 88f; John Rowning, *A Compendious System of Natural Philosophy*, 4th edition (London, 1745), part 2, 6; and others.

64 Michael Faraday, 'Thoughts on Ray-Vibrations', *Experimental Researches in Electricity*, 3 vols. (London, 1839–55), vol. 3, 449.

65 James Challis, 'A Theory of Molecular Forces', *Phil. Mag.*, 19 (1860), 93ff.

66 This is strengthened by the fact that these speculations were prompted by the work of van der Waals, who employed Clausius's notion of 'sphere of action'. Van der Waals stated that 'we need only take into account (in considering the force on any given particle) those other particles which are within a sphere of very small radius having the particle as centre, and termed the "sphere of action", the forces themselves becoming insensible at distances greater than the radius of the sphere', *Physical Memoirs* (London, 1890), vol. 1 (part 3), 342 (English translation of work cited in note 59).

67 Maxwell, 'Atom', *Papers*, vol. 2, 448.

68 Manuscript cited in note 62.

69 Maxwell, *Papers*, vol. 2, 448.

70 *Ibid.*, 33.

71 *Ibid.*, 448.

72 *Sir Isaac Newton's Mathematical Principles of Natural Philosophy*, trans. Motte-Cajori (Berkeley, 1934), 398f.

73 *Ibid.*, 399. For a discussion of Newton's third rule, see J. E. McGuire, 'The Origin of Newton's Doctrine of Essential Qualities', *Centaurus*, **12** (1968), 233–60; and *id.*, 'Atoms and the "Analogy of Nature": Newton's Third Rule of Philosophizing', *Studies in History and Philosophy of Science*, **1** (1970), 3–58.

74 This is clearly stated in James Challis, 'On Newton's "Foundation of all Philosophy"', *Phil. Mag.*, **26** (1863), 280–92. Challis argued that 'the experience of the *senses* relative to matter is necessary and sufficient for revealing to us the universal properties of the ultimate constituents of the masses' (*op. cit.*, 282). Challis told Maxwell that his theories were 'strictly within the rules of the Newtonian principles of Philosophy' (Challis to Maxwell, 10 June 1861, U.L.C. Add. MSS 7655). William Whewell took a different view, regarding the third rule as 'a mode of reasoning far from conclusive', *Philosophy of the Inductive Sciences*, 2nd edition, 2 vols. (London, 1847), vol. 2, 289. Whewell remarked that, according to Newton, 'the properties of bodies depend on the attractions and repulsions of the particles. Therefore, among other properties of bodies, their hardness depends on such forces. But if the hardness *of the bodies* depends upon the forces, the repulsion, for instance on the particles, upon what does the hardness *of the particles* depend? What progress do we make in explaining the properties of bodies, when we assume the same properties in our explanation? and to what purpose do we assume that the particles *are* hard?' *Ibid.*, vol. 1, 432.

75 Quoted by Campbell and Garnett, *op. cit.*, note 8, 439.

76 Manuscript on 'The Dimensions of Physical Quantities', U.L.C. Add. MSS 7655. This probably dates from the same period as the other remarks quoted.

77 This letter has been published in H. T. Bernstein, 'J. Clerk Maxwell on the History of the Kinetic Theory of Gases', *Isis*, **54** (1963), 210ff.

78 U.L.C. Add. MSS 7655.

79 Maxwell to Stokes, 18 December 1866, *op. cit.*, note 39, vol. 2, 27.

80 William Thomson and P. G. Tait, *Treatise on Natural Philosophy* (Oxford, 1867), vi.

81 Manuscript on 'Remarks on the Classification of the Physical Sciences', U.L.C. Add. MSS 7655. Probably an early draft of *Matter and Motion* (London, 1877).

82 Maxwell, *Matter and Motion*, section 36.

83 Maxwell, 'Molecules', *Papers*, vol. 2, 374.

84 Quoted by Campbell and Garnett, *op. cit.*, note 8, 438.

85 Maxwell, *Papers*, vol. 2, 374. Maxwell was *not* discussing the applicability of the *dynamical* method to the treatment of *individual* molecules; having denied the 'analogy of Nature', he had questioned the transference of the laws of dynamics to unobservable particles. This will be discussed further below, but here he was discussing the treatment of entities that could be *observed*.

86 Maxwell, 'On Loschmidt's Experiments on Diffusion in relation to the Kinetic Theory of Gases', *Papers*, vol. 2, 343–50.

87 He used the word 'dynamical' in his paper 'On the Dynamical Evidence of the Molecular Constitution of Bodies', *ibid.*, 418–38, where he spoke of 'dynamical principles' (*ibid.*, 421) and the 'application . . . of dynamical methods to chemical science' (*ibid.*, 429), but only in a *general* sense, not in the sense discussed above.

88 Maxwell, 'The Kinetic Theory of Gases', *Nature*, **16** (1877), 242. This was a review of H. W. Watson, *Treatise on the Kinetic Theory of Gases* (Oxford, 1876).

89 Manuscript 'On the Motions and Encounters of Molecules', U.L.C. Add. MSS 7655. This was written on the back of a draft of the *Treatise on Electricity and Magnetism* (Oxford, 1873), and so probably dates from *c.* 1870. Maxwell was not arguing that such a 'different event' was incompatible with the probability prediction.

90 For example, in Descartes, *Principles of Philosophy*, part IV, articles 204ff; see *Descartes: Philosophical Writings*, trans. and ed. G. E. M. Anscombe and P. T. Geach (London, 1966), 237f. Maxwell was familiar with the *Principles of Philosophy* which he quoted in his essay on 'Science and Free Will', published in Campbell and Garnett, *op. cit.*, note 8, 436. For the problem of certainty see H. G. van Leeuwen, *The Problem of Certainty in English Thought, 1630–1690* (The Hague, 1963).

91 Joseph Turner, 'Maxwell on the Logic of Dynamical Explanation', *Philosophy of Science*, **23** (1956), 36–47.

92 Maxwell, *Papers*, vol. 2, 418.

93 *Ibid.*, 374.

94 *Ibid.*

95 See J. F. W. Herschel, *Preliminary Discourse on the Study of Natural Philosophy*, new edition (London, 1851), 38, where Herschel argued that the discoveries of chemistry showed that atoms were '*exactly alike* in all their properties', and these discoveries 'effectually destroy the idea of an eternal *self-existent matter*, by giving to each of its atoms the essential characters, at once, of a *manufactured article*, and a subordinate agent'.

96 Maxwell, *Papers*, vol. 2, 376. Maxwell was criticized by his friend C. J. Monro, who pointed out that the traditional argument from design 'owes much of its virtue to complexity and variety', while the new argument exemplified 'uniformity for the sake of uniformity'. He argued that 'Uniformity . . . is not as such the sign of a manufactured article, except as it may be the sign of an imperfect manufacturer . . . who does not vary them according to the interests connected with them', *Nature*, 10 (1874), 481. As Maxwell said in a letter of 22 November 1876 to C. J. Ellicott, Bishop of Gloucester and Bristol, his extension of this argument in his 'Atom' article was intended to meet this criticism, for Maxwell was thinking of 'a uniformity intended and accomplished by the same wisdom and power of which uniformity, accuracy, symmetry, consistency, and continuity of plan are as important attributes as the contrivance of the special ability of each individual thing', Campbell and Garnett, *op. cit.*, note 8, 393. See also 'Atom', *Papers*, vol. 2, 483f. This argument was also used in B. Stewart and P. G. Tait, *Paradoxical Philosophy: A Sequel to the Unseen Universe* (London, 1878), 89, 105f, but opposed by W. K. Clifford, 'The First and Last Catastrophe', *Lectures and Essays*, ed. L. Stephen and F. Pollock, 2 vols. (London, 1879), vol. 1, 191-227.

97 Maxwell, *Papers*, vol. 2, 376. Maxwell was probably referring to the spectroscopic work of William Huggins, who had recently published 'On the Spectrum of the Great Nebula in Orion, and on the Motions of some Stars towards or from Earth', *Proc. Roy. Soc.*, 20 (1872), 370-93. Huggins's paper 'Further Observations on the Spectra of some of the Stars and Nebulae', *Phil. Trans.*, 158 (1868), 529-64, included a note by Maxwell, 'On the Influence of the Motions of the Heavenly bodies on the Index of Refraction of Light', *ibid.*, 532-5. For a discussion of spectroscopy and chemical evolution, see W. H. Brock, 'Lockyer and the Chemists: The First Dissociation Hypothesis', *Ambix*, 16 (1969), 81-99, and W. V. Farrar, 'Nineteenth-century Speculations on the Complexity of the Chemical Elements', *Brit. J. Hist. Sci.*, 2 (1965), 314ff.

98 *Ibid.*, 377.

99 *Ibid.*, 376.

100 *Ibid.* These remarks on immutable created atoms may be compared with Newton's famous statement in Query 31. See *Opticks*, *op. cit.*, note 63, 400.

101 *Ibid.*, 377.

102 In his *Natural Theology*, Chalmers argued that design was not indicated by the mere operation of laws but by the dispositions or 'collocations' of matter, for 'mere laws, without collocations, would have afforded no security against a turbid and disorderly chaos', *Select Works of Thomas Chalmers*, ed. W. Hanna (Edinburgh, 1857), vol. 5, 116. He also stated that 'these laws and properties, though perfectly sufficient to account for the working of the planetary mechanism, are not sufficient to account for the original collocation of its parts. They may account for the operation of the machine, but not for the fabrication of it.' (*ibid.*, 120). A similar remark was made by Herschel, *loc. cit.*, note 95, and in B. Stewart and P. G. Tait, *The Unseen Universe: or Physical Speculations on a Future State*, 3rd edition (London, 1875), 167.

103 Maxwell, *Papers*, vol. 2, 482ff.

104 Maxwell, *Theory of Heat*, 5th edition (London, 1877), 328f.

105 Maxwell to Tait, 11 December 1867, quoted by C. G. Knott in *Life and Scientific Work of Peter Guthrie Tait* (Cambridge, 1911), 214.

106 *Ibid.*

107 Maxwell, *op. cit.*, note 104, 329. For a discussion of the 'demon' and the second law of thermodynamics, see M. J. Klein, 'Maxwell, his Demon, and the Second Law of Thermodynamics', *American Scientist*, 58 (1970), 84-97.

108 Joseph Turner, *op. cit.*, note 91, 44, seems to me to be wrong in arguing that the 'demon' showed the *temporary* nature of the statistical method, for in fact it served to illustrate the range of application of this method. For a similar view to mine see Klein, *op. cit.*, note 107.

109 That the 'demon' would perform work in observing the molecules was shown by L.

Brillouin, 'Maxwell's Demon Cannot Operate', *Journal of Applied Physics*, **22** (1951), 334–7.

[110] William Thomson, 'The Sorting Demon of Maxwell' (1879), in *Popular Lectures and Addresses*, 3 vols. (London, 1889–94), vol. 1, 137–41, and also 'The Kinetic Theory of the Dissipation of Energy', *Nature*, **9** (1874), 441–4.

[111] Maxwell to Tait, undated letter quoted by Knott, *op. cit.*, note 105, 215.

[112] Maxwell, *op. cit.*, note 104, 328.

[113] See my 'Maxwell and the Modes of Consistent Representation', *Arch. Hist. Exact Sci.*, **6** (1970), 171–213.

[114] Maxwell, *Treatise on Electricity and Magnetism* (Oxford, 1873), section 105 (1st edition only).

[115] *Ibid.*, section 110.

[116] *Ibid.*, sections 553–67.

[117] *Ibid.*, section 554.

[118] *Ibid.*, section 567.

[119] *Ibid.*, section 567.

[120] *Ibid.*, sections 568–77.

[121] *Ibid.*, section 574.

[122] *Ibid.*, section 107 (1st edition only).

[123] *Ibid.*, section 552.

[124] Maxwell, *Papers*, vol. 2, 228f.

[125] L. Wittgenstein, *Tractatus Logico-Philosophicus*, trans. D. F. Pears and B. F. McGuinness (London, 1961), 6.35.

[126] I wish to express my gratitude to Mr J. E. McGuire for his advice during the preparation of this paper, and to Dr Joan Bromberg for comments. The research reported in this paper was done at the University of Leeds

Martin J. Klein

Maxwell, His Demon, and the Second Law of Thermodynamics

Maxwell saw the second law as statistical, illustrated this with his demon, but never developed its theory

By the mid-sixties of the last century the science of thermodynamics had reached a certain level of maturity. One could already describe it, in the words James Clerk Maxwell would use a few years later, as "a science with secure foundations, clear definitions, and distinct boundaries" (*1*). As one sign of the maturity of the subject, Rudolf Clausius, one of its creators, reissued his principal papers on thermodynamics as a book in 1864 (*2*). He also set aside his protracted efforts to find the simplest and most general form of the second law of thermodynamics in order to meet the need for convenient working forms of the thermodynamic equations, forms suitable for dealing with the variety of experimental situations to which the theory was being applied (*3*).

Another indication of the maturity of the subject was the appearance in 1868 of Peter Guthrie Tait's book, *Sketch of Thermodynamics* (*4*). This consisted of a revision of two articles Tait had already published on the history of the recent developments in the theory of heat, supplemented by a brief treatment of the principles of thermodynamics. Tait did not claim to have written a comprehensive treatise, but his book did make the basic concepts and methods available to students.

One of his reasons for writing the book was, in fact, his feeling of "the want of a short and ele-

Martin J. Klein, Professor of the History of Physics at Yale, teaches both physics and the history of science at the University. A graduate of Columbia, he holds a Ph.D. from M.I.T. (1948). He has worked on various problems in thermodynamics and statistical mechanics, and most recently has been studying the development of physics in the nineteenth and twentieth centuries. His papers on Planck, Einstein, Gibbs, and others have appeared in a number of journals. His book, Paul Ehrenfest, Volume 1, The Making of a Theoretical Physicist *(North-Holland Publishing Co., Amsterdam), will appear this winter. Address: Department of the History of Science and Medicine, Yale University, 56 Hillhouse Avenue, New Haven, Conn. 06520.*

mentary textbook" for use in his own classes (*4*, p. iii). Another reason was Tait's desire to set the historical record straight, which for him meant urging the claims of his compatriots, James Prescott Joule and William Thomson (later Lord Kelvin), against those of the Germans who had contributed along similar lines—Julius Robert Mayer, Hermann von Helmholtz, and Clausius. Since Tait admitted in his preface that he might have taken "a somewhat too British point of view" (*4*, p. v), it is not surprising that his book became the center of a stormy controversy, but that controversy is not our concern here (*5*).

Before sending his manuscript off to the publisher, Tait wrote to Maxwell, asking him to apply his critical powers to it. Tait was already expecting trouble over his assignment of priorities and credit, since both Clausius and Helmholtz had been sent parts of the manuscript and had reacted negatively (*5a*, pp. 216–17; *6*). Maxwell was an old friend; the two men had been together at school, at the University of Edinburgh and at Cambridge. They shared a variety of scientific interests and carried on a particularly lively and vigorous correspondence (*7*). It was not at all unusual for Maxwell to read the manuscripts or proofs of his friends' books and to "enrich them by notes, always valuable and often of the quaintest character," as Tait himself wrote (*8*). This time Maxwell provided his enrichment even before he saw Tait's book.

Maxwell wrote Tait that he would be glad to see his manuscript, although he did not "know in a controversial manner the history of thermodynamics" and so was not prepared to join his friend in waging the priority wars. "Any contributions I could make to that study," he went on, "are in the way of altering the point of view here and there for clearness or variety, and picking holes here and there to ensure strength and stability" (*9*). Maxwell proceeded to pick such a hole—in the second law of thermody-namics itself.

Since its original appearance in Sadi Carnot's memoir of 1824, the principle that would eventually become the second law was always formulated as a completely general statement, as free of exceptions as Newton's laws of motion or his law of universal gravitation. What Maxwell challenged was just this universal, invariable validity of the second law. His challenge took the strange form of what we now call Maxwell's demon, an argument of the "quaintest character" indeed. This was Maxwell's way of ex-pressing his insight into the peculiar nature of the second law of thermodynamics: it was not a law that could be reduced ultimately to dynamics, but it expressed instead the statistical regularity of systems composed of unimaginably large numbers of molecules.

Maxwell's views on the nature of the second law, expressed in brief passages and passing remarks, were never developed into a systematic statistical mechanics, but they show how clearly he saw to the heart of the matter. He was insisting on the statistical character of the second law at a time when Rudolf Clausius and Ludwig Boltzmann were trying to show that it was a strictly mechanical theorem. His writ-ings on this subject show, in their fragmentary character as well as in their penetration, that quality which Tait summed up in a sentence: "It is thoroughly characteristic of the man that his mind could never bear to pass by any phenomenon with-out satisfying itself of at least its general nature and causes" (*8*, pp. 319–20).

The demon and molecular statistics

Carnot formulated his general result in these words: "The motive power of heat is independent of the agents employed to realize it; its quantity is fixed solely by the temperatures of the bodies between which is effected, finally, the transfer of the caloric" (*10*). As the last word indicates, Carnot was using the caloric theory of heat, so that for him heat was a conserved fluid: as much heat was rejected at the low temperature as had been absorbed at the high temperature, when work was performed by a cyclic process. Carnot's proof made use of the impossibility of perpetual motion, the impossibility, that is, of "an unlimited creation of motive power without con-sumption either of caloric or of any other agent what-ever" (*10*, p. 12).

When the possibility of transforming work into heat, or heat into work, in a fixed proportion was con-clusively demonstrated in the 1840s, the basis for Carnot's principle seemed to be lost (*11*). Caloric was not conserved and Carnot's proof no longer held. It was Clausius who saw that the equivalence of work and heat could be made compatible with Carnot's principle, if the latter were modified only slightly (*12*). Whereas Carnot had said that heat, Q, must be transferred from a hot body to a cold one when work, W, is done in a cyclic process, one could now say instead that when heat Q is absorbed from the hot body, only the difference, $Q - W$, is rejected as heat to the cold body. This revised form of Carnot's assumption allowed for the equivalence of heat and work, and, according to Clausius, it could still serve as the basis for a proof of Carnot's theorem. But something more than the usual impossibility of perpetual motion had to be invoked as a postulate to carry out the proof.

Clausius repeated Carnot's indirect reasoning, prov-ing his result by showing that assuming the converse led one to an evidently intolerable conclusion. For Carnot this had been the appearance of perpetual motion; for Clausius it was something different. "By repeating these two processes alternately it would be possible, without any expenditure of force or any other change, to transfer as much heat as we please from a *cold* to a *hot* body, and this is not in accord with the other relations of heat, since it al-ways shows a tendency to equalize temperature dif-ferences and therefore to pass from *hotter* to *colder* bodies" (*13*). This was the new assumption Clausius needed for the creation of a thermodynamics based on both the equivalence of heat and work (the first law) and Carnot's principle. He phrased it more compactly a few years later: "Heat can never pass from a colder to a warmer body without some other change, connected therewith, occurring at the same time" (*14*). Modern textbook formulations of this second law of thermodynamics are careful to specify that cyclic processes are being considered and that the "other change" in question is the performance of ex-ternal work on the system, but these specifications were implicit in Clausius' statement. The point to be stressed here is the universality of the statement, the presence of the word "never," for example, in the second quotation from Clausius.

It was here that Maxwell chose to "pick a hole" when he wrote to Tait in December 1867. He sug-gested a conceivable way in which, "if two things are in contact, the hotter" could "take heat from the colder without external agency." Maxwell considered a gas in a vessel divided into two sections, A and B, by a fixed diaphragm. The gas in A was assumed to be hotter than the gas in B, and Maxwell looked at the implications of this assumption from the molecular point of view. A higher temperature meant a higher average value of the kinetic energy of the gas molecules in A compared to those in B. But, as Maxwell had shown some years earlier, each sample of gas would necessarily contain molecules having velocities of all possible magnitudes. "Now," Maxwell wrote, "conceive a finite being who knows the paths and velocities of all the molecules by simple inspection but who can do no work except open and close a hole in the diaphragm by means of a slide without mass." This being would be assigned to open the hole for an approaching molecule in A only when that molecule had a velocity less than the root mean square velocity of the molecules in B. He would allow a molecule from B to pass through the hole into A only when its velocity exceeded the root mean square velocity of the molecules in A. These two procedures were to be carried out alternately, so that the numbers of molecules in A and B would not change. As a result of this process, however, "the energy in A is increased and that in B diminished; that is, the hot system has got hotter and the cold colder and yet no work has been done, only the intelligence of a very observant and neat-fingered being has been employed." If one could only deal with the molecules directly and individually in the manner of this supposed being, one could violate the second law. "Only we can't," added Maxwell, "not being clever enough" (*9*).

This is the first time that Maxwell's talented little being appeared on paper. Thomson immediately gave him the name "demon," by which he has been known ever since (*5a*, p. 214; *15*). Thomson used this name only in its original meaning, a supernatural being, and did not want to suggest any evil intentions on the part of this being who could reverse the common tendency of nature. In his letter to Tait, Maxwell probably did not make sufficiently clear his reason for introducing this fanciful construction. He described "the chief end" of his demon soon afterwards in these words: "to show that the 2nd law of thermodynamics has only a statistical certainty" (*5a*, p. 215). He meant that while it would require the action of the demon to produce an observable flow of heat from a cold body to a hotter one, this process is occurring spontaneously all the time, on a submicroscopic scale. The possibility of the demon's existence is less significant than the actuality of the statistical distribution of molecular velocities in a gas at equilibrium. This statistical character of a system composed of an enormous number of molecules, which would form

the basis for the demon's actions, necessarily leads to spontaneous fluctuations, including fluctuations that take heat from a cold body to a hotter one.

Maxwell came a little closer to saying these things explicitly when he repeated his argument a few years later in a letter to John William Strutt (later Lord Rayleigh). This time he referred to the possibility of a complete reversal of the motion of all particles in the world, thereby reversing the sequence in which events normally occur. This possibility was quite consistent with the assumption that "this world is a purely dynamical system." In this time-reversed state the trend would always be away from equilibrium; such behavior would be in flagrant violation of the second law. Maxwell knew, of course, that "the possibility of executing this experiment is doubtful," but he did not "think it requires such a feat to upset the 2nd law of thermodynamics." It could be done more easily with the help of the demon, now described more graphically as "a doorkeeper very intelligent and exceedingly quick, with microscopic eyes," who would be "a mere guiding agent, like a pointsman on a railway with perfectly acting switches who should send the express along one line and the goods along another." The demon argument was introduced, however, by this sentence: "For if there is any truth in the dynamical theory of gases, the different molecules in a gas of uniform temperature are moving with very different velocities." That was the essential thing; the demon only served to make its implications transparently clear. Maxwell even drew an explicit "moral" from his discussion: "The 2nd law of thermodynamics has the same degree of truth as the statement that if you throw a tumblerful of water into the sea, you cannot get the same tumblerful of water out again" (*16*).

It is, after all, not surprising that Maxwell should have been ready to take the consequences of the velocity distribution so seriously: he was the one who had introduced this concept into physics. Maxwell became interested in the molecular theory of gases in 1859 when he read Clausius' papers on the subject in the *Philosophical Magazine* (*17*). Clausius had made use of the idea of the average distance traveled by a molecule between its collisions with the other molecules of the gas. It was Maxwell, however, who showed how the theory could be subjected to experimental test, as he derived the relationships between Clausius' mean free path and the measurable coefficients of viscosity, thermal conductivity, and diffusion. Again, although Clausius had remarked several times that "actually the greatest possible variety exists among the velocities of the several molecules" in a gas, he made no attempt to analyze the nature of this "variety" but simply used the average molecular velocity. Maxwell saw at once that an analysis of how molecular velocities were distributed would be fundamental to the development of the theory.

As early as May 1859, Maxwell wrote to George Gabriel Stokes about his work on the theory of gases, commenting, "Of course my particles have not all the same velocity, but the velocities are distributed according to the same formula as the errors are distributed in the theory of least squares" (*18*). He presented a derivation of this velocity distribution law in his first paper on gases in 1860, pointing out that molecular collisions would continually alter the individual velocities, and that what he found was "the average number of particles whose velocities lie between given limits after a great number of collisions among a great number of equal particles" (*19*). This relationship became even clearer in a new derivation of the distribution law that Maxwell published in 1866 (*20*). This time he calculated the effect of collisions on the distribution law and found the equilibrium distribution as that distribution which would be unchanged by collisions—the stationary law. This velocity distribution formed the basis of all the calculations of the properties of gases that Maxwell carried out, and it is quite natural that it should also have been the basis for his criticism of the second law of thermodynamics. Although this statistical approach seemed natural to Maxwell, it was very different from contemporary efforts to probe into the meaning of the second law.

Attempts at mechanical explanation

In 1866 Ludwig Boltzmann wrote a paper, "On the Mechanical Meaning of the Second Law of Thermodynamics" (*21*). It was his first scientific work of any significance and the first serious attempt to give a general mechanical interpretation of the second law. Boltzmann began by referring to the "peculiarly exceptional position" of the second law and to the "roundabout and uncertain methods" by which physicists had tried to establish it, contrasting this with the first law, whose identity with the energy principle had been known "for a long time already." This "long time" was only about fifteen years, but Boltzmann was only twenty-two himself. He announced his goal with all the self-assurance of his age: "It is the purpose of this article to give a purely analytical, completely general proof of the second law of thermodynamics, as well as to discover the theorem in mechanics that corresponds to it."

Boltzmann was pursuing the classic program of physics, "tracing the phenomena of nature back to the simple laws of mechanics" (*22*). Since the first law could be clearly understood by introducing the energy of molecular motions, why not the second, too? Boltzmann apparently persuaded himself that he had achieved his goal, but for all his sweeping claims his success was very limited. To evaluate it we must state more precisely what he was trying to explain.

The statement that "heat can never pass from a colder to a warmer body without some other change occurring" had been an adequate basis for Clausius' first thermodynamic studies, but he felt that it was "incomplete, because we cannot recognize therein, with sufficient clearness, the real nature of the theorem" (*14*, p. 81). He was more satisfied with another form which he deduced from this a few years later and then expressed very compactly in 1865, in a paper which might well have stimulated Boltzmann's work (*3*). Clausius' results were these: For every thermodynamic system there exists a function, *S*, which is a function of the thermodynamic state of the system. *S*, which he named the entropy, is defined by the differential relationship,

$$dS = \frac{dQ}{T} \qquad (1)$$

where *dQ* is the heat supplied to the system in a *reversible* infinitesimal process and *T* is the absolute temperature of the system. (The notation *dQ*, not used by Clausius, emphasizes that *dQ* is not an exact differential.) For processes that are *irreversible*, one can only state the inequality,

$$dS > \frac{dQ}{T}. \qquad (2)$$

In order to give the second law a mechanical explanation, Boltzmann would have had to find mechanical expressions for all of the quantities appearing in (1) and (2) and would have had to show that these mechanical quantities, functions of the molecular coordinates and momenta, do indeed satisfy the relationships satisfied by their thermodynamic counterparts. All of this should be done for a mechanical system of very general character. Boltzmann had certainly tried to do just these things. He was least successful in dealing with irreversible processes; his brief discussion of one particular example threw no light on the molecular basis for irreversibility.

Boltzmann did give a detailed justification for the idea, already expressed by others, that temperature was a measure of the average kinetic energy of a molecule. He also proved a very interesting mechanical theorem, a generalization of the principle of least action, on the strength of which he claimed to have given a mechanical explanation of the second law. This theorem will be discussed later; it is enough for the present to point out that Boltzmann could prove it only under a very restrictive assumption. He had to limit himself to periodic systems. For a system whose entire molecular configuration repeats itself after a time, τ, he found a mechanical counterpart to the entropy, S. Boltzmann's equation for the entropy of such a system had the form,

$$S = \Sigma \ln(T\tau)^2 + \text{constant}, \qquad (3)$$

where the sum is over all molecules. The absolute temperature, T, is the kinetic energy of one molecule averaged over the period,

$$T = \frac{1}{\tau} \int_0^\tau \left(\frac{1}{2} mv^2\right) dt. \qquad (4)$$

Since the period, τ, appears explicitly in the entropy equation one is inclined to guess that the periodicity of the system is an essential aspect of the theorem. Boltzmann tried to extend his proof to nonperiodic systems, where the particle orbits are not closed, but his argument was not cogent. It concluded rather lamely with the remark that "if the orbits are not closed in a finite time, one may still regard them as closed in an infinite time" (23). (It may be worth noting, however, that one can evaluate the entropy, with the help of (3), for a very simple model of a gas—a collection of particles bouncing back and forth between the walls of a container of volume V, all particles moving with the same speed, v. The result does depend linearly on the quantity $\ln (VT^{3/2})$, as it should for an ideal gas of point particles.)

Boltzmann was not the only physicist who tried to reduce the second law to a theorem in mechanics. Rudolf Clausius had been thinking about the second law since 1850; "the second law of thermodynamics is much harder for the mind to grasp than the first," he wrote once (3, p. 353). This is not the place to follow the evolution of his ideas, but it must be pointed out that Clausius arrived at a very particular way of looking at the second law (24). He introduced a concept that he named the disgregation, intended as a measure of "the degree in which the molecules of a body are dispersed." It was to be a thermodynamic state function, denoted by Z, related to the total work, internal as well as external, done by a system in a reversible process. This relationship was fixed by the equation,

$$dL = TdZ \qquad (5)$$

where dL represents the total work, an inexact differential. (Clausius considered the internal energy, U, of a system to be the sum of two terms, both state functions—the heat in the body, H, and the internal work, I. The total work dL was the sum of dI and the usual external work, dW, or PdV.) It was (5) that Clausius saw as the ultimate thermodynamic formulation of the second law: "the effective force of heat is proportional to the absolute temperature" (25). And it was (5) for which Clausius tried to find a mechanical interpretation.

Clausius' first attempt, in 1870, did not succeed, but it could hardly be called a failure since it led him to the virial theorem (25). The following year he was convinced that he had solved the problem, as he entitled his paper, "On the Reduction of the Second Law of Thermodynamics to General Mechanical Principles" (26). This title sounds very much like that of Boltzmann's paper of 1866, and with good reason. Clausius had independently discovered the theorem published by Boltzmann five years earlier. Although the results were the same, there were some differences in approach. Boltzmann had been looking for a mechanical interpretation of entropy and its properties, while Clausius gave disgregation the central position in the theory. The two functions are simply related, however, and the entropy Clausius derived from his mechanical expression for disgregation was identical with the one Boltzmann had found directly (see (3) above).

Boltzmann wasted no time in pointing out his considerable priority in having established this mechanical analogue of the second law (27). He showed that all of Clausius' basic equations were identical with his own, apart from notation, reinforcing the point by reproducing verbatim the relevant pages of his earlier article. "I think I have established my priority," Boltzmann concluded, adding, "I can only express my pleasure that an authority with Mr. Clausius' reputation is helping to spread the knowledge of my work on thermodynamics" (27, p. 236).

Clausius had, of course, overlooked Boltzmann's original memoir. He had moved from Zürich to Würzburg in 1867 and again to Bonn in 1869, and the resulting "extraordinary demands" on his time and energy had prevented him from keeping up with the literature properly. He obviously granted Boltzmann's claim to priority for all the results common to both papers, but Clausius was not convinced that Boltzmann's arguments were as general or as sound as his own, and he proceeded to discuss some of these matters in detail (28).

Limitations of the second law

Maxwell observed this and later disputes over the mechanical interpretation of the second law with detachment—and no little amusement. "It is rare sport to see those learned Germans contending for the priority of the discovery that the 2nd law of $\theta\Delta$cs [thermodynamics] is the Hamiltonsche Princip," he wrote to Tait, "when all the time they *assume* that the temperature of a body is but another name for the vis viva of one of its molecules, a thing which was suggested by the labours of Gay Lussac, Dulong, etc., but first deduced from dynamical statistical considerations by dp/dt [i.e. Maxwell: see Appendix]. The Hamiltonsche Princip, the while, soars along in a region unvexed by statistical considerations, while the German Icari flap their waxen wings in nephelococcygia amid those cloudy forms which the ignorance and finitude of human science have invested with the incommunicable attributes of the invisible Queen of Heaven" (*29*).

The prize for which "those learned Germans" were contending was an illusion: the second law was not a dynamical theorem at all, but an essentially statistical result.

Maxwell expressed some of his own ideas on the meaning of the second law in his *Theory of Heat*, published in 1871 (*30*). This book appeared as one of a series, described by the publisher as "text-books of science adapted for the use of artisans and of students in public and science schools." They were meant to be "within the comprehension of working men, and suited to their wants," with "every theory ... reduced to the stage of direct and useful application" (*31*). Maxwell's book did not quite fit this description. Tait thought that some of it was probably "more difficult to follow than any other of his writings" (!) and that as a whole it was "*not* an elementary book." His explanation of this fact was interesting, and probably accurate. "One of the few knowable things which Clerk-Maxwell did not know," he wrote, "was the distinction which most men readily perceive between what is easy and what is hard. What *he called* hard, others would be inclined to call altogether unintelligible." As a consequence Maxwell's book contained "matter enough to fill two or three large volumes without undue dilution (perhaps we should rather say, *with the necessary dilution*) of its varied contents" (*8*, p. 320). Maxwell did not hesitate to include discussions of the latest work in thermodynamics in the successive editions of his book; one wonders what his intended audience of "artisans and students" made of something like Willard Gibbs's thermodynamic surface,

which Maxwell treated at some length, less than two years after the publication of Gibbs's paper (*32*).

In discussing the second law, Maxwell emphasized that Carnot's principle does not follow from the first law, but must instead be deduced from an independent assumption, hence a second law. He quoted Thomson's and Clausius' versions of this law, both of which asserted, in effect, the impossibility of a cyclic process converting the heat of a body into work without allowing heat to pass from that body to a colder one. He advised the student to compare the various statements of the law so as "to make himself master of the fact which they embody, an acquisition which will be of much greater importance to him than any form of words on which a demonstration may be more or less compactly constructed." And then in his next two paragraphs Maxwell went to the crux of the question.

> Suppose that a body contains energy in the form of heat, what are the conditions under which this energy or any part of it may be removed from the body? If heat in a body consists in a motion of its parts, and if we were able to distinguish these parts, and to guide and control their motions by any kind of mechanism, then by arranging our apparatus so as to lay hold of every moving part of the body, we could, by a suitable train of mechanism, transfer the energy of the moving parts of the heated body to any other body in the form of ordinary motion. The heated body would thus be rendered perfectly cold, and all its thermal energy would be converted into the visible motion of some other body.

> Now this supposition involves a direct contradiction to the second law of thermodynamics, but is consistent with the first law. The second law is therefore equivalent to a denial of our power to perform the operation just described, either by a train of mechanism, or by any other method yet discovered. Hence, if the heat consists in the motion of its parts, the separate parts which move must be so small or so impalpable that we cannot in any way lay hold of them to stop them [*30*, pp. 153–54].

This argument, so deceptively simple in appearance, brought out the point that had escaped Boltzmann and Clausius, among others. Those processes that are declared to be impossible by the second law are perfectly consistent with the laws of mechanics. The second law must, therefore, express some essentially nonmechanical aspect of nature. If it is to receive an explanation at the molecular level, that explanation must refer to the smallness of molecules, or, equivalently, to their enormous numbers. This is really the same point of view that Maxwell had already expressed privately in his demon argument. He made the connection himself in the last chapter of his book, which dealt briefly with the molecular theory of matter. In a section entitled "Limitation of the Second Law of Thermodynamics," Maxwell remarked that this law "is undoubtedly true as long as we can deal with bodies only in mass, and have no power of perceiving or handling the separate molecules of which they are made up." The status of the second law would be very different if we had the powers of "a being whose faculties are so sharpened that he can follow every molecule in its course." Maxwell described how the second law could be flouted by such a demon, just as he had described it in his letters to Tait and Strutt. As a consequence, one had to be careful about extending conclusions "drawn from our experience of bodies consisting of an immense number of molecules" to the "more delicate observations and experiments" that might be made if individual molecules could be perceived and handled. Unless that should become possible we were "compelled to adopt ... the statistical method of calculation, and to abandon the strict dynamical method" (*30*, pp. 328–29).

The inadequacy of mechanical explanation

Maxwell returned to these considerations a few years later, when he was asked to review the second edition of Tait's *Sketch of Thermodynamics*. Written only a year or so before Maxwell's fatal illness, this review contains his final reflections on the subject of thermodynamics, presented in his most brilliant style. (As Tait himself remarked in another connection, "No living man has shown a greater power of condensing the whole marrow of a question into a few clear and compact sentences than Maxwell" [*8*, p. 321]). Much of Maxwell's review was devoted to the second law, since he thought that the manner in which an author handled this thorny subject formed "the touchstone of a treatise on thermodynamics" (*1*, p. 667).

The review offered a new variation on Maxwell's old theme of the irreducibility of the second law to pure dynamics. The whole point of the second law depends on the distinction between two modes of communicating energy from one body to another, heat and work. "According to the molecular theory," Maxwell observed, "the only difference between these two kinds of communication of energy is that

the motions and displacements which are concerned in the communication of heat are those of molecules, and are so numerous, so small individually, and so irregular in their distribution, that they quite escape all our methods of observation; whereas when the motions and displacements are those of visible bodies consisting of great numbers of molecules moving altogether, the communication of energy is called work" (*1*, p. 669). If one supposed that individual molecular motions could be followed, as one would have to do in a dynamical molecular theory, then "the distinction between work and heat would vanish." At the molecular level there is no mechanical distinction between work and heat, and so no attempt to deduce the second law from purely dynamical principles, however satisfactory it might appear, could be a "sufficient explanation" of this law (*1*, p. 671).

This conclusion has a certain irony about it, and Maxwell was probably quite aware of that. The second law denies the possibility of perpetual motion machines of the second kind: no matter how ingenious one of these devices may seem to be, one can be certain that in some way or other its existence would violate the laws of nature. Maxwell had cast his conclusion in precisely the same form: no matter how convincing a purely dynamical proof of the second law might seem to be, it could not adequately explain the limited convertibility of heat into work.

Maxwell might have observed—but did not—that one of the subjects for dispute between "those learned Germans" was precisely the proper way of describing work and heat at the molecular level. Boltzmann (*21*, pp. 24–28) imagined a process in which each molecule was supplied with the same amount of energy, ϵ. The sum of ϵ for all molecules was his way of representing the heat added to the system, but he gave no indication of *how* this ϵ was to be supplied to each molecule. Boltzmann did have to require that this energy went either into work done against external forces or into an increase of the kinetic energy of that particular molecule, explicitly excluding its partial transfer to other molecules. This might be reasonable enough on the average, but the nature of this average was never analyzed. Boltzmann also made no attempt to clarify how the work done by the individual molecules, represented only very schematically, was to be related to the work done by the gas in displacing a piston under pressure. The coordinate of the piston, that is to say, the volume of the gas, not being a molecular coordinate, never appeared in his equations.

Clausius (*28*) criticized Boltzmann's treatment of

some of these points, and this was the reason he did not grant Boltzmann's absolute priority for the mechanical derivation of the second law. His own way of treating the work involved making the potential energy function depend on a parameter. This parameter, in turn, which varied from one orbit to another, was assumed to change uniformly with time as the particle went through a complete orbit. It must be remembered that Clausius, like Boltzmann, could make even reasonably precise arguments only when the particles moved in closed orbits, that is, for a periodic system. Boltzmann was not happy about Clausius' way of "allowing the laws of nature to vary with time," and never adopted this procedure in his later discussions of the problem (*33*).

Perhaps the best way of seeing the difficulty of separating work and heat in a mechanical theory is to look at the particularly clear exposition of the Boltzmann-Clausius theorem given by Paul Ehrenfest (*34*). One considers a system whose Lagrangian depends on a set of generalized coordinates, q, the corresponding generalized velocities, $\dot{q}$, and a parameter, a, such as the volume in the case of a gas. The system is assumed to be periodic, and to remain periodic (but with a changed period) in a variation from the original orbit to a neighboring orbit. This variation is of the kind considered in the principle of least action, i.e. nonsimultaneous, but the two orbits are also assumed to differ because the parameter has the value $a + \Delta a$ rather than a on the new orbit. By the usual variational procedures Ehrenfest derived the equation,

$$\Delta \int_0^\tau 2T \, dt = \tau(\Delta E + A \, \Delta a). \tag{6}$$

The Δ represents the change in the generalized variation just described. T is the kinetic energy, E is the total energy, and τ is the period of the system. The quantity $\overline{A}$ is defined by the equations,

$$\overline{A} = \frac{1}{\tau} \int_0^\tau A \, dt; \qquad A = \frac{\partial L}{\partial a}, \tag{7}$$

so that $(-A)$ is the generalized force that must be exerted on the system to hold the parameter, a, constant, and $\overline{A}$ is its time average. In the standard treatment of the principle of least action there is no variation of a parameter, a, and the variation of the path is carried out at constant total energy, E. As a result the variation of the action, which is just the time integral of the kinetic energy, vanishes.

When the parameter, a, is varied slowly, so that the variation occurs during a time long compared to the

period of the motion, the external work done by the system is just $\overline{A} \, \Delta a$. In this case the change in energy, ΔE, is just the negative of the work done, and the complete variation of the action, (6), still vanishes. This slow variation is the Ehrenfest adiabatic process, so important in the old quantum theory (*35*). When the variation is not carried out at this very slow pace the right-hand side of (6) need not vanish. *If* one still calls $\overline{A}\Delta a$ the work, ΔW, done by the system, *then* it is proper to identify $\Delta E + \Delta W$ with ΔQ, the heat supplied to the system. In that case (6) leads directly to the equation,

$$2\Delta(\tau \overline{T}) = \tau \Delta Q. \tag{8}$$

This is easily rewritten in the form,

$$\frac{\Delta Q}{\overline{T}} = \Delta \ln (\overline{T}\tau)^2, \tag{9}$$

which is equivalent to (3), the Boltzmann-Clausius result, when the average kinetic energy is set equal to the temperature.

The argument hinges on the identification of $\overline{A}\Delta a$ with the work done by the system, but there is no compelling reason for this identification. The work is the integral, $\int_a^{a + \Delta a} A \, da$, and this is not equivalent to $\overline{A} \, \Delta a$ when the time of the variation is of the order of, or less, than the period. There is no obvious way of distinguishing two separate modes of energy transfer as heat and work in such a process. This is an illustration of Maxwell's general statement that mechanical explanations of the second law can never be adequate, no matter how impressive their outward appearance may be.

Boltzmann and statistical mechanics

Maxwell was not the one to develop the statistical mechanics that does explain the second law. He was apparently satisfied to have recognized that "the truth of the second law [is] of the nature of a strong probability...not an absolute certainty" (*1*, p. 671), that it depended in an essential way on the unimaginably large number of molecules that constitute macroscopic bodies. It was Boltzmann who undertook the task of creating a statistical theory that would make clear just how a mechanical system of so many particles could show the behavior required by the laws of thermodynamics. But Boltzmann found his starting point in Maxwell's work, for which he had a profound admiration.

At the time when Boltzmann tried to account for the

second law in purely mechanical terms, he was apparently unfamiliar with what Maxwell had written on the theory of gases. When he quoted the relationship between the pressure of a gas and the velocities of its molecules, he referred to Krönig, Rankine, and Clausius, but did not mention Maxwell or his law for the distribution of molecular velocities (*36*). We know that Boltzmann was learning to read English at this time—in order to read Maxwell's papers on electromagnetism (*37*). He returned to the theory of gases in 1868, however, with fresh ideas prompted by his study of Maxwell's new analysis of the kinetic theory (*38*). Boltzmann had embarked on a series of lengthy memoirs in which the statistical description of the gas was absolutely central to his treatment.

By the time Clausius was criticizing the fine points of his mechanical interpretation of the second law, Boltzmann was already committed to the statistical approach. In that same year, 1871, he offered a new proof of the law, but this time it was a statistical mechanical, rather than a mechanical, proof (*39*). This new proof dealt only with the equilibrium aspect of the second law—that is, with the existence of the entropy as a thermodynamic state function related to heat and temperature in the proper way, through equation (1). Work and heat were now distinguished with the help of the distribution function: roughly speaking, a change in the total energy produced by a change in the molecular potential energy with a fixed distribution was work, whereas heat was identified with a change in the energy due only to a change in the distribution. The exponential energy distribution at equilibrium played an important part in the analysis. The essential features of Boltzmann's argument have survived the transition from classical to quantum physics, and it is still to be found in textbooks on statistical mechanics (*40*).

A year later Boltzmann was able to provide a molecular basis for the other aspect of the second law, the increase of the entropy of an isolated system whenever an irreversible process occurs (*41*). This came as a by-product of an investigation into the uniqueness of the Maxwell-Boltzmann equilibrium distribution. Boltzmann's result, the famous *H*-theorem, was based on his analysis of how the distribution evolved in time as a result of binary molecular collisions. Although much more limited in its scope than his discussion of equilibrium, the *H*-theorem offered the first insight into the nature of irreversibility.

It must be emphasized, however, that while Boltz-

mann made constant use of the statistical distribution of molecular velocities and energies, the result he asserted was supposed to be a certainty and not just a probability. The *H*-theorem of 1872 said that entropy would *always* increase (*41*, p. 345). Boltzmann did not revise this statement until 1877, when Josef Loschmidt pointed out that it was untenable in its original form (*42*). Since the equations of motion of the molecules do not distinguish between the two senses in which time might flow (that is, they are invariant to the replacement of t by $-t$), the time reversal of any actual motion is an equally legitimate solution of the equations. As a consequence, for any motion of the molecules in which the entropy of the gas increased with time, one could construct another motion in which the entropy decreased with time, in apparent contradiction to the second law. It was only in his reply to Loschmidt's criticism that Boltzmann recognized "how intimately the second law is connected to the theory of probability," and that the increase in entropy can only be described as very highly probable, but not as certain. He elaborated this view in a major article later that same year, in which he formulated the relationship between the entropy of a thermodynamic state and the number of molecular configurations compatible with that state (*43*). Entropy became simply a measure of this "thermodynamic probability."

Boltzmann's work can be viewed legitimately as a development of the insight first expressed by Maxwell—an extended, detailed, and quantitative development of a brief qualitative insight, to be sure, but a natural development, all the same. Nevertheless Maxwell seems to have taken little or no interest in these papers by Boltzmann. He did follow some particular aspects of Boltzmann's work in statistical mechanics; Maxwell's last scientific work was a new analysis of the equipartition theorem, taking Boltzmann's 1868 memoir as its starting point and presenting an alternate way of handling some of the difficult assumptions (*44*). Maxwell was certainly aware of much of Boltzmann's other work. Henry William Watson's little book on the kinetic theory, which appeared in 1876 (*45*), followed Boltzmann's methods and included a modified version of Boltzmann's first statistical derivation of the existence of an entropy function. Watson acknowledged "much kind assistance" from Maxwell in his Preface, and Maxwell also reviewed the book for *Nature* (*46*). But nowhere did Maxwell discuss Boltzmann's statistical mechanical theory of the second law of thermodynamics. It is not even mentioned in his review of Tait, where it would have been completely appropriate.

There is no obvious explanation for the peculiar lack of intellectual contact between Maxwell and Boltzmann at this one point. It is true that their styles were very different. Boltzmann found Maxwell hard to understand because of his terseness (*38*, p. 49); Maxwell found the great length of Boltzmann's discussions to be "an equal stumbling block" and wanted to reduce one of his papers to "about six lines" (*47*). It may well be that Maxwell simply never read Boltzmann's memoirs of 1877, and so missed the pleasure of seeing the relationship between entropy and probability.

Fluctuations and the demon

Maxwell conjured up his demon as a way of giving life to the difficult idea that the second law of thermodynamics is a statistical truth and not a dynamical certainty. This idea caught on quickly in Maxwell's circle. William Thomson incorporated it into his own thinking and elaborated it in a paper on the kinetic theory of energy dissipation. He went so far as to imagine an army of Maxwell's demons stationed at the interface of a hot and a cold gas, each member of this "ideal army" being armed with "a club, or, as it were, a molecular cricket bat," and described the variety of ways in which such an army could control molecular processes (*48*). But even though Thomson was playful enough to endow the demon "with arms and hands and fingers—two hands and ten fingers suffice" (*49*), he knew very well why they had been called into being. Thomson's paper of 1874 raised the reversibility paradox with which Loschmidt would confront Boltzmann a few years later, and also showed that it was no real paradox, in much the way Boltzmann would. Thomson went further. He calculated the probability of the fluctuations that are an inescapable aspect of the statistical theory, showing that while it was not impossible that one would find all the oxygen molecules in a vessel of air in the left-most fifth of the container, the probability of this event was staggeringly small.

Tait also absorbed the statistical molecular approach to the second law. He pointed out in his lectures that molecular processes taking energy from a colder to a warmer body are "constantly going on, but on a very limited scale, in every mass of a gas." This fact did not interfere with the validity of Carnot's theorem and could be safely ignored for "the enormous number of particles in a cubic inch of even the most rarefied gas" (*15*, pp. 119–20). But Tait also found the existence of such fluctuations to be a convenient stick with which to beat his old antagonist, Clausius, commenting that the demon argument was "absolutely fatal to Clausius' reasoning."

This was, of course, an exaggerated version of what Maxwell had originally said. He had looked for possible limitations of the second law, but he had certainly never intended to destroy it. Clausius, used to Tait's onslaughts and practiced in countering them with equal vigor, had a proper answer to this new attack: "I believe I can summarize my reply to Mr. Tait's objection in the brief remark that my law is concerned, not with what heat can do with the help of demons, but rather with what it can do by itself" (*50*). He saw no reason why the existence of fluctuations should be considered as contradicting the average behavior described by the second law.

Maxwell's own view was not essentially different. He saw no conflict between the two very different ways of establishing thermodynamics. "The second law," he wrote, "must either be founded on our actual experience in dealing with real bodies of sensible magnitude, or else deduced from the molecular theory of these bodies, on the hypothesis that the behaviour of bodies consisting of millions of molecules may be deduced from the theory of the encounters of pairs of molecules, by supposing the relative frequency of different kinds of encounters to be distributed according to the laws of probability (*1*, pp. 669–70).

Real experimental support for the statistical molecular theory did not come until the early years of this century, but then it came in strength. A whole series of fluctuation phenomena was studied quantitatively—the Brownian motion, critical opalescence, density fluctuations in colloidal suspensions—and the statistical theory accounted for all of them. By 1912, Maryan von Smoluchowski could give an invited lecture with the "revolutionary sounding" title "Experimentally Verifiable Molecular Phenomena that Contradict Ordinary Thermodynamics" (*51*). A decade earlier "it would have been foolhardy to have spoken so disrespectfully of the traditional formulation of thermodynamics," at least on the continent of Europe. There was now good reason for taking Maxwell's statistical approach completely seriously. The hole Maxwell had picked in the second law had become plainly visible (*52*).

Smoluchowski's brilliant analysis of the fluctuation phenomena showed that one could observe violations of almost all the usual statements of the second law by dealing with sufficiently small systems. The trend toward equilibrium, the increase of entropy, and so on, could not be taken as certainties. The one statement that could be upheld, even in the presence of fluctuations, was the impossibility of a perpetual motion of the second kind. No device could ever be made that would use the existing fluctuations to convert heat completely into work on a macroscopic scale. For any such device would have to be constituted of molecules and would therefore itself be subject to the same chance fluctuations. To *use* the molecular fluctuations one would have to construct a device whose action would not be limited by them. "Only we can't," as Maxwell had said, "not being clever enough."

Appendix. On Maxwell's Signature

James Clerk Maxwell often signed letters to such friends as Thomson and Tait with the signature dp/dt. He also used this derivative as a nom de plume for the witty verses on scientific subjects that he published in *Nature* (53). It is not hard to guess that he was making private reference to an equation of the form

$$\frac{dp}{dt} = JCM \qquad (A1)$$

so that dp/dt simply represented his initials. But what was the equation, and where did it come from? The late D. K. C. MacDonald recently described it as one of Maxwell's four thermodynamic relations (54), derived by him in the *Theory of Heat* from the geometry of isothermal and adiabatic curves (30, pp. 165–69), and now commonly derived from the equality of the mixed second derivatives of the various thermodynamic potentials. MacDonald's statement is technically correct but historically misleading. To Maxwell the relationship in (A1) expressed the second law of thermodynamics itself.

Carnot's statement of his fundamental theorem said that the motive power of heat depends only on the temperatures between which heat is transferred in the working of an engine. This was translated into mathematical terms by Émile Clapeyron in 1834 (55). A slightly modified version of the argument runs in the following way.

Consider an infinitesimal Carnot cycle consisting of an isothermal expansion at temperature $(t + dt)$ an adiabatic expansion which cools the system down to temperature t, an isothermal compression at temperature t, and a final adiabatic compression back to the initial state, all processes being carried out reversibly. Since the cycle is infinitesimal it can be represented as a parallelogram in the pressure-volume diagram. The area of this parallelogram is the work, ΔW, done per cycle and it has the value

$$\Delta W = (dp)\,(dV) \qquad (A2)$$

where dp and dV are, respectively, the difference in pressure between the two isotherms and the difference in volume in either isothermal step. The efficiency of the cycle is the ratio of ΔW to ΔQ, where ΔQ is the heat absorbed in the isothermal expansion. Carnot's theorem states that this efficiency, "the motive power of heat," depends only on the temperatures t and $t + dt$, which means that it can be expressed as $C(t)dt$ since dt is infinitesimal. Here $C(t)$ is a universal function (the Carnot function) of the temperature t, this temperature, t, being measured on any arbitrary scale. If one introduces the mechanical equivalent of heat, J, to allow for the fact that heat and work were expressed in different units, the equation expressing Carnot's theorem can be written in the form

$$\frac{\Delta W}{J\Delta Q} = C(t) \ dt. \tag{A3}$$

The quantity of heat absorbed is, however, proportional to the extent of the expansion, dV, so that one has the equation

$$\Delta Q = M \ dV \tag{A4}$$

where M is the coefficient of proportionality, the heat absorbed per unit volume change in an isothermal expansion. With the help of (A2) and (A4), the efficiency equation now becomes

$$\frac{(dp)}{J} \frac{(dV)}{M (dV)} = C \ dt \tag{A5}$$

or, with a slight rearrangement,

$$\frac{dp}{dt} = JCM. \tag{A1}$$

This is the basis of the assertion made by Maxwell's and Tait's biographers that (A1) represents the second law of thermodynamics (56).

There is, however, a little more to the story than that. It is obvious that Maxwell's use of dp/dt depends in an essential way on the notation used to express this result, but not all the notation in (A1) was standard. Pressure and temperature were commonly denoted by p and t. The quantities on the other side of the equation had no standard designation. In his first papers on thermodynamics, William Thomson had used J for the mechanical equivalent, probably in honor of Joule, and M for the quantity then usually denoted by dQ/dV (57). But it is C that is really interesting.

Clapeyron first made explicit use of the universal function of temperature whose existence is called for by Carnot's theorem. He did call it $C(t)$, but Clapeyron's $C(t)$ is essentially the *reciprocal* of the function defined by (A3). The central importance of this universal function was recognized by Clapeyron, who evaluated it numerically from several different kinds of data to establish its universality. Clausius used C as Clapeyron had, and also confirmed that C was equal to the ideal gas temperature (58). In modern notation $C(t)$, as used by Clapeyron and Clausius, is proportional to the absolute temperature.

Thomson did not use this notation. He wrote the equation we have called (A1) in the form

$$\frac{dp}{dt} = \mu M, \tag{A6}$$

where μ was the universal function of temperature, which Thomson called the Carnot function. The function μ incorporates the mechanical equivalent and is the integrating factor for the inexact differential dQ.

Where, then, did Maxwell get the particular form of the Carnot theorem which allowed him to use dp/dt as his signature? The first use of $C(t)$ in the form of (A3) and the first appearance of (A1) occur together in that same *Sketch of Thermodynamics* which called forth the Maxwell demon. It was Tait who renamed the Carnot function, making his $C(t)$ the reciprocal of the absolute temperature, and who thereby put JCM into the second law of thermodynamics (4, p. 91). It is not very likely that this was fortuitous. The Tait–Maxwell correspondence is full of verbal joking of various sorts. Both men wrote well, and often playfully; both were sensitive to questions of terminology and notation.

Tait actually commented on his old friend's thermodynamic signature in his notice of Maxwell's scientific work: "This nom de plume was suggested to him by me from the occurrence of his initials in the well-known expression of the second Law of Thermodynamics (for whose establishment on thoroughly valid grounds he did so much) $dp/dt = JCM$" (8, p. 321).

The first appearance of dp/dt in the Maxwell–Tait correspondence is on a postcard from Tait to Maxwell early in 1871 (59). Tait addressed Maxwell as dp/dt, and added an explanatory parenthesis: "[= JCM (T''s Thermodynamics § 162]." This is a reference to the paragraph of his *Sketch* in which (A1) is stated. T′ is the shorthand designation for Tait, just as T was used to designate Thomson, their famous book being referred to as T and T′ by the inner circle.

There is, however, an even earlier use of dp/dt by Maxwell. It occurs in a letter to Thomson in April 1870 (60), almost a year before Tait's card pointing out that dp/dt is equivalent to JCM, but well over a year after the publication of Tait's book. This suggests that Maxwell had already noticed the equation that Tait probably redesigned for his benefit and did not need to have it pointed out explicitly to him. He was certainly clever enough.

Acknowledgments

This work was supported in part by a grant from the National Science Foundation. I thank Dr. Elizabeth Garber for many informative discussions on Maxwell, and my colleague Professor Derek J. de Solla Price for the use of his copy of the Cambridge University collection of Maxwell correspondence.

Notes

1. J. C. Maxwell, "Tait's *Thermodynamics*," *Nature 17* (1878), 257. Reprinted in *The Scientific Papers of James Clerk Maxwell*, ed. W. D. Niven (Cambridge, 1890), Vol. 2, 660–71. Quotation from p. 662.

2. R. Clausius, *Abhandlungen über die mechanische Wärmetheorie* (Braunschweig, 1864).

3. R. Clausius, "Über verschiedene für die Anwendung bequeme Formen der Hauptgleichungen der mechanischen Wärmetheorie," *Pogg. Ann. 125* (1865), 353.

4. P. G. Tait, *Sketch of Thermodynamics* (Edinburgh, 1868).

5. For further discussion of this controversy see: (a) C. G. Knott, *Life and Scientific Work of Peter Guthrie Tait* (Cambridge, 1911), 208–26. Referred to below as Knott, *Tait*. (b) M. J. Klein, "Gibbs on Clausius," *Historical Studies in the Physical Sciences 1* (1969), 127–49.

6. R. Clausius, *Die Mechanische Wärmetheorie*, 2d ed. Vol. 2 (Braunschweig, 1879), 324–30.

7. Knott, *Tait*, contains extensive excerpts from this correspondence as well as a description of the relationship of Tait and Maxwell. Also see L. Campbell and W. Garnett, *The Life of James Clerk Maxwell* (London, 1882).

8. P. G. Tait, "Clerk-Maxwell's Scientific Work," *Nature 21* (1880), 321.

9. J. C. Maxwell to P. G. Tait, 11 December 1867. Reprinted in Knott, *Tait*, 213–14.

10. S. Carnot, *Reflections on the Motive Power of Fire*, trans. R. H. Thurston, ed. E. Mendoza (New York, 1960), 20. This volume also contains papers by É. Clapeyron and R. Clausius. It is referred to below as Mendoza reprint.

11. See, e.g., E. Mach, *Die Principien der Wärmelehre*, 3d ed. (Leipzig, 1919), 269–71. Also see M. J. Klein, n. 5, for further references.

12. R. Clausius, "Über die bewegende Kraft der Wärme, und die Gesetze, welche sich daraus für die Wärmelehre selbst ableiten lassen," *Pogg. Ann. 79* (1850), 368,500. Trans. by W. F. Magie in Mendoza reprint. Also see J. W. Gibbs, "Rudolf Julius Emanuel Clausius," *Proc. Amer. Acad. 16* (1889), 458. Reprinted in *The Scientific Papers of J. Willard Gibbs* (New York, 1906), Vol. 2, 261.

13. R. Clausius in Mendoza reprint, 134.

14. R. Clausius, "On a Modified Form of the Second Fundamental Theorem in the Mechanical Theory of Heat," *Phil. Mag. 12* (1856), 86.

15. Also see P. G. Tait, *Lectures on Some Recent Advances in Physical Science*, 2d ed. (London, 1876), 119, and Sir William Thomson, Baron Kelvin, *Mathematical and Physical Papers*, Vol. 5 (Cambridge, 1911), 12, 19.

16. J. C. Maxwell to J. W. Strutt, 6 December 1870. Reprinted in R. J. Strutt, *Life of John William Strutt, Third Baron Rayleigh* (Madison, 1968), 47.

17. R. Clausius, "The Nature of the Motion Which We Call Heat," *Phil. Mag. 14* (1857), 108; "On the Mean Lengths of the Paths Described by the Separate Molecules of Gaseous Bodies," *Phil. Mag. 17* (1859), 81. Both are reprinted in S. G. Brush, *Kinetic Theory*, Vol. 1 (Oxford, 1965).

18. J. C. Maxwell to G. G. Stokes, 30 May 1859. Quoted by Brush (n. 17), 26–27.

19. J. C. Maxwell, "Illustrations of the Dynamical Theory of Gases," *Phil. Mag. 19* (1860), 19; *20* (1860), 21. *Scientific Papers*, Vol. 1, 377–409. Quotation from p. 380.

20. J. C. Maxwell, "On the Dynamical Theory of Gases," *Phil. Mag. 32* (1866), 390; *35* (1868) 129, 185. *Scientific Papers*, Vol. 2, 26–78.

21. L. Boltzmann, "Über die mechanische Bedeutung des zweiten Hauptsatzes der Wärmetheorie," *Wiener Berichte 53* (1866), 195. Reprinted in L. Boltzmann, *Wissenschaftliche*

Abhandlungen, ed. F. Hasenöhrl (Leipzig, 1909), Vol. 1, 9–33. This collection will be referred to as Boltzmann, *Wiss. Abh.*, and page references to Boltzmann's work are made to this reprint.

22. H. Hertz, *The Principles of Mechanics Presented in a New Form*, trans. D. E. Jones and J. T. Walley (Reprinted New York, 1956), Author's Preface.

23. Boltzmann, *Wiss. Abh.*, Vol. 1, 30. Some years later Boltzmann proved that nonperiodic systems (open orbits) could not be handled by these methods. See L. Boltzmann, "Bemerkungen über einige Probleme der mechanischen Wärmetheorie," *Wiener Berichte 75* (1877), 62, or *Wiss. Abh.*, Vol. 2, 122–48.

24. R. Clausius, "On the Application of the Theorem of the Equivalence of Transformations to the Internal Work of a Mass of Matter," *Phil. Mag. 24* (1862) 81, 201. Also see M. J. Klein (n. 5) and E. E. Daub, "Atomism and Thermodynamics," *Isis 58* (1967), 293.

25. R. Clausius, "On a Mechanical Theorem Applicable to Heat," *Phil. Mag. 40* (1870), 122. Reprinted in Brush, *Kinetic Theory*, 172–78.

26. R. Clausius, "Über die Zurückführung des zweiten Hauptsatzes der mechanischen Wärmetheorie auf allgemeine mechanische Principien," *Pogg. Ann. 142* (1871), 433.

27. L. Boltzmann, "Zur Priorität der Auffindung der Beziehung zwischen dem zweiten Hauptsatze der mechanischen Wärmetheorie und dem Prinzip der kleinsten Wirkung," *Pogg. Ann. 143* (1871), 211; *Wiss. Abh.*, Vol. 1, 228–36.

28. R. Clausius, "Bemerkungen zu der Prioritätsreclamation des Hrn. Boltzmann," *Pogg. Ann. 144* (1871), 265.

29. J. C. Maxwell to P. G. Tait, 1 December 1873. Reprinted in Knott, *Tait*, 115–16.

30. J. C. Maxwell, *Theory of Heat* (London, 1871). My quotations are from the 4th London edition of 1875.

31. *Ibid.* Advertisement of the publisher (Longmans, Green and Co.) for the series, printed at the end of the text.

32. Maxwell, *Heat*, 4th ed., 195–208. For a detailed discussion of Gibbs's influence on Maxwell and Maxwell's appreciation of Gibbs see E. Garber, "James Clerk Maxwell and Thermodynamics," *Amer. Jour. Phys. 37* (1969) 146.

33. L. Boltzmann, *Vorlesungen über die Prinzipe der Mechanik* (Leipzig, 1904), Vol. 2, 162–64.

34. P. Ehrenfest, "On Adiabatic Changes of a System in Connection with the Quantum Theory," *Proc. Acad. Amst. 19* (1916), 591. Reprinted in P. Ehrenfest, *Collected Scientific Papers*, ed. M. J. Klein (Amsterdam, 1959), 393–97.

35. M. J. Klein, *Paul Ehrenfest. The Making of a Theoretical Physicist* (Amsterdam, 1970), chapters 10–11.

36. L. Boltzmann, n. 21, p. 21.

37. L. Boltzmann, *Populäre Schriften* (Leipzig, 1905), 96.

38. L. Boltzmann, "Studien über das Gleichgewicht der lebendigen Kraft zwischen bewegten materiellen Punkten," *Wiener Berichte 58* (1868), 517. *Wiss. Abh.*, Vol. 1, 49–96.

39. L. Boltzmann, "Analytischer Beweis des zweiten Hauptsatzes der mechanischen Wärmetheorie aus den Sätzen über das Gleichgewicht der lebendigen Kraft," *Wiener Berichte 63* (1871), 712. *Wiss. Abh.*, Vol. 1, 288–308.

40. See, e.g., E. Schrödinger, *Statistical Thermodynamics* 2d ed. (Cambridge, 1952), 10–14.

41. L. Boltzmann, "Weitere Studien über das Wärmegleichgewicht unter Gasmolekülen," *Wiener Berichte 66* (1872), 275. *Wiss. Abh.*, Vol. 1, 316–402.

42. L. Boltzmann, "Bemerkungen über einige Probleme der mechanischen Wärmetheorie," *Wiener Berichte 75* (1877), 62. *Wiss. Abh.*, Vol. 2, 116–22.

43. L. Boltzmann, Über die Beziehung zwischen dem zweiten Hauptsatze der mechanischen Wärmetheorie und der Wahrscheinlichkeitsrechnung respektive den Sätzen über das Wärmegleichgewicht," *Wiener Berichte 76* (1877), 373. *Wiss. Abh.*, Vol. 2, 164–223.

44. J. C. Maxwell, "On Boltzmann's Theorem on the Average Distribution of Energy in a System of Material Points," *Trans. Cambr. Phil. Soc. 12* (1879), 547. *Scientific Papers*, Vol. 2 713–41.

45. H. W. Watson, *A Treatise on the Kinetic Theory of Gases* (Oxford, 1876).

46. J. C. Maxwell, "The Kinetic Theory of Gases," *Nature 16* (1877), 242. This is not reprinted in the *Scientific Papers*.

47. J. C. Maxwell to P. G. Tait, August 1873. Quoted in Knott, *Tait*, 114.

48. W. Thomson, "The Kinetic Theory of the Dissipation of Energy," *Nature 9* (1874), 441. *Papers*, Vol. 5, 13.

49. W. Thomson, "The Sorting Demon of Maxwell," *Papers*, Vol. 5, 21.

50. R. Clausius, n. 6, p. 316. Clausius' comments on Maxwell's demon are discussed by L. Rosenfeld, "On the Foundations of Statistical Thermodynamics," *Acta Physica Polonica 14* (1955), 37–38.

51. M. v. Smoluchowski, "Experimentell nachweisbare, der üblichen Thermodynamik widersprechende Molekularphänomene," *Phys. Zeits. 13* (1912), 1069.

52. A recent analysis of the relationship between Maxwell's demon and information theory can be found in L. Brillouin, *Science and Information Theory* 2d ed. (New York, 1962), 162–82.

53. These verses are reprinted in the Campbell and Garnett biography of Maxwell (n. 7).

54. D. K. C. MacDonald, *Faraday, Maxwell, and Kelvin* (New York, 1964), 62–63, 98–99. The derivative dp/dt would now be written more carefully as $(\partial p/\partial t)_V$.

55. É. Clapeyron, "Memoir on the Motive Power of Heat," in Mendoza reprint, pp. 73–105.

56. Knott, *Tait*, p. 101; Campbell and Garnett, *Maxwell*, pp. ix–x.

57. W. Thomson, "On the Dynamical Theory of Heat," *Trans. Roy. Soc. Edinburgh 20* (1851), 261. Reprinted in W. Thomson, *Mathematical and Physical Papers*, Vol. 1 (Cambridge, 1882), 174–316. See especially p. 187.

58. R. Clausius, n. 12.

59. P. G. Tait to J. C. Maxwell, 1 February 1871.

60. J. C. Maxwell to W. Thomson, 14 April 1870. (This letter and the preceding one are in the Cambridge University collection of Maxwell correspondence.)

LIFE, THERMODYNAMICS, AND CYBERNETICS

By L. BRILLOUIN

Cruft Laboratory, Harvard University*

HOW is it possible to understand life, when the whole world is ruled by such a law as the second principle of thermodynamics, which points toward death and annihilation? This question has been asked by many scientists, and, in particular, by the Swiss physicist, C. E. Guye, in a very interesting book.[1] The problem was discussed at the Collège de France in 1938, when physicists, chemists, and biologists met together and had difficulty in adjusting their different points of view. We could not reach complete agreement, and at the close of the discussions there were three well defined groups of opinion:

(*A*) Our present knowledge of physics and chemistry is practically complete, and these physical and chemical laws will soon enable us to explain life, without the intervention of any special "life principle."

(*B*) We know a great deal about physics and chemistry, but it is presumptuous to pretend that we know all about them. We hope that, among the things yet to be discovered, some new laws and principles will be found that will give us an interpretation of life. We admit that life obeys all the laws of physics and chemistry at present known to us, but we definitely feel that something more is needed before we can understand life. Whether it be called a "life principle" or otherwise is immaterial.

(*C*) Life cannot be understood without reference to a "life principle." The behavior of living organisms is completely different from that of inert matter. Our principles of thermodynamics, and especially the second one, apply only to dead and inert objects; life is an exception to the second principle, and the new principle of life will have to explain conditions contrary to the second law of thermodynamics.

Another discussion of the same problems, held at Harvard in 1946, led to similar conclusions and revealed the same differences of opinion.

In summarizing these three points of view, I have of course introduced some oversimplifications. Recalling the discussions, I am certain that opinions *A* and *B* were very clearly expressed. As for opinion *C*, possibly no one dared to state it as clearly as I have here, but it was surely in the minds of a few scientists, and some of the points introduced in the discussion lead logically to this opinion. For instance, consider a living organism; it has special properties which enable it to resist destruction, to heal its wounds, and to cure occasional sickness. This is very strange behavior, and nothing similar can be observed about inert matter. Is such behavior an exception to the second principle? It appears so, at least superficially, and we must be prepared to

* *Now Director of Electronic Education, International Business Machines Corporation, New York, N. Y.*

[1] *L'évolution physico-chimique* (Paris, E. Chiron, 1922).

accept a "life principle" that would allow for some exceptions to the second principle. When life ceases and death occurs, the "life principle" stops working, and the second principle regains its full power, implying demolition of the living structure. There is no more healing, no more resistance to sickness; the destruction of the former organism goes on unchecked and is completed in a very short time. Thus the conclusion, or question: What about life and the second principle? Is there not, in living organisms, some power that prevents the action of the second principle?

The Attitude of the Scientist

The three groups as defined in the preceding section may be seen to correspond to general attitudes of scientists towards research: (*A*) strictly conservative, biased against any change, and interested only in new development and application of well established methods or principles; (*B*) progressive, open-minded, ready to accept new ideas and discoveries; (*C*) revolutionary, or rather, metaphysical, with a tendency to wishful thinking, or indulging in theories lacking solid experimental basis.

In the discussion just reviewed, most non-specialists rallied into group *B*. This is easy to understand. Physicists of the present century had to acquire a certain feeling for the unknown, and always to be very cautious against over-confidence. Prominent scientists of the previous generation, about 1900, would all be classed in group *A*. Common opinion about that time was that everything was known and that coming generations of scientists could only improve on the accuracy of experiments and measure one or two more decimals on the physical constants. Then some new laws were discovered: quanta, relativity, and radioactivity. To cite more specific examples, the Swiss physicist Ritz was bold enough to write, at the end of the nineteenth century, that the laws of mechanics could not explain optical spectra. Thirty years passed before the first quantum mechanical explanation was achieved. Then, about 1922, after the first brilliant successes of quantum mechanics, things came to a standstill while experimental material was accumulating. Some scientists (Class *A*) still believed that it was just a question of solving certain very complicated mathematical problems, and that the explanation would be obtained from principles already known. On the contrary, however, we had to discover wave mechanics, spinning electrons, and the whole structure of the present physical theories. Now, to speak frankly, we seem to have reached another dead-end. Present methods of quantum mechanics appear not to be able to explain the properties of fundamental particles, and attempts at such explanations look decidedly artificial. Many scientists again believe that a new idea is needed, a new type of mathematical correlation, before we can go one step further.

All this serves to prove that every physicist must be prepared for many new discoveries in his own domain. Class *A* corresponds to cautiousness. Before abandoning the safe ground of well established ideas, says the cautious scientist, it must be proved that these ideas do not check with experiments. Such was the case with the Michelson-Morley experiment. Nevertheless, the same group of people were extremely reluctant to adopt relativity.

Attitude *B* seems to be more constructive, and corresponds to the trend of scientific research through past centuries; attitude *C,* despite its exaggeration, is far from being untenable. We have watched many cases of new discoveries leading to limitations of certain previous "laws." After all, a scientific law is not a "decree" from some supernatural power; it simply represents a systematization of a large number of experimental results. As a consequence, the scientific law has only a limited validity. It extends over the whole domain of experimentation, and maybe slightly beyond. But we must be prepared for some strange modifications when our knowledge is expanded much farther than this. Many historical examples could be introduced to support this opinion. Classical mechanics, for instance, was one of the best-established theories, yet it had to be modified to account for the behavior of very fast particles (relativity), atomic structure, or cosmogony.

Far from being foolish, attitude *C* is essentially an exaggeration of *B;* and any scholar taking attitude *B* must be prepared to accept some aspects of group *C,* if he feels it necessary and if these views rest upon a sound foundation.

To return to the specific problem of life and thermodynamics, we find it discussed along a very personal and original line in a small book published by the famous physicist E. Schrödinger.[2] His discussion is very interesting and there are many points worth quoting. Some of them will be examined later on. In our previous classification, Schrödinger without hesitation joins group *B*:

> We cannot expect [he states] that the "laws of physics" derived from it [from the second principle and its statistical interpretation] suffice straightaway to explain the behavior of living matter. . . . We must be prepared to find a new type of physical law prevailing in it. Or are we to term it a non-physical, not to say a super-physical law?[3]

The reasons for such an attitude are very convincingly explained by Schrödinger, and no attempt will be made to summarize them here. Those who undertake to read the book will find plenty of material for reflection and discussion. Let us simply state at this point that there is a problem about "life and the second principle." The answer is not obvious, and we shall now attempt to discuss that problem systematically.

The Second Principle of Thermodynamics, Its Successes and Its Shortcomings

Nobody can doubt the validity of the second principle, no more than he can the validity of the fundamental laws of mechanics. However, the question is to specify its domain of applicability and the

[2] E. Schrödinger, *What is Life?* (London, Cambridge University Press, and New York, The Macmillan Company, 1945).
[3] *Ibid.,* p. 80.

chapters of science or the type of problems for which it works safely. We shall put special emphasis on all cases where the second principle remains silent and gives no answer. It is a typical feature of this principle that it has to be stated as an inequality. Some quantity, called "entropy," cannot decrease (under certain conditions to be specified later); but we can never state whether "entropy" simply stays constant, or increases, or how fast it will increase. Hence, the answer obtained from the second principle is very often evasive, and keeps a sibyllic character. We do not know of any experiment telling *against* the second principle, but we can easily find many cases where it is useless and remains dumb. Let us therefore try to specify these limitations and shortcomings, since it is on this boundary that life plays.

Both principles of thermodynamics apply only to an isolated system, which is contained in an enclosure through which no heat can be transferred, no work can be done, and no matter nor radiation can be exchanged.[4] The first principle states that the total energy of the system remains constant. The second principle refers to another quantity called "entropy," S, that may only increase, or at least remain constant, but can never decrease. Another way to explain the situation is to say that the total amount of energy is conserved, but not its "quality." Energy may be found in a high-grade quality, which can be transformed into mechanical or electrical work (think of the energy of compressed air in a tank, or of a charged electric battery); but there are also low-grade energies, like heat. The second principle is often referred to as a principle of energy degradation. The increase in entropy means a decrease in quality for the total energy stored in the isolated system.

Consider a certain chemical system (a battery, for instance) and measure its entropy, then seal it and leave it for some time. When you break the seal, you may again measure the entropy, and you will find it increased. If your battery were charged to capacity before sealing, it will have lost some of its charge and will not be able to do the same amount of work after having been stored away for some time. The change may be small, or there may be no change; but certainly the battery cannot increase its charge during storage, unless some additional chemical reaction takes place inside and makes up for the energy and entropy balance. On the other hand, life feeds upon high-grade energy or "negative entropy."[5] A decrease in high-grade energy is tantamount to a loss of food for living organisms. Or we can also say that living organisms automatically destroy first-

---

[4] The fundamental definition must always start with an isolated system, whose energy, total mass, and volume remain constant. Then, step by step, other problems may be discussed. A body at "constant temperature" is nothing but a body enclosed in a large thermostat, that is, in a big, closed, and isolated tank, whose energy content is so large that any heat developed in the body under experience cannot possibly change the average temperature of the tank. A similar experimental device, with a closed tank containing a large amount of an ideal gas, leads to the idea of a body maintained at constant pressure and constant temperature. These are secondary concepts derived from the original one.

[5] Schrödinger, p. 72.

quality energy, and thus contribute to the different mechanisms of the second principle. If there are some living cells in the enclosure, they will be able for some time to feed upon the reserves available, but sooner or later this will come to an end and death then becomes inevitable.

The second principle means *death by confinement,* and it will be necessary to discuss these terms. Life is constantly menaced by this sentence to death. The only way to avoid it is to prevent confinement. Confinement implies the existence of perfect walls, which are necessary in order to build an ideal enclosure. But there are some very important questions about the problem of the existence of perfect walls. Do we really know any way to build a wall that could not let any radiation in or out? This is theoretically almost impossible; practically, however, it can be done and is easily accomplished in physical or chemical laboratories. There is, it is true, a limitation to the possible application of the second principle, when it comes to highly penetrating radiation, such as ultra-hard rays or cosmic rays; but this does not seem to have any direct connection with the problem of life and need not be discussed here.

Time and the second principle. The second principle is a death sentence, but it contains no time limit, and this is one of the very strange points about it. The principle states that in a closed system, S will increase and high-grade energy must decrease; but it does not say how fast. We have even had to include the possibility that nothing at all might happen, and that S would simply remain constant. The second principle is an arrow pointing to a direction along a one-way road, with no upper or lower speed limit. A chemical reaction may flash in a split second or lag on for thousands of centuries.

Although time is not a factor in the second principle, there is, however, a very definite connection between that principle and the definition of time. One of the most important features about time is its irreversibility. Time flows on, never comes back. When the physicist is confronted with this fact he is greatly disturbed. All the laws of physics, in their elementary form, are reversible; that is, they contain the time but not its sign, and positive or negative times have the same function. All these elementary physical laws might just as well work backward. It is only when phenomena related to the second principle (friction, diffusion, energy transferred) are considered that the irreversibility of time comes in. The second principle, as we have noted above, postulates that time flows always in the same direction and cannot turn back. Turn the time back, and your isolated system, where entropy (S) previously was increasing, would now show a decrease of entropy. This is impossible: evolution follows a one-way street, where travel in the reverse direction is strictly forbidden. This fundamental observation was made by the founders of thermodynamics, as, for instance, by Lord Kelvin in the following paragraphs:

If Nature Could Run Backward[6]

If, then, the motion of every particle of matter in the universe were precisely reversed at any instant, the course of nature would be simply reversed forever after. The bursting bubble of foam at the foot of a waterfall would reunite and descend into the water; the thermal motions would reconcentrate their energy and throw the mass up the fall in drops re-forming into a close column of ascending water. Heat which had been generated by the friction of solids and dissipated by conduction, and radiation with absorption, would come again to the place of contact and throw the moving body back against the force to which it had previously yielded. Boulders would recover from the mud the materials required to rebuild them into their previous jagged forms, and would become reunited to the mountain peak from which they had formerly broken away. And if, also, the materialistic hypothesis of life were true, living creatures would grow backward, with conscious knowledge of the future but with no memory of the past, and would become again, unborn.

But the real phenomena of life infinitely transcend human science, and speculation regarding consequences of their imagined reversal is utterly unprofitable. Far otherwise, however, is it in respect to the reversal of the motions of matter uninfluenced by life, a very elementary consideration of which leads to the full explanation of the theory of dissipation of energy.

This brilliant statement indicates definitely that Lord Kelvin would also be classed in our group *B,* on the basis of his belief that there is in life something that transcends our present knowledge. Various illustrations have been given of the vivid description presented by Lord Kelvin. Movie-goers have had many opportunities to watch a waterfall climbing up the hill or a diver jumping back on the springboard; but, as a rule, cameramen have been afraid of showing life going backward, and such reels would certainly not be authorized by censors!

In any event, it is a very strange coincidence that life and the second principle should represent the two most important examples of the impossibility of time's running backward. This reveals the intimate relation between both problems, a question that will be discussed in a later section.

Statistical interpretation of the second principle. The natural tendency of entropy to increase is interpreted now as corresponding to the evolution from improbable toward most probable structures. The brilliant theory developed by L. Boltzmann, F. W. Gibbs, and J. C. Maxwell explains entropy as a physical substitute for "probability" and throws a great deal of light upon all thermodynamical processes. This side of the question has been very clearly discussed and explained in Schrödinger's book[2] and will not be repeated here.

Let us, however, stress a point of special interest. With the statistical theory, entropy acquires a precise mathematical definition as the logarithm of probability. It can be computed theoretically, when a physical model is given, and the theoretical value compared with experiment. When this has been found to work correctly, the same physical model can be used to investigate problems outside the reach of classical thermodynamics and especially problems involving time. The questions raised

[6] William Thompson (Lord Kelvin) in the *Proceedings of the Royal Society of Edinburgh 8:* 325-331. 1874. Quoted in *The Autobiography of Science,* F. R. Moulton and J. J. Shifferes. Editors (New York. 1945), p. 468.

in the preceding section can now be answered; the rate of diffusion for gas mixtures, the thermal conductivity of gases, the velocity of chemical reactions can be computed.

In this respect, great progress has been made, and in a number of cases it can be determined *how fast* entropy will actually increase. It is expected that convenient models will eventually be found for all of the most important problems; but this is not yet the case, and we must distinguish between those physical or chemical experiments for which a detailed application of statistical thermodynamics has been worked out, and other problems for which a model has not yet been found and for which we therefore have to rely on classical thermo-dynamics without the help of statistics. In the first group, a detailed model enables one to answer the most incautious questions; in the second group, questions involving time cannot be discussed.

Distinction between two classes of experiments where entropy remains constant. The entropy of a closed system, as noted, must increase, or at least remain constant. When entropy increases, the system is undergoing an *irreversible* transformation; when the system undergoes a *reversible* transformation, its total entropy remains constant. Such is the case for reversible cycles discussed in textbooks on thermo-dynamics, for reversible chemical reactions, etc. However, there is *another case* where no entropy change is observed, a case that is usually ignored, about which we do not find a word of discussion in textbooks, simply because scientists are at a loss to explain it properly. This is the case of systems in *unstable equilibrium*. A few examples may serve to clarify the problem much better than any definition.

In a private kitchen, there is a leak in the gas range. A mixture of air and gas develops (unstable equilibrium), but nothing happens until a naughty little boy comes in, strikes a match, and blows up the roof. Instead of gas, you may substitute coal, oil, or any sort of fuel; all our fuel reserves are in a state of unstable equilibrium. A stone hangs along the slope of a mountain and stays there for years, until rains and brooklets carry the soil away, and the rock finally rolls down-hill. Substitute waterfalls, water reservoirs, and you have all our reserves of "white fuel." Uranium remained stable and quiet for thou-sands of centuries; then came some scientists, who built a pile and a bomb and, like the naughty boy in the kitchen, blew up a whole city. Such things would not be permitted if the second principle were an active principle and not a passive one. Such events could not take place in a world where this principle was strictly enforced.

All this makes one thing clear. All our so-called power reserves are due to systems in unstable equilibrium. They are really reserves of negative entropy—structures wherein, by some sort of miracle, the normal and legitimate increase of entropy does not take place, until man, acting like a catalytic agent, comes and starts the reaction.

Very little is known about these systems of unstable equilibrium. No explanation is given. The scientist simply mumbles a few embarrassed words about "obstacles" hindering the reaction, or "potential energy walls" separating systems that should react but do not. There is a hint in these vague attempts at explanation, and, when properly developed, they should constitute a practical theory. Some very interesting attempts at an interpretation of *catalysis,* on the basis of quantum mechanics, have aroused great interest in scientific circles. But the core of the problem remains. How is it possible for such tremendous negative entropy reserves to stay untouched? What is the mechanism of *negative catalysis,* which maintains and preserves these stores of energy?

That such problems have a stupendous importance for mankind, it is hardly necessary to emphasize. In a world where oil simply waits for prospectors to come, we already watch a wild struggle for fuel. How would it be if oil burned away by itself, unattended, and did not wait passively for the drillers?

Life and Its Relations with the Second Principle

We have raised some definite questions about the significance of the second principle, and in the last section have noted certain aspects of particular importance. Let us now discuss these, point by point, in connection with the problem of life maintenance and the mechanism of life.

Closed systems. Many textbooks, even the best of them, are none too cautious when they describe the increase of entropy. It is customary to find statements like this one: "The entropy of the universe is constantly increasing." This, in my opinion, is very much beyond the limits of human knowledge. Is the universe bounded or infinite? What are the properties of the boundary? Do we know whether it is tight, or may it be leaking? Do entropy and energy leak out or in? Needless to say, none of these questions can be answered. We know that the universe is expanding although we understand very little of how and why. Expansion means a moving boundary (if any), and a moving boundary is a leaking boundary; neither energy nor entropy can remain constant within. Hence, it is better not to speak about the "entropy of the universe." In the last section we emphasized the limitations of physical laws, and the fact that they can be safely applied only within certain limits and for certain orders of magnitude. The whole universe is too big for thermodynamics and certainly exceeds considerably the reasonable order of magnitude for which its principles may apply. This is also proved by the fact that the Theory of Relativity and all the cosmological theories that followed always involve a broad revision and drastic modification of the laws of thermodynamics, before an attempt can be made to apply them to the universe as a whole. The only thing that we can reasonably discuss is the entropy of a conceivable closed structure. Instead of the very mysterious universe, let us speak of our home, the earth. Here we stand on familiar ground. The earth is not a closed system. It is constantly receiving energy and negative entropy from outside—radiant heat from the sun, gravitational energy from sun and moon (provoking sea tides), cosmic radiation from unknown origin, and so on. There is also a certain amount of outward leak, since the earth itself radiates energy and entropy. How does the balance stand? Is it positive or negative? It is very doubtful whether any scientist can answer this question, much less such a question relative to the universe as a whole.

The earth is not a closed system, and life feeds upon energy and negative entropy leaking into the earth system. Sun heat and rain make crops (remember April showers and May flowers), crops provide food, and the cycle reads: first, creation of unstable equilibriums (fuels, food, waterfalls, etc.); then, use of these reserves by all living creatures.

Life acts as a catalytic agent to help destroy unstable equilibrium, but it is a very peculiar kind of catalytic agent, since it profits by the operation. When black platinum provokes a chemical reaction, it does not seem to care, and does not profit by it. Living creatures care about food, and by using it they maintain their own unstable equilibrium. This is a point that will be considered later.

The conclusion of the present section is this: that the sentence to "death by confinement" is avoided by living in a world that is not a confined and closed system.

The role of time. We have already emphasized the silence of the second principle. The direction of any reaction is given, but the velocity of the reaction remains unknown. It may be zero (unstable equilibrium), it may remain small, or it may become very great. Catalytic agents usually increase the velocity of chemical reactions; however, some cases of "anticatalysis" or "negative catalysis" have been discovered, and these involve a slowing down of some important reactions (e.g., oxidation).

Life and living organisms represent a most important type of catalysis. It is suggested that a systematic study of positive and negative catalysts might prove very useful, and would in fact be absolutely necessary before any real understanding of life could be attained.

The *statistical interpretation* of entropy and *quantum mechanics* are undoubtedly the tools with which a theory of catalysis should be built. Some pioneer work has already been done and has proved extremely valuable, but most of it is restricted, for the moment, to the most elementary types of chemical reactions. The work on theoretical chemistry should be pushed ahead with great energy.

Such an investigation will, sooner or later, lead us to a better understanding of the mechanisms of "unstable equilibrium." New negative catalysts may even make it possible to stabilize some systems that otherwise would undergo spontaneous disintegration, and to preserve new types of energies and negative entropies, just as we now know how to preserve food.

We have already emphasized the role of living organisms as catalytic agents, a feature that has long been recognized. Every biochemist now thinks of ferments and yeasts as peculiar living catalysts, which help release some obstacle and start a reaction, in a system in unstable equilibrium. Just as catalysts are working within the limits of the second principle, so living organisms are too. It should be noted, however, that catalytic action in itself is something which is not under the jurisdiction of the second principle. Catalysis involves the velocity of chemical reactions, a feature upon which the second principle remains silent. Hence, in this first respect, life is found to operate along the border of the second principle.

However, there is a second point about life that seems to be much more important. Disregard the very difficult problem of birth and reproduction. Consider an adult specimen, be it a plant or an animal or man. This adult individual is a most extraordinary example of a chemical system in unstable equilibrium. The system is unstable, undoubtedly, since it represents a very elaborate organization, a most improbable structure (hence a system with very low entropy, according to the statistical interpretation of entropy). This instability is further shown when death occurs. Then, suddenly, the whole structure is left to itself, deprived of the mysterious power that held it together; within a very short time the organism falls to pieces, rots, and goes (we have the wording of the scriptures) back to the dust whence it came.

Accordingly, a living organism is a chemical system in unstable equilibrium maintained by some strange "power of life," which manifests itself as a sort of *negative catalyst*. So long as life goes on, the organism maintains its unstable structure and escapes disintegration. It slows down to a considerable extent (exactly, for a lifetime) the normal and usual procedure of decomposition. Hence, a new aspect of life. Biochemists usually look at living beings as possible catalysts. But this same living creature is himself an unstable system, held together by some sort of internal anticatalyst! After all, a poison is nothing but an active catalyst, and a good drug represents an anticatalyst for the final inevitable reaction: death.

N. Wiener, in his *Cybernetics,* takes a similar view when he compares enzymes or living animals to Maxwell demons, and writes: "It may well be that enzymes are metastable Maxwell demons, decreasing entropy. . . . We may well regard living organisms, such as Man himself, in this light. Certainly the enzyme and the living organism are alike metastable: the stable state of an enzyme is to be deconditioned, and the stable state of a living organism is to be dead. All catalysts are ultimately poisoned: they change rates of reaction, but not true equilibrium. Nevertheless, catalysts and Man alike have sufficiently definite states of metastability to deserve the recognition of these states as relatively permanent conditions."[7]

Living Organisms and Dead Structures

In a discussion at Harvard (1946), P. W. Bridgman stated a funda-

[7] Norbert Wiener, *Cybernetics, or Control and Communication in the Animal and the Machine* (New York, John Wiley and Sons, 1948), p. 72.

mental difficulty regarding the possibility of applying the laws of thermodynamics to any system containing living organisms. How can we compute or even evaluate the entropy of a living being? In order to compute the entropy of a system, it is necessary to be able to create or to destroy it in a reversible way. We can think of no reversible process by which a living organism can be created or killed: both birth and death are irreversible processes. There is absolutely no way to define the change of entropy that takes place in an organism at the moment of its death. We might think of some procedure by which to measure the entropy of a dead organism, albeit it may be very much beyond our present experimental skill, but this does not tell us anything about the entropy the organism had just before it died.

This difficulty is fundamental; it does not make sense to speak of a quantity for which there is no operational scheme that could be used for its measurement. The entropy content of a living organism is a completely meaningless notion. In the discussion of all experiments involving living organisms, biologists always avoid the difficulty by assuming that the entropy of the living objects remains practically constant during the operation. This assumption is supported by experimental results, but it is a bold hypothesis and impossible to verify.

To a certain extent, a living cell can be compared to a flame: here is matter going in and out, and being burned. The entropy of a flame cannot be defined, since it is not a system in equilibrium. In the case of a living cell, we may know the entropy of its food and measure the entropy of its wastes. If the cell is apparently maintained in good health and not showing any visible change, it may be assumed that its entropy remains practically constant. All experimental measures show that the entropy of the refuse is larger than that of the food. The transformation operated by the living system corresponds to an increase of entropy, and this is presented as a verification of the second principle of thermodynamics. But we may have some day to reckon with the underlying assumption of constant entropy for the living organism.

There are many strange features in the behavior of living organisms, as compared with dead structures. The evolution of species, as well as the evolution of individuals, is an irreversible process. The fact that evolution has been progressing from the simplest to the most complex structures is very difficult to understand, and appears almost as a contradiction to the law of degradation represented by the second principle. The answer is, of course, that degradation applies only to the whole of an isolated system, and not to one isolated constituent of the system. Nevertheless, it is hard to reconcile these two opposite directions of evolution. Many other facts remain very mysterious: reproduction, maintenance of the living individual and of the species, free will, etc.

A most instructive comparison is presented by Schrödinger[8] when he points to similarities and differences between a living organism, such as a cell, and one of the most elaborate structures of inanimate matter,

[8] Schrödinger, pp. 3 and 78.

a crystal. Both examples represent highly organized structures con-
containing a very large number of atoms. But the crystal contains only a few types of atoms, whereas the cell may contain a much
greater variety of chemical constituents. The crystal is always more
stable at very low temperatures, and especially at absolute zero. The
cellular organization is stable only within a given range of temperatures.
From the point of view of thermodynamics this involves a very different type of organization.

When distorted by some stress, the crystal may to a certain extent
repair its own structure and move its atoms to new positions of equilibrium, but this property of self-repair is extremely limited. A similar
property, but exalted to stupendous proportions, characterizes living
organisms. The living organism heals its own wounds, cures its sick-
nesses, and may rebuild large portions of its structure when they have
been destroyed by some accident. This is the most striking and unexpected behavior. Think of your own car, the day you had a flat tire, and
imagine having simply to wait and smoke your cigar while the hole
patched itself and the tire pumped itself to the proper pressure, and
you could go on. This sounds incredible.[9] It is, however, the way nature
works when you "chip off" while shaving in the morning. There is no
inert matter possessing a similar property of repair. That is why so
many scientists (class B) think that our present laws of physics and
chemistry do not suffice to explain such strange phenomena, and that
something more is needed, some very important law of nature that has
escaped our investigations up to now, but may soon be discovered.
Schrödinger, after asking whether the new law required to explain the
behavior of living matter (see page 556) might not be of a super-
physical nature, adds: "No, I do not think that. For the new principle that is involved is a genuinely physical one. It is, in my opinion,
nothing else than the principle of quantum theory over again."[10]
This is a possibility, but it is far from certain, and Schrödinger's
explanations are too clever to be completely convincing.

There are other remarkable properties characterizing the ways of
living creatures. For instance, let us recall the paradox of Maxwell's
demon, that submicroscopical being, standing by a trapdoor and opening it only for fast molecules, thereby selecting molecules with highest
energy and temperature. Such an action is unthinkable, on the submicroscopical scale, as contrary to the second principle.[11] How does it

---

[9] The property of self-repairing has been achieved in some special devices. A self-
sealing tank with a regulated pressure control is an example. Such a property, however, is not realized in most physical structures and requires a special control device,
which is a product of human ingenuity, not of nature.

[10] Schrödinger. p. 81.

[11] Wiener discusses very carefully the problem of the Maxwell demon (*Cybernetics*,
pp. 71-72). One remark should be added. In order to choose the fast molecules,
the demon should be able to see them: but he is in an enclosure in equilibrium at constant temperature. where the radiation must be that of the black body. and it is
impossible to see anything in the interior of a black body. The demon simply does not
see the particles. unless we equip him with a torchlight. and a torchlight is obviously
a source of radiation not at equilibrium. It pours negative entropy into the system.

(*Continued on following page*)

become feasible on a large scale? Man opens the window when the weather is hot and closes it on cold days! Of course, the answer is that the earth's atmosphere is not in equilibrium and not at constant temperature. Here again we come back to the unstable conditions created by sunshine and other similar causes, and the fact that the earth is not a closed isolated system.

The very strange fact remains that conditions forbidden on a small scale are permitted on a large one, that large systems can maintain unstable equilibrium for large time-intervals, and that life is playing upon all these exceptional conditions on the fringe of the second principle.

Entropy and Intelligence

One of the most interesting parts in Wiener's *Cybernetics* is the discussion on "Time series, information, and communication," in which he specifies that a certain "amount of information is the negative of the quantity usually defined as entropy in similar situations."[12]

This is a very remarkable point of view, and it opens the way for some important generalizations of the notion of entropy. Wiener introduces a precise mathematical definition of this new negative entropy for a certain number of problems of communication, and discusses the question of time prediction: when we possess a certain number of data about the behavior of a system in the past, how much can we predict of the behavior of that system in the future?

In addition to these brilliant considerations, Wiener definitely indicates the need for an extension of the notion of entropy. "Information represents negative entropy"; but if we adopt this point of view, how can we avoid its extension to all types of intelligence? We certainly must be prepared to discuss the extension of entropy to scientific knowledge, technical know-how, and all forms of intelligent thinking. Some examples may illustrate this new problem.

Take an issue of the New York *Times*, the book on Cybernetics, and an equal weight of scrap paper. Do they have the same entropy? According to the usual physical definition, the answer is "yes." But for an intelligent reader, the amount of information contained in these three bunches of paper is very different. If "information means negative entropy," as suggested by Wiener, how are we going to measure this new contribution to entropy? Wiener suggests some practical and numerical definitions that may apply to the simplest possible problems of this kind. This represents an entirely new field for investigation and a most revolutionary idea.

Under these circumstances, the demon can certainly extract some fraction of this negative entropy by using his gate at convenient times. Once we equip the demon with a torchlight, we may also add some photoelectric cells and design an automatic system to do the work, as suggested by Wiener. The demon need not be a living organism, and intelligence is not necessary either. The preceding remarks seem to have been generally ignored, although Wiener says: the demon can only act on information received and this information represents a negative entropy.

[12] Wiener, Chap. III, p. 76.

Many similar examples can be found. Compare a rocky hill, a pyramid, and a dam with its hydroelectric power station. The amount of "know-how" is completely different, and should also correspond to a difference in "generalized entropy," although the physical entropy of these three structures may be about the same. Take a modern large-scale computing machinery, and compare its entropy with that of its constituents before the assembling. Can it reasonably be assumed that they are equal? Instead of the "mechanical brain," think now of the living human brain. Do you imagine its (generalized) entropy to be the same as that for the sum of its chemical constituents?

It seems that a careful investigation of these problems, along the directions initiated by Wiener, may lead to some important contributions to the study of life itself. Intelligence is a product of life, and a better understanding of the power of thinking may result in a new point of discussion concerning this highly significant problem.

Let us try to answer some of the questions stated above, and compare the "value" of equal weights of paper: scrap paper, New York *Times*, *Cybernetics*. To an illiterate person they have the same value. An average English-reading individual will probably prefer the New York *Times*, and a mathematician will certainly value the book on Cybernetics much above anything else. "Value" means "generalized negative entropy," if our present point of view be accepted. The preceding discussion might discourage the reader and lead to the conclusion that such definitions are impossible to obtain. This hasty conclusion, however, does not seem actually to be correct. An example may explain the difficulty and show what is really needed.

Let us try to compare two beams of light, of different colors. The human eye, or an ultraviolet photo-cell, or an infrared receiving cell will give completely different answers. Nevertheless, the entropy of each beam of light can be exactly defined, correctly computed, and measured experimentally. The corresponding definitions took a long time to discover, and retained the attention of most distinguished physicists (e.g., Boltzman, Planck). But this difficult problem was finally settled, and a careful distinction was drawn between the intrinsic properties of radiation and the behavior of the specific receiving set used for experimental measurements. Each receiver is defined by its "absorption spectrum," which characterizes the way it reacts to incident radiations. Similarly, it does not seem impossible to discover some criterion by which a definition of generalized entropy could be applied to "information," and to distinguish it from the special sensitivity of the observer. The problem is certainly harder than in the case of light. Light depends only upon one parameter (wave length), whereas a certain number of independent variables may be required for the definition of the "information value," but the distinction between an absolute intrinsic value of information and the absorption spectrum of the receiver is indispensable. Scientific information represents certainly a sort of negative entropy for Wiener, who knows how to use it for prediction, and may be of no value whatsoever to a non-scientist. Their respective absorption spectra are completely different.

Similar extensions of the notion of entropy are needed in the field of biology, with new definitions of entropy and of some sort of absorption spectrum. Many important investigations have been conducted by biologists during recent years, and they can be summarized as "new classifications of energies." For inert matter, it suffices to know energy and entropy. For living organisms, we have to introduce the "food value" of products. Calories contained in coal and calories in wheat and meat do not have the same function. Food value must itself be considered separately for different categories of living organisms. Cellulose is a food for some animals, but others cannot use it. When it comes to vitamins or hormones, new properties of chemical compounds are observed, which cannot be reduced to energy or entropy. All these data remain rather vague, but they all seem to point toward the need for a new leading idea (call it principle or law) in addition to current thermodynamics, before these new classifications can be understood and typical properties of living organisms can be logically connected together. Biology is still in the empirical stage and waits for a master idea, before it can enter the constructive stage with a few fundamental laws and a beginning of logical structure.

In addition to the old and classical concept of physical entropy, some bold new extensions and broad generalizations are needed before we can reliably apply similar notions to the fundamental problems of life and of intelligence. Such a discussion should lead to a reasonable answer to the definition of entropy of living organisms and solve the paradox of Bridgman (pages 563-564).

A recent example from the physical sciences may explain the situation. During the nineteenth century, physicists were desperately attempting to discover some mechanical models to explain the laws of electromagnetism and the properties of light. Maxwell reversed the discussion and offered an electromagnetic theory of light, which was soon followed by an electromagnetic interpretation of the mechanical properties of matter. We have been looking, up to now, for a physico-chemical interpretation of life. It may well happen that the discovery of new laws and of some new principles in biology could result in a broad redefinition of our present laws of physics and chemistry, and produce a complete change in point of view.

In any event, two problems seem to be of major importance for the moment: a better understanding of catalysis, since life certainly rests upon a certain number of mechanisms of negative catalysis; and a broad extension of the notion of entropy, as suggested by Wiener, until it can apply to living organisms and answer the fundamental question of P. W. Bridgman.

Information, Measurement, and Quantum Mechanics [1]

Jerome Rothstein

*Solid State Devices Section, Thermionics Branch, Evans Signal Laboratory,
Belmar, New Jersey*

RECENT DEVELOPMENTS IN COMMU-
NICATION THEORY use a function
called the entropy, which gives a measure
of the quantity of information carried by
a message. This name was chosen because of the
similarity in mathematical form between informational entropy and the entropy of statistical mechanics. Increasing attention is being devoted to the
connection between information and physical entropy
(*1–9*), Maxwell's demon providing a typical opportunity for the concepts to interact.

It is the purpose of this paper to present a short
history of the concepts of entropy and information,
to discuss information in physics and the connection
between physical and informational entropies, and to
demonstrate the logical identity of the problem of
measurement and the problem of communication.
Various implications for statistical mechanics, thermodynamics, and quantum mechanics, as well as the
possible relevance of generalized entropy for biology,
will be briefly considered. Paradoxes and questions of
interpretation in quantum mechanics, as well as reality, causality, and the completeness of quantum
mechanics, will also be briefly examined from an informational viewpoint.

Information and Entropy

Boltzmann's discovery of a statistical explanation
for entropy will always rank as one of the great
achievements in theoretical physics. By its use, he was
able to show how classical mechanics, applied to billiard-ball molecules or to more complicated mechanical
systems, could explain the laws of thermodynamics.
After much controversy (arising from the reversibility
of mechanics as opposed to the irreversibility of
thermodynamics), during which the logical basis of
the theory was recast, the main results were firmly
based on the abstract theory of measurable sets. The
function Boltzmann introduced depends on how
molecular positions and momenta range over their
possible values (for fixed total energy), becoming
larger with increasing randomness or spread in these
molecular parameters, and decreasing to zero for a
perfectly sharp distribution. Entropy often came to
be described in later years as a measure of disorder,
randomness, or chaos. Boltzmann himself saw later

[1] Presented in shorter form before the American Physical
Society Feb. 1, 1951, and before a physics seminar at Purdue
University Feb. 21, 1951.

that statistical entropy could be interpreted as a
measure of missing information.

A number of different definitions of entropy have
been given, the differences residing chiefly in the em-
ployment of different approximations or in choosing
a classical or quantal approach. Boltzmann's classical
and Planck's quantal definitions, for example, are,
respectively,

$$S = -k \int f \log f \, d\tau,$$
$$\text{and} \quad S = k \log P.$$

Here k is Boltzmann's constant, f the molecular distribution function over coordinates and momenta, $d\tau$
an element of phase space, and P the number of independent wave functions consistent with the known
energy of the system and other general information,
like requirements of symmetry or accessibility.

Even before maturation of the entropy concept,
Maxwell pointed out that a little demon who could
"see" individual molecules would be able to let fast
ones through a trap door and keep slow ones out. A
specimen of gas at uniform temperature could thereby
be divided into low and high temperature portions,
separated by a partition. A heat engine working between them would then constitute a *perpetuum mobile*
of the second kind. Szilard (*1*), in considering this
problem, showed that the second law of thermodynamics could be saved only if the demon paid for the
information on which he acted with entropy increase
elsewhere. If, like physicists, the demon gets his information by means of measuring apparatus, then the
price is paid in full. He was led to ascribe a thermodynamical equivalent to an item of information. If one
knew in which of two equal volumes a molecule was
to be found, he showed that the entropy could be reduced by $k \log 2$.

Hartley (*2*), considering the problem of transmitting information by telegraph, concluded that an
appropriate measure of the information in a message
is the logarithm of the number of equivalent messages
that might have been sent. For example, if a message
consists of a sequence of n choices from k symbols,
then the number of equivalent messages is k^n, and
transmission of any one conveys an amount of information $n \log k$. In the hands of Wiener (*3, 4*),
Shannon (*5*), and others, Hartley's heuristic begin-
nings become a general, rigorous, elegant, and powerful theory related to statistical mechanics and promis-
ing to revolutionize communication theory. The ensemble of possible messages is characterized by a quantity

completely analogous to entropy and called by that name, which measures the information conveyed by selection of one of the messages. In general, if a sub-ensemble is selected from a given ensemble, an amount of information equal to the difference of the entropies of the two ensembles is produced. A communication system is a means for transmitting information from a source to a destination and must be capable of transmitting any member of the ensemble from which the message is selected. Noise introduces uncertainty at the destination regarding the message actually sent. The difference between the a priori entropy of the ensemble of messages that might have been selected and the a posteriori entropy of the ensemble of messages that might have given rise to the received signal is reduced by noise so that less information is conveyed by the message.

It is clear that Hartley's definition of quantity of information agrees with Planck's definition of entropy if one correlates equivalent messages with independent wave functions. Wiener and Shannon generalize Hartley's definition to expressions of the same form as Boltzmann's definition (with the constant k suppressed) and call it entropy. It may seem confusing that a term connoting lack of information in physics is used as a measure of amount of information in communication, but the situation is easily clarified. If the message to be transmitted is known in advance to the recipient, no information is conveyed to him by it. There is no initial uncertainty or doubt to be resolved; the ensemble of a priori possibilities shrinks to a single case and hence has zero entropy. The greater the initial uncertainty, the greater the amount of information conveyed when a definite choice is made. In the physical case the message is not sent, so to speak, so that physical entropy measures how much physical information is missing. Planck's entropy measures how uncertain we are about what the actual wave function of the system is. Were we to determine it exactly, the system would have zero entropy (pure **case**), and our knowledge of the system would be maximal. The more information we lose, the greater the entropy, with statistical equilibrium corresponding to minimal information consistent with known energy and physical make-up of the system. We can thus equate physical information and negative entropy (or negentropy, a term proposed by Brillouin [9]). Szilard's result can be considered as giving thermodynamical support to the foregoing.

MEASUREMENT AND COMMUNICATION

Let us now try to be more precise about what is meant by information in physics. Observation (measurement, experiment) is the only admissible means for obtaining valid information about the world. Measurement is a more quantitative variety of observation; e.g., we observe that a book is near the right side of a table, but we measure its position and orientation relative to two adjacent table edges. When we make a measurement, we use some kind of procedure and apparatus providing an ensemble of possible results. For measurement of length, for example, this ensemble of a priori possible results might consist of: (*a*) too small to measure, (*b*) an integer multiple of a smallest perceptible interval, (*c*) too large to measure. It is usually assumed that cases (*a*) and (*c*) have been excluded by selection of instruments having a suitable range (on the basis of preliminary observation or prior knowledge). One can define an entropy for this a priori ensemble, expressing how uncertain we are initially about what the outcome of the measurement will be. The measurement is made, but because of experimental errors there is a whole ensemble of values, each of which could have given rise to the one observed. An entropy can also be defined for this a posteriori ensemble, expressing how much uncertainty is still left unresolved after the measurement. We can define the quantity of physical information obtained from the measurement as the difference between initial (a priori) and final (a posteriori) entropies. We can speak of position entropy, angular entropy, etc., and note that we now have a quantitative measure of the information yield of an experiment. A given measuring procedure provides a set of alternatives. Interaction between the object of interest and the measuring apparatus results in selection of a subset thereof. When the results of this process of selection become known to the observer, the measurement has been completed.

It is now easy to see that there is an analogy between communication and measurement which actually amounts to an identity in logical structure. Fig. 1

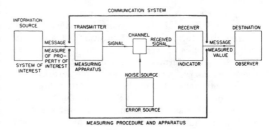

Fig. 1.

shows this less abstractly. The blocks and upper captions follow Shannon's characterization of a communication system; the lower captions give analogous terms for a measuring apparatus. The system of interest corresponds to the information source, the observer to the destination for which the message is intended. The message corresponds to a measure of the property of interest, which is often encoded by the transmitter or measuring apparatus into a signal consisting of information-bearing variations of some physical quantity, often quite distinct from the one of direct interest. The signal, corrupted by noise or errors, is decoded by the receiver or indicator and presented as a message or measured value at the output of the system. Calibration in measurement is, in part, the analog of distortion correction in communication. In practice a communication or measuring system often consists of a number of subsystems in series, intermediate ones serving as destinations for their predecessors and as sources for their successors. The sensory and nervous apparatus of the observer can be considered the ultimate system, which, together with instruments, operations, and apparatus, constitutes the means whereby the mind of the scientist communicates with, or acquires information about, the universe.

PHYSICAL CONSEQUENCES OF THE INFORMATION VIEWPOINT

Some implications of the informational viewpoint must be considered. First of all, the entropy of information theory is, except for a constant depending on choice of units, a straightforward generalization of the entropy concept of statistical mechanics. Information theory is abstract mathematics dealing with measurable sets, with choices from alternatives of an unspecified nature. Statistical mechanics deals with sets of alternatives provided by physics, be they wave functions, as Planck's quantal definition, or the complexions in phase space of classical quantum statistics. Distinguishing between identical particles (which leads to Gibbs' paradox and nonadditivity of entropy) is equivalent to claiming information that is not at hand, for there is no measurement yielding it. When this nonexistent information is discarded, the paradox vanishes. Symmetry numbers, accessibility conditions, and parity are additional items of (positive or negative) information entering into quantal entropy calculations.

Second, we can formulate the statistical expression of the second law of thermodynamics rather simply in terms of information: Our information about an isolated system can never increase (only by measurement can new information be obtained). Reversible processes conserve, irreversible ones lose information.

Third, all physical laws become relationships between types of information, or information functions collected or constructed according to various procedures. The difference between classical or quantum mechanics, on one hand, and classical or quantum statistics, on the other, is that the former is concerned with theoretically maximal information, the latter with less than the maximal. From the present viewpoint, therefore, classical and quantum mechanics are limiting cases of the corresponding statistics, rather than separate disciplines. The opposite limiting cases —namely, minimum information or maximum entropy —relate to the equilibrium distributions treated in texts on statistical mechanics. The vast, almost virgin field of nonequilibrium physics lies between these two extremes.

It is tempting to speculate that living matter is distinguished, at least in part, by having a large amount of information coded in its structure. This information would be in the form of "instructions" (constraints) restricting the manifold of possibilities for its physicochemical behavior. Perhaps instructions for developing an organism are "programmed" in the

genes, just as the operation of a giant calculating machine, consisting of millions of parallel or consecutive operations, is programmed in a control unit. Schroedinger, in a fascinating little book, *What Is Life?* views living matter as characterized by its "disentropic" behavior, as maintaining its organization by feeding on "negative entropy," the thermodynamic price being a compensating increase in entropy of its waste products. Gene stability is viewed as a quantum effect, like the stability of atoms. In view of previous discussion, the reader should have no trouble fitting this into the informational picture above.

Returning to more prosaic things, we note, fourth, that progress either in theory of measurement or in theory of communication will help the other. Their logical equivalence permits immediate translation of results in one field to the other. Theory of errors and of noise, of resolving power and minimum detectable signal, of best channel utilization in communication and optimal experimental design are three examples of pairs where mutual cross-fertilization can be confidently expected.

Fifth, absolutely exact values of measured quantities are unattainable in general. For example, an infinite amount of information is required to specify a quantity capable of assuming a continuum of values. Only an ensemble of possibly "true" or "real" values is determined by measurement. In classical mechanics, where the state of a system is specified by giving simultaneous positions and momenta of all particles in the system, two assumptions are made at this point—namely, that the entropy of individual measurements can be made to approach zero, and furthermore that this can be done simultaneously for all quantities needed to determine the state of the system. In other words, the ensembles can be made arbitrarily sharp in principle, and these sharp values can be taken as "true" values. In current quantum mechanics the first assumption is retained, but the second is dropped. The ensembles of position and momenta values cannot be made sharp simultaneously by any measuring procedure. We are left with irreducible ensembles of possible "true" values of momentum, consistent with the position information on hand from previous measurements. It thus seems natural, if not unavoidable, to conclude that quantum mechanics describes the ensemble of systems consistent with the information specifying a state rather than a single system. The wave function is a kind of generating function for all the information deducible from operational specification of the mode of preparation of the system, and from it the probabilities of obtaining possible values of measurable quantities can be calculated. In communication terminology, the stochastic nature of the message source—i.e., the ensemble of possible messages and their probabilities— is specified, but not the individual message. The entropy of a given state for messages in x-language, p-language, or any other language, can be calculated in accordance with the usual rules. It vanishes in the language of a given observable if, and only if, the state is an eigenstate of that observable. For an eigenstate of an operator commuting with the Hamiltonian, all entropies are constant in time, analogous to equilibrium distributions in statistical mechanics. This results from the fact that change with time is expressed by a unitary transformation, leaving inner products in Hilbert space invariant. The corresponding classical case is one with maximal information where the entropy is zero and remains so. For a wavepacket representing the result of a position measurement, on the other hand, the distribution smears out more and more as time goes on, and its entropy of position increases. We conjecture, but have not proved, that this is a special case of a new kind of quantal H-theorem.

Sixth, the informational interpretation seems to resolve some well-known paradoxes (*10*). For example, if a system is in an eigenstate of some observable, and a measurement is made on an incompatible observable, the wave function changes instantaneously from the original eigenfunction to one of the second observable. Yet Schroedinger's equation demands that the wave function change continuously with time. In fact, the system of interest and the measuring equipment can be considered a single system that is unperturbed and thus varying continuously. This causal anomaly and action-at-a-distance paradox vanishes in the information picture. Continuous variation occurs so long as no new information is obtained incompatible with the old. New information results from measurement and requires a new representative ensemble. The system of interest could "really" change continuously even though our information about it did not. It does no harm to believe, as Einstein does, in a "real" state of an individual system, so long as one remembers that quantum mechanics does not permit an operational definition thereof. The Einstein-Podolsky-Rosen paradox (*11*), together with Schroedinger's (*12*) sharpening of it, seems to be similarly resolved. Here two systems interact for a short time and are then completely separated. Measurement of one system determines the state of the other. But the kind of measurement is under the control of the experimenter, who can, for example, choose either one of a pair of complementary observables. He obtains one of a pair of incompatible wave functions under conditions where an objective or "real" state of the system cannot be affected. If the wave function describes an individual system, one must renounce all belief in its objective or "real" state. If the wave function only bears information and describes ensembles consistent therewith, there is no paradox, for an individual system can be compatible with both of two inequivalent ensembles, as long as they have a nonempty intersection. The kind of information one gets simply varies with the kind of measurement one chooses to make.

REALITY, CAUSALITY, AND THE COMPLETENESS OF QUANTUM MECHANICS

We close with some general observations.

First, it is possible to believe in a "real" objective state of a quantum-mechanical system without contradiction. As Bohr and Heisenberg have shown, states of simultaneous definite position and definite momentum in quantum mechanics are incompatible because they refer to simultaneous results of two mutually exclusive procedures. But, if a variable is not measured, its corresponding operation has not been performed, and so unmeasured variables need not correspond to operators. Thus there need be no conflict with the quantum conditions. If one denies simultaneous reality to position and momentum then EPR forces the conclusion that one or the other assumes reality only when measured. In accepting this viewpoint, should one not assume, for consistency, that electrons in an atom have no reality, because any attempt to locate one by a photon will ionize the atom? The electron then becomes real (i.e., is "manufactured") only as a result of an attempt to measure its position. Similarly, one should also relinquish the continuum of space and time, for one can measure only a countable infinity of locations or instants, and even this is an idealization, whereas a continuum is uncountable. If one admits as simultaneously real all positions or times that *might* be measured, then for consistency simultaneous reality of position and momentum must be admitted, for either one might be measured.

Second, it is possible to believe in a strictly causal universe without contradiction. Quantum indeterminacy can be interpreted as reflecting the impossibility of getting enough information (by measurement) to permit prediction of unique values of all observables. A demon who can get physical information in other ways than by making measurements might then see a causal universe. Von Neumann's proof of the impossibility of making quantum mechanics causal by the introduction of hidden parameters assumes that these parameters are values that internal variables can take on, the variables themselves satisfying quantum conditions. Causality and reality (i.e., objectivity) have thus been rejected on similar grounds. Arguments for their rejection need not be considered conclusive for an individual system if quantum mechanics be viewed as a Gibbsian statistical mechanics of ensembles.

The third point is closely connected with this—namely, that quantum mechanics is both incomplete in Einstein's sense and complete in Bohr's sense (*13*). The former demands a place in the theory for the "real" or objective state of an individual system; the latter demands only that the theory correctly describe what will result from a specified operational procedure—i.e., an ensemble according to the present viewpoint. We believe there is no reason to exclude the possibility that a theory may exist which is complete in Einstein's sense and which would yield quantum mechanics in the form of logical inferences. In the communication analogy, Bohr's operational viewpoint corresponds to demanding that the ensemble of possible messages be correctly described by theory when the procedure determining the message source is given with maximum detail. This corresponds to the attitude of the telephone engineer who is concerned with transmitting the human voice but who is indifferent to the meaning of the messages. Einstein's attitude implies that the messages may have meaning, the particular meaning to be conveyed determining what message is selected. Just as no amount of telephonic circuitry will engender semantics, so does "reality" seem beyond experiment as we know it. It seems arbitrary, however, to conclude that the problem of reality is meaningless or forever irrelevant to science. It is conceivable, for example, that a long sequence of alternating measurements on two noncommuting variables carried out on a single system might suggest new kinds of regularity. These would, of course, have to yield the expectation values of quantum mechanics.

References

1. SZILARD, L. *Z. Physik,* **53**, 840 (1929).
2. HARTLEY, R. V. L. *Bell System Tech. J.,* **7**, 535 (1928).
3. WIENER, N. *Cybernetics.* New York: Wiley (1950).
4. ———. *The Extrapolation, Interpolation and Smoothing of Time Series.* New York: Wiley (1950).
5. SHANNON, C. E. *Bell System Tech. J.,* **27**, 279, 623 (1948) ; *Proc. I. R. E.,* **37**, 10 (1949).
6. TULLER, W. G. *Proc. I. R. E.,* **37**, 468 (1949).
7. GABOR, D. *J. Inst. Elec. Engrs. (London),* Pt. III, **93**, 429 (1946) ; *Phil. Mag.,* **41**, 1161 (1950).
8. MACKAY, D. M. *Phil. Mag.,* **41**, 289 (1950).
9. BRILLOUIN, L. *J. Applied Phys.,* **22**, 334, 338 (1951).
10. REICHENBACH, H. *Philosophical Foundations of Quantum Mechanics.* Berkeley : Univ. Calif. Press (1944).
11. EINSTEIN, A., PODOLSKY, B., and ROSEN, N. *Phys. Rev.,* **47**, 777 (1935).
12. SCHROEDINGER, E. *Proc. Cambridge Phil. Soc.,* **31**, 555 (1935) ; **32**, 466 (1936).
13. BOHR, N. *Phys. Rev.,* **48**, 696 (1935).

How subjective is entropy?

Kenneth Denbigh

The idea that entropy is perhaps not fully objective has been around for a long time, and is by no means solely the consequence of modern information theory. Hints in that direction are already to be found in Maxwell, Boltzmann and Gibbs, and were related to the view that subjectivity is connected with incompleteness of knowledge.

In his remarks on the probabilistic foundations of statistical mechanics, Gibbs[1] says that probability refers to something which is 'imperfectly known', and he also speaks of thermodynamic experiments as being made on bodies whose states 'are certainly not known to us exactly'. And again in his discussion on the dispersion of a band of colour in a stirred liquid, in relation to Liouville's theorem, he points out that the colour appears to become more uniformly spread, but only if *our* considerations relate to samples of fluid whose thickness is much greater than the thickness of the colour filaments.

Similar views are to be found in Tolman.[2] Perhaps the most forthright expression is that of G. N. Lewis.[3] 'The increase in entropy comes when a *known* distribution goes over into an *unknown* distribution. . . Gain in entropy always means loss of information, and nothing more. It is a subjective concept, but we can express it in its least subjective form, as follows. If, on a page, we read the description of a physicochemical system, together with certain data which help to specify the system, the entropy of the system is determined by these specifications. If any of the essential data are erased, the entropy becomes greater; if any essential data are added, the entropy becomes less.'

Later expressions of the same viewpoint are to be found in Born, Reichenbach, Brillouin and many others. 'Irreversibility', says Born,[4] is 'a consequence of the explicit introduction of ignorance into the fundamental laws.'

It will be useful to examine the thesis of the alleged subjectivity of entropy by starting with thermodynamics, and then going on to statistical mechanics and information theory. But first let me distinguish between two different senses of 'objectivity' (and conversely of 'subjectivity'). 'Objectivity', I suggest, has two commonly used meanings:[5, 6] (*i*) A broad, or weak, meaning which refers to statements which can be *publicly agreed* (philosophers sometimes refer to this as intersubjectivity) and (*ii*) a more restricted, or stronger, meaning, much used in science, which refers to statements about things which can be said to exist, or about events which can be said to occur, quite independently of man's thoughts and perceptions, or of his presence in the world.

Kenneth Denbigh, FRS, is currently director of the Council for Science and Society, 3/4 St Andrews Hill, London EC4V 5BY.

In the following I shall be concerned with the status of entropy in this second sense. But notice that neither meaning seems directly related to matters concerning incompleteness of knowledge. States of affairs might be 'imperfectly known', as Gibbs put it, without this appearing to carry any *necessary* implication of subjectivity. Yet this is an involved issue, relating to realist versus positivist interpretations of science, and it would be out of place to discuss it in full although it will be implicit in much of what follows.

Thermodynamic entropy
The word 'entropy' was coined by Clausius from a Greek word for transformation. Clausius regarded entropy as a measure of the 'transformation content' of a body, meaning presumably its capacity for change. This would appear to be an objective property of the body, when specified as to its circumstances. Yet it is better to turn to the defining equation, which refers to a transfer of heat when carried out under reversible conditions: $dS \equiv (dq/T)_{rev}$. Of course this only yields *changes* of entropy, $S_2 - S_1$, between states 1 and 2 when these are connectible by a reversible path. Yet the magnitude of this entropy change is clearly fully objective *so long as* the temperatures and the heat quantities along this path are also fully objective. Normally I believe they are. To be sure there are certain situations where a heat quantity or a temperature may be *ambiguous*, although this is not to say necessarily subjective. For example if a fluid is in turbulent motion, this motion is continually decaying, and it may be difficult to decide precisely how much of the total kinetic energy is to be counted as mechanical energy of the fluid eddies, at any moment, and how much is to be counted as thermal energy.

A similar argument in favour of the objectivity of $S_2 - S_1$ may be based on the Gibbs equation

$$dU = TdS - pdV + \Sigma \mu_i dn_i,$$

in view of the nature of the variables U, V and the n_i.

On the other hand, Grad[7] has maintained that there are several choices for thermodynamic entropy. He instances the case of a chemical reaction; if it is slow, he says, we have the choice of two distinct entropies which are functions of different variables. This is a familiar point to the chemist, for it is a question of whether we 'idealise' by regarding the reaction as being so slow that all of the dn_i may be taken as being independent of each other; or whether we idealise by regarding the reaction as being sufficiently fast for it to be at equilibrium—or for the reagents to have effectively disappeared. Yet idealisations of this kind have little bearing on the issue of subjectivity; it is rather a matter of the goodness of an approximation, and this is well illustrated by the alternative forms which can be given to the Phase Rule for a reactive system.[8]

Grad[9] has also rightly remarked that a change in the estimate of an entropy can occur 'when some relevant facet of the problem at hand has changed, even if only in the mind of the observer.' A case in point is that of Third Law entropies; the scientist may well have to change his tabulated values as soon as he learns that the substances in question contain previously unknown isotopes, or that the crystals of these substances have a residual randomness at the lowest attainable temperatures, or for reasons concerning nuclear spins. But the fact that an entropy value is changed, or is not changed, according to whether it is known, or is not known, that such factors are operative is surely no more an indication of subjectivity than would be the change in the value of almost any other physical property when new factors become known. After all we do not regard the age of a rock stratum as being subjective simply because the estimate of its age is subject to revision! To be sure the case of entropy is a little more involved since, as Grad points out, we may wish to use different measures for different purposes—for example we may wish to neglect the difference between oxygen and nitrogen in matters relating to the flow of air in a wind tunnel.

The chemist uses his Third Law entropies consistently, according to well-recognised conventions. In particular any entropy within the nucleus is taken as zero, if only because it is entirely beyond calculation in the present state of knowledge. What saves the situation, as far as chemistry is concerned, is that the unknown nuclear entropies can be assumed to remain constant during the occurrence of chemical processes for which one wishes to calculate *changes* of entropy. The same applies to the entropy of isotope mixing for this too will cancel out—except, of course, in processes where there is a separation or a mixing of the isotopes. (If we had the requisite semi-permeable membranes which would allow of a reversible mixing process, the entropy of mixing of unlike substances could be measured calorimetrically.)

What seems to me a strong argument *against* the charge of subjectivity is the normally very satisfactory agreement which obtains between calorimetric entropies, on the one hand, and spectroscopic entropies, on the other, when all well-understood factors have been allowed for. The two sorts of entropy are calculated by use of *two virtually independent theories*; the former depends on classical thermodynamics and the integration of dq/T; the latter depends on statistical mechanics and the use of spectroscopic data for evaluating the partition function. Certainly discrepancies between the two methods do occur; but in instances such as CO and N_2O the reasonable assumption that there is an end-to-end randomness of these linear molecules in the crystal, at the lowest temperature, has brought the calorimetric entropy into close agreement with the spectroscopic entropy. This kind of numerical convergence gives good support to the view that the calculated entropies correspond to an objective reality, even though this can only be approached and perhaps never fully attained.

But let us consider a counter-argument put forward by Jaynes,[10] with all of his characteristic vigour. He begins by remarking that a given *physical* system can correspond to many different *thermodynamic* systems, according to the choice of the variables which are used for specifying its state. This is true, and is fully in line with what has been said above. However he goes on to say: 'From this we see that entropy is an anthropomorphic concept, not only in the well-known statistical sense that it measures the extent of human ignorance as to the microstate. *Even at the purely phenomenological level, entropy is an anthropomorphic concept.* For it is a property, not of the physical system, but of the particular experiments you or I choose to perform on it.' (His italics.)

This last sentence, which is used to entail the previous one, is remarkably tendentious! There is no need to bring in 'you or I'; that sentence could equally well have been written: 'It is a property of the variables required to specify the physical system under the conditions of the particular experiment.' Yet Jaynes proceeds to fortify his charge of anthropomorphism by making reference to the engineer's steam tables. Since steam is a polar substance, he says, its entropy 'depends appreciably on the electric field strength present. It must always be understood implicitly . . . that the electric field was not inadvertently varied from one measurement to the next.'

Well of course—but there is nothing here which is peculiar to entropy! The values of many other 'properties of steam' (to use conventional scientific language) will also be dependent on the field strength, and will be ambiguous if the field is not specified, along with the other state variables.

Rather than accepting that entropy is an anthropomorphic concept, I prefer the way in which the matter is expressed by Hobson,[11] who in other respects is close to Jaynes. He says that, instead of speaking of the entropy of the physical system, we should speak of 'the entropy of the data'. He then remarks that this does not render entropy subjective; for it is an observable quantity and is determined by the observable data, such as energy, volume and composition. It is thus relative, not to the observer, but to the observer's data. This way of putting the matter takes good care of my own points about isotopes *etc*; for the observed data might, or might not, include information about the presence of isotopes as part of the system's composition variables.

Let us accept then that thermodynamic entropies are relative to the data, but without conceding subjectivity, and proceed to see how the matter stands when entropy is interpreted in the light of statistical mechanics.

Statistical mechanical entropies

Quite a number of statistical quantities can be defined whose behaviour more or less resembles that of thermodynamic entropy. Gibbs himself discussed three such quantities, over and above the earlier Boltzmann–Planck definition, and others have been devised subsequently. Gibbs was right, I think, to call them 'entropy analogues' since the term 'entropy' had already been pre-empted by Clausius for the purposes of classical thermodynamics. As is well-known the various analogues differ from each other by small terms; furthermore some of them are not completely additive, or do not increase in irreversible adiabatic processes. Therefore it remains somewhat problematic whether thermodynamic entropy can be completely 'reduced' to any one of them.[9, 10, 12]

Yet this is to move ahead too quickly. Let us first remind ourselves that the founders of statistical mechanics (SM) believed that thermodynamics had to be explained in terms of more fundamental theory—an entirely legitimate view, and especially so since classical thermodynamics was entirely at a loss to deal with fluctuation phenomena. The development of SM has resulted in remarkable contributions both to the basic understanding of thermodynamics, and to the solving of problems which previously were quite intractable.

Treatises on the subject typically begin by saying that probability theory has to be used because the precise mechanical state of a system containing, say, 10^{23} particles 'cannot be known to us'. Is this a declaration of subjectivity? It needs to be said, in the first place, that the kind of probabilities used in SM are not necessarily subjective probabilities—*ie* those which relate to personal beliefs about unique events, such as the horse which will win tomorrow's Derby. On the contrary, SM uses either the frequency interpretation of probability or the inductive logic interpretation[11] such as is implied by the assertion that the probability is $\frac{1}{2}$ of an even number being obtained in the throw of an unbiased die. Neither of these usages carries subjective connotations; indeed the numerical assessments of these probabilities, in various situations, could be carried out by a suitable automaton coupled to a computer.

As for the point about things which 'cannot be known to us', this of course is entirely true—and yet the introduction of 'us' is quite unnecessary! Entropy, like other macroscopic properties, is required as a function of other macroscopic variables and these are quite insufficient to specify the microscopic state of the system in question. To be sure in the case of entropy, in the SM treatment, we *also* need to use a certain amount of knowledge, or a certain number of assumptions, about the molecular mechanics. In particular we are concerned with the limitation created by Liouville's theorem, and we need to make an important assumption about the probabilities of the occurrence of individual quantum states being proportional, at equilibrium, to an exponential function of their energies (or some alternative assumption of a statistical kind). In short, if we wish to speak of entropy as being a matter of 'lack of information' about the precise micro-state prevailing at any instant, this (I suggest) is to use the term 'information' without specifically human connotation. Here again suitable automata and computers could be used in the performance of standardised SM investigations.

Perhaps the matter needs to be dealt with in a little more detail, giving careful consideration to a remark made by Jaynes.[10] Entropy, he states, can be said, in a subjective sense, to measure 'our *degree of ignorance* as to the true unknown microstate . . .' This may seem difficult to reconcile with what has already been said about thermodynamic entropy. However, in my view, it is quite unnecessary to bring human powers of knowledge—or lack of it—into the picture. Jaynes' remark, though undoubtedly illuminating in a certain sense, is quite superfluous to the actual scientific discussion.

To see that this is so, let us follow through the relevant parts of the statistical mechanical treatment, cutting a few corners for the sake of brevity. We consider a Gibbsian ensemble of macroscopically identical systems which are capable of exchanging energy with a very large heat bath and are in a state of equilibrium. Then the mean energy of the systems is

$$\langle E \rangle = \Sigma P_i E_i \tag{1}$$

where P_i is the probability of a system being in a quantum state whose momentary energy eigenvalue is E_i. The summation is over all accessible quantum states, including degenerate states. A variation of the mean energy is thus given by

$$d\langle E \rangle = \Sigma P_i dE_i + \Sigma E_i dP_i \tag{2}$$

Now the first term on the right hand side represents a change in $\langle E \rangle$ due to changes in the eigenvalues, E_i, and these latter changes are determined, according to quantum mechanics, by changes in external variables such as the volume. So long as the changes in these external variables take place slowly enough, so that the systems of the ensemble never depart more than infinitesimally from equilibrium, it can therefore be argued that the first term on the RHS corresponds wholly to what, in thermodynamic terms, is the mean of the reversible work done on each of the systems. If so, the second term must correspond to the mean of the reversible intakes of heat:

$$\langle dq \rangle = \Sigma E_i dP_i \tag{3}$$

A reversible heat effect may therefore be interpreted as being due to changes in the probabilities with which the various energy levels are occupied. So far, then, there is no necessary implication of subjectivity!

Consider now the entropy analogue:

$$S' = -k\Sigma P_i \log P_i \tag{4}$$

where the summation is again over all quantum states, so that $\Sigma P_i = 1$ and $\Sigma dP_i = 0$. We thus obtain

$$dS' = -k\Sigma \log P_i dP_i \tag{5}$$

In the situation in question, where equilibrium is essentially maintained, the probabilities are given by the Gibbs' familiar canonical distribution:

$$P_i = Q^{-1} e^{\beta E_i} \tag{6}$$

where β is a constant and Q is the partition function, or 'sum-over-states'. Hence from (3), (5) and (6);

$$dS' = -k\beta \Sigma E_i dP_i = -k\beta d\langle q \rangle \tag{7}$$

As is well-known, $-k\beta$ can be identified as $1/T$. Therefore we recover the familiar thermodynamic expression $dS = (dq/T)_{rev}$ where the mean sign, $\langle q \rangle$, is no longer necessary since the fluctuations about the mean can be shown to be extremely small in the case of the macroscopic systems we are considering.

This brief argument, summary though it is, indicates that the entropy analogue (4) can be related to heat and temperature without requiring any appeal to 'ignorance', or to lack of information. The use of these notions is redundant in the strictly scientific context, even though they may be important from a more philosophical viewpoint.

Another familiar entropy analogue is that of Boltzmann and Planck:

$$S'' = \log W \tag{8}$$

W was called the number of 'complexions' of the system, but in modern terms it is the number of quantum states accessible to an isolated system having the energy E. No doubt some of the original impetus for the subjective view of entropy arose from a contemplation of this expression; for of course it is entirely true that 'we cannot know' which particular one, out of all the W possible quantum states, the system momentarily occupies at any instant. Yet it needs once again to be asked: Is this really relevant to the physics of the situation? It would seem a quite unnecessary gloss on the significance of (8) to introduce human powers of knowing. Consider a single molecule and suppose that the degeneracy of one of its eigenvalues has been assigned the value 2. Since we do not normally regard it as a subjective matter that it is not known which of these two states the molecule momentarily occupies, there seems no good reason why we need take a different attitude in regard to W. For W too is essentially a degeneracy, although it relates to a whole macroscopic system when its energy lies in a very narrow range E to $(E + \delta E)$.

There is however another line of argument within SM which has been taken to imply that entropy is subjective. So far I have been discussing equilibrium situations, but suppose we wish to prove that one of the entropy analogues increases during an irreversible process? This was a problem which greatly troubled Gibbs, as may be seen from his Chapter 12. His own preferred analogue was similiar to (4), except that it was expressed in a pre-quantal form and was an integral over a continuous range of the coordinates and momenta. He showed that it has a larger value when the probabilities are given by (6) than it would have for any other probability distribution yielding the same mean energy in the ensemble. Yet it was an inescapable, if unwelcome, consequence of Liouville's theorem that the analogue *remains constant* during an irreversible process at constant energy.

Hence arose the problem of discovering a modified analogue which would display irreversible increase. Boltzmann had, of course, previously used kinetic theory for this purpose, but his H-theorem only applied to dilute gases, and even then required some questionable assumptions. In order to achieve a more general treatment on Gibbsian lines, the Ehrenfests, Tolman and others (foreshadowed by Gibbs himself) adopted the device of *coarse graining*. It was the apparent necessity for this which gave rise to the view that an entropy analogue which will satisfactorily display irreversibility must contain subjective elements since the degree of coarse graining is arbitrarily chosen.

Tolman, in his quantum statistical mechanics (where the same problem arises) defined coarse graining as follows: '... we regard ourselves as making observations of only limited accuracy ... As in the classical mechanics, we thus define the coarse-grained probability for a state as the mean of fine-grained probabilities taken over neighbouring states of nearly identical properties.' The summation in (4) is therefore taken over *groups* of quantum states. A number of authors have regarded this kind of procedure as a fiddle, and have looked for alternative methods of demonstrating irreversibility independently of thermodynamics. Nevertheless coarse graining has remained the standard method of approach, at least until recently, so we must inquire whether it implies subjectivity.

Tolman seems half to agree that it does. Since the value of $-\Sigma P_i \log P_i$ is greater 'the less exactly the quantum mechanical state of the system is specified, this provides the reason for the statement sometimes made that the entropy of a system is a measure of the degree of our ignorance as to

its condition.' But he goes on to say: 'From a precise point of view, however, it seems more clarifying to emphasise that entropy can be regarded as a quantity which is thermodynamically *defined* . . . and statistically *interpreted* . . .' (My italics.) In other words, for Tolman the word 'entropy' is to be understood as it is in thermodynamics; SM provides nothing more than a possibly fallible interpretation.

He proceeds to point out that the coarse-grained probabilities become identical with the fine-grained probabilities in the case of equilibrium states whose variables can be measured. This means that the coarse graining device has no bearing on the statistical mechanics of equilibrium states—for example in regard to the calculation of thermodynamic quantities from spectroscopic data where one proceeds up to the limit of specification permitted by quantum mechanics. It follows that any subjectivity which might be attributed to coarse graining carries no implications for thermodynamics where entropy changes are strictly defined only for reversible changes.

However Grünbaum[13] has gone further and has argued that, even when coarse graining is adopted, this need not carry any implications of anthropomorphism. Confining his attention to classical SM, he admits that the charge of subjectivity is made plausible by the fact that the magnitude of an entropy change depends on the human choice of the size of the finite cells into which the position–velocity phase space is partitioned. One can even find types of partitioning which can manifest a diminution of entropy with time! But this fact, he argues, relates only to a single system. As soon as we consider a union U of ensembles it follows that: 'For any and every partition, the common initial entropy of all the systems in U will either have increased *in a vast majority* of the systems by the time $t + \Delta t$, or it will have remained the same.' In other words it is shown that, after averaging over all macrostates having a particular initial value of W (in eqn 8), relative to a partition however it might be chosen, the entropy either increases or remains constant. Grünbaum therefore concludes that the objective physical significance of a coarse-grained entropy is not impugned by the conceptual process of coarse-graining and 'cannot be held to be merely expressive of human ignorance of the underlying microprocesses.'

As has been said, various alternative methods of demonstrating irreversible entropy increase are being explored. The difficulties are formidable. For whereas classical thermodynamics *starts* from the empirical observation that certain types of process cannot be reversed (*ie* the Clausius or Kelvin impossibility statements), SM has somehow to *prove* that this is so. The major difficulty is that the laws of classical and quantum mechanics are t-invariant, and thus allow of the recurrence of states arbitrarily close to the initial state. Thus irreversibility remains a very live problem, as may be seen from the recent reviews by Wehrl[14] and Penrose.[15] Nevertheless the various difficulties seem in no way to invalidate the existence of entropy as an objective property of the data relating to equilibrium states.

Information theory and Brillouin's 'Principle'
The view that entropy is a measure of 'ignorance' has appeared to obtain a good deal of support from the side of information theory. Yet the question has to be asked: Which entropy are we talking about?

Consider a sequence of symbols; for instance the 26 letters of the alphabet. It was shown by Shannon that, so long as each symbol occurs independently of the previous ones, the mean 'information' per symbol can be described conveniently by the function $-\Sigma P_i \log P_i$, where the summation is over the various symbols and the P_i refer to their probabilities of occurrence. (If the sequence happened to be a meaningful sentence, the successive symbols would not be independent and, in that case, conditional probabilities would need to be used in the formula.) Shannon made it clear that his usage of the word 'information' was highly technical; it was simply a question of finding a suitable measure for the 'uncertainty' which existed before a sequence was chosen. Shannon's measure has therefore no bearing whatsoever on *meaning*. For example the sequence 'Arrive Sunday' has no greater value of the foregoing function than has some alternative, but meaningless, arrangement of the symbols.

Shannon gave his function the name 'entropy' and Tribus[16] has described how this came about. Apparently Shannon's previous intentions were to call it either 'information' or 'uncertainty', but when he discussed the matter with von Neumann the latter suggested that it be named 'entropy'. 'It is already in use under that name', von Neumann is reported to have said, 'and besides, it will give you a great edge in debates because nobody really knows what entropy is anyway.'

In my view von Neumann did science a disservice! There are, of course, good mathematical reasons why information theory and statistical mechanics both require functions having the same formal structure. They have a common origin in probability theory, and they also need to satisfy certain common requirements such as additivity. Yet this formal similarity does not imply that the functions necessarily signify or represent the same concepts. The term 'entropy' had already been given a well-established physical meaning in thermodynamics, and it remains to be seen under what conditions, if any, thermodynamic entropy and information are mutually interconvertable. They may be so in some contexts, but not in others. As Popper[17] has very clearly put it, it needs to be shown whether or not the P_i 'are probabilities of the same attributes of the same system.'

In the absence of this demonstration there is a good deal to be said for denoting the function $H \equiv \Sigma P_i \log P_i$ by an entirely neutral term. Tisza[18] calls it 'the dispersal' of the particular probability distribution, and this seems admirable. The reader will perhaps recall that as long ago as 1945 Guggenheim[19] used a similar term, namely 'spread', although he was primarily concerned with the thermodynamic context. The best verbalisation for explaining entropy, he said, is that it measures the 'spread' over the accessible quantum states.

Nevertheless the last three decades have seen a partial merging of SM and information theory, especially by Jaynes,[20] Tribus,[21] Hobson[11] and Katz.[22] Jaynes takes his point of departure from what he regards as a general rule of statistical inference, and this remains controversial.[23, 24] But leaving that aside, the partial merging of the two disciplines has resulted, in my view, in disbenefits as well as benefits. The application of information theory in thermodynamic contexts has certainly been very helpful in an heuristic sense, and a couple of examples will be quoted later. On the other hand the proliferation of 'entropies' has

led to confusion, and there has occurred a tendency, as already noticed, to make charges of subjectivity in contexts where they are unjustified.

And again there has been a too ready acceptance—although not by any of the authors mentioned—of the generality of Brillouin's 'Negentropy Principle'. This has encouraged the idea, referred to above, that almost any form of 'information' is freely interconvertable (after appropriate change of sign) into thermodynamic entropy, or vice versa. My own view is that the interconvertability thesis can be maintained only in certain special cases where it becomes trivially true, due to the reference to 'information' being unnecessary.

Brillouin's work followed on from earlier studies by Szilard, Demers and Raymond on the subject of Maxwell's Demon. Using the entropy analogue $S = k \log W$, we have, in any process where W is made to diminish from an initial value W_0 to a smaller final value W_1:

$$S_0 - S_1 = k \log W_0/W_1$$

Brillouin takes this entropy reduction as the gain, I, in what he calls 'the bound information' about the system, and thus he writes

$$I \equiv S_0 - S_1 = k \log W_0/W_1$$

If the system is now left to evolve spontaneously, as an isolated system, then from the Second Law $\Delta S_1 \geqslant 0$. Hence for the two processes taken together he writes

$$\Delta(S_0 - I) \geqslant 0$$

(The foregoing are equations 12.1, 12.3 and 12.9 from his book.[25] In his 12.9 he surprisingly included what he calls 'free information'; that 'which occurs when the possible cases are regarded as abstract and have no specified physical significance.' However in his original papers[26] on the subject, free information was *not* included, and neither is it dealt with elsewhere in the book.)

Little exception can be taken to the foregoing since the 'bound information' is really nothing more than *a name* given by Brillouin to the entropy change $S_0 - S_1$, a change which he admits 'must be furnished by some external agent whose entropy will increase.' However something more significant than a mere naming seems to be involved when he proceeds to re-write the equation as 'a reversible reaction: $I \rightleftharpoons N$' (where $N = -S$). This is his 'Negentropy Principle of Information', or 'Generalisation of Carnot's Principle'. What has to be questioned, I think, is whether *all forms* of information, when this term is understood in Shannon's sense, can be changed into negentropy, if the latter is understood in the thermodynamic sense. If not, what are the restrictions which would define the scope of Brillouin's principle?

Brillouin gives many interesting and illuminating examples relating to the obtaining of 'information' in the form of a measurement. The higher is the accuracy which is demanded, the greater must be the compensating entropy increase. On the other hand the only example he provides of his 'reversible reaction' proceeding in the reverse direction—*ie* the use of 'information' to reduce entropy—lies in his discussion of Maxwell's Demon. The following is a slight paraphrase of Brillouin's account, differing from his only in so far as the notion of 'information' will not be used; it is unnecessary. To be sure the Demon must be able to *distinguish* between the gas molecules—but the energy

114 *Maxwell's Demon*

transfer which is here involved can be discussed entirely in thermodynamic terms.

As in Brillouin, I assume that the Demon uses something equivalent to an electric torch to illuminate the molecules. Let T_0 be the temperature of the gas and Demon; then if the temperature T_1 of the filament in the torch is sufficiently greater than T_0, the relationship $h\nu > kT_0$ will be satisfied and the light scattered by the gas molecules can be distinguished by the Demon from the background of black body radiation in the enclosure. Let E be the energy radiated by the filament during the duration of the Demon's efforts. This is absorbed as heat within the enclosure. Therefore these two aspects, radiation and absorption, of the overall process are attended by entropy increase since they are equivalent to the transfer of energy E from a temperature T_1 to a lower temperature T_0.

Let us turn to a third aspect—the operation of the Demon. 'He' needs at least one quantum, $h\nu$, of energy per molecule for the purpose of distinguishing between the gas molecules in regard to their suitability for being allowed to pass through the trap door. This energy enters his 'eye', or photocell, and is degraded as heat. The Demon's own entropy is thereby increased by an amount $h\nu/T_0$. Finally we turn to the effect of the Demon's passing of a particular molecule through the trap door. This can *diminish* the entropy of the gas by a factor of the order $k \log(W_0 - \delta W)/W_0$. Here W_0 is the original number of complexions of the gas (in both compartments), and $W_0 - \delta W$ is the number of complexions after the segregation in, say, the right hand compartment of one additional molecule.

Hence the entropy change in these two processes, per molecule transferred, is:

$$h\nu/T_0 + k \log(W_0 - \delta W)/W_0 \doteq k(h\nu/kT_0 - \delta W/W_0)$$

This is positive since $\delta W/W_0 \ll 1$ and $h\nu/kT_0 > 1$. The overall entropy change in all four processes therefore satisfies the Second Law—although, in a more refined treatment, it would be shown that it does so only on the average.

The point of my paraphrase has thus been to show that Brillouin's treatment of the Demon problem can be carried through entirely in thermodynamic terms and does not require the use of 'information'. He, on the other hand, writes as follows: 'The torch is a source of radiation not in equilibrium. It pours negative entropy into the system. From this negative entropy the demon obtains information. Using this information, he operates the trap door, and rebuilds negative entropy, thus completing a cycle:

negentropy $\longrightarrow$ information $\longrightarrow$ negentropy.'

This seems to me a fallacious way of putting the matter. The Demon does not have to be thought of as 'obtaining information'; indeed the Demon could be replaced by a mechanical device, (as was admitted by Szilard in his earlier treatment). Furthermore there is no necessity for the process to be conceived as occurring in successive stages in which negentropy is converted into information and then back into negentropy; it is simply a matter of the summation of various entropy terms, as in so many other physicochemical situations.

What may be conceded however is that the general ideas of information theory have been very useful in this example in a purely heuristic sense. They have enabled the investi-gator to appreciate that the Demon must be able to distinguish between the gas molecules by physical means. In that respect information theory can truly be said to have contributed to *the process of solving* the problem of Maxwell's Demon; but once the essential idea has been obtained, the solution can be carried through without any reference to information theory.

And indeed a too literal application of this theory could actually have led to errors. For it might fail to bring out the important point that the Demon's 'information' is relevant only if it is used quickly enough! If, instead of immediately opening the shutter, the Demon had punched out a tape containing the message 'Here is a suitable molecule coming', and had then put the tape into a computer-robot system to operate the shutter, the opportunity for transmitting the molecule into the other chamber would have passed by long ago.

In general it seems difficult to conceive of many situations in which 'information', as applied so fruitfully by Shannon in the context of communications engineering, can be made use of by humans, or by automata, for the purpose of seizing hold of the momentary fluctuations which occur within physicochemical systems. Of course it must be accepted that the Second Law is a statistical law, and is true only on the average. Therefore it would not be really shocking (although very, very surprising) if we did sometimes succeed in trapping such systems in slightly low entropy states. On the other hand it would be exceedingly shocking, as well as surprising, if a sequence of symbols on a piece of paper, or inscribed on a magnetic tape, or held in someone's head, were ever capable of being the *cause* of such an event. It is entirely outside our experience that an item of information of that kind could truly be regarded as the originating mechanism (as distinct from an instruction about what to do) of an overall reduction of entropy at some arbitrary later time.

A further point may be made, and this is no less important for being semantic. Consider the irreversible expansion of a gas from a volume V_1 into a larger total volume V_2. The information theorists speak of there being a 'loss of information' in this process, and they suppose it to be monotonic apart from minute fluctuations. But let us look at the matter in a different way. Initially the gas was in a well-defined and knowable equilibrium state, of volume V_1, and finally it again reaches a well-defined and knowable equilibrium state, of volume V_2. Nevertheless all sorts of eddies and surges occur during the course of the process and these are unknowable and unpredictable, especially if the vessel has an irregular shape. The 'knowability' of the state of the gas evidently passes through a minimum. Therefore, if it is contended that there is a monotonic loss of information, this seems to require that the notion of information must be understood as being quite distinct from the notions of knowability and unpredictability. This raises a problem of what is meant by 'information' in contexts very different from those of Shannon's applications.

It is of interest that the Jaynes school makes singularly little mention of Brillouin's interconvertability thesis, and indeed Jaynes himself[27] gave an explicit warning: '. . . we have to emphasize that "information-theory entropy" S_I and the experimental thermodynamic entropy S_e are entirely different concepts. Our job cannot be to *postulate* any relation between them; it is rather to *deduce* whatever relations we can from known mathematical and physical facts.'

This agrees with my own views. Perhaps what is needed is the formulation of certain rules of procedure, methodological rules, which would clarify the meaning of information in physicochemical contexts, together with the circumstances under which lack of information can legitimately be counted as thermodynamic entropy. The previous quotation from Popper provides a good beginning, and some further hints are to be found in Tisza[18] and Watanabe.[28] The reader may also wish to consult the work of Penrose,[12] Jauch and Báron.[29] Lindblad[30, 31] and Skagerstam.[32]

Distinction needs also to be made between the foregoing considerations about *correctness*, on the one hand, and the undoubted *heuristic value* of information theory, on the other. A further good example of the latter is provided in Bekenstein's well-known paper[33] on the thermodynamics of black holes. Bekenstein follows Hawking in assuming that the entropy of a black hole is related to its surface area, and he first adduces arguments in favour of a linear relationship. He then goes on to inquire about the factors which may determine the proportionality constant.

Since a hole is fully characterised, from the viewpoint of an external observer, by the use of only three parameters (mass, charge and angular momentum), Bekenstein argues that its entropy is essentially a measure of the inaccessibility, to the outside observer, of information about the hole's internal configurations. He then proposes that there are two factors within the proportionality constant: one of them is chosen on dimensional grounds as being the square of the Planck length; and the other is log 2. This is obtained by posing the question: What is the absolute minimum of information which is lost when a particle disappears into a black hole? Before it enters the hole there is one bit of information, namely the affirmative answer to the question whether the particle exists or not. After it has entered, this amount of information is lost, since it can no longer be known whether or not the particle still exists. Hence his conjecture that the proportionality constant contains the factor log 2.

No doubt this simple theory, put forward in the springtime of an entirely new field of research, may not prove to be entirely correct. I quote it only to indicate that the argument would probably not have occurred to a pure thermodynamicist unversed in the outlook of information theory.

Conclusion

My general conclusion is that the subjectivity thesis, relating to entropy, remains unproved, and in my view can be largely dispelled by careful attention to the logic of the matter, and to its linguistic expression.

To this it may be added that irreversibility is a much more direct aspect of experience than is entropy itself. Of course they are closely bound up, for the entropy concept is capable of reflecting the fact that there are processes which occur in a particular sequence of states, ABC . . . , which do not occur—or exceedingly rarely—in the reverse sequence . . . CBA. The final point I want to make is that, even if it were successfully demonstrated that the entropy concept contains a subjective element, the same could hardly be said about the world's pervasive irreversibility.

Many expositions of the Second Law concentrate their attention, naturally enough, on isolated laboratory systems, initially prepared in a non-equilibrium state. The relevant concept, says Grad,[9] when viewing the subsequent evolution of a system, even one which is deterministic, 'is the progressive weakening of the property of continuous dependence on the initial conditions.' Of course this is entirely relevant, but the question which is seldom asked is: How is it ever possible to prepare a system in a non-equilibrium state in the first place?

Of course the answer is self-evident once the question has been posed: the possibility of preparing such systems depends on the existence of an environment which is also in a non-equilibrium state. We can prepare laboratory systems in chosen initial conditions only by extracting them, so to speak, from the capacity for change—Clausius' 'transformation content'—displayed by the whole of the world around us. Even to set up such a simple laboratory system as one consisting of a block of material at 1000 °C requires free energy sources such as are provided by oil or coal deposits. The existence of these, in their turn, may be traced back to the nuclear reactions taking place in the Sun and stars.[34] This all-pervasive capacity for change within the universe is surely independent of man's presence and is thus fully objective.

References

1. J. W. Gibbs, *Elementary principles in statistical mechanics.* Yale, 1902.
2. R. C. Tolman, *The principles of statistical mechanics.* Oxford, 1938.
3. G. N. Lewis, *Science,* 1930, *LXXI,* 569.
4. Max Born, *Natural philosophy of cause and chance.* Oxford, 1949.
5. K. G. Denbigh, *An inventive universe.* London: Hutchinson, 1975.
6. B. D'Espagnat, *Conceptual foundations of quantum mechanics,* 2nd Edn. Reading, Mass: W. A. Benjamin, 1976.
7. H. Grad, *Delaware seminar in the foundations of physics,* (M. Bunge ed). Berlin: Springer-Verlag, 1967.
8. K. G. Denbigh, *The principles of chemical equilibrium,* 4th Edn. p 187. Cambridge, 1981.
9. H. Grad, *Communications on Pure and Applied Maths,* 1961, *XIV,* 323.
10. E. T. Jaynes, *Am. J.Phys.* 1965, **33,** 391.
11. A. Hobson, *Concepts in statistical mechanics.* New York: Gordon and Breach, 1971.
12. O. Penrose, *Foundations of statistical mechanics.* Oxford: Pergamon, 1970.
13. A. Grünbaum in *Entropy and information,* (L. Kubát and J. Zeman eds). Prague: Academia, 1975.
14. A. Wehrl, *Rev. Mod. Phys.,* 1978, **50,** 221.
15. O. Penrose, *Rep. Prog. Phys.,* 1979, **42,** 1937.
16. M. Tribus, *Boelter anniversary volume.* McGraw Hill, 1963.
17. K. R. Popper in *The philosophy of Karl Popper,* Vol. I, p 130, (P. A. Schilpp ed). LaSalle: Open Court, 1974.
18. L. Tisza, *Generalized thermodynamics,* MIT Press, 1966.
19. E. A. Guggenheim, *Research,* 1949, **2,** 450.
20. E. T. Jaynes, *Phys. Rev.,* 1957, **106,** 620; 1957, **108,** 171.
21. M. Tribus, *Thermostatics and thermodynamics.* Van Nostrand, 1961.
22. A. Katz, *Principles of statistical mechanics.* San Francisco: Freeman, 1967.
23. J. S. Rowlinson, *Nature (London),* 1970, **225,** 1196.
24. E. T. Jaynes in *The maximum entropy formalism,* (R. D. Levine and M. Tribus eds). MIT Press, 1979.
25. L. Brillouin, *Science and information theory.* New York: Academic Press, 1962.
26. L. Brillouin, *J. Appl. Phys.,* 1953, **24,** 1152; 1954, **25,** 595.
27. E. T. Jaynes in *Information theory and statistical mechanics,* (K. W. Ford ed). New York: Benjamin, 1963.
28. S. Watanabe, *Knowing and guessing.* Wiley, 1969.
29. J. M. Jauch and J. G. Báron, *Helv. Phys. Acta,* 1972, **45,** 220.
30. G. Lindblat, *Commun. Maths. Phys.,* 1973, **33,** 305.
31. G. Lindblat, *J. Stat. Phys.,* 1974, **11,** 231.
32. B. K. Skagerstam, *J. Stat. Phys.,* 1975, **12,** 449.
33. J. D. Bekenstein, *Phys. Rev. D,* 1973, **7,** 2333.
34. See also my *Three concepts of time,* forthcoming from Springer-Verlag.

On the Relation Between Information and Energy Systems
A Family of Maxwell's Demons

DR ALVIN M. WEINBERG

Director, Institute for Energy Analysis, Oak Ridge Associated Universities, Oak Ridge, Tennessee, USA

Maxwell's Demon uses information to save free energy. However, as Brillouin has shown, the energy required by the demon in acquiring information just equals the energy he saves. Modern microprocessor controls on internal combustion engines are macroscopic Maxwell demons. They increase engine efficiency by continuously optimizing operating parameters. The market system is a social Maxwell demon; by sending price signals to the consumer, it causes him to use energy more efficiently. As the scale of the demon increases, so does the ratio of energy saved to energy used by the demon. The amount of energy that can be saved by intervention of intelligence is further limited by the time available for the intervention. Time, energy and information thus form a triad, as was first pointed out by D. Spreng.

Into 1980 fell the 109th birthday of Maxwell's Demon. The ingenious little fellow first appeared in Maxwell's *Theory of Heat*, published in 1871.[1] Maxwell wrote: 'let us suppose that a vessel is divided into two portions, *A* and *B*, by a division in which there is a small hole, and that a being who can see the individual molecules opens and closes this hole, so as to allow only the swifter molecules to pass from *A* to *B*, and only the slower ones to pass from *B* to *A*. He will thus, without expenditure of work raise the temperature of *B* and lower that of *A*, in contradiction to the second law of thermodynamics.' In other words, a heat engine that produces work could be operated on this temperature difference perpetually, or at least until the demon got tired. That the resolution of this paradox might have something to do with information was hinted at by M. von Smoluchowski in the book, *Lectures on the Kinetic Theory of Matter and Electricity*, published in 1914.[2] Smoluchowski wrote (p. 89): 'There is no automatic, permanently effective perpetual motion machine, in spite of molecular fluctuations, but such a device might perhaps function regularly if it were operated by intelligent beings.'

SZILARD'S ARGUMENT

Leo Szilard, one of the fathers of nuclear energy, first resolved the paradox by establishing a quantitative connection between information and entropy. In a remarkable paper first published in 1929 in the *Zeitschrift für Physik* and reprinted in 1964 in, of all places, the American journal *Behavioral Science* under the title 'On the Decrease of Entropy in a Thermodynamic System by the Intervention of Intelligent Beings', Szilard showed that the second law of thermodynamics would not be violated if the entropy *S* of the system increased by an amount

$$\Delta S = k \ln 2 \qquad (1)$$

(where k = Boltzmann's constant = 1.38×10^{-23} joules per degree Kelvin), every time the demon measured the speed of a molecule in order to decide whether or not to open the trap-door.[3] This increase in entropy just balances the *decrease* in entropy associated with the appearance of a higher speed molecule in the right-hand box. In this way the paradox is resolved since the entropy of the system informed-demon-plus-segregated-gas is the same as that of the system uninformed-demon-plus-unsegregated-gas. We can therefore quantify the information in the demon: per measurement he makes, or per bit, it is

$$\Delta I = -k \ln 2 \qquad (2)$$

the negative sign signifying that for each increase in information, there is a corresponding decrease in the actual physical entropy of the gas.

Szilard's argument implies that the connection between information and entropy is intrinsic and real, not incidental and analogic. Pushed further, one would have to concede, as Eugene Wigner has explained to me, that entropy itself has anthropomorphic connotations. For example, as a red liquid and a blue liquid are mixed, their degree of mixing, and therefore the entropy of the system, depends on how well an observer can keep track of the smaller and smaller globules of each liquid. An observer with very sharp eyesight can keep track of individual globules that are too small to be seen by one with poor eyesight. For him, the two liquids are really not mixed, and in principle he could fish out the blue from the red. The entropy, as he measures it, would therefore differ from that of the observer with poorer eyesight.

Szilard's ideas appear in the work of C. Shannon[4] and later in that of L. Brillouin;[5] Shannon, entirely independently of Szilard, derived a formula equivalent to Eqn (2). But Shannon, when he speaks of entropy of information, is using it in an analogic sense: he makes no direct connection with the classical, phenomenological concept of entropy:

$$\Delta S = \frac{\text{Amount of heat transferred in a reversible process}}{\text{Temperature at which heat is transferred}} \quad (3)$$

$$= \frac{\Delta Q}{T}$$

as a state variable characterizing a thermodynamic system. Indeed, according to M. Tribus,[6] Shannon attributes his use of the word entropy to John von Neumann, who pointed out to him that 'no one knows what entropy really is so in a debate you will always have the advantage'.

DUALITY OF ENTROPY AND INFORMATION

In this essay I shall adopt Szilard's point of view – that on a molecular level there is an intrinsic connection, even a duality, between information and entropy: increase in information corresponds to a diminution of physical entropy. Moreover – if one does not count the energy required to acquire the information – intelligent intervention on a microscopic level allows one to extract more useful work than would have been possible without this intervention. But, as Brillouin explained in detail, energy must be expended in order to let the demon make his measurement. Thus, the entropy decrease in the demon requires an expenditure of energy:

$$\Delta Q = T\Delta S \approx 10^{-23}T \text{ joules per bit} \quad (4)$$

or, at room temperature, $\Delta Q \approx 3 \times 10^{-21}$ joules per bit. This expenditure of energy just balances the energy derived from the segregation of the molecules in the box. Thus, if we call E_A the extra energy made available by the demon's intervention and E_D the energy required for the demon to operate, then their ratio is

$$R = \frac{E_A}{E_D} = 1 \quad (5)$$

It will be my purpose to show that this almost bizarre connection between information and entropy has analogies also on a macroscopic, physical level; and even on a social, institutional level. Moreover, as the level of aggregation increases, the energy saved by astute intervention of information processing devices – that is, by control – can greatly exceed the energy expended in operation of the devices, unlike Maxwell's Demon where, as seen in Eqn (5), the two energies are equal.

WHY ENTROPY?

My essay is called 'On the Relation Between Information and Energy Systems'; so far I have written mostly about information or control and entropy. Yet a moment's reflection should make clear that it is entropy, not energy *per se*, that is of primary interest – that the energy crisis is a misnomer. The first law of thermodynamics states that energy can be neither created nor destroyed: in what sense then are we in an energy crisis, since the amount of energy always remains the same?

The answer, of course, is that we lack useful energy, that is, energy in a form that enables us to extract work, to heat a cold chicken, or to drive a chemical reaction. Various so-called state functions measure how much useful work can be derived from, say, the energy in a piece of coal, or a compressed gas, or a tank of hot water. These state functions include the Helmholtz free energy, F; the Gibbs free energy, G; and the engineer's availability, A. The appropriate state function depends upon whether the transformation is being performed at constant temperature, F; or at constant pressure and temperature, G; or in an environment at a fixed temperature and pressure that differs from that of the system performing the work, A. All these functions are linear functions of the entropy, and the coefficient of the entropy term is negative. Because the coefficient is negative, the higher the entropy of the system, the less useful work can be derived from it. Thus, insofar as man's transactions involve converting the energy in a chemical or nuclear or solar system into useful work, such transactions are most efficient – that is, can be accomplished with the least expenditure of

DR ALVIN M. WEINBERG is Director of the Institute for Energy Analysis, which he was instrumental in establishing at Oak Ridge Associated Universities in January 1974. For more than a quarter of a century Weinberg was director of the Oak Ridge National Laboratory, one of the world's great scientific and technological institutions. For his role in the development of nuclear reactors, Weinberg shared the Atoms for Peace Award in 1960 and was one of the first recipients of the E. O. Lawrence Memorial Award. He was awarded the first Heinrich Hertz Prize on the 150th anniversary of the University of Karlsruhe, FRG, in 1975. In 1980 he received the US Department of Energy's Enrico Fermi Award for especially meritorious contributions to the development of atomic energy. He is a member of the National Academy of Sciences and the National Academy of Engineering.
Address: Institute for Energy Analysis, Oak Ridge Associated Universities, PO Box 117, Oak Ridge, Tennessee 37830, USA.

useful energy – if the entropy of the system initially is as small as possible.

A simple example might make this clearer. Suppose an electric heater is energized by an amount ΔW_E of electric energy. The heater supplies an amount of heat $\Delta Q \approx \Delta W_E$ to a hot water tank, thus raising its absolute temperature to T. The electrical energy represented in the electric current flowing in the heater is by convention regarded as being work– that is, energy with zero entropy. If this electricity were run through a motor, all this electrical energy, except for frictional losses, could in principle be converted to mechanical work, ΔW_M. On the other hand, once the electrical energy is converted into an amount of heat ΔQ at temperature T, the entropy of the hot water has increased by an amount $\Delta S = \Delta Q/T$. A heat engine energized by the hot water could generate an amount of mechanical energy that is less than the energy in the electricity by at least the added entropy multiplied by the temperature T_0 at which the heat is rejected. Thus, the maximum possible work ΔW_{max} supplied by the heat engine from the increment of heat ΔQ is

$$\Delta W_{max} \leqslant \Delta Q - T_0 \Delta S = \Delta Q(1 - T_0/T) \qquad (6)$$

We see that the higher the operating temperature T, that is, the lower the entropy change, the greater the amount of work we can extract from the increment of heat, ΔQ.

To take another example, suppose we are trying to heat a house 10 degrees above the outside temperature. From the point of view I have delineated, we ought to use as heat source a relatively low temperature source (say a geothermal well) rather than a high quality, low entropy source (say a bucket of coal). Even though the amount of energy required to heat the house is the same in both cases, we are being wasteful in the second case because in addition to heating the house we could have extracted more useful work out of the low entropy bucket of coal than out of the high entropy geothermal well.

MACROSCOPIC MAXWELL DEMONS

As stated, the crisis is not simply energy: it is energy of high quality – that is, energy at low entropy. The 17 million barrels of oil that flowed each day through the Straits of Hormuz before the Iran–Iraq war represented a critical supply of energy at low entropy. Our national interest in the United States, not to speak of the world's interest, required us to utilize this precious supply of energy at low entropy as efficiently as possible.

Until the advent of microcomputers and other ways of handling information, the path to higher efficiency, and therefore better utilization of our limited supply of oil, in conversion to mechanical work depended primarily on reducing the entropy change in the conversion by increasing the temperature of the working fluid – for example, the inlet temperature of the aircraft gas turbine has increased from about 760 K to 1600 K in the past 30 years. The theoretical Carnot efficiency of aircraft turbines has increased from about 30% to 60%, the actual efficiency from about 15% to about 30%.

Materials limit the improvements in efficiency that can be achieved through increasing temperatures. Fortunately there is an entirely different approach to increasing efficiency, an approach in the spirit of Maxwell's Demon, that is not limited by the temperature that a turbine blade can withstand without failing. I refer of course to the use of micro-sensors and microcomputers to monitor and control the conversion of chemical energy into work in an engine, so as to minimize the increase in entropy in the process.

Recently, General Motors placed a full-page advertisement in *Parade* (6 October 1980), a Sunday newspaper magazine that circulates very widely. To quote. 'Computer Command Control . . . allows GM to achieve the highest Corporate Average Fuel Economy. . . . A solid-state electronic control module monitors oxygen in the exhaust, engine speed, and engine coolant temperature through three highly specialized sensors. . . . Analyzing this information at thousands of calculations per second, it then adjusts the air/fuel mixture in the carburetor to optimize combustion. . . .'

I do not think I am stretching a point too much by referring to such microprocessor control systems as macroscopic Maxwell Demons. According to E. F. Walker, head of the General Motors Electronics Department, the energy saved by the Computer Command Control is about twice the energy required to operate the system, i.e. $R \approx 2$.

The General Motors Computer Command Control is one of an ever-growing class of information processing devices that are improving the efficiency of conversion of chemical energy to work. Although most improvements in automobile efficiency stem from reduction in weight of cars – the average miles per gallon for General Motors cars is expected to reach 31 by 1985 – intervention of microprocessors, according to Daimler-Benz, might improve efficiencies in Mercedes engines by another 5 or 10% (personal communication, E. Schmidt).

SYSTEMS MAXWELL DEMONS

Another class of information-handling device that can save energy is exemplified by the automatic control systems for heating units in large buildings. These systems, as described in *Energy User News*, try to match use of energy with actual demand for energy. In this sense they might be described as Systems Maxwell Demons – as they make a whole system, consisting of user of energy and producer of energy, operate more efficiently. For example, with the Fabri-Tek system, a guest activates the heating or air conditioning in his room with his room key – in effect, only occupied rooms are conditioned. But such devices, unlike the GM Computer Command Control, impact on the guests' convenience, a point to which I shall return later. To quote from *Energy User News*, 'Every time a customer would leave the room, he'd have to pull his key out, and when he came back the room would be cold... It takes 2 hours to warm a room from 60 °F to 70 °F. Not very many customers are willing to wait that long.'[7]

Another example of how information control saves energy on a system scale is the Flight Management Computer: according to Robin Wilson of Trans World Airlines, use of such computers to optimize flight plans saves 2% of the total fuel used in the TWA system. Optimizing the flight plan for the Concorde saves even more fuel – 5% – since the Concorde uses so much more fuel per kilometer than does a subsonic plane.

The late Pat Haggerty of Texas Instruments, in his speech 'Shadow and Substance', offered a far more expansive view of the possibilities for saving energy through intervention by microprocessors.[8] To begin with, he found a correlation between the use of Active Element Groups (AEG) and energy saved in automobiles and households. He defined an AEG as a transistor plus its associated circuitry, including diodes, resistors, capacitors, printed circuit boards, etc. From this correlation, he estimated that 53×10^{15} Btu of energy, out of an estimated total of 180×10^{15} Btu, could be saved in the United States in the year 2000, if 1.4×10^{13} AEGs could be installed by that time. In 1977 the US semiconductor industry produced 4×10^{11} AEGs. Haggerty considered that by 2000 this number would grow to 2×10^{16} AEGs; thus, only 1/1000 of the yearly production at that time would be used in a variety of ways for engine and process control and for a substitution of transfer of information instead of a transfer of people. In addition, I suppose a general rationalization of planning, through use of computers, would save altogether 53×10^{15} Btu – compared to the 80×10^{15} Btu we used in 1980. I am unable to evaluate Haggerty's extraordinary prediction of how microprocessors will greatly reduce our energy demand. I suppose he himself would have conceded that the correlation on which he bases his speculations, automobiles and households, is probably insufficient to make such great extrapolations. Nevertheless, one cannot help but be impressed by such extraordinary optimism about the future of microprocessors.

SOCIAL MAXWELL DEMONS

I have described how information can be traded for energy on a microscopic scale Maxwell's Demon, though in that case the energy expended by the demon actually equals the energy saved; on a macroscopic physical scale GM Computer Command Control; and on a macroscopic systems scale. It is possible to push the hierarchy further: we can find many examples of how clever use of information can save energy on what might be described as a social scale.

Consider the effect of price on consumption of fuel. When oil cost $2 per barrel, industrial processes, as well as cars, were designed with little regard for their fuel efficiency. With oil costing $30 per barrel, the market has transmitted signals to innumerable users of gasoline that it is to their advantage to buy cars that are fuel-efficient. This in turn has sent signals to Detroit: design a fuel-efficient car. There are sophisticated buyers out there who will buy such cars.

We see this trade-off between knowledge and energy in several ways here: the buyer is more sophisticated about the importance of fuel efficiency, and so he demands an efficient car; the automobile manufacturer must exercise ingenuity in designing a more efficient car.

In a broader sense, the whole effort to conserve energy requires re-education of innumerable energy consumers. This re-education may come from exhortation or from the impetus of the market place.[9] The price mechanism apparently has worked: the United States used 8% less oil in 1980 than in 1979, and our oil imports dropped from 8.5×10^6 barrels per day in 1975 to 7×10^6 barrels per day in 1980. Though some of this has come about because of recession, or a mild winter, much of it must be attributed to the decontrol of oil prices.

It is evident that the ratio of energy saved to energy expended in placing the information system in place – in this instance, the decontrol of oil prices – must be enormous. Thus, I would put forth the conjecture that if R is the ratio of energy saved by intervention of an information control system to the energy expended in the information system, then as the scale of the intervention increases, so does the ratio R. I illustrate this in the following table:

$R = 1$	for microscopic Maxwell Demon
$R \approx 2\text{–}100$	for microprocessor control
$R \to \infty$	social interventions, for example price system.

THE ROLE OF TIME

In the previous examples I have suggested that information, primarily its manifestation as control, can be used to save energy; and that this way of increasing efficiency through use of, say, microprocessors is a more delicate and sophisticated approach than is the use of higher temperatures. Yet going to higher temperature to increase efficiency in a sense can be subsumed under the general heading of information: we go to higher temperatures only by using higher strength alloys, or by applying more powerful methods for design of components. Development and deployment of such alloys is therefore itself a manifestation of the use of information. In a broader sense then, both higher temperatures and use of microprocessors are captured in the word information. Moreover, this trade-off between information and energy is reciprocal: clever use of information can save energy; or energy can be used to compensate for lack of information, as when a reactor engineer overdesigns a pressure vessel because he does not know just how to estimate the effect of radiation on its strength.

Daniel Spreng, a Swiss physicist, has pointed out there is another great trade-off: this is between time and energy.[10] If we do things slowly we use less energy than if we do them fast: haste makes waste. For this there is a good thermodynamic basis. Reversible processes are more efficient than are irreversible ones, but reversible processes go infinitely slowly. Indeed, all of classical thermodynamics assumes that we are immortal since it treats only reversible processes. This trade-off between time and energy we see in many everyday ways: the American 55 mile per hour speed limit saves oil (energy) but it costs time; if we match perfectly the quality of energy at the end use (heating a room, for example) with the energy of the source, it would take all day to heat the room. Remember here the Fabri-Tek users' complaints that they have to wait for their room to be heated.

SPRENG'S TRIAD

Spreng thus conceives energy, time and information as forming a triad: each in some sense can be traded off for the other two. He summarizes these trade-offs in what I call the Spreng triangle (Fig. 1). To quote from Spreng, 'In this diagram each point inside the triangle represents a possible mix of energy, information, and time necessary to accomplish a certain task. When much available energy is employed, the point will be indicated at the upper left side of the triangle; if less energy is required, the point moves towards the opposite corner marked with $E = 0$. Two methods to accomplish a job with the same requirement of available energy will be represented by points lying on a line parallel to the side of maximum available energy use. Near the corners of the triangle are the situations of the starving philosopher (near $E = 0$) who employs much information and time to accomplish his task; of a primitive man, perhaps in a slash-and-burn society (near $I = 0$) who, because of little information, requires much time and energy (a large area of forest) to meet his needs; and of the "industrial man" (near $t = 0$) who with much energy and information accomplishes things very quickly.

'The diagram underlines the fact that energy conservation measures, ΔE, can be simultaneously the substitution of time, Δt, and the substitution of information, ΔI, for energy. For instance, increasing the efficiency by slowing down heat flows, i.e. by reducing the output rate or increasing the size of equipment, has to be done with expertise and know-how. Or, the educational process to disseminate energy conservation know-how requires time and patience.

'As Figure 1 suggests, information and time can also be substituted for one another: if we have lots of time, we do not need information, but can apply trial-and-error approaches to solving a problem; if we have little time, we are happy if we know which is the fastest way. In fact, the main function of applying electronic devices in the last few decades has been to make more time available for saving labor and speeding up the flow of information.'

THE CENTRALITY OF TIME

In the great energy debates, the role of time, unlike the role of information, seems largely to have been ignored. The extreme polarization of the debate was exemplified by the views of two presidential candidates, Barry Commoner and Ronald Reagan. According to Commoner we can, even now, shift to a solar-based society and turn away from what are called hard technologies, the centralized electric power stations fueled with coal or nuclear sources. This shift implies far more vigorous conservation measures than we have already taken. As presidential candidate Ronald Reagan, by contrast, saw few dangers in proceeding with our centralized energy production methods, including nuclear; and though he accepted conservation and solar energy as desirable, he placed these at a lower priority.

On energy policy I have much more sympathy with President Reagan's view than with Dr Commoner's. I have two reasons for my position. First, the energy

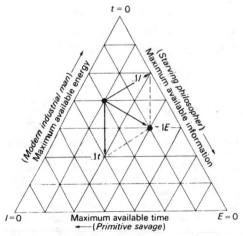

Figure 1. The Spreng triangle.

crisis we seek to resolve is not a general energy crisis; it is our dependence on unreliable foreign oil. From this viewpoint, replacing oil with nuclear- or coal-generated electricity makes sense. And even though the use of low entropy electricity for heating houses – a job that can be accomplished with poorer quality energy sources – offends the sensibilities of energy radicals, it turns out not only to be convenient, but economical at the present price of oil.

But the main reason why I favor a predominantly centralized, hard energy system is that, on the whole, it is less intrusive and makes far fewer demands on our individual use of time than do Commoner's soft systems. The decentralized systems based largely on the Sun and wind are inherently less reliable than are the centralized systems based on fossil or nuclear sources. A society based primarily on solar systems will tend to be an intermittent society: what we can do at any time will depend upon the vagaries of the weather. To be sure, farming and outdoor construction are already beset with such intermittency. But to impose such intermittency on all our activities seems to me to be an enormous price to pay for the alleged advantage of being able to control one's own private electrical system.

I am puzzled that the role of time, indeed its centrality, has been largely ignored in the energy debate. Yet both on a theoretical thermodynamic basis, as well as a practical basis, time is of the essence. One can even argue that time is our most valuable resource, and that the value of energy and, as Spreng says, of information, is to give us more freedom to allocate our time. To return to Spreng's triad, I have here speculated on how information saves energy: I have only touched upon how information saves time. Yet, in the long run, the impact of information on our freedom to allocate time may be even more important than its impact on our use of energy. In previewing the Computer Age, I would suggest that the reorganization of our use of time may be the most profound and lasting social effect of the extraordinary advances in the handling of information that have largely resulted from the work of ever more efficient computing machinery.

This review is based on the Keynote Address to the 1980 National Conference of the Association of Computing Machinery, 'Previewing the Computer Age' held at Nashville, Tennessee; it was delivered on 27 October 1980.

LITERATURE CITED

1. James Clerk Maxwell, *Theory of Heat*, 3rd Edn, republication of 1872 edition. AMS Press, Inc., New York (1972).
2. Marian von Smoluchowski, *Lectures on the Kinetic Theory of Matter and Electricity*, Leipzig–Berlin (1914).
3. Leo Szilard, On the decrease of entropy in a thermodynamic system by the intervention of intelligent beings. *Behav. Sci.* 9(4) (October 1964).
4. Claude Shannon, A mathematical theory of communication, *Bell Syst. Tech. J.* 27, 379, 623 (1948).
5. Leon Brillouin, *Science and Information Theory*, Academic Press, New York (1956).
6. Myron Tribus and Edward C. McIrvine, *Sci. Am.* 225, 179–188 (1971).
7. Lodging industry wary of automated energy controls. *Energy User News* 5 (39) (29 September 1980).
8. Patrick E. Haggerty, 'Shadow and Substance', presented at Semicon/West Annual Banquet, San Francisco, California (25 May 1977).
9. The role of the market as an information-feedback system has been an important thread in economic theory; see, for example, Tjalling C. Koopmans, Efficient allocation of resources, *Econometrica* (October 1951) pp. 445–465. I am grateful to W. Gilmer and D. Weinberg for pointing this out to me.
10. Daniel T. Spreng, On time, information, and energy conservation. ORAU/IEA-78-22(R). Institute for Energy Analysis, Oak Ridge Associated Universities, Oak Ridge, Tennessee (December 1978).

Note added in proof: In a paper, J. Beckenstein, Energy cost of information transfer. *Phys. Rev. Lett.* 623(46) (1981) places a lower bound on the amount of energy that must be associated with the transfer of a bit of information in a given time. His result is based on the second law of thermodynamics as generalized to systems involving black holes!

The manuscript was received 20 March 1981

CHAPTER 3

Maxwell's Demon and Information Acquisition

ON THE DECREASE OF ENTROPY IN A THERMODYNAMIC SYSTEM BY THE INTERVENTION OF INTELLIGENT BEINGS

Leo Szilard

Translated by Anatol Rapoport and Mechthilde Knoller from the original article "Über die Entropiever-minderung in einem thermodynamischen System bei Eingriffen intelligenter Wesen." Zeitschrift für Physik, 1929, 53, 840–856.

∽

The objective of the investigation is to find the conditions which apparently allow the construction of a perpetual-motion machine of the second kind, if one permits an intelligent being to intervene in a thermodynamic system. When such beings make measurements, they make the system behave in a manner distinctly different from the way a mechanical system behaves when left to itself. We show that it is a sort of a memory faculty, manifested by a system where measurements occur, that might cause a permanent decrease of entropy and thus a violation of the Second Law of Thermodynamics, were it not for the fact that the measurements themselves are necessarily accompanied by a production of entropy. At first we calculate this production of entropy quite generally from the postulate that full compensation is made in the sense of the Second Law (Equation [1]). Second, by using an inanimate device able to make measurements—however under continual entropy production—we shall calculate the resulting quantity of entropy. We find that it is exactly as great as is necessary for full compensation. The actual production of entropy in connection with the measurement, therefore, need not be greater than Equation (1) requires.

∽

THERE is an objection, already historical, against the universal validity of the Second Law of Thermodynamics, which indeed looks rather ominous. The objection is embodied in the notion of Maxwell's demon, who in a different form appears even nowadays again and again; perhaps not unreasonably, inasmuch as behind the precisely formulated question quantitative connections seem to be hidden which to date have not been clarified. The objection in its original formulation concerns a demon who catches the fast molecules and lets the slow ones pass. To be sure, the objection can be met with the reply that man cannot in principle foresee the value of a thermally fluctuating parameter. However, one cannot deny that we can very well measure the value of such a fluctuating parameter and therefore could certainly gain energy at the expense of heat by arranging our intervention according to the results of the measurements. Presently, of course, we do not know whether we commit an error by not including the intervening man into the system and by disregarding his biological phenomena.

Apart from this unresolved matter, it is known today that in a system left to itself no "perpetuum mobile" (perpetual motion machine) of the second kind (more exactly, no "automatic machine of continual finite work-yield which uses heat at the lowest temperature") can operate in spite of the fluctuation phenomena. A perpetuum mobile would have to be a machine which in the long run could lift a weight at the expense of the heat content of a reservoir. In other words, if we want to use the fluctuation phenomena in order to gain energy at the expense of heat, we are in the same position as playing a game of chance, in which we may win certain amounts now and then, although the expectation value of the winnings is zero or negative. The same applies to a system where the intervention from outside is performed strictly periodically, say by periodically moving machines. We consider this as established (Szilard, 1925) and intend here only to consider the difficulties that occur when intelligent beings intervene in a system. We shall try to discover the quantitative relations having to do with this intervention.

Smoluchowski (1914, p. 89) writes: "As far as we know today, there is no automatic, permanently effective perpetual motion machine, in spite of the molecular fluctuations, but such a device might, perhaps, function regularly if it were appropriately operated by intelligent beings. . . ."

A perpetual motion machine therefore is possible if—according to the general method of physics—we view the experimenting man as a sort of *deus ex machina*, one who is continuously and exactly informed of the existing state of nature and who is able to start or interrupt the macroscopic course of nature at any moment without expenditure of work. Therefore he would definitely not have to possess the ability to catch single molecules like Maxwell's demon, although he would definitely be different from real living beings in possessing the above abilities. In eliciting any physical effect by action of the sensory

as well as the motor nervous systems a degradation of energy is always involved, quite apart from the fact that the very existence of a nervous system is dependent on continual dissipation of energy.

Whether—considering these circumstances—real living beings could continually or at least regularly produce energy at the expense of heat of the lowest temperature appears very doubtful, even though our ignorance of the biological phenomena does not allow a definite answer. However, the latter questions lead beyond the scope of physics in the strict sense.

It appears that the ignorance of the biological phenomena need not prevent us from understanding that which seems to us to be the essential thing. We may be sure that intelligent living beings—insofar as we are dealing with their intervention in a thermodynamic system—can be replaced by non-living devices whose "biological phenomena" one could follow and determine whether in fact a compensation of the entropy decrease takes place as a result of the intervention by such a device in a system.

In the first place, we wish to learn what circumstance conditions the decrease of entropy which takes place when intelligent living beings intervene in a thermodynamic system. We shall see that this depends on a certain type of coupling between different parameters of the system. We shall consider an unusually simple type of these ominous couplings.[1] For brevity we shall talk about a "measurement," if we succeed in coupling the value of a parameter y (for instance the position co-ordinate of a pointer of a measuring instrument) at one moment with the simultaneous value of a fluctuating parameter x of the system, in such a way that, from the value y, we can draw conclusions about the value that x had at the moment of the "measurement." Then let x and y be uncoupled after the measurement, so that x can change, while y retains its value for some time. Such measurements are not harmless interventions. A system in which such measurements occur shows a sort of memory

[1] The author evidently uses the word "ominous" in the sense that the possibility of realizing the proposed arrangement threatens the validity of the Second Law.—*Translator*

faculty, in the sense that one can recognize by the state parameter y what value another state parameter x had at an earlier moment, and we shall see that simply because of such a memory the Second Law would be violated, if the measurement could take place without compensation. We shall realize that the Second Law is not threatened as much by this entropy decrease as one would think, as soon as we see that the entropy decrease resulting from the intervention would be compensated completely in any event if the execution of such a measurement were, for instance, always accompanied by production of $k \log 2$ units of entropy. In that case it will be possible to find a more general entropy law, which applies universally to all measurements. Finally we shall consider a very simple (of course, not living) device, that is able to make measurements continually and whose "biological phenomena" we can easily follow. By direct calculation, one finds in fact a continual entropy production of the magnitude required by the above-mentioned more general entropy law derived from the validity of the Second Law.

The first example, which we are going to consider more closely as a typical one, is the following. A standing hollow cylinder, closed at both ends, can be separated into two possibly unequal sections of volumes V_1 and V_2 respectively by inserting a partition from the side at an arbitrarily fixed height. This partition forms a piston that can be moved up and down in the cylinder. An infinitely large heat reservoir of a given temperature T insures that any gas present in the cylinder undergoes isothermal expansion as the piston moves. This gas shall consist of a single molecule which, as long as the piston is not inserted into the cylinder, tumbles about in the whole cylinder by virtue of its thermal motion.

Imagine, specifically, a man who at a given time inserts the piston into the cylinder and somehow notes whether the molecule is caught in the upper or lower part of the cylinder, that is, in volume V_1 or V_2. If he should find that the former is the case, then he would move the piston slowly downward until it reaches the bottom of the cylinder. During this slow movement of the piston the molecule stays, of course, above the piston.

However, it is no longer constrained to the upper part of the cylinder but bounces many times against the piston which is already moving in the lower part of the cylinder. In this way the molecule does a certain amount of work on the piston. This is the work that corresponds to the isothermal expansion of an ideal gas—consisting of one single molecule—from volume V_1 to the volume $V_1 + V_2$. After some time, when the piston has reached the bottom of the container, the molecule has again the full volume $V_1 + V_2$ to move about in, and the piston is then removed. The procedure can be repeated as many times as desired. The man moves the piston up or down depending on whether the molecule is trapped in the upper or lower half of the piston. In more detail, this motion may be caused by a weight, that is to be raised, through a mechanism that transmits the force from the piston to the weight, in such a way that the latter is always displaced upwards. In this way the potential energy of the weight certainly increases constantly. (The transmission of force to the weight is best arranged so that the force exerted by the weight on the piston at any position of the latter equals the average pressure of the gas.) It is clear that in this manner energy is constantly gained at the expense of heat, insofar as the biological phenomena of the intervening man are ignored in the calculation.

In order to understand the essence of the man's effect on the system, one best imagines that the movement of the piston is performed mechanically and that the man's activity consists only in determining the altitude of the molecule and in pushing a lever (which steers the piston) to the right or left, depending on whether the molecule's height requires a down- or upward movement. This means that the intervention of the human being consists only in the coupling of two position co-ordinates, namely a co-ordinate x, which determines the altitude of the molecule, with another co-ordinate y, which determines the position of the lever and therefore also whether an upward or downward motion is imparted to the piston. It is best to imagine the mass of the piston as large and its speed sufficiently great, so that the thermal agitation of the piston at the temperature in question can be neglected.

In the typical example presented here, we wish to distinguish two periods, namely:

1. The period of *measurement* when the piston has just been inserted in the middle of the cylinder and the molecule is trapped either in the upper or lower part; so that if we choose the origin of co-ordinates appropriately, the x-co-ordinate of the molecule is restricted to either the interval $x > 0$ or $x < 0$;

2. The period of *utilization of the measurement,* "the period of decrease of entropy," during which the piston is moving up or down. During this period the x-co-ordinate of the molecule is certainly not restricted to the original interval $x > 0$ or $x < 0$. Rather, if the molecule was in the upper half of the cylinder during the period of measurement, i.e., when $x > 0$, the molecule must bounce on the downward-moving piston in the lower part of the cylinder, if it is to transmit energy to the piston; that is, the co-ordinate x has to enter the interval $x < 0$. The lever, on the contrary, retains during the whole period its position toward the right, corresponding to downward motion. If the position of the lever toward the right is designated by $y = 1$ (and correspondingly the position toward the left by $y = -1$) we see that during the period of measurement, the position $x > 0$ corresponds to $y = 1$; but afterwards $y = 1$ stays on, even though x passes into the other interval $x < 0$. We see that in the utilization of the measurement the coupling of the two parameters x and y disappears.

We shall say, quite generally, that a parameter y "measures" a parameter x (which varies according to a probability law), if the value of y is directed by the value of parameter x at a given moment. A measurement procedure underlies the entropy decrease effected by the intervention of intelligent beings.

One may reasonably assume that a measurement procedure is fundamentally associated with a certain definite average entropy production, and that this restores concordance with the Second Law. The amount of entropy generated by the measurement may, of course, always be greater than this fundamental amount, but not smaller. To put it precisely: we have to distinguish here between two entropy values. One of them, $\bar{S}_1$, is produced when during the measurement y assumes the value 1, and the other, $\bar{S}_2$, when y assumes the value -1. We cannot expect to get general information about $\bar{S}_1$ or $\bar{S}_2$ separately, but we shall see that *if* the amount of entropy produced by the "measurement" is to compensate the entropy decrease affected by utilization, the relation must always hold good.

$$e^{-\bar{S}_1/k} + e^{-\bar{S}_2/k} \leqq 1 \qquad (1)$$

One sees from this formula that one can make one of the values, for instance $\bar{S}_1$, as small as one wishes, but then the other value $\bar{S}_2$ becomes correspondingly greater. Furthermore, one can notice that the magnitude of the interval under consideration is of no consequence. One can also easily understand that it cannot be otherwise.

Conversely, as long as the entropies $\bar{S}_1$ and $\bar{S}_2$, produced by the measurements, satisfy the inequality (1), we can be sure that the expected decrease of entropy caused by the later utilization of the measurement will be fully compensated.

Before we proceed with the proof of inequality (1), let us see in the light of the above mechanical example, how all this fits together. For the entropies $\bar{S}_1$ and $\bar{S}_2$ produced by the measurements, we make the following Ansatz:

$$\bar{S}_1 = \bar{S}_2 = k \log 2 \qquad (2)$$

This ansatz satisfies inequality (1) and the mean value of the quantity of entropy produced by a measurement is (of course in this special case independent of the frequencies w_1, w_2 of the two events):

$$\bar{S} = k \log 2 \qquad (3)$$

In this example one achieves a decrease of entropy by the isothermal expansion:[2]

$$- \bar{s}_1 = -k \log \frac{V_1}{V_1 + V_2} ;$$
$$\qquad\qquad\qquad\qquad (4)$$
$$- \bar{s}_2 = -k \log \frac{V_2}{V_1 + V_2} ,$$

[2] The entropy generated is denoted by $\bar{s}_1$, $\bar{s}_2$.

depending on whether the molecule was found in volume V_1 or V_2 when the piston was inserted. (The decrease of entropy equals the ratio of the quantity of heat taken from the heat reservoir during the isothermal expansion, to the temperature of the heat reservoir in question). Since in the above case the frequencies w_1, w_2 are in the ratio of the volumes V_1, V_2, the mean value of the entropy generated is (a negative number):

$$\bar{s} = w_1 \cdot (+\bar{s}_1) + w_2 \cdot (+\bar{s}_2) =$$

$$\frac{V_1}{V_1 + V_2} k \log \frac{V_1}{V_1 + V_2} + \qquad (5)$$

$$\frac{V_2}{V_1 + V_2} k \log \frac{V_1}{V_1 + V_2}$$

As one can see, we have, indeed

$$\frac{V_1}{V_1 + V_2} k \log \frac{V_1}{V_1 + V_2} + \frac{V_2}{V_1 + V_2}$$

$$(6)$$

$$\cdot k \log \frac{V_2}{V_1 + V_2} + k \log 2 \geqq 0$$

and therefore:

$$\bar{S} + \bar{s} \geqq 0. \qquad (7)$$

In the special case considered, we would actually have a full compensation for the decrease of entropy achieved by the utilization of the measurement.

We shall not examine more special cases, but instead try to clarify the matter by a general argument, and to derive formula (1). We shall therefore imagine the whole system—in which the co-ordinate x, exposed to some kind of thermal fluctuations, can be measured by the parameter y in the way just explained—as a multitude of particles, all enclosed in one box. Every one of these particles can move freely, so that they may be considered as the molecules of an ideal gas, which, because of thermal agitation, wander about in the common box independently of each other and exert a certain pressure on the walls of the box—the pressure being determined by the temperature. We shall now consider two of these molecules as chemically different and, in principle, separable by semipermeable walls, if the co-ordinate x for one molecule is in a preassigned interval while the corresponding co-ordinate of the other molecule falls outside that interval. We

also shall look upon them as chemically different, if they differ only in that the y co-ordinate is $+1$ for one and -1 for the other.

We should like to give the box in which the "molecules" are stored the form of a hollow cylinder containing four pistons. Pistons A and A' are fixed while the other two are movable, so that the distance BB' always equals the distance AA', as is indicated in Figure 1 by the two brackets. A', the bottom, and B, the cover of the container, are impermeable for all "molecules," while A and B' are semipermeable; namely, A is permeable only for those "molecules" for which the parameter x is in the preassigned interval, i.e., (x_1, x_2), B' is only permeable for the rest.

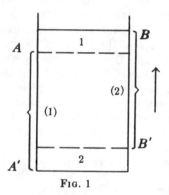

FIG. 1

In the beginning the piston B is at A and therefore B' at A', and all "molecules" are in the space between. A certain fraction of the molecules have their co-ordinate x in the preassigned interval. We shall designate by w_1 the probability that this is the case for a randomly selected molecule and by w_2 the probability that x is outside the interval. Then $w_1 + w_2 = 1$.

Let the distribution of the parameter y be over the values $+1$ and -1 in any proportion but in any event independent of the x-values. We imagine an intervention by an intelligent being, who imparts to y the value 1 for all "molecules" whose x at that moment is in the selected interval. Otherwise the value -1 is assigned. If then, because of thermal fluctuation, for any "molecule," the parameter x should come out of the preassigned interval or, as we also may put it, if the "molecule" suffers a monomolecular chemical reaction with regard to x (by which it is transformed from a species that can pass the semipermeable piston A into a species for which the piston is impermeable), then the parameter y retains its value 1 for the time being, so that the "molecule," because of the value of the parameter y, "remembers" during the whole following process that x originally was in the preassigned interval. We shall see immediately what part this memory may play. After the intervention just discussed, we move the piston, so that we separate the two kinds of molecules without doing work. This results in two containers, of which the first contains only the one modification and the second only the other. Each modification now occupies the same volume as the mixture did previously. In one of these containers, if considered by itself, there is now no equilibrium with regard to the two "modifications in x." Of course the ratio of the two modifications has remained $w_1 : w_2$. If we allow this equilibrium to be achieved in both containers independently and at constant volume and temperature, then the entropy of the system certainly has increased. For the total heat release is 0, since the ratio of the two "modifications in x" $w_1 : w_2$ does not change. If we accomplish the equilibrium distribution in both containers in a reversible fashion then the entropy of the rest of the world will decrease by the same amount. Therefore the entropy increases by a negative value, and, the value of the entropy increase per molecule is exactly:

$$\bar{s} = k(w_1 \log w_1 + w_2 \log w_2). \qquad (9)$$

(The entropy constants that we must assign to the two "modifications in x" do not occur here explicitly, as the process leaves the total number of molecules belonging to the one or the other species unchanged.)

Now of course we cannot bring the two gases back to the original volume without expenditure of work by simply moving the piston back, as there are now in the container—which is bounded by the pistons BB'—also molecules whose x-co-ordinate lies outside of the preassigned interval and for which the piston A is not permeable any longer. Thus one can see that the calculated decrease of entropy (Equation [9]) does not mean a contradiction of the Second Law. *As*

long as we do not use the fact that the molecules in the container BB', by virtue of their co-ordinate y, "remember" that the x-co-ordinate for the molecules of this container originally was in the preassigned interval, full compensation exists for the calculated decrease of entropy, by virtue of the fact that the partial pressures in the two containers are smaller than in the original mixture.

But now we can use the fact that all molecules in the container BB' have the y-co-ordinate 1, and in the other accordingly -1, to bring all molecules back again to the original volume. To accomplish this we only need to replace the semipermeable wall A by a wall A^*, which is semipermeable not with regard to x but with regard to y, namely so that it is permeable for the molecules with the y-co-ordinate 1 and impermeable for the others. Correspondingly we replace B' by a piston B'^*, which is impermeable for the molecules with $y = -1$ and permeable for the others. Then both containers can be put into each other again without expenditure of energy. The distribution of the y-co-ordinate with regard to 1 and -1 now has become statistically independent of the x-values and besides we are able to re-establish the original distribution over 1 and -1. Thus we would have gone through a complete cycle. The only change that we have to register is the resulting decrease of entropy given by (9):

$$\bar{s} = k(w_1 \log w_1 + w_2 \log w_2). \qquad (10)$$

If we do not wish to admit that the Second Law has been violated, we must conclude *that the intervention which establishes the coupling between y and x, the measurement of x by y, must be accompanied by a production of entropy.* If a definite way of achieving this coupling is adopted and if the quantity of entropy that is inevitably produced is designated by S_1 and S_2, where S_1 stands for the mean increase in entropy that occurs when y acquires the value 1, and accordingly S_2 for the increase that occurs when y acquires the value -1, we arrive at the equation:

$$w_1 S_1 + w_2 S_2 = \bar{S} \qquad (11)$$

In order for the Second Law to remain in force, this quantity of entropy must be greater than the decrease of entropy $\bar{s}$, which according to (9) is produced by the utilization of the measurement. Therefore the following inequality must be valid:

$$\bar{S} + \bar{s} \geq 0$$

$$w_1 S_1 + w_2 S_2 \tag{12}$$
$$+ k(w_1 \log w_1 + w_2 \log w_2) \geq 0$$

This equation must be valid for any values of w_1 and w_2,[3] and of course the constraint $w_2 + w_2 = 1$ cannot be violated. We ask, in particular, for which w_1 and w_2 and given S-values the expression becomes a minimum. For the two minimizing values w_1 and w_2 the inequality (12) must still be valid. Under the above constraint, the minimum occurs when the following equation holds:

$$\frac{S_1}{k} + \log w_1 = \frac{S_2}{k} + \log w_2 \tag{13}$$

But then:

$$e^{-S_1/k} + e^{-S_2/k} \leq 1. \tag{14}$$

This is easily seen if one introduces the notation

$$\frac{S_1}{k} + \log w_1 = \frac{S_2}{k} + \log w_2 = \lambda; \tag{15}$$

then:

$$w_1 = e^{\lambda} \cdot e^{-S_1/k}; \quad w_2 = e^{\lambda} \cdot e^{-S_2/k}. \tag{16}$$

If one substitutes these values into the inequality (12) one gets:

$$\lambda e^{\lambda}(e^{-S_1/k} + e^{-S_2/k}) \geq 0. \tag{17}$$

Therefore the following also holds:

$$\lambda \geq 0. \tag{18}$$

If one puts the values w_1 and w_2 from (16) into the equation $w_1 + w_2 = 1$, one gets

$$e^{-S_1/k} + e^{-S_2/k} = e^{-\lambda}. \tag{19}$$

And because $\lambda \geq 0$, the following holds:

$$e^{-S_1/k} + e^{-S_2/k} \leq 1. \tag{20}$$

This equation must be universally valid, if thermodynamics is not to be violated.

As long as we allow intelligent beings to perform the intervention, a direct test is

[3] The increase in entropy can depend only on the types of measurement and their results but not on how many systems of one or the other type were present.

not possible. But we can try to describe simple nonliving devices that effect such coupling, and see if indeed entropy is generated and in what quantity. Having already recognized that the only important factor is a certain characteristic type of coupling, a "measurement," we need not construct any complicated models which imitate the intervention of living beings in detail. We can be satisfied with the construction of this particular type of coupling which is accompanied by memory.

In our next example, the position co-ordinate of an oscillating pointer is "measured" by the energy content of a body K. The pointer is supposed to connect, in a purely mechanical way, the body K—by whose energy content the position of the pointer is to be measured—by heat conduction with one of two intermediate pieces, A or B. The body is connected with A as long as the co-ordinate—which determines the position of the pointer—falls into a certain preassigned, but otherwise arbitrarily large or small interval a, and otherwise if the co-ordinate is in the interval b, with B. Up to a certain moment, namely the moment of the "measurement," both intermediate pieces will be thermally connected with a heat reservoir at temperature T_0. At this moment the insertion A will be cooled reversibly to the temperature T_A, e.g., by a periodically functioning mechanical device. That is, after successive contacts with heat reservoirs of intermediate temperatures, A will be brought into contact with a heat reservoir of the temperature T_A. At the same time the insertion B will be heated in the same way to temperature T_B. Then the intermediate pieces will again be isolated from the corresponding heat reservoirs.

We assume that the position of the pointer changes so slowly that all the operations that we have sketched take place while the position of the pointer remains unchanged. If the position co-ordinate of the pointer fell in the preassigned interval, then the body was connected with the insertion A during the above-mentioned operation, and consequently is now cooled to temperature T_A.

In the opposite case, the body is now heated to temperature T_B. Its energy content becomes—according to the position of the pointer at the time of "measurement"— small at temperature T_A or great at temperature T_B and will retain its value, even if the pointer eventually leaves the preassigned interval or enters into it. After some time, while the pointer is still oscillating, one can no longer draw any definite conclusion from the energy content of the body K with regard to the momentary position of the pointer but one can draw a definite conclusion with regard to the position of the pointer at the time of the measurement. Then the measurement is completed.

After the measurement has been accomplished, the above-mentioned periodically functioning mechanical device should connect the thermally isolated insertions A and B with the heat reservoir T_0. This has the purpose of bringing the body K—which is now also connected with one of the two intermediate pieces—back into its original state. The direct connection of the intermediate pieces and hence of the body K—which has been either cooled to T_A or heated to T_B—to the reservoir T_0 consequently causes an increase of entropy. This cannot possibly be avoided, because it would make no sense to heat the insertion A reversibly to the temperature T_0 by successive contacts with the reservoirs of intermediate temperatures and to cool B in the same manner. After the measurement we do not know with which of the two insertions the body K is in contact at that moment; nor do we know whether it had been in connection with T_A or T_B in the end. Therefore neither do we know whether we should use intermediate temperatures between T_A and T_0 or between T_0 and T_B.

The mean value of the quantity of entropy S_1 and S_2, per measurement, can be calculated, if the heat capacity as a function of the temperature $\bar{u}(T)$ is known for the body K, since the entropy can be calculated from the heat capacity. We have, of course, neglected the heat capacities of the intermediate pieces. If the position co-ordinate of the pointer was in the preassigned interval at the time of the "measurement," and accordingly the body in connection with insertion A, then the entropy conveyed to the heat reservoirs during successive cooling was

$$\int_{T_A}^{T_0} \frac{1}{T} \frac{d\bar{u}}{dT}. \tag{21}$$

However, following this, the entropy withdrawn from the reservoir T_0 by direct contact with it was

$$\frac{\bar{u}(T_0) - \bar{u}(T_A)}{T_0}. \tag{22}$$

All in all the entropy was increased by the amount

$$S_A = \frac{\bar{u}(T_A) - \bar{u}(T_0)}{T_0} + \int_{T_A}^{T_0} \frac{1}{T} \frac{d\bar{u}}{dT} dT. \tag{23}$$

Analogously, the entropy will increase by the following amount, if the body was in contact with the intermediate piece B at the time of the "measurement":

$$S_B = \frac{\bar{u}(T_B) - \bar{u}(T_0)}{T_0} + \int_{T_B}^{T_0} \frac{1}{T} \frac{d\bar{u}}{dT} dT. \tag{24}$$

We shall now evaluate these expressions for the very simple case, where the body which we use has only two energy states, a lower and a higher state. If such a body is in thermal contact with a heat reservoir at any temperature T, the probability that it is in the lower or upper state is given by respectively:

$$p(T) = \frac{1}{1 + g e^{-u/kT}}$$
$$q(T) = \frac{g e^{-u/kT}}{1 + g e^{-u/kT}} \tag{25}$$

Here u stands for the difference of energy of the two states and g for the statistical weight. We can set the energy of the lower state equal to zero without loss of generality. Therefore:[4]

$$S_A = q(T_A) k \log \frac{q(T_A) p(T_0)}{q(T_0) p(T_A)}$$
$$+ k \log \frac{p(T_A)}{p(T_0)}$$
$$S_B = p(T_B) k \log \frac{q(T_0) p(T_B)}{q(T_B) p(T_0)}$$
$$+ k \log \frac{q(T_B)}{q(T_0)} \tag{26}$$

Here q and p are the functions of T given

[4] See the Appendix.

by equation (25), which are here to be taken for the arguments T_0, T_A, or T_B.

If (as is necessitated by the above concept of a "measurement") we wish to draw a dependable conclusion from the energy content of the body K as to the position co-ordinate of the pointer, we have to see to it that the body surely gets into the lower energy state when it gets into contact with T_B. In other words:

$$p(T_A) = 1, q(T_A) = 0;$$
$$p(T_B) = 0, q(T_B) = 1. \tag{27}$$

This of course cannot be achieved, but may be arbitrarily approximated by allowing T_A to approach absolute zero and the statistical weight g to approach infinity. (In this limiting process, T_0 is also changed, in such a way that $p(T_0)$ and $q(T_0)$ remain constant.) The equation (26) then becomes:

$$S_A = -k \log p(T_0);$$
$$S_B = -k \log q(T_0) \tag{28}$$

and if we form the expression $e^{-S_A/k} + e^{-S_B/k}$, we find:

$$e^{-S_A/k} + e^{-S_B/k} = 1. \tag{29}$$

Our foregoing considerations have thus just realized the smallest permissible limiting care. The use of semipermeable walls according to Figure 1 allows a complete utilization of the measurement: inequality (1) certainly cannot be sharpened.

As we have seen in this example, a simple inanimate device can achieve the same essential result as would be achieved by the intervention of intelligent beings. We have examined the "biological phenomena" of a nonliving device and have seen that it generates exactly that quantity of entropy which is required by thermodynamics.

APPENDIX

In the case considered, when the frequency of the two states depends on the temperature according to the equations:

$$p(T) = \frac{1}{1 + ge^{-u/kT}} ; q(T) = \frac{ge^{-u/kT}}{1 + ge^{-u/kT}} \tag{30}$$

and the mean energy of the body is given by:

$$\bar{u}(T) = uq(T) = \frac{uge^{-u/kT}}{1 + ge^{-u/kT}}, \tag{31}$$

the following identity is valid:

$$\frac{1}{T}\frac{d\bar{u}}{dT} = \frac{d}{dT}\left\{\frac{\bar{u}(T)}{T} + k \log\left(1 + e^{-u/kT}\right)\right\}. \tag{32}$$

Therefore we can also write the equation:

$$B_A = \frac{\bar{u}(T_A) - \bar{u}(T_0)}{T_0} + \int_{T_A}^{T_0} \frac{1}{T}\frac{d\bar{u}}{dT} dT \tag{33}$$

as

$$S_A = \frac{\bar{u}(T_A) - \bar{u}(T_0)}{T_0}$$
$$+ \left\{\frac{\bar{u}(T)}{T} + k \log(1 + ge^{-u\,kT})\right\}_{T_A}^{T_0}, \tag{34}$$

and by substituting the limits we obtain:

$$S_A = \bar{u}(T_A)\left(\frac{1}{T_0} - \frac{1}{T_A}\right) + k \log\frac{1 + ge^{-u/kT_0}}{1 + ge^{-u/kT_A}}. \tag{35}$$

If we write the latter equation according to (25):

$$1 + ge^{-u/kT} = \frac{1}{p(T)} \tag{36}$$

for T_A and T_0, then we obtain:

$$S_A = \bar{u}(T_A)\left(\frac{1}{T_0} - \frac{1}{T_A}\right) + k \log\frac{p(T_A)}{p(T_0)} \tag{37}$$

and if we then write according to (31):

$$\bar{u}(T_A) = uq(T_A) \tag{38}$$

we obtain:

$$S_A = q(T_A)\left(\frac{u}{T_0} - \frac{u}{T_A}\right) + k \log\frac{p(T_A)}{p(T_0)}. \tag{39}$$

If we finally write according to (25):

$$\frac{u}{T} = -k \log\frac{q(T)}{gp(T)} \tag{40}$$

for T_A and T_0, then we obtain:

$$S_A = q(T_A) k \log\frac{p(T_0)}{q(T_0)}\frac{q(T_A)}{p(T_A)}$$
$$+ k \log\frac{p(T_A)}{p(T_0)}. \tag{41}$$

We obtain the corresponding equation for S_B, if we replace the index A with B. Then we obtain:

$$S_B = q(T_B)\, k \log \frac{p(T_0)}{q(T_0)} \frac{q((T_B)}{p((T_B)} + k \log \frac{p(T_B)}{p(T_0)}. \quad (42)$$

Formula (41) is identical with (26), given, for S_A, in the text.

We can bring the formula for S_B into a somewhat different form, if we write:

$$q(T_B) = 1 - p(T_B), \quad (43)$$

expand and collect terms, then we get

$$S_B = p(T_B)\, k \log \frac{q(T_0)}{p(T_0)} \frac{p(T_B)}{q(T_B)} + k \log \frac{q(T_B)}{q(T_0)}. \quad (44)$$

This is the formula given in the text for S_B.

REFERENCES

Smoluchowski, F. *Vorträge über die kinetische Theorie der Materie u. Elektrizitat.* Leipzig: 1914.

Szilard, L. Zeitschrift fur Physik, 1925, 32, 753.

Maxwell's Demon Cannot Operate: Information and Entropy. I

L. Brillouin

International Business Machines Corporation, Poughkeepsie and New York, New York

(Received September 18, 1950)

In an enclosure at constant temperature, the radiation is that of a "blackbody," and the demon cannot see the molecules. Hence, he cannot operate the trap door and is unable to violate the second principle. If we introduce a source of light, the demon can see the molecules, but the over-all balance of entropy is positive. This leads to the consideration of a cycle

Negentropy→Information→Negentropy

for Maxwell's demon as well as for the scientist in his laboratory. Boltzmann's constant k is shown to represent the smallest possible amount of negative entropy required in an observation.

I. MAXWELL'S DEMON

THE Sorting demon was born in 1871 and first appeared in Maxwell's *Theory of Heat* (p. 328), as "a being whose faculties are so sharpened that he can follow every molecule in his course, and would be able to do what is at present impossible to us····. Let us suppose that a vessel is divided into two portions A and B by a division in which there is a small hole, and that a being who *can see the individual molecules* opens and closes this hole, so as to allow only the swifter molecules to pass from A to B, and only the slower ones to pass from B to A. He will, thus, without expenditure of work raise the temperature of B and lower that of A, in contradiction to the second law of thermodynamics."[1]

The paradox was considered by generations of physicists, without much progress in the discussion, until Szilard[2] pointed out that the demon actually transforms "information" into "negative entropy"—we intend to investigate this side of the problem in a moment.

Another contribution is found in a recent paper by the present author.[3]

In order to select the fast molecules, the demon should be able to see them (see Maxwell, passage reproduced in italics); but he is in an enclosure in equilibrium at constant temperature, where the radiation must be that of the blackbody, and it is impossible to see anything in the interior of a black body. It would not help to raise the temperature. At "red" temperature, the radiation has its maximum in the red and obtains exactly the same intensity, whether there are

no molecules or millions of them in the enclosure. Not only is the intensity the same but also the fluctuations. The demon would perceive radiation and its fluctuations, he would never see the molecules.

No wonder Maxwell did not think of including radiation in the system in equilibrium at temperature T. Blackbody radiation was hardly known in 1871, and it took 30 more years before the thermodynamics of radiation was clearly understood and Planck's theory developed.

The demon cannot see the molecules, hence, he cannot operate the trap door and is unable to violate the second principle.

II. INFORMATION MEANS NEGATIVE ENTROPY

Let us, however, investigate more carefully the possibilities of the demon. We may equip him with an electric torch and enable him to see the molecules. The torch is a source of radiation not in equilibrium. It pours negative entropy into the system. From this negative entropy the demon obtains "informations." With these informations he may operate the trap door and rebuild negative entropy, hence, completing a cycle:

$$\text{negentropy} \rightarrow \text{information} \rightarrow \text{negentropy}. \quad (1)$$

We coined the abbreviation "negentropy" to characterize entropy with the opposite sign. This quantity is very useful to consider and already has been introduced by some authors, especially Schrödinger.[4] Entropy must always increase, and negentropy always decreases. Negentropy corresponds to "grade" of energy in Kelvin's discussion of "degradation of energy."

---

[1] The full passage is quoted by J. H. Jeans, *Dynamical Theory Gases* (Cambridge University Press, London, 1921), third edition, p. 183.

[2] L. Szilard, Z. Physik **53**, 840–856 (1929).

[3] L. Brillouin, Am. Scientist **37**, 554–568 (1949), footnote to p. 565; **38**, 594 (1950).

[4] E. Schrödinger, *What is Life?* (Cambridge University Press, London, and The Macmillan Company, New York, 1945).

We shall discuss more carefully the new cycle (1) for the demon and show later on how it extends to man and scientific observation.

The first part of the cycle, where negentropy is needed to obtain information, seems to have been generally overlooked. The second transformation of information into negentropy was very clearly discussed by L. Szilard[2] who did the pioneer work on the question.

Our new cycle (1) compares with C. E. Shannon's[5] discussion of telecommunications, which can be stated this way:

information→telegram→negentropy on the cable→
        telegram received→information received.   (2)

Shannon, however, compares information with positive entropy, a procedure which seems difficult to justify since information is lost during the process of transmission, while entropy is increased. Norbert Wiener[6] recognized this particular feature and emphasized the similarity between information and negentropy.

Our new cycle (1) adds another example to the general theory of information. We shall now discuss this problem in some detail.

III. ENTROPY BALANCE FOR MAXWELL'S DEMON

In order to discuss an entropy balance, the first question is to define an isolated system, to which the second principle can be safely applied. Our system is composed of the following elements:

1. A charged battery and an electric bulb, representing the electric torch.

2. A gas at constant temperature T_0, contained in Maxwell's enclosure, with a partition dividing the vessel into two portions and a hole in the partition.

3. The demon operating the trap door at the hole. The whole system is insulated and closed.

The battery heats the filament at a high temperature T_1.

$$T_1 \gg T_0.   (3)$$

This condition is required, in order to obtain visible light,

$$h\nu_1 \gg kT_0,   (4)$$

that can be distinguished from the background of blackbody radiation in the enclosure at temperature T_0. During the experiment, the battery yields a total energy E and no entropy. The filament radiates E and an entropy S_f,

$$S_f = E/T_1.   (5)$$

If the demon does not intervene, the energy E is absorbed in the gas at temperature T_0, and we observe a

[5] C. E. Shannon and Warren Weaver, *The Mathematical Theory of Communication* (University of Illinois Press, Urbana, Illinois, 1949).
[6] N. Wiener, *Cybernetics* (John Wiley and Sons, Inc., New York, 1948).

global increase of entropy

$$S = E/T_0 > S_f > 0   (6)$$

Now let us investigate the work of the demon. He can detect a molecule when at least one quantum of energy $h\nu_1$ is scattered by the molecule and absorbed in the eye of the demon (or in a photoelectric cell, if he uses such a device).[7] This represents a final increase of entropy

$$\Delta S_d = h\nu_1/T_0 = kb   h\nu_1/kT_0 = b \gg 1   (7)$$

according to condition (4).

Once the information is obtained, it can be used to decrease the entropy of the system. The entropy of the system is

$$S_0 = k \ln P_0   (8)$$

according to Boltzmann's formula, where P_0 represents the total number of microscopic configurations (Planck's "complexions") of the system. After the information has been obtained, the system is more completely specified. P is decreased by an amount p and

$$P_1 = P_0 - p   \Delta S_i = S - S_0 = k\Delta(\log P) = -k(p/P_0).   (9)$$

It is obvious that $p \ll P_0$ in all practical cases. The total balance of entropy is

$$\Delta S_d + \Delta S_i = k(b - p/P_0) > 0,   (10)$$

since $b \gg 1$ and $p/P_0 \ll 1$. The final result is still an increase of entropy in the isolated system, as required by the second principle. All the demon can do is to recuperate a small part of the entropy and use the information to decrease the degradation of energy.

In the first part of the process [Eq. (7)], we have an increase of entropy ΔS_d, hence, a change ΔN_d in the negentropy:

$$\Delta N_d = -kb < 0,   \text{a decrease.}   (7a)$$

From this lost negentropy, a certain amount is changed into information, and in the last step of the process [Eq. (9)], this information is turned into negentropy again:

$$\Delta N_i = k(p/P_0) > 0,   \text{an increase.}   (9a)$$

This justifies the general scheme (1) of Sec. II.

Let us discuss more specifically the original problem of Maxwell. We may assume that, after a certain time, the demon has been able to obtain a difference of temperature ΔT:

$$
\begin{aligned}
T_B > T_A & & T_B = T + \tfrac{1}{2}\Delta T \\
T_B - T_A = \Delta T & & T_A = T - \tfrac{1}{2}\Delta T.
\end{aligned}   (11)
$$

On the next step, the demon selects a fast molecule in A [kinetic energy $\tfrac{3}{2}kT(1+\epsilon_1)$] and directs it into B. Then he selects a slow molecule in B, $\tfrac{3}{2}kT(1-\epsilon_2)$ and lets it enter into A. In order to see these two molecules,

[7] We may replace the demon by an automatic device with a "magic eye" which opens the trap door at convenient instants of time. This is a mere problem of devising some ingenious gadget, and it does not modify the general conditions of the problem.

the demon had to use two light quanta, hence, an increase of entropy, similar to the one computed in Eq. (7):

$$\Delta S_d = 2kb, \quad b = h\nu/kT \gg 1. \tag{12}$$

The exchange of molecules results in an energy transfer

$$\Delta Q = \tfrac{3}{2}kT(\epsilon_1 + \epsilon_2) \tag{13}$$

from A to B, which corresponds to a decrease of the total entropy, on account of (11):

$$\Delta S_i = \Delta Q\left(\frac{1}{T_B} - \frac{1}{T_A}\right) = -\Delta Q\frac{\Delta T}{T^2} = -\tfrac{3}{2}k(\epsilon_1 + \epsilon_2)\frac{\Delta T}{T}. \tag{14}$$

The quantities ϵ_1 and ϵ_2 will usually be small but may exceptionally reach a value of a few units. ΔT is much smaller than T, hence,

$$\Delta S_i = -\tfrac{3}{2}k\eta \quad \eta \ll 1$$

and

$$\Delta S_d + \Delta S_i = k(2\bar{b} - \tfrac{3}{2}\eta) > 0. \tag{15}$$

Carnot's principle is actually satisfied.

Szilard, in a very interesting paper[2] published in 1929, discussed the second part of the process (1). He first considered simplified examples, where he could prove that additional information about the structure of the system could be used to obtain work and represented a potential decrease of entropy of the system. From these general remarks he inferred that the process of physical measurement, by which the information could be obtained, must involve an increase of entropy so that the whole process would satisfy Carnot's principle. Szilard also invented a very curious (and rather artificial) model on which he could compute the amount of entropy corresponding to the first part of the process, the physical measurement yielding the information.

In the examples selected by Szilard, the most favorable one was a case with just two complexions in the initial state,

$$P_0 = 2. \tag{16}$$

The information enabled the observer to know which one of the two possibilities was actually obtained.

$$P_1 = 1,$$

hence,

$$\Delta S_i = k(\ln P_0 - \ln P_1) = k\ln 2 < k, \tag{17}$$

since the natural logarithms of base e are used in Boltzmann's formula. Even in such an oversimplified example, we still obtain an inequality similar to (10),

$$\Delta S_d + \Delta S_i = k(b - \ln 2) > 0, \tag{18}$$

and Carnot's principle is not violated.

Szilard's discussion was completed by J. von Neumann and by P. Jordan in connection with statistical problems in quantum mechanics.[8]

[8] J. von Neumann, *Math. Grundlagen der Quantum Mechanik* (Verlag. Julius Springer, Berlin, 1932). P. Jordan, Philosophy of Science **16**, 269–278 (1949).

IV. ENTROPY AND OBSERVATION IN THE LABORATORY

The physicist in his laboratory is no better off than the demon. Every observation he makes is at the expense of the negentropy of his surroundings. He needs batteries, power supply, compressed gases, etc., all of which represent sources of negentropy. The physicist also needs light in his laboratory in order to be able to read ammeters or other instruments.

What is the smallest possible amount of negentropy required in an experiment? Let us assume that we want to read an indication on an ammeter. The needle exhibits a brownian motion of oscillation, with an average kinetic energy $(\tfrac{1}{2})kT$ and an average total energy

$$\bar{E}_t = kT. \tag{19}$$

G. Ising[9] considers that an additional energy

$$E_m \geqslant 4\bar{E}_t = 4kT \tag{20}$$

is required to obtain a correct reading. Let us be more optimistic and assume

$$\Delta E_m \geqslant kT. \tag{21}$$

This energy is dissipated in friction and viscous damping in the ammeter, after the physicist has performed the reading. This means an increase of entropy ΔS (or a decrease of negentropy)

$$-\Delta N = \Delta S \geqslant kT/T = k. \tag{22}$$

Boltzmann's constant k thus appears as the lower limit of negentropy required in an experiment.

Instead of reading an ammeter, the physicist may be observing a radiation of frequency ν. The smallest observable energy is $h\nu$, and it must be absorbed somewhere in the apparatus in order to be observed, hence,

$$-\Delta N = \Delta S \geqslant h\nu/T, \tag{23}$$

a quantity that must be greater than k, if it is to be distinguished from blackbody radiation at temperature T. We thus reach the conclusion that

$$-\Delta N = \Delta S \geqslant \begin{cases} k \\ h\nu/T \end{cases} \quad \text{(whichever is greater),} \tag{24}$$

represents the limit of possible observation.

A more compact formula can be obtained by the following assumptions: let us observe an oscillator of frequency ν. At temperature T, it obtains an average number

$$n = 1/(e^{h\nu/kT} - 1) \tag{25}$$

of quanta of energy $h\nu$. In order to make an observation, this number n must be increased by a quantity that is materially larger than n and its fluctuations; let us assume

$$\Delta n \geqslant n + 1. \tag{26}$$

[9] G. Ising, Phil. Mag. **51**, 827–834 (1926); M. Courtines, *Les Fluctuations dans les Appareils de Mesures* (Congres Intern. d'Electricité, Paris, 1932), Vol. 2.

This means at least one quantum for high frequencies ν, when n is almost zero. For very low frequencies, formula (26) requires Δn of the order of n, as in formula (21).

Observation means absorption of Δn quanta $h\nu$, hence, a change in entropy

$$-\Delta N = \Delta S = \frac{\Delta n}{T} h\nu \geqslant \frac{h\nu}{T}\left[\frac{1}{e^{h\nu/kT}-1}+1\right] \quad (27)$$

or

$$-\Delta N = \Delta S \geqslant k\left[\frac{x}{e^x-1}+x\right] = k\frac{x}{1-e^{-x}} \quad x = h\nu/kT. \quad (28)$$

This formula satisfies the requirements stated in Eq. (24).

R. C. Raymond[10] recently published some very interesting remarks on similar subjects. He was especially concerned with the original problem of Shannon, Wiener, and Weaver, namely, the transmission of information through communication channels. He succeeded in applying thermodynamic definitions to the entropy of information and discussed the application of the second principle to such problems.

The limitations to the possibilities of measurements, as contained in our formulas, have nothing to do with the uncertainty relations. They are based on entropy, statistical thermodynamics, Boltzmann's constant, all quantities that play no role in the uncertainty principle.

The physicist making an observation performs the first part of process (1); he transforms negative entropy into information. We may now ask the question: can the scientist use the second part of the cycle and change information into negentropy of some sort? Without directly answering the question, we may risk a suggestion. Out of experimental facts, the scientist builds up scientific knowledge and derives scientific laws. With

these laws he is able to design and build machines and equipment that nature never produced before; these machines represent most unprobable structures,[11] and low probability means negentropy? Let us end here with this question mark, without attempting to analyze any further the process of scientific thinking and its possible connection with some sort of generalized entropy.

APPENDIX

A few words may be needed to justify the fundamental assumption underlying Eq. (26). We want to compute the order of magnitude of the fluctuations in a quantized resonator. Let n_a be the actual number of quanta at a certain instant of time, and $\bar{n}$ the average number as in Eq. (26).

$$n_a = \bar{n} + m, \quad (29)$$

where m is the fluctuation. It is easy to prove the following result

$$\langle m^2 \rangle_{Av} = \bar{n}(\bar{n}+1) = \bar{n}^2 + \bar{n}. \quad (30)$$

For large quantum numbers, $\langle m^2 \rangle_{Av}^{\frac{1}{2}}$ is of the order of magnitude of $\bar{n}$; hence, when we add n more quanta $h\nu$, we obtain an increase of energy that is only of the order of magnitude of the average fluctuations. This certainly represents the lower limit for an observation.

Formula (29) is obtained in the following way: We first compute the partition function Z (Planck's Zustandssumme) for the harmonic oscillator

$$Z = \Sigma e^{-nx} = \frac{1}{1-e^{-x}} \quad x = h\nu/kT. \quad (31)$$

Next we compute the average $\bar{n}$

$$\bar{n} = \frac{\Sigma n e^{-nx}}{z} = -\frac{1}{z}\frac{\partial z}{\partial x} = \frac{e^{-x}}{1-e^{-x}} = \frac{1}{e^x-1}, \quad (32)$$

which is our Eq. (25). Then we obtain

$$\langle n^2 \rangle_{Av} = \frac{1}{z}\Sigma_1 n^2 e^{-nx} = \frac{1}{z}\frac{\partial^2 z}{\partial x^2} = \frac{e^{-x}+e^{-2x}}{(1-e^{-x})^2}, \quad (33)$$

and finally

$$\langle m^2 \rangle_{Av} = \langle n^2 \rangle_{Av} - (\bar{n})^2 = \frac{e^{-x}+e^{-2x}-e^{-2x}}{(1-e^{-x})^2} = \frac{1}{1-e^{-x}}\cdot\frac{1}{e^x-1} = \bar{n}^2 + \bar{n}, \quad (34)$$

which is our formula (30). Hence, our assumption (26) is completely justified.

[10] R. C. Raymond, Phys. Rev. **78**, 351 (1950); Am. Scientist **38**, 273–278 (1950).

[11] L. Brillouin, Am. Scientist **38**, 594 (1950).

The Well-Informed Heat Engine

RICHARD C. RAYMOND

The Pennsylvania State College, State College, Pennsylvania

(Received July 21, 1950)

The failure of a heat engine to defeat the second law of thermodynamics by using density fluctuations to convert heat to work without leaving other changes in the universe is usually explained by saying that the fluctuations of the engine itself would defeat such an operation or that the microscopic nature of the fluctuations prevents their being put to a macroscopic use. It is shown here that with a proper definition of stored information, a heat engine can be made to convert heat to work without other changes in its immediate system, provided that an outside observer creates in the system a negative information entropy equal to the negative entropy change involved in the operation of the engine. This equivalence of a communication entropy change to a thermodynamic entropy change leads to the definition of the entropy of a nonequilibrium system as the algebraic sum of the thermodynamic entropy which the system would have at equilibrium and the information entropy necessary to construct the specified state from the equilibrium state.

THE suggestion that a heat engine might be built to convert heat into work without leaving other changes in the universe has been discussed briefly by a number of writers. In a modern textbook[1] on kinetic theory the possibility is dismissed by the statement that the second law of thermodynamics applies only to normal or average behavior of macroscopic systems, or by the statement that any such machine would itself be subject to fluctuations which would prevent its successful operation. Fluctuations of appreciable magnitude are apparent in a case such as that of Brownian motion, and it seems difficult to imagine that any set of fluctuations could cancel any other set of fluctuations

for any appreciable period of time. It is, therefore, of interest to examine a theoretical heat engine which operates on the basis of density fluctuations in a gas to determine in what way changes must be left in the universe as a result of its operation. It will be interesting also in this connection to examine a case of physical relationship between the information entropy defined by Hartley,[2] Shannon,[3] and Wiener[4] and the common thermodynamic entropy.

The Engine

Figure 1 shows the heat engine which will be discussed, and Fig. 2 illustrates its cycle of

[1] E. H. Kennard, *Kinetic Theory of Gases* (McGraw-Hill Book Company, Inc., New York, 1938), p. 368.

[2] R. V. L. Hartley, Bell System Tech. J. **7**, 535 (1928).
[3] C. E. Shannon, Bell System Tech. J. **27**, 379 (1948).
[4] N. Wiener, *Cybernetics* (John Wiley & Sons, Inc., New York, 1948).

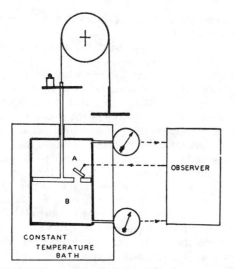

Fig. 1. Heat engine and observer. The observer watches the gauges and controls the gate in the piston to operate the engine through a cycle in which heat is absorbed and work is done without leaving other changes in the system which does not include the observer.

operation. The engine consists of a cylinder fitted with a piston which divides the total volume of the cylinder into an upper part A and a lower part B. The piston is connected with a piston rod of negligible diameter which moves weights and weight pans in such a way as to do mechanical work. The cylinder is fitted with pressure gauges at both ends and surrounded by a constant temperature bath. The piston is provided with a gate under the control of an external observer who manipulates the gate in response to the time average readings of the pressure gauges in order to carry out the desired thermodynamic cycle. The system to be considered in the computations includes the cylinder, piston, weight pans and weights and the constant temperature bath but does not include the observer. This choice of system boundaries makes it possible to compute the contribution of the observer to the system in terms of negative information entropy and makes it unnecessary to consider in detail the processes of the observer.

The operating cycle of the engine is diagrammed in Fig. 2, which shows the pressure in part A of the cylinder plotted against the volume of part A as the cycle of operation is carried out. The cycle starts at O. In process OQ the

following steps are carried out: (a) the piston is locked in place so that the volume cannot change, and the gate is opened; (b) after a time interval sufficient to make the distribution of molecules of gas between parts A and B random with respect to the initial distribution the gate is closed, and time average readings of the two pressure gauges are taken over intervals sufficiently long to insure accurate indication of the distribution of gas molecules between the two chambers; (c) if point Q has been attained, the gate is locked, and the piston is loaded and released for a reversible isothermal expansion through process QX. If point Q has not been reached, the piston is kept in position, and the gate is opened for a time interval sufficient to insure a new random distribution and then closed again as in (b) above. No heat is exchanged with the bath in process OQ, but the entropy of the system is reduced through the storage of information in the system by the observer.

In process QX heat is added to the cylinder from the bath, and an equivalent amount of work is done. At point X the piston is again locked in position and the gate is opened. Steps similar to that in process OQ are repeated until point Y is reached. Again the entropy of the system is reduced through the storage of information. In process YO the gate is locked, the piston

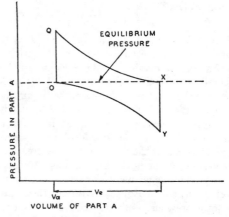

Fig. 2. Operating cycle of the heat engine. In process OQ random fluctuations result in increase in pressure in part A of the cylinder. Process QX is a reversible isothermal expansion of part A. Process XY is a fluctuation reversing that of process OQ, and process YO is an isothermal expansion of part B which returns the cylinder to its original condition.

is unlocked and a reversible isothermal expansion is carried out, resulting in an absorption of heat from the bath with an equal output of work. At point O the gate is opened, returning the cylinder and piston to its original condition and leaving the system unchanged except for the disappearance of a certain amount of heat and the performance of an equal amount of mechanical work.

The following symbols will be used in the mathematical discussion of the entropy changes involved in the engine cycle.

V_a = initial and final volume of part A,

V_b = initial and final volume of part B,

$V = V_a + V_b$,

N_a = equilibrium number of molecules in part A when the volume is V_a,

N_b = equilibrium number of molecules in part B when the volume is V_b,

$N = N_a + N_b$,

N_e = number of molecules shifted from part B to part A in process OQ,

V_e = increase in volume of the part A during process QX.

If the gas molecules in the cylinder are so chosen that the gas obeys the perfect gas equation of state the work done and the heat absorbed in the two reversible isothermal processes QX and YO are each given by

$$W = N_e kT[\log[(V_a + V_e)/V_a] + \log[V_b/(V_b - V_e)]], \quad (1)$$

where k is Boltzmann's constant and T is the temperature of the bath. If the contribution of the observer in manipulating the engine could be ignored, this would be accompanied by a decrease in the entropy of the system without other changes. We shall now see, however, that with the proper choice of the definition for information stored in the system by the observer we can demonstrate that the negative entropy created in the system by the information storage process is equal to the change in entropy resulting from the work indicated in Eq. (1). We may then make use of a previous result[5] to show that the communication of this information from the observer to the system has resulted in an increase of the entropy of the large system including the observer which is larger than the decrease in

the entropy in the small system due to information storage.

The plausibility of the definition of quantity of information to be adopted may be justified in the manner used by Wiener.[4] When the gate is closed in the piston and the piston is locked in position in the cylinder in such a way that the pressures on the two sides of the piston are not equal, then the system is not in equilibrium, and the relationship between the pressures may be taken to indicate an item of information, such as a number, stored in the system. Process OQ, the method of storing the number in the system, will on the average require a number of trials to reach point Q, and the number of digits used to express this number of trials will be proportional to the logarithm of the number. The amount of information stored in the cylinder when it is not in equilibrium will thus be taken as the logarithm of the number of trials which are necessary, on the average, to establish the particular nonequilibrium state. If we designate the nonequilibrium state in terms of N_e, the number of displaced molecules, we may compute the probability of state e and the expected number of trials necessary to establish state e by the simple probability assumptions of the kinetic theory. If the probability that state e exists on any closing of the gate is P_e, the probable number of trials necessary to establish state e is $1/P_e$, and the information content of the system is defined as

$$D_e = \log(1/P_e) = -\log P_e. \quad (2)$$

Assuming that all the molecules are independent, as in a perfect gas, the probability of state e in performing process OQ is

$$P_e = (V_a/V)^{(N_a + N_e)}(V_b/V)^{(N_b - N_e)} N! / (N_a + N_e)!(N_b - N_e)! \quad (3)$$

When the numbers of molecules are large and the deviation from equilibrium is appreciable, the first terms of Stirling's approximation for the factorial may be used to write Eq. (2) as

$$D_e \doteq (N_a + N_e)\log(N_a + N_e) + (N_b - N_e)\log(N_b - N_e) + N \log V - (N_a + N_e)\log V_a - (N_b - N_e)\log V_b - N \log N. \quad (4)$$

If $N_e = 0$, and if $N_a/V_a = N_b/V_b$ the information

[5] R. C. Raymond, Am. Scientist **38**, 273 (1950).

storage involved in closing the gate on the system as given by Eq. (4) disappears. If, however, the second term of the Stirling approximation is used, the total is not zero. We have,

$$D_0 \doteq \tfrac{1}{2} \log(2\pi N_a N_b/N). \tag{5}$$

Information is stored in the system at the completion of steps OQ and XY. Some information is lost in the system on opening the gate at the completion of steps QX and YO. The net information stored in the system in the performance of its cycle may be determined by writing Eqs. (4) and (5) in forms appropriate to points Q, X, Y, and O and then taking the sum of information inputs at point Q and Y, less the sum of information losses at points X and O. This process results in

$$D_c = N_e[\log(V_a + V_e)/V_a + \log V_b/(V_b - V_e)]. \tag{6}$$

This result is identical with Eq. (1) except for the factor kT, and it indicates that the information entropy stored in the system during the cycle may be regarded as a negative physical entropy. This point of view suggests further that the entropy of the system in a nonequilibrium state characterized by e may be defined as

$$S = S_{eq} - kD_e, \tag{7}$$

where S_{eq} is the entropy which the system has with the gate open at equilibrium.

The observer has been omitted from the system because it is of interest to consider his contribution to the creation of negative entropy in the system through the storage of information without considering his particular physical processes. No observer yet considered has proved capable of storing information in any system without degrading an amount of energy sufficient to make the total entropy change in a system, including the observer, positive. The second law is therefore not in danger through the treatment of information as a form of negative physical entropy. The use of the entropy definition of Eq. (7) helps in explaining the selective decrease of entropy in some systems in apparent contradiction to the second law, and a careful consideration of the information storage possible in a system assists in distinguishing equilibrium systems from steady state systems. If, for instance, the two sides of the piston in the cylinder of Fig. 1 were filled to the same pressure with identical molecules, the old thermodynamics would predict no change in entropy on the opening of the gate. Classical statistical mechanics would predict a change in entropy, and the wave-mechanical statistical mechanics would predict no change. Information theory shows that the closing of the gate on any predetermined distribution of the molecules requires some number of trials and that the system with the gate closed therefore contains stored information and a lower entropy than the system with the gate open. The total entropy of the sum of two masses of identical gas at constant temperature and pressure is therefore larger than the sum of the entropies of the separate masses under the information theory and the classical statistical mechanics, whereas this inequality does not exist in statistical wave mechanics or in classical thermodynamics.

Well-Informed Heat Engine: Efficiency and Maximum Power*

C. Finfgeld and S. Machlup

Western Reserve University, Cleveland, Ohio

(Received July 6, 1959)

Further analysis is presented of a thought experiment due to Raymond, which permits an apparent violation of the second law of thermodynamics (the conversion of heat into work by a cyclic process), utilizing spontaneous fluctuations, and supplying the negentropy in the form of information obtained by counting. The thermodynamic efficiency of the heat engine itself is unity; considering the engine and counting demon together preserves the sanctity of the second law. An expression is derived for the power delivered by the engine, and the maximum value of this expression is studied as a function of the various parameters.

I. INTRODUCTION

ATTEMPTS to design a heat engine that would violate the second law of thermodynamics by converting heat into work without leaving other changes in the universe frequently utilize the services of a counting demon. The (Maxwell) demon counts particles in order to detect spontaneous fluctuations from equilibrium, which can then be used to do work.

An ingenious variation of such a device has been discussed by Raymond.[1] In his "well-informed heat engine" the demon does not have to have quick reactions to the passage of particles, and is thus less obvious than Maxwell's efficient doorman. He operates a gate in the piston separating the two halves of a cylinder surrounded by the heat bath. He opens and closes it at will, measuring the pressure (or, what is the same thing, counting the particles) in his half of the cylinder after each closing. If the pressure exceeds a certain value (point Q in Fig. 1) he unlocks the piston and allows it to do work. Then he locks it in its new position and continues the open-close-count routine until the pressure falls below Y, when he unlocks the piston to do some more work, and so forth. Raymond shows (see Appendix) that the negentropy needed for the resulting conversion of heat into work is exactly that of the information supplied by the demon when he reads the pressure gauge (or counts particles) just after one of his improbable "successful" closings. The negentropy of information is defined as $k \ln M$, where M is the number of alternatives among which the information

* Supported in part by contract with the U. S. Atomic Energy Commission.
[1] R. C. Raymond, Am. J. Phys. 19, 109 (1951).

decides, or, more conventionally, $1/M$ is the probability of being in the state which the information describes.

Purely as an exercise, i.e., in order to deepen our understanding of a situation in which spontaneous fluctuations from equilibrium are connected very simply with a macroscopic phenomenon, we set ourselves the task of calculating (1) the efficiency and (2) the power output of the Raymond engine.

II. EFFICIENCY

Since the engine converts all the heat it takes from the heat bath into work, its efficiency, defined as

$$\eta = \text{work out/heat in},$$

is obviously unity. That such details as friction

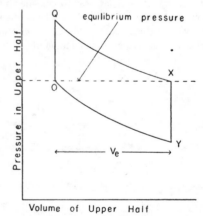

FIG. 1. The Raymond cycle on a pV diagram: Beginning at point O, the demon only releases the piston if a fluctuation has brought the pressure to Q, whereupon he allows an isothermal expansion QX. Here he waits until a fluctuation brings the pressure to Y. The isothermal contraction YO now completes the cycle.

have been neglected does not bother us; but 100% efficiency is that of a heat engine operating into a "cold" reservoir at absolute zero. The only thing to which this would correspond is the demon, so we must include him in our analysis. We must ask for the efficiency of the demon.

This poses a conceptual problem. Since the demon's output is not work but information, how is his efficiency defined? Let us, for simplicity, make him a counting demon. The process of counting the particles must, of course, require the expenditure of entropy. It is here that the sanctity of the second law of thermodynamics is preserved. Since the information output is measured as an entropy, we may follow Brillouin[2] and define the demon's efficiency as the entropy ratio,

$$\eta_{demon} = \frac{\text{negentropy of information gained}}{\text{entropy added to obtain it}}. \quad (1)$$

In counting one (classical) particle, the demon gains exactly one *bit* of information: namely, that this particle is in his half of the enclosure, i.e., the information distinguishes between two alternatives; the corresponding negentropy is $k\ln2$. To count, however, the demon must "see" the particles, e.g., by reflecting light off them. In order that this reflected light signal be distinguishable from the background "noise" of the blackbody radiation there must be in some radiation degree of freedom an amount of energy E considerably greater than kT, the mean blackbody (equilibrium) energy per degree of freedom. This energy E, supplied by the demon, increases the entropy of the system by at least E/T. The total change in entropy due to the act of counting one particle is thus greater than

$$E/T - k\ln2.$$

Since the signal-to-noise criterion requires that $E/T > k$, this entropy change is always positive. The demon himself can be considered a heat engine equipped with a flashlight: its filament must be hotter than the enclosure it illuminates. Energy, supplied by the flashlight battery, is degraded in being radiated into the enclosure.

The efficiency of the demon can thus be delimited. From the definition, Eq. (1),

$$\eta_{demon} < k\ln2/(E/T) < \ln2.$$

[2] L. Brillouin, *Science and Information Theory* (Academic Press, New York, 1956), Chap. 13.

In order not to gain the impression that ln2 (=69%) is anywhere near the actual efficiency it must be remembered that on the overwhelming number of observations which show that the points Q or Y have not been reached, the demon must reopen the door, relinquishing the information he has gained at such high cost in entropy.[3]

III. MAXIMUM POWER

The average power $\mathcal{P}$ delivered by the engine is the work W done per cycle divided by the average time t necessary to perform one cycle:

$$\mathcal{P} = W/t. \quad (2)$$

The average length of a cycle t is the product of the length of time per observation τ times the average number of observations $1/P$ per cycle:

$$t = \tau/P. \quad (3)$$

The number $1/P$ is simply the sum of the average number $1/P_e$ of observations necessary to attain state e (corresponding to point Q) plus the average number $1/P_{e'}$ needed to attain state e' (point Y):

$$1/P = 1/P_e + 1/P_{e'}. \quad (4)$$

The notation has been chosen so that P_e is the probability that the nonequilibrium state e exists on any closing of the gate:

$$P_e = (\tfrac{1}{2})^N N!/(\tfrac{1}{2}N+N_e)!(\tfrac{1}{2}N-N_e)!. \quad (5)$$

Each of the N particles has a probability $\tfrac{1}{2}$ of being in either half. The state e (point Q) is that in which an excess number N_e are in the upper half; thus $\tfrac{1}{2}N+N_e$ above, $\tfrac{1}{2}N-N_e$ below.

Similarly, the state e' (point Y) has an equal number $\tfrac{1}{2}N$ in top and bottom, but the top has volume $\tfrac{1}{2}V+V_e$, the bottom $\tfrac{1}{2}V-V_e$, so the probability is

$$P_{e'} = \left(\frac{\tfrac{1}{2}V+V_e}{V}\right)^{\tfrac{1}{2}N}\left(\frac{\tfrac{1}{2}V-V_e}{V}\right)^{\tfrac{1}{2}N}\frac{N!}{(\tfrac{1}{2}N)!^2}. \quad (6)$$

Since the excess volume V_e is proportional to N_e,

$$V_e/V = N_e/N,$$

this can be written

$$P_{e'} = [\tfrac{1}{4}-(N_e^2/N^2)]^{\tfrac{1}{2}N}[N!/(\tfrac{1}{2}N)!^2]. \quad (6')$$

[3] This cuts down the net efficiency by the factor P [Eq. (7)], where $1/P$ is the expected number of observations per cycle.

Combining Eqs. (4)–(6') we have

$$P=\frac{P_e P_{e'}}{P_e+P_{e'}}=\frac{N![\frac{1}{4}-(N_e^2/N^2)]^{\frac{1}{2}N}}{2^N(\frac{1}{4}-[N_e^2/N^2])^{\frac{1}{2}N}(\frac{1}{2}N+N_e)!(\frac{1}{2}N-N_e)!+(\frac{1}{2}N)!^2}. \tag{7}$$

The work W is entirely performed along the two isotherms QX and YO. For an ideal gas,

$$W=N_e kT[\ln(\tfrac{1}{2}V+V_e)$$
$$-\ln\tfrac{1}{2}V-\ln(\tfrac{1}{2}V-V_e)+\ln\tfrac{1}{2}V]$$
$$=N_e kT\ln[(1+2N_e/N)/(1-2N_e/N)]. \tag{8}$$

Since it may be assumed that τ, the time between observations, is independent of N_e and N, the dependence of the power $\mathcal{P}$ on these variables can now be studied. Combining Eqs. (2), (3), (7), and (8) we have

$$\mathcal{P}=WP/\tau$$
$$=(kT/\tau)PN_e \ln[(1+2N_e/N)/(1-2N_e/N)].$$

The function

$$\mathfrak{F}\equiv PN_e \ln[(1+2N_e/N)/(1-2N_e/N)]$$

vanishes for $N_e=0$ and for $N_e=\frac{1}{2}N$. For constant N, it has one maximum with respect to variation of N_e. Its maximum value, always less than unity, decreases with increasing N. Thus, for $N=4$ the maximum is attained at $N_e=1$ (obviously) and $\mathfrak{F}_{\max}=13\%$. For large N, Stirling's approximation in the form $n!=(2\pi n)^{-\frac{1}{2}}n^n e^{-n}$ gives the asymptotic expression, good to order $1/N$,

$$\mathfrak{F}=(2\pi N)^{-\frac{1}{2}}u^2 \exp(-\tfrac{1}{2}u^2),$$

where $u^2=4N_e^2/N$. This attains its maximum value $\mathfrak{F}_{\max}=(2/\pi e^2 N)^{\frac{1}{2}}$ [i.e., goes inversely as the square root of the number of particles] at $u^2=2$, or $N_e=(\frac{1}{2}N)^{\frac{1}{2}}$.

We may still investigate the dependence of the time τ between observations on the physical variables of the system. If the demon can count the particles in negligible time, τ is simply the relaxation time, thus, the average time for a particle to get from the upper to the lower half. This is evidently the shortest time in which the distribution of particles can change appreciably. To minimize τ it is evident that the particles should interfere little with each other's motion, i.e., that the pressure should be low. We may therefore approximate τ by the average time taken by a particle to move half the height of the cylinder, h:

$$\tau=h/(kT/m)^{\frac{1}{2}}. \tag{9}$$

The power output then becomes

$$\mathcal{P}=(kT)^{\frac{3}{2}}h^{-1}m^{-\frac{1}{2}}\mathfrak{F}. \tag{10}$$

The prescription for maximizing it is thus: low pressure, high temperature, light gas, short cylinder. If there is a need to emphasize that we are dealing with a *thought experiment*, the numbers should be convincing: For $\tau=10^{-5}$ sec and $kT=5\times10^{-21}$ joule (room temperature), we have $kT/\tau=5\times10^{-16}$ w, which must still be multiplied by the tiny fraction $\mathfrak{F}$ to obtain the power output.

The authors would like to thank Professor J. W. Weinberg for helpful discussions.

APPENDIX

Proof that the negentropy needed for the conversion of heat into work in the engine is exactly equal to the *net* negentropy of information supplied by the counting demon on a "successful" count.

When closing the gate on point Q (attainment of state e) and counting, the negentropy of information stored is $-k\ln P_e$ [see Eq. (5)]. Similarly, at point Y the demon contributes an informational negentropy $-k\ln P_{e'}$ [Eq. (6)]. On opening the gate at X, however, an amount of information $-k\ln P_X$ is given up, where

$$P_X=\left(\frac{\frac{1}{2}V+V_e}{V}\right)^{\frac{1}{2}N+N_e}\left(\frac{\frac{1}{2}V-V_e}{V}\right)^{\frac{1}{2}N-N_e}$$

$$\times\frac{N!}{(\frac{1}{2}N+N_e)!(\frac{1}{2}N-N_e)!}.$$

Similarly, at O there is an information loss $-k\ln P_0$ on opening the gate, where

$$P_0=(\tfrac{1}{2})^{\frac{1}{2}N}(\tfrac{1}{2})^{\frac{1}{2}N}[N!/(\tfrac{1}{2}N)!^2].$$

The net gain in negentropy of information is

$$-k\ln P_e+k\ln P_X-k\ln P_{e'}+k\ln P_0$$
$$=-k\ln(P_e/P_X)(P_{e'}/P_0)$$
$$=-kN_e \ln[(1+2V_e/V)/(1-2V_e/V)].$$

This is precisely the entropy one obtains by dividing the heat converted (work done) in one cycle [Eq. (8)] by the temperature T.

Some Comments on Entropy and Information

PHILIP RODD

Cornell University, Ithaca, New York

(Received 26 June 1963)

Information is quantitatively defined in terms of probability, and the statistical interpretation of entropy is given. Entropy change and information are shown to be related on a physical basis, treating a simple volume expansion as an example. Maxwell's demon is discussed as an example of an irreversible process. The argument used by Brillouin in his discussion of the demon is corrected. A generalized second law of thermodynamics is set forth.

SINCE information is a measure of order and the concept "entropy" is a measure of disorder, it is logical that there should be a relation between the two. To see this relation it is first necessary to define both terms and to assign quantitative measures to them.

To define information, consider a situation in which a number P of possible events may occur. We then consider the outcome of this situation to be "uncertain." The amount of uncertainty connected with this situation should depend on the total number of possible events, P. It can be shown[1] that the uncertainty U must take the following form:

$$U = K \ln P,$$

where K is an arbitrary constant. We can now define information by saying it is the amount by which the uncertainty of an event has been reduced. Thus,

$$I = U_1 - U_2.$$

In functional form,

$$I = K \ln(P_1/P_2).$$

To define entropy statistically, consider an isolated system whose energy we know to within a certain small range, and let there be n states accessible to the system at this energy. In equilibrium, the n states are equally probable, and the entropy is given by

$$S = k \ln n,$$

where k is Boltzmann's constant.

The question has been posed as to whether the connection between entropy and information is limited to a mathematical similarity or whether there is really some physical connection. We show that there is a definite physical relation between the two. Suppose that a physical system has a number W_0 of equally likely microstates. If the system is changed in some way, for instance if the volume is changed, the number of microstates available to the system changes to W_1. According to our formula for information, the information necessary to specify this change is $K \ln(W_0/W_1)$. If we take $K = k$, we get information in thermodynamic units. Then,

$$I = k \ln(W_0/W_1) \ \text{erg/°C}.$$

[1] Myron Tribus, *Thermostatics and Thermodynamics* (D. Van Nostrand, Company, Inc., Princeton, New Jersey, 1959).

The change in thermodynamic entropy corresponding to the physical change discussed above is

$$S_1 - S_0 = k \ln(W_1/W_0).$$

Therefore, $S_0 - S_1 = I$, or

$$S_1 = S_0 - I.$$

This formula has led to the statement that information is the equivalent of "negentropy."[2] That is, as our information about a physical system increases, its entropy must decrease, or in other words, "entropy measures the lack of information" about the exact state of a system.[2]

To further illustrate the physical connection between entropy and information, consider a gas consisting of N molecules confined in a volume V_0 with entropy S_0. If we expand this gas to volume V_1, the entropy increases the increase being given by

$$S_1 - S_0 = k \ln(W_1/W_0).$$

When we increase the volume of the gas, the number of microstates available to each molecule increases also, since all microstates with position coordinates corresponding to location in the new volume are included. Let us represent the volume in phase space which is accessible to a molecule by $\Delta p_x \Delta p_y \Delta p_z \Delta x \Delta y \Delta z$. Since $\Delta p_q \Delta q \geqslant \hbar$, the number of microstates per molecule, W, cannot be greater than $(\Delta p_x \Delta p_y \Delta p_z \Delta x \Delta y \Delta z / \hbar^3)$. If the physical volume of the gas is increased, the volume in phase space accessible to a molecule becomes $\Delta p_x \Delta p_y \Delta p_z (\Delta x + \delta x)(\Delta y + \delta y)(\Delta z + \delta z)$. The ratio of thermodynamic probabilities, W_1/W_0, corresponding to these two different physical volumes is $\{[(\Delta x + \delta x)(\Delta y + \delta y)(\Delta z + \delta z)]/\Delta x \Delta y \Delta z\}$. Therefore,

$$W_1/W_0 = V_1/V_0,$$

and

$$S_1 - S_0 = k \ln(V_1/V_0) \text{ per molecule},$$
$$S_1 - S_0 = Nk \ln(V_1/V_0) \text{ for the entire gas}.$$

How much information about the gas is lost in this volume expansion? Before the expansion, each molecule is known to be in the volume V_0. The number of locations each molecule can occupy, P_0, is $V_0/\Delta V$, where ΔV is the smallest volume measurable. After expansion, the molecule can be found somewhere in V_1. Thus the

new number of available locations, P_1, equals $V_1/\Delta V$. Thus,

$$I = k \ln(P_0/P_1) = k \ln(V_0/V_1) < 0.$$

In other words, since we know its position less exactly, we have lost information about the molecule. For the entire gas,

$$I = Nk \ln(V_0/V_1).$$

Therefore, $S_0 - S_1 = I$, or,

$$S_1 = S_0 - I, \text{ the negentropy principle of information.}$$

The conclusion we draw from this example is that the entropy increase of the gas was accompanied by an information loss.

Now we ask whether information corresponds to an entropy change in an irreversible process. In answering this question, some light is also shed on the problem of Maxwell's demon. The difficulty engendered by Maxwell's demon is that if one has a device which is sophisticated enough to act like a demon, the second law of thermodynamics can be violated. But the demon is in an enclosure which is in constant temperature equilibrium, thus making it impossible to see anything, since the radiation in the enclosure is uniform blackbody radiation. Therefore, can the demon actually see the individual atoms? If he cannot see, or by some other method distinguish them, obviously, he cannot separate the fast ones from the slow ones. However, suppose the demon has a flashlight, i.e., a source of radiation not in equilibrium with the enclosure. He can use this radiation to get information and thus decrease the entropy of the system. The following argument is a corrected form of the one set forth by Brillouin.[2] Analyzing the process, we see that to be of use in distinguishing particles, the flashlight must supply a beam whose energy $h\nu$ is greater than kT_0, where T_0 is the temperature of the enclosure. To produce the light beam, the filament in the flashlight bulb must be heated to some temperature $T_1 > T_0$. Assume that no energy is radiated by the filament during the heating process, thus the entropy increase of the filament during the temperature change is $m_{fil} c_{fil} \ln(T_1/T_0)$. Once the filament reaches the temperature T_1 and begins to radiate, there is no further entropy change, since the filament does not change in state. (The entropy flow is $-E/T_1$ where E is the total energy of the radiated light, and the entropy production is $+E/T_1$.) For the demon to received information about a

[2] Leon Brillouin, *Science and Information Theory* (Academic Press, Inc., New York, 1962), 2nd ed.

molecule, let one quantum of energy $h\nu$ be scattered by the molecule and absorbed by the demon. Since $h\nu/T_0 > k$, let $h\nu/T_0 = kb$, where $b > 1$. The entropy increase of the demon owing to the absorption of this quantum of energy is $\Delta S_d = h\nu/T_0 = kb$.

The entropy of the gas in its original state can be given as: $S = k \ln P$. The action of the demon changes the number of microstates available to the gas from P to $P - p_1$. Therefore,

$$\Delta S_{gas} = k(\ln(P - p_1) - \ln P)$$
$$= k \ln[1 - (p_1/P)].$$

Since $p_1/P \ll 1$, $\ln[1 - (p_1/P)] \cong -p_1/P$. The entropy change of the flashlight battery in this process is zero.

Thus, defining the isolated system as the filament, demon, gas, and battery, we get the following for $(\Delta S)_{isolated}$:

$$(\Delta S)_{isolated} = \Delta S_{fil} + \Delta S_{dem} + \Delta S_{gas} + \Delta S_{bat}$$
$$= m_{fil} c_{fil} \ln(T_1/T_0) + k(b - p_1/P) + 0.$$

Since $b > 1$, and $p_1/P < 1$, we can write

$$(\Delta S)_{isolated} > 0.$$

Thus we see that in actuality, Maxwell's demon does not violate the second law, since the entropy of the isolated system increases. Also, note that heating the filament of the flashlight bulb is an irreversible process, which makes the entire process irreversible. Due to this irreversibility, the entropy has increased even though the information about the system has increased. Therefore, for an irreversible process, we may write:

$$S_0 - S_0 < I.$$

CONCLUSIONS

(1) Thermodynamic entropy and information are physically related in the sense that both are measures of randomness.

(2) Combining the statements for reversible and irreversible processes, we may write

$$S_0 - S_1 < I,$$

or,

$$S_1 - S_0 + I \geqslant 0.$$

Remember that in terms of uncertainties, $I = U_0 - U_1$. Thus,

$$S_1 - S_0 - (U_1 - U_0) \geqslant 0.$$

Therefore, we may set forth a generalized second law of thermodynamics:

$$\Delta(S - U) \geqslant 0.$$

From *Light and Information* by D Gabor

§ 5.   A Further Paradox: "A Perpetuum Mobile of the Second Kind"

We see that the conviction that one cannot get something for nothing, "not even an observation", leads to the first result of the quantum theory of light, that monochromatic light is perceived in discrete quanta [†]. It will now be shown that this belief can be based on one of the strongest convictions of the physicist; the belief in the Second Principle of Thermodynamics.

For our purpose it will be best to formulate this principle in the orthodox way: No cyclically operating machine is possible which produces work at the expense of the heat in *one* store.

This great principle has always remained a challenge to physicists by the extreme generality which it claims, and it can be safely said that something has always been learned every time one tried to break through it. One of the most fruitful ideas in this direction came from Clerk Maxwell, who posed the question of demons opening a valve for fast molecules in a gas, and shutting it for slow ones. This led to the even simpler question: Why not spring-load the valve, so that only a fast molecule can open it? This was answered only by SMOLU-CHOWSKI in his classical papers [1912–13]. These, however, did not deal with the question of an "intelligent demon". L. SZILÁRD took this up [in 1929], and cleared the ground first by showing that a simple observation, which amounts to a selection from n equally likely possibilities, enables the observer to decrease the entropy of the system observed by a maximum of

$$k \log n.$$

Hence, in order to save the Second Principle, it must be assumed that such an observation could not be made by any "demon", intelligent or mechanical, without an entropy increase of *at least* this amount. Szilárd proved this in detail in one example [††].

[†] It may be recalled that the existence of light quanta or photons was historically first inferred by EINSTEIN [1905] from the fluctuations of black radiation. Einstein obtained this by boldly applying the fluctuation law of statistical mechanics which he had previously discovered to the radiation in a black cavity. L. SZILÁRD showed [in 1925] that this fluctuation law is indeed a thermodynamical necessity.

[††] Here is a somewhat simplified account of Szilárd's work. He considers a molecule performing Brownian motion in a cylinder. At some instant this volume is divided into two parts by a shutter. An observation is made to

We now consider a *Perpetuum Mobile* similar to Szilárd's, in that it is based on Brownian motion, but different in so far as we aim to obtain large gains of entropy, and that we are using light for the

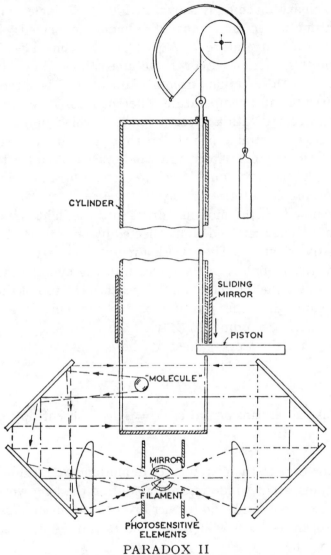

PARADOX II

Fig. 7. "Perpetuum mobile of second kind"

determine which part-volume contains the molecule, and the shutter, now serving as a piston, is moved so that the one-molecule gas expands until it fills the whole volume. It is easy to see that the expectation value of the entropy gain is maximum if the two part volumes are equal, and in this case the entropy decrease is $k \log 2$, corresponding to a binary choice. But the generalisation to an n-fold selection is so obvious, that we thought it fairer to formulate Szilárd's result in this more general form.

observations. This will enable us to prove once more the failure of the classical theory, and to learn a few somewhat surprising facts about the properties of photons.

The imaginary machine is shown in Fig. 7. A single "molecule" is in thermal motion in an evacuated cylinder, connected with a large heat store at a temperature T. A part of the cylinder walls is transparent, and this fraction $1/X$ of the volume is flooded by a light beam, coming from both directions from a filament, which is the only part of the apparatus at a temperature different from T. We can imagine this filament coated with a selective emitter, which emits and absorbs only a narrow spectral range $d\nu$, so that the light is nearly monochromatic. The mirrors, lenses and windows are assumed to be ideal, so that the light stream could circulate without losses for an indefinite time if nothing came into its way.

Assume now that the molecule drifts into the light stream. A part of the light will be scattered, and collected by one or the other or both photosensitive elements. These work a relay which sets the mechanism in motion. A frictionless piston slides into the cylinder, and will be slowly raised by the molecule, until it reaches the top of the cylinder. A cam ensures that the pressure of the molecule is always very nearly balanced according to Boyle's law. Thus the expansion is isothermic, and the work gained at the expense of the heat in the store is

$$kT \log X, \tag{12}$$

where X is the expansion ratio, $X = V/v$. The entropy decrease is

$$k \log X. \tag{13}$$

At the same time as the piston is set in motion two ideal mirrors slide over the transparent windows, so that during the long working phase of the device there can be no further loss of light, even if the molecule should happen — as it will from time to time — to visit the part volume v again.

The process can be cyclically repeated †, if the work gained, $kT \log X$, is larger than the energy lost from the light beam. In this case a part of the work is used to restore the energy to the filament, and we have

---

† In order to show the final part of the cycle a few modifications should be added to Fig. 7. One may imagine, for example, that at the stop the piston is again slipped out sideways, and does work on a machine, say an electric generator, while descending to its original position.

indeed a cyclically operating perpetuum mobile of the second kind.

This of course cannot be true, but it is not easy to see where we have gone wrong. The evident objection against frictionless pistons, ideal mirrors, selective emitters etc. can be discarded. These are all thermo-dynamically sound assumptions, and have been used in the classical imaginary experiments of Boltzmann and Willy Wien. The disturbing feature of the problem is that, however high we assume the minimum energy δ_0 required for an observation, we can always make the expansion ratio $X = V/v$ so large that

$$kT \log X > \varepsilon_0.$$

But X depends on that part of the volume into which light has *not* penetrated at all, according to our assumptions. Unless we can explain that a loss of light energy from the ordered beam has taken place somewhere in the cycle, which increases at least with the logarithm of the *unexplored* volume, we cannot disprove the perpetuum mobile.

Before showing that classical light theory has no answer to this question, it may be mentioned that classical *statistics* has an answer, but one which we cannot accept. If, with Max Planck and Max von Laue we apply Boltzmann's statistical method to the degrees of freedom of light which we have previously discussed, it is easy to show that *any* amount of energy ε_0 when passing from the ordered state, in which it fills the partial volume v and the solid angle Ω, to the disordered state in which it fills the whole volume of the apparatus (necessarily larger than V), and the solid angle 4π thereby increases the entropy of the system by more than

$$k \left(\log \frac{V}{v} + \log \frac{4\pi}{\Omega} \right). \tag{14}$$

But this is merely a mathematical expression, so contrived that the second principle shall be satisfied. It is useless unless classical theory can also explain how this entropy change has come about, i.e. unless it provides a mechanism by which the filament must lose an energy at least equal to $kT \log V/v$. It will now be shown that there is, in fact, no such classical mechanism.

The energy loss required to save the Second Principle can have taken place in three phases of the cycle:

1. During the transient process which proceeds the steady state of the beam, when the sliding mirrors are removed from the windows after the completed cycle.

2. During the waiting time, before the molecule has appeared in the part-volume v, provided that there is a possibility for the light energy to be scattered by the molecule while it is still *outside* the volume v. This energy would be either absorbed by the walls of the cylinder, or if the walls are not absorbing, it would escape through the windows.

3. During the working phase. A certain amount of radiation is imprisoned in the cylinder when the windows are shut. This will be either dissipated to the walls by the molecule, or merely disordered, in which case it will escape when the windows are opened again for the next cycle.

Let us see first what classical theory has to say regarding these three possibilities.

Ad 1. There is indeed, by Huygens' Principle, a transient process, during which the wavelets emitted by the progressing wavefront explore the whole available space, before they destroy each other by interference outside v. But the energy consumed or disordered in this process must be proportional to the final *intensity*, and this can be made as small as we like, as will be shown in a moment.

Ad 2. Scattering outside the space v can be made as small as we like, as according to classical theory the intensity can be made to fall off very sharply, e.g. as $\exp\left[-(x/x_0)^2\right]$ with the distance x from the beam edge.

Ad 3. The imprisoned radiation is proportional to the intensity.

It remains to be shown that the intensity can in fact be made as small as we like. Let ε_0 be the energy necessary to make the relay work. This is estimated in Appendix IV; here we require only the evident result that it is in no way dependent on the potential expansion X. Let $I_\nu \, d\nu$ be the light-flux per unit time, Δt the mean waiting time, of the order of the "return time" of the molecule. The mean time which it spends in v will be of the order $\Delta t \cdot v/V = \Delta t/X$; this is the time during which the observation must be made. If κ is the fraction of the flux which is in the mean successfully scattered by the molecule on to the photosensitive elements, we have the relation

$$\kappa I_\nu \, d\nu \Delta t/X > \varepsilon_0. \tag{15}$$

The factor κ causes no difficulties, as it can be made of the order unity just in the most favourable case for large gains, when v is made so small that it is entirely filled by the molecule. Thus, however large ε_0 or X, we can keep the intensity $I_\nu \, d\nu$ as low as we like, if only we make Δt sufficiently large, and this we can achieve by using a large and sluggish "molecule". Such a machine would operate very slowly, but it would none the less certainly break through the Second Principle in the long run.

But there is a hidden assumption here, which we must mention. This is that we can make I_ν as large as we like [†], relative to the background of black radiation at the temperature T which fills the whole space. Experience (Wien's Law) confirms that this is possible if we make the filament sufficiently hot. But this is a datum which we take directly from experience, the classical theory of light and thermodynamics have nothing to say on this point. (Classical statistics has something to say, but we are not here concerned with disproving classical statistics.) This is an essential assumption, as otherwise we could not expect the mechanism to pick out the weak signal from the background. We will return to it later.

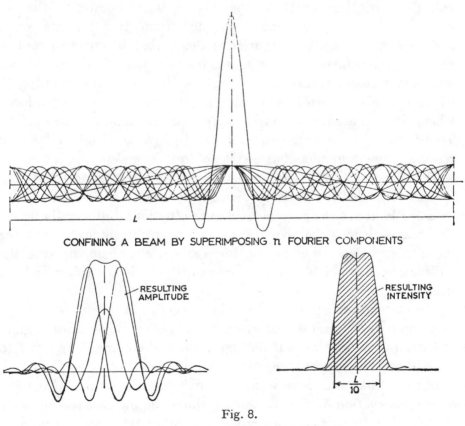

CONFINING A BEAM BY SUPERIMPOSING n FOURIER COMPONENTS

RESULTING AMPLITUDE

RESULTING INTENSITY

$\frac{L}{10}$

Fig. 8.
(cf. Appendix IV, p. 143)

[†] While keeping $I_\nu d\nu$ very small.

Thus the conclusion is that, on the basis of the classical light theory, we cannot disprove this perpetuum mobile. But even elementary quantum theory is not sufficient. A single quantum $h\nu$ is sufficient for an observation, or at any rate a small number of quanta, if there is sufficient certainty that the photons do not come from the thermal background. But however large $h\nu$, we can still make the expansion ratio X so large that the gain exceeds the loss.

But the modern quantum theory of radiation easily accounts for this queer phenomenon. The essence of this method is that it uses classical theory to the point of decomposing the general field into simple components which can be easily quantized: plane waves, or in the case of cavities, eigenfunctions. In our case plane waves will be appropriate, because we have not to deal with a closed cavity during the waiting time, when the windows are open, but we will talk of these, for simplicity, as "modes", or "Fourier components". Evidently only the vertical dimension of the cylinder is of importance; thus we can restrict our explanations to one dimension. It is a fundamental and elementary result of Fourier analysis, that in order to confine non-zero amplitudes essentially to a fraction $1/X$ of an interval, we must superimpose at least X components. This is illustrated in Fig. 8, where it is also shown how amplitude distributions can be produced which are essentially flat inside a region, and almost zero outside. That is to say *in order to confine a beam of light to a fraction $1/X$ of a volume, we must simultaneously excite at least X modes.*

The question now arises how strongly must we excite them. The answer is evidently: strongly enough, so that the peak in v rises sufficiently above the general level of fluctuations. Sufficiently means that the peak must be about X times stronger in intensity than the mean energy level due to the fluctuations elsewhere, because the molecule spends about X times more time outside the volume v than inside it.

The calculations are carried out in Appendix IV. Here we mention only the result, which is that every one of the X modes must contain in the mean about one half photon inside the volume V, in order to have about an even chance for a correct observation.

But what happens if we want to avoid this danger (i.e. making a wrong observation during the waiting time) and increase the intensity sufficiently? In this case we fall into another trap; we imprison at least $\frac{1}{2}X$ photons, and these will be dissipated by the molecule during the long "working phase". Thus the Second Principle is amply safeguarded, because the dissipated energy is at least

$$\tfrac{1}{2}Xh\nu,$$

and this is always larger than $kT \log X$, because

$$h\nu > kT, \qquad \tfrac{1}{2}X > \log X. \tag{16}$$

The first relation follows from the fact that a relay at temperature T cannot be safely worked by an energy less than kT, the second is a purely mathematical relation. It shows also that the more we try to gain, the more we are going to lose, because for large X the logarithm of X will be very much smaller than $\tfrac{1}{2}X$.

Thus the Second Principle reveals a rather curious and unexpected property of light. One could call it the "ubiquitousness of photons", and sum it up in the form: *Very weak beams of light cannot be concentrated.*

But lest this demonstration might have given the impression that one can sit down and work out the laws of nature from purely imaginary experiments, it will be useful to remember that an important element of experience has gone into our proof; the fact that the thermal spectrum falls off at short wavelengths. We cannot get something for nothing, not even an observation, far less a law of nature! But it remains remarkable how small a hint from experience is sometimes sufficient to reveal phenomena apparently quite unconnected with it [†].

IV. NOTES TO THE PERPETUUM MOBILE PROBLEM

The minimum energy required to operate safely a relay of any kind at a temperature T can be estimated from NYQUIST's theorem [1928] which states that the noise power for one degree of freedom, in a frequency range Δf is

$$kT\Delta f. \tag{1}$$

The relay, in our case, has to expect a signal during a time interval of the order $\Delta t/X$, if Δt is the mean waiting time. Thus the *optimum* setting of the frequency band Δf transmitted to the relay is of the order

$$\Delta f = \frac{X}{\Delta t}. \tag{2}$$

An instrument set in this way will integrate the signal over a time of the order $1/\Delta f$, and if the signal energy received is ε_0, the mean signal power during this time is about $\varepsilon_0 \Delta f$. As this must exceed the noise power 1, the minimum perceptible energy, received during the interval $1/\Delta f$ or less will be indeed of the order kT.

Fourier analysis of restricted beams. Fig. 8 illustrates an example of the series

$$\sum_1^n \cos 2\pi \frac{kz}{L} = \frac{\cos (\pi(n+1)z/L) \sin (\pi n z/L)}{\sin (\pi z/L)}, \tag{3}$$

that is to say it consists of n equal harmonic components, which have all the same phase at $z = 0$ and substantially destroy each other by interference outside an interval of about L/n. This function also satisfies exactly the boundary condition "amplitude zero at $z = \pm \frac{1}{2}L$" if n is an even number.

It is also shown in Fig. 8 how three such wave-sets can be superimposed in order to produce an amplitude which is substantially flat inside an interval L/n, and vanishes even a little more rapidly outside this interval than the function (3). In this second example $2n$ modes are excited, because the functions (3), shifted to z_0 can be written

$$\sum_n^1 \cos \frac{2\pi k(z - z_0)}{L} =$$

$$\sum \cos \left(\frac{2\pi k z_0}{L}\right) \cos \left(\frac{2\pi k z}{L}\right) + \sum \sin \left(\frac{2\pi k z_0}{L}\right) \sin \left(\frac{2\pi k z}{L}\right),$$

i.e. *sin* components are excited, as well as *cos* components. In order to satisfy the boundary conditions at $z = \pm \frac{1}{2}L$ only *one* condition must be imposed on the components, because they are periodic in L. Note that it is not necessary to impose the boundary conditions on every component separately, because they are coherent. That is to say the components need not be eigenfunctions of the interval L.

The fluctuations of the intensity. Assume that we have decomposed the beam into plane waves inside the volume V, by the scheme just described. (We neglect the fact that we have two beams going in opposite directions, requiring at least $2X$ components for their description, as even X waves will give us a sufficiently sharp criterion.) Plane waves can be directly quantized, due to their "particle-like" classical properties. (HEITLER [1944], p. 18.) We assume that each of those waves, $1 \ldots i \ldots n$ contains an integer number of quanta,

q_i inside the volume V. If n is a reasonably large number, the probability of an additional quantum appearing in any one of the Fourier components is small, we can therefore, at least approximately, apply the law of Poisson's distribution, according to which the probability of the i-th mode containing q_i photons is

$$e^{-\bar{q}_i} \frac{\bar{q}_i{}^{q_i}}{q_i!}. \tag{4}$$

For simplicity we assume that the mean value

$$\bar{q}_i = \frac{q}{n} \tag{5}$$

is the same for all components, q being the total number of quanta in the beam inside V.

The probability of scattering taking place at any point in the volume is proportional to the classically calculated intensity, but with the assumption that the energies in the modes are distributed according to the law (4). As we need only compare the intensities, or probabilities in a point outside the volume v with those inside it, we can use quantum units, and write for the probability

$$P = (\Sigma \sqrt{q_i} \cos \phi_i)^2 + (\Sigma \sqrt{q_i} \sin \phi_i)^2. \tag{6}$$

The ϕ_i here are the classically defined relative phases (relative to any one of the components), they do not fluctuate. It is simpler to replace these by complex unit vectors

$$c_i = e^{i\phi_i}, \tag{7}$$

so that the probability appears in the form

$$P = (\Sigma c_i \sqrt{q_i})(\Sigma c_k{}^* \sqrt{q_k}). \tag{8}$$

Outside v we assume that the c_i form a closed polygon

$$\Sigma c_i = 0, \tag{9}$$

so that the intensity or probability would be zero if all the q_i were exactly equal. We now take account of their fluctuations, by writing

$$q_i = \bar{q}_i + \delta q_i = \frac{q}{n} + \delta q_i$$

and

$$\sqrt{q_i} = \left(\frac{q}{n}\right)^i \left[1 + \frac{1}{2}\frac{n}{q}\,\delta q_i - \frac{1}{8}\left(\frac{n}{q}\right)^2 \delta q_i^2 + \ldots\right]. \quad (10)$$

We shall have to use the second approximation, as n/q will turn out to be of the order 2, and this is not sufficient to justify the first approximation. With the condition (9) this gives for the mean probability of scattering

$$\overline{P}_0 = \frac{q}{n}\overline{\left[\sum c_i\left(\frac{1}{2}\frac{n}{q}\,\delta q_i - \frac{1}{8}\left(\frac{n}{q}\right)^2 \delta q_i^2\right)\right]} \times$$

$$\overline{\left[\sum c_k{}^*\left(\frac{1}{2}\frac{n}{q}\,\delta q_k - \frac{1}{8}\left(\frac{n}{q}\right)^2 \delta q_k^2\right)\right]} =$$

$$n\left(\frac{q}{n}\right)\left[\frac{1}{4}\left(\frac{n}{q}\right)^2\overline{\delta q_i^2} + \frac{1}{64}\left(\frac{n}{q}\right)^4\overline{\delta q_i^4}\right], \quad (11)$$

where we have assumed that the fluctuations are independent in the mean, $\overline{\delta q_i \delta q_k} = 0$. For the Poisson distribution eq. (4),

$$\overline{\delta q_i^2} = \bar{q}_i = \frac{q}{n}, \quad \overline{\delta q_i^4} = \bar{q}_i + 3\bar{q}_i^2 = \frac{q}{n} + 3\left(\frac{q}{n}\right)^2. \quad (12)$$

Substituting these into (11) the probability outside v is found to be

$$\overline{P}_0 = \tfrac{1}{4}n\left[1 + \frac{3}{16}\frac{n}{q} + \frac{1}{16}\left(\frac{n}{q}\right)^2\right]. \quad (13)$$

Inside v all Fourier components are in phase, i.e. $c_i = 1$, and the corresponding probability P_i is, by eq. (8), in the mean

$$\overline{P}_i = (n\bar{q}_i{}^i)^2 = nq. \quad (14)$$

If now we want at least an even chance for a correct observation, we must postulate

$$\overline{P}_i \geq (X - 1)\overline{P}_0, \quad (15)$$

because the molecule will spend in the mean $X - 1$ times more time outside the inside v. For simplicity we will write X instead of $X - 1$, and write $n = kX$, where k, as we have previously seen, must be at least unity if the beam be confined to the fraction $1/X$ of the volume. Substituting (13) and (14) into (15) we thus obtain the condition

$$4\frac{q}{X} > 1 + \tfrac{3}{16}k\frac{X}{q} + \tfrac{1}{16}k^2\left(\frac{X}{q}\right)^2 \quad (16)$$

for approximately even chance of a successful observation of the molecule. A few values are

$$k \qquad 1 \qquad 2 \qquad 3$$

$$q/X > 0.45 \qquad 0.54 \qquad 1.0.$$

Thus even for the smallest possible number $k = 1$ we have for the minimum number of quanta lost during the cycle

$$q > 0.45\,X > \log X$$

which, as we have shown in the text, amply safeguards the Second Principle.

References

BOHR, N. and L. ROSENFELD, 1933, Mat. Fys. Medd. Dan. Vid. Selsk. **12**, No. 8; 1950, Phys. Rev. **68**, 794.

BOOKER, H. G., J. A. RATCLIFFE and D. H. SHINN, 1950, Phil. Trans. Roy. Soc. A **242**, 579.

BORN, M., 1949, Ann. Inst. Henri Poincaré, Paris **11**, 1.

DE BROGLIE, L., 1947, Reprinted in Optique Electronique et Corpusculaire (Hermann & Cie, Paris, 1950) p. 227.

DUFFIEUX, P. M., 1950, Réunion d'Opticiens, Ed. Rev. d'Optique, Paris, 1950 lists the works of this author between 1935 and 1938.

EDDINGTON, A., Sir, 1939, The Philosophy of Physical Sciences (Cambridge).

EINSTEIN, A., 1905, Ann. d. Phys. [4] **17**, 132.

GABOR, D., 1946, Journ. I.E.E. **93**, III 429; *Ibid.*, 1947, **94**, III, 369; 1949, Proc. Roy. Soc. A **197**, 454; 1950, Phil. Mag. [7] **41**, 1161; Nature **166**, 724; 1951, Proc. Phys. Soc. B **64**, 449.

HEITLER, W., 1944, The Quantum Theory of Radiation (Oxford, 2d Ed.).

v. LAUE, M., 1914, Ann. Physik [4] **44**, 1197; *Ibid.* [4] **48**, 668.

MACKAY, D. M., 1950, Phil. Mag. [7] **41**, 189.

MOTT, N. F. and H. S. W. MASSEY, 1949, Theory of Atomic Collisions (Oxford).

NYQUIST, H., 1928, Phys. Rev. **32**, 753.

OSWALD, J., 1949, C. R. Acad. Sci. Paris **229**, 21.

PLANCK, M., 1924, Ber. Preuss. Akad. Wiss. Berlin **24**, 442.

VAN DER POL, B., 1950, U.R.S.I. report, Geneva, unpublished.

SHANNON, C. E., 1948, Bell. Syst. T. J. **27**, 379, 623, reprinted in SHANNON, C. E. and W. WEAVER, 1949, The Math. Theor. of Comm., Urbana, Illinois; 1949, Proc. I.R.E. **37**, 10.

v. SMOLUCHOWSKI, M., 1912, Phys. Zeitschr. **13**, 1069; *Ibid.* **14**, 261.

SOMMERFELD, A., 1950, Vorlesungen über theoret. Physik, Bd. IV, Optik (Dieterich, Wiesbaden).

SZILÁRD, L., 1925, Z. Physik **32**, 753; 1929, *Ibid.* **53**, 840.

WHITTAKER, E. T., 1915, Univ. of Edinburgh, Math. Dept. Res. Paper No. 8.

WIENER, N., 1949, "Stationary Time Series" and "Cybernetics" (Chapman & Hall).

Entropy, Information and Szilard's Paradox

by **J. M. Jauch**

Dept. of Theoretical Physics, University of Geneva,
and Dept. of Mathematics, University of Denver

and **J. G. Báron**

Rye, New York

(15. XII. 71)

This essay is presented in homage to Professor Markus Fierz, whose long-standing interest in statistical physics is well known, on the occasion of his 60th birthday.

Abstract. Entropy is defined as a general mathematical concept which has many physical applications. It is found useful in classical thermodynamics as well as in information theory. The similarity of the formal expressions in the two cases has misled many authors to identify entropy of information (as measured by the formula of Shannon) with negative physical entropy. The origin of the confusion is traced to a seemingly paradoxical thought experiment of Szilard, which we analyze herein. The result is that this experiment cannot be considered a justification for such identification and that there is no paradox.

1. Introduction

There is a widespread belief that the physical entropy used in thermodynamics is more or less closely related to the concept of information as used in communication theory.

This thesis has been made precise and explicit, primarily by Brillouin [1], who is of the opinion that both concepts should be united by identifying information (suitably normalized) by establishing an equivalence relation with negative physical entropy (called 'negentropy' by him), which then together satisfy a generalized principle of Clausius.

This point of view, however, is not universally accepted by those physicists who have thought about the question. We quote here as an example an explicit denial of such identification, by ter Haar [2], who writes in his textbook on statistical mechanics:

'The relationship between entropy and lack of information has led many authors, notably Shannon, to introduce "entropy" as a measure for the information transmitted by cables and so on, and in this way entropy has figured largely in recent discussions on information theory. It must be stressed here that the entropy introduced in information theory is *not* a thermodynamic quantity and that the use of the same term is rather misleading. It was probably introduced because of a rather loose use of the term "information".'

We want to elaborate ter Haar's point of view and discuss the reasons why we believe that the two concepts should not be identified.

One can trace the origin of this identification to a paper by Szilard [3], published in 1929, which discusses a particular version of Maxwell's demon and an apparent violation of the second law of thermodynamics.

The emphasis in that paper is on the intelligence of the 'demon', who, by utilizing the 'information' gained by observation of the detailed properties of a thermodynamic system, could use this information for the manipulation of a macroscopic gadget which could extract mechanical energy from the fluctuations of a thermodynamic system and thus produce a *perpetuum mobile* of the second kind.

Szilard based his version on a remark by Smoluchowski which was published in the latter's lectures on the kinetic theory of matter [4]. Smoluchowski said, 'As far as our present knowledge is concerned there does not exist a permanently working *automatic perpetuum mobile* in spite of molecular fluctuations, but such a contraption could function *if it were operated by intelligent beings in a convenient manner . . .*' (italics ours).

This statement seems to imply that the second law of thermodynamics could somehow be violated in the presence of intelligent beings and that this possible violation would be associated with the acquisition and retention of knowledge by such beings. It is with this in mind that Szilard contructed his thought experiment.

Although in a subsequent passage, Smoluchowski expressed considerable doubt ('recht zweifelhaft') about this possibility, Szilard proposed to elucidate the conjectured role of the intelligent being in creating the uncompensated entropy decrease. He described an idealized heat engine that seemingly functioned with continuous decrease of entropy. In order to save the second law, Szilard conjectured that the intelligent being (we shall call him 'the observer') must perform measurements in order to operate the engine, and that this process is in principle connected with a compensating increase of entropy.

We shall discuss Szilard's thought experiment in section 4 of this paper. Here we merely point out that this experiment provoked much discussion and, in our opinion, misinterpretation. We mention in particular the discussion by von Neumann [5], who transferred considerations of this kind into the realm of quantum mechanics with reference to the measuring process.

Many aspects of the measuring process in quantum mechanics are still controversial. Szilard's conjecture mentioned above has led many commentators [6] to believe that the measuring process in quantum mechanics is connected in an essential manner with the presence of a conscious observer who registers in his mind an effect, and that this conscious awareness is responsible for the oft-discussed, paradoxical 'reduction of the wave packet'.

We expect to show that the presence of a conscious observer in Szilard's experiment is not necessary; he can be replaced by an automatic device with no consciousness at all. Interestingly, Szilard noted this himself; toward the end of his paper, he concluded:

> 'As we have seen with this example, a simple, inanimate device can do exactly the same, as far as the essentials are concerned, as the intervention of an intelligent being would accomplish.'

It is strange that Szilard seemed not to realize that an automatic version of the intelligent observer contradicts the conclusion of Smoluchowski, according to which such mechanisms are not possible. As a matter of fact, the solution of the paradox in the case of the living observer is the same as that which Smoluchowski indicated for the explanation of the mechanical demon: The demon is himself subject to fluctuations, just as the system which he tries to control. To use a medical analogy, the demon who wants to operate the molecular trap is like a patient with a severe case of Parkinson's disease trying to thread a fast-vibrating needle!

We shall not question the analysis of the problem given by Smoluchowski; we shall consider this aspect of the problem as solved. From this it follows that Szilard's conjecture is not proven by his experiment.

2. The Classical Notion of Entropy

Entropy as a basic notion of science was introduced by Clausius to summarize thermal behavior of systems in equilibrium or changing in reversible fashion in the second principle of thermodynamics.

Boltzmann [8] and Gibbs [9] defined entropy of non-equilibrium states and entropy changes of irreversible processes in purely mechanical terms. Their theory was more general; it also explained how the same thermodynamic process can be irreversible from the phenomenological point of view—and completely reversible from the purely mechanical point of view. This paradoxical situation was cleared up by statistical interpretation of thermodynamic entropy.

Increase in generality resulted in some ambiguity of the notion of entropy. The reason for this is that in any statistical consideration a more or less arbitrary model must be used. Expressed differently, the system may be described at different levels (see H. Grad [7]).

We shall return to the significance of these ambiguities later in this section. First we briefly review some special features of the statistical interpretation of thermo-dynamic entropy.

In thermodynamics one may specify a homogeneous thermal system by a certain number of extensive variables $x_1, \ldots x_n$ which usually have a simple physical interpretation (volume, surface, magnetic moment, etc.).

The generalized forces $y_1, \ldots y_n$ associated with these variables are homogeneous functions of them, such that the element of work δA delivered by the system to the surrounding is related to the differentials $dx_r (r = 1, \ldots n)$ by

$$\delta A = \sum_{r=1}^{n} y_r \, dx_r. \tag{1}$$

Mathematically, (1) is a differential form defined on an open region of $\mathbb{R}^n$, the Euclidean space of n dimensions.

The first principle of thermodynamics which expresses conservation of energy for a conservative system states that for an adiabatic system (that is, a thermally isolated system), this differential form is total. That means that there exists a function $U(x_1, \ldots x_n)$ of the extensive variables x_r, which is itself extensive, such that

$$\delta A = -dU \tag{2}$$

Physically interpreted, this equation says that the work delivered to the outside by an adiabatic system is exactly compensated by the loss of internal energy.

If the system is not adiabatic, then equation (2) is no longer true and must be generalized to

$$\delta Q = dU + \delta A \tag{3}$$

where now δQ is the differential of the amount of heat added to the system in a reversible manner.

We may consider equation (3) as a new differential form in $n + 1$ variables where $U = x_0$ may be defined as the new variable. Each of the generalized forms y_r is then a function of all the variables $x_0, x_1, \ldots, x_n$.

The differential form (3) is of a special kind which admits an integrating factor $T(x_0, x_1, \ldots x_n)$ such that the form

$$dS = \frac{\delta Q}{T} \tag{4}$$

is the total differential of an extensive function $S(x_0, x_1, \ldots x_n)$. This function is the entropy and the integrating factor (suitably normalized) is the absolute temperature of the system.[1])

The second principle of thermodynamics says that in a spontaneous evolution of a closed system not in equilibrium, the entropy always increases and attains its maximum value for the state of equilibrium.

Definition (4) determines the thermodynamic entropy only up to a constant of integration.

Boltzmann's statistical definition is given by the famous formula,

$$S = k \ln W \tag{5}$$

where W represents a probability for the system specified by the thermodynamic variables based on some appropriate statistical mode. This formula was apparently never written down by Boltzmann; yet it appears on his tombstone and indeed is one of the most important advances in statistical physics. For the practical application of this formula, one usually goes through the following procedure:

a) One assumes (explicitly or implicitly) an a priori probability. In phase space of a classical system it is given by a convenient selection of a volume element.

b) One then imposes constraints in agreement with a certain number of external parameters characterizing the thermodynamic state of the system.

c) One then calculates the probability of such constrained systems on the basis of the a priori probability field assumed.

d) Finally, one calculates a maximum value of this probability under the assumed constraints to obtain an expression for W.

The W thus calculated is in an arbitrary normalization. This arbitrariness corresponds to the constant of integration for the thermodynamic entropy S.

Boltzmann's theoretical interpretation of the entropy gives immediate insight into two important properties which are characteristic for the thermodynamic, and, as we shall see, for all other forms of entropy. They are:

a) *Extensity*

If there are two independent systems with their respective probabilities W_1 and W_2, then the joint system has a probability

$$W = W_1 W_2. \tag{6}$$

---

[1]) It seems not to be generally known that the existence of the integrating factor, hence the existence of the function entropy, is a consequence of the first principle of thermodynamics for conservative systems under reversible quasistatic variations. This was discovered by T. Ehrenfest [12]. A new proof of this statement will be given in a subsequent publication.

Hence

$$S = S_1 + S_2 = k \ln (W_1 W_2).$$ (7)

b) *Maximum property*

Any system outside the equilibrium state will have a probability $W < W_0$, the equilibrium probability.
Hence

$$S = k \ln W < k \ln W_0 = S_0,$$ (8)

since $\ln W$ is a monotonic function.

The arbitrariness in the definition of W, and thus the ambiguity of S, is brought out explicitly if we turn now to the definition for W used by Boltzmann and others in the derivation of the so-called H-theorem.

Here one considers the phase space Γ of a classical system endowed with a probability measure $\rho(P)$, $P \in \Gamma$. $\rho(P)$ is assumed to be a positive function, normalized by

$$\int_\Gamma \rho(P) d\Omega = 1$$ (9)

and interpreted to represent the probability of finding the system at the point P in phase space. We have written $d\Omega$ for the volume element in phase space.

One can define a quantity $\eta = \ln \rho$ and its average

$$\sigma = \int_\Gamma \rho \ln \rho \, d\Omega = \bar\eta$$ (10)

and one can then show that this quantity reaches its maximum value under the subsidiary condition

$$\int \epsilon \rho d\Omega = E = \text{constant}$$ (11)

provided it has the form of the canonical distribution

$$\rho = e^{(\psi - \epsilon)/\theta}.$$ (12)

However, the quantity σ is a constant under the evolution in time. This is true for any σ of the form (10) for any ρ.

One obtains a more suitable statistical definition for the entropy if one uses the process of 'coarse-graining'. Physically, this corresponds to the process which one would use for describing a system, the state of which is incompletely known. It is carried out in the following manner:

One divides the phase space into a certain number of cells with volume Ω_i and defines

$$P_i = \frac{1}{\Omega_i} \int_{\Omega_i} \rho \, d\Omega.$$

It follows then that

$$\sum_i P_i \Omega_i = 1.$$

The coarse-grained density is defined as

$$P(x) = P_i \quad \text{if } x \in \Omega_i$$

and

$$\sum \equiv \sum_i P_i \ln P_i \, \Omega_i = \int_\Gamma P \ln P \, d\Omega.$$

Hence

$$\sum = \overline{\ln P}.$$

One can then prove that $\sum$ is a decreasing function in time, reaching its minimum value for the canonical distribution provided that the mean energy is kept constant.

This suggests that $-k\sum$ could be identified with the thermodynamic entropy when the system is away from equilibrium.

This result shows quite clearly that there are several ways of defining and interpreting statistical entropy. The arbitrariness is connected with both the assumed probability field and with the nature of constraints used in the coarse-graining process. Both Boltzmann [8] and Gibbs [9] were aware of these ambiguities in the statistical interpretation of thermodynamic variables. Boltzmann says, for example:

'I do not believe that one is justified to consider this result as final, at least not as long as one has not defined very precisely what one means by the most probable state distribution.'

Gibbs is still more explicit:

'It is evident that there may be more than one quantity defined for finite values of the degrees of freedom, which approach the same limiting form for infinitely many degrees of freedom. There may be, therefore, and there are, other quantities which may be thought to have some claim to be regarded as temperature and entropy with respect to systems of a finite number of freedoms.'

As an example of two different ways of interpreting entropy, we mention the mixing problem discussed by Gibbs.

If a blue and a red liquid are mixed, there will result after a while a purplish mixture which cannot be unmixed by further agitation.

In this case the statistical entropy increases if the coarse-graining size is much larger than the average size of the volume element that has a definite (unmixed) color. On the other hand, the statistical entropy remains constant if the volume element having a definite color is much larger than the coarse-graining size. Only on the molecular level, e.g., in the diffusion process of two different gases, can this entropy be related to thermodynamic entropy; it increases in the diffusion process by

$$S = R \log 2,$$

provided that the volumes of the two kinds of gases are equal. The so-called paradox of Gibbs results from the confusion of two different kinds of entropy, based on different statistical models.

All that we have said in this section has been said before. Nevertheless, we felt reiteration useful to emphasize the polymorphic nature of statistical entropy. It is precisely this non-uniqueness which makes the concept so versatile.

3. The Definition of Entropy as a Mathematical Concept

In this section we will define the notion of entropy in an abstract setting without reference to its interpretations. It will be seen that a suitable definition will immediately reveal the range of its applications to a variety of situations, including thermodynamic entropy and the notion of 'information'.

Before proceeding with the formal definition, let us give a heuristic description of what we seek in order to achieve sufficient motivation for the mathematical definitions.

We wish to establish between two measures a relationship which represents a quantitative expression for the variability of one with respect to the other. As an example, let us consider the probability of the outcome of one of two alternatives, head or tail in flipping a coin. If the coin is 'true' then the a priori probability for either of the two events is $\frac{1}{2}$. However, if the experiment is made and the coin has been observed, then this probability is changed and is now 0 for one and 1 for the other event. The observation, or the specification, has restricted the variability and as a result a certain quantity which we wish to define—entropy—has decreased.

This quantity should have the property that it behaves additively for independent events, so that if the coin is flipped twice, then the entropy for the two observations should be twice that for one. As we shall see, these properties determine the quantity almost uniquely.

Proceeding now to the formal definition, what we need first of all is a measure space; by this we mean the triplet $(X, \mathscr{S}, \mu)$ where X is a non-empty set, $\mathscr{S}$ a collection of subsets of X, and μ a normalized finite measure on $\mathscr{S}$. We assume that the subsets of $\mathscr{S}$ are closed under the formation of complements and countable unions (hence also countable intersections), and we call such a collection a *field* of subsets.

The measure μ is a positive, countably additive set function defined for the sets of $\mathscr{S}$ such that

$$\mu(X) = 1, \quad \mu(\varnothing) = 0 \quad (\varnothing = \text{null set}).$$

Let $S \in \mathscr{S}$ be such that $\mu(S) = 0$, then we say the set S has μ-measure zero. Two different measures μ and ν on $\mathscr{S}$ are said to be *equivalent* if they have exactly the same sets of measure zero. We write $\mu \sim \nu$ so that

$$\mu \sim \nu \Leftrightarrow \{\mu(S) = 0 \Leftrightarrow \nu(S) = 0\}.$$

A more general concept is *absolute continuity*. We say μ is absolutely continuous with respect to another measure ν if

$$\nu(R) = 0 \Rightarrow R \text{ is } \mu\text{-measurable and } \mu(R) = 0.$$

We then write

$$\mu \propto \nu.$$

The relation $\propto$ is a partial order relation between different measures since

1. $\mu \propto \mu$
2. $\mu \propto \nu$ and $\nu \propto \rho \Rightarrow \mu \propto \rho$.

Two measures are equivalent if and only if $\mu \propto \nu$ and $\nu \propto \mu$.

A function f on X is called $L^1(\nu)$ if it is measurable with respect to ν and if

$$\int_X |f| \, d\nu < \infty.$$

It is convenient to identify functions which differ only on a set of measure zero with respect to a measure v. In this case we write for two such functions

$f_1 = f_2$ a.e. $[v]$.

where a.e. stands for 'almost everywhere'.

For any measure v and $f \in L^1(v)$ ($f \geqslant 0$ a.e. $[v]$) we can define a measure μ_f by setting

$$\mu_f(R) = \int_R f \, dv \qquad (13)$$

and it is easy to verify that $\mu_f < v$.

More interesting is the converse, which is the content of one of the Radon-Nikodym theorems [10].

If $\mu \propto v$ then there exists a uniquely defined $f \geqslant 0$ a.e. $[v]$ and $f \in L^1(v)$ such that

$\mu = \mu_f$

The function f so defined is called the Radon-Nikodym derivative and is often written as

$$f = \frac{d\mu}{dv}. \qquad (14)$$

If X_1 and X_2 are two measure spaces with measures μ_1 and μ_2, respectively, then we can define the product measure μ_{12} on $X_1 \times X_2$ as follows: On every set of the form $S_1 \times S_2$ with $S_1 \in \mathcal{S}_1$ and $S_2 \in \mathcal{S}_2$ we set

$$\mu_{12}(S_1 \times S_2) = \mu_1(S_1) \, \mu_2(S_2).$$

There is then a unique continuation of this measure by additivity to the field of all sets generated by the sets of the form $S_1 \times S_2$. This is called the *product measure*.

If $\mu_1 \propto v_1$ and $\mu_2 \propto v_2$ then one can prove that

$$\mu_{12} < v_{12} \quad \text{and} \quad f_{12} = \frac{d\mu_{12}}{dv_{12}} = \frac{d\mu_1}{dv_1} \frac{d\mu_2}{dv_2} = f_1 f_2.$$

We have now all the concepts needed for the definition of *entropy*. If $\mu \propto v$ and $f = d\mu/dv$ we define entropy of μ with respect to v by

$$H(\mu, v) = \int f \ln f \, dv. \qquad (15)$$

It has the following properties

1. $H(\mu, \mu) = 0$.
2. $H(\mu, v) \geqslant 0$ for $\mu \propto v$.
3. $H(\mu_{12}, v_{12}) = H(\mu_1, v_1) + H(\mu_2, v_2)$.

We verify them as follows:

1. is obvious, since $f = 1$ for $\mu = v$,
2. we prove as follows: Let $f = 1 + \phi$. Since

$$\int_X d\mu = \int_X \frac{d\mu}{dv} dv = 1 = \int_X dv$$

it follows that $\int \phi \, dv = 0$. Therefore

$$0 = \int_X f \ln (f - \phi) dv = \int_X f \ln f \left(1 - \frac{\phi}{f}\right) dv$$

$$= \int_X f \ln f + \int_X f \ln \left(1 - \frac{\phi}{f}\right) dv$$

Here we use the inequality

$$\ln \left(1 - \frac{\phi}{f}\right) < \frac{-\phi}{f}$$

so that the second term is

$$\int_X f \ln \left(1 - \frac{\phi}{f}\right) dv < - \int \phi \, dv = 0.$$

Thus we have verified

$$0 < \int f \ln f \, dv$$

3.   follows from the definition $f_{12} = f_1 f_2$ and Fubini's theorem:

$$\int f_1 f_2 \ln (f_1 f_2) \, dv_{12} = \int f_1 f_2 (\ln f_1 + \ln f_2) \, dv_1 \, dv_2$$

$$= \int f_1 \ln f_1 \, dv_1 + \int f_2 \ln f_2 \, dv_2$$

$$= H(\mu_1, v_1) + H(\mu_2, v_2).$$

We illustrate the foregoing with a few examples:

As a first example we consider a finite sample space X consisting of n objects. For the a priori measure v we choose the value $1/n$ for each element of X. The family of sets $\mathcal{S}$ is the class of all subsets of X. The measure of any subset S with k elements is then given by $v(S) = k/n$.

For the measure μ we choose the value 1 on one particular element of X and zero for all others. Let A denote this element and denote by B any other element of X. We have then

$$v(B) = \frac{1}{n} \quad B \in X, \quad \mu(A) = 1$$

$$\mu(B) = 0 \text{ for } A \neq B.$$

If $S \in \mathcal{S}$ is any subset of X and if $v(S) = 0$ then it follows that $S = \phi$. Therefore $\mu(S) = 0$ also, and μ is absolutely continuous with respect to v: $\mu \propto v$. We can easily calculate the values of the Radon-Nikodym derivative $f = d\mu/dv$. It has the values

$$f(A) = n, \quad f(B) = 0 \quad \text{for } A \neq B$$

where A is that particular element for which $v(A) = 1$.

We obtain now for the entropy as we have defined it

$$H(\mu, \nu) = \int f \ln f \, d\nu = \sum_B f(B) \ln f(B) \cdot \frac{1}{n} = \ln n. \tag{16}$$

We observe that this is a very simple, special case of Boltzmann's formula, since n can be interpreted as the number of 'states' which are contained in a set X of n elements.

One can generalize this example a little to bring it closer to the use of 'entropy in information theory'. Let us assume as before that the a priori probability on the elements A_i of X has the value $\nu(A_i) = 1/n$ $(i = 1, \ldots, n)$. For the measure μ, however, we assume $\mu(A_i) = p_i$ where $p_i \geqslant 0$ and $\sum_i^n = 1, p_i = 1$. The positive number p_i represents the probability with which the element A_i appears for instance in a message with an alphabet of n letters. If $p_i = 1/n$ the message is completely garbled; if it is $=1$ for one A_i and $=0$ for the others, it is clear. We consider now the intermediate case.

If $\nu(S) = 0$ for some set $S \in \mathcal{S}$ then $S = \phi$; hence again as before $\mu(S) = 0$ so that μ is absolutely continuous with respect to $\nu : \mu \propto \nu$.

Furthermore

$$\frac{du}{d\nu}(A_i) \equiv f(A_i) = np_i.$$

This follows from the formula

$$\int_S \frac{d\mu}{d\nu} \, d\nu = \mu(S).$$

When we calculate the entropy in this case, we obtain

$$H(\mu, \nu) = \sum_{i=1}^n np_i \ln(np_i) \cdot \frac{1}{n} = \ln n + \sum_{i=1}^n p_i \ln p_i. \tag{17}$$

This expression reaches its minimum value 0 for $p_i = 1/n$ and its maximum value $\ln n$ for $p_k = 1$ for $k = i$, $p_k = 0$ for $k \neq i$.

In information theory [11] one uses the quantity $I = -\sum_{i=1}^n p_i \ln p_i$ as a measure of the information contained in the one-letter message and we may therefore write

$$H(\mu, \nu) = \ln n - I.$$

Our definition of entropy is therefore in this case, apart from a constant, $\ln n$ equal to the negative entropy of the measure μ with respect to ν.

The abstract mathematical concept of entropy introduced here is at the basis of numerous different applications of this notion in physics as well as in other fields. This was recently emphasized by Grad [7]. Mathematicians use this concept as a versatile research tool in mathematical probability theory.

As has been emphasized, the use of the word entropy should not lead to confusion of the mathematical concept defined here with the physical concept of thermodynamic entropy. The concept introduced here relates two measures, one of which is absolutely continuous with respect to the other and has at this stage of abstraction nothing to do with any particular physical system. The misleading use of the same word for mathematical and for physical entropy is well-entrenched; it is now unavoidable. We use it in the general sense; its special meanings should be clear from the context.

4. Szilard's Paradox

Many authors who have tried to identify thermodynamic entropy with information (or rather, its negative) refer explicitly to the thought experiment of Szilard which seemed to lead to a violation of the second principle of thermodynamics unless the loss of entropy in the hypothetical experiment, so it is alleged, is compensated by a gain of information by some observer. In this section we describe Szilard's thought experiment and present an analysis to show that it cannot be considered a basis for the alleged identity and interchangeability of these two kinds of entropy.

In our description of Szilard's thought experiment, we follow closely von Neumann's version. We make only minor, physically irrelevant changes in the experimental set-up to make it more convenient for analysis and to avoid extreme idealizations.

In the experiment, a rigid, hollow, heat-permeable cylinder, closed at both ends, is used. It is fitted with a freely moveable piston with a hole large enough for the molecule to pass easily through it. The hole can be closed from outside. All motions are considered reversible and frictionless. The cylinder is in contact with a very large heat reservoir to keep the temperature of the entire machine constant.

Within the cylinder is a gas consisting of a single molecule. At the beginning of the experiment, the piston is in the middle of the cylinder and its hole is open so that the molecule can move (almost) freely from one side of the piston to the other. The hole is then closed, trapping the molecule in one half of the cylinder.

The observer now determines the location of the molecule by a process called by Szilard 'Messung', meaning measurement. If it is found to the left of the piston (see figure), the observer attaches a weight to the piston with a string over a pulley so that the pressure is almost counterbalanced. He then moves the piston very slowly to the right, thereby raising the weight. When the piston reaches the end of the cylinder, the hole in the piston is opened and the piston is moved back to the middle of the cylinder, reversibly and without effect on the gas. At the end of this process the starting position has been reached, except that a certain amount of heat energy Q from the heat reservoir has been transformed into potential energy A of the weight lifted.

Although Szilard does not mention this, obviously the same procedure can be used if the molecule happens to be trapped on the other side of the cylinder after the closing of the piston's hole.

By repeating the process a large number of times (say, N), an arbitrarily large quantity of heat energy $Q = NA$ from the reservoir is transformed into potential energy without any other change in the system. This violates the second principle of thermodynamics.

In order to 'save' the second law, Szilard assumes that the observation of the molecule, for determining in which half of the cylinder it is contained, is in principle connected with an exactly compensating increase of entropy of the observer.

Before analyzing the experiment, a few remarks are in order concerning admissibility of procedures in idealized experiments. In this we are helped by a statement of von Neumann (p. 359 of his book, Ref. [5]): 'In phenomenological thermodynamics each conceivable process constitutes valid evidence, provided that it does not conflict with the two fundamental laws of thermodynamics.' To this we add: 'If an idealization is in conflict with a law that is basic to the second law, then it cannot be used as evidence for violation of the second law.'

Now this is precisely what is happening in the case of Szilard's experiment. Obviously, frictionless motion, reversible expansion and heat transfer, and infinitely large reservoir are all admissible under these criteria. Even the single-molecule gas is admissible so long as it satisfies the gas laws. However, at the exact moment when the piston is in the middle of the cylinder and the opening is closed, the gas violates the law of Gay-Lussac because the gas is compressed to half its volume without expenditure of energy. We therefore conclude that the idealizations in Szilard's experiment are inadmissible in their actual context.

It is of further interest to analyze that phase of the experiment during which the hole in the piston is closed. This phase is almost a replica of the expansion phase of a

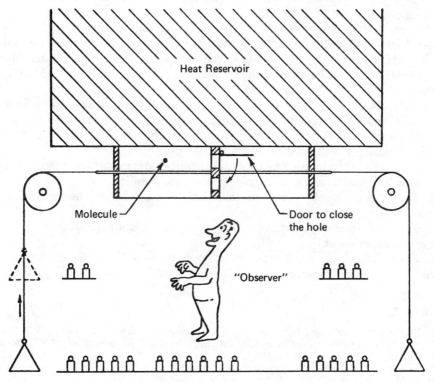

Szilard's thought experiment

Carnot cycle. Szilard believed that during this phase there is an uncompensated decrease in entropy, since during this interval the entropy of the heat reservoir decreases while at the same time the entropy of the gas increases by the same amount. The entropy of the entire system (piston, gas and reservoir) remains constant because the system is closed and the changes are reversible. Thus there is nothing to be compensated for by the alleged increase of entropy of the observer during observation.

Finally, and perhaps most importantly, there is an unacceptable assumption in Szilard's interpretation of his experiment. He believed that the observer must *know* on which side of the piston the molecule is located in order that he may start the piston moving in the right direction. This knowledge is unnecessary, as is the pushing of the piston by the observer. The piston starts moving—under the idealized conditions of the experiment—by the pressure of the gas.

The automatic device, referred to in section 1, which can completely replace the observer, could work as follows:

Near the mid-plane of the cylinder and on both its sides are electrical contacts in its walls. When activated by the piston's motion along them, they operate mechanisms which attach a weight to the piston in whichever direction it moves. Thus a weight is lifted and the engine performs work, without interference by a conscious observer.

5. Summary and Concluding Remarks

Entropy is a fundamental mathematical concept, which relates two measures on a measure space in a certain manner.

The concept has many different applications, including thermodynamics (where it was first discovered) and information theory. It is also applicable in quantal systems, for example, and in random variables of any kind. The fact that entropy can be applied to many fields is no excuse for confusing its different meanings when applied to physical systems or mathematical constructions.

In particular, the identification of entropy of information (as defined by Shannon) as equivalent with negative thermodynamic entropy is unfounded and a source of much confusion. We have traced the origin of this confusion to the paradox of Szilard. Analysis of Szilard's paradox has shown specifically that:

1. Szilard's experiment is based on an inadmissible idealization; therefore it cannot be used for examining the principles of thermodynamics.

2. The observer needs no information about the location of the molecule at the beginning of the experiment.

3. There is no uncompensated entropy change in the system during the expansion phase of the experiment.

4. Thus, Szilard's thought experiment does not work; it is no paradox; and has nothing to do with information.

REFERENCES

[1] L. BRILLOUIN, *Science and Information Theory* (Academic Press, New York, N.Y. 1956).
[2] D. TER HAAR, *Elements of Statistical Mechanics* (Rinehart and Co., New York, N.Y. 1954, p. 161.
[3] L. SZILARD, Z. Phys. *53*, 840 (1929).
[4] B. VON SMOLUCHOWSKI, *Vorträge über die kinetische Theorie der Materie und Elektrizität* (Leipzig 1914), esp. p. 89.
[5] J. VON NEUMANN, *Mathematische Grundlagen der Quantenmechanik*, p. 212 (1932).
[6] F. LONDON and E. BAUER, *La Théorie de l'Observation en Mécanique Quantique*, Actual. scient. ind. *775* (Hermann, Paris 1939).
[7] H. GRAD, *The Many Faces of Entropy*, Comm. Pure Appl. Math. *XIV*, 323 (1961).
[8] L. BOLTZMANN, Collected Papers, No. 42, p. 193.
[9] W. GIBBS, *Elementary Principles in Statistical Mechanics*, Dover Press, p. 169.
[10] S. K. BERBERIAN, *Measure and Integration* (MacMillan & Co., New York, N.Y. 1962), esp. p. 160 seq.
[11] C. L. SHANNON and W. WEAVER, *Mathematical Theory of Communication*. (Univ. of Illinois Press, 1949).
[12] P. and T. EHRENFEST, *The Conceptual Foundations of the Statistical Approach in Mechanics*, transl. from the German by M. T. MORAVCSIK (Cornell Univ. Press, 1959), esp. Preface to the translation, by T. EHRENFEST-AFANASSJEWA. See also T. EHRENFEST, *Die Grundlagen der Thermodynamik* (Leiden 1956); A. LANDE, *Axiomatische Begründung der Thermodynamik*, Handbuch der Physik *IX*; A. H. WILSON, *Thermodynamics and Statistical Mechanics* (Cambridge Univ. Press, 1960), esp. §2.5, p. 24 seq.

Information Theory and Thermodynamics

by **Olivier Costa de Beauregard**

Laboratoire de Physique Theorique associé an CNRS, Institut Henri Poincaré, 11 rue Pierre et Marie Curie, 75005 Paris, France

and **Myron Tribus**

Xerox Corporation, Webster, New York, USA

(19. XI. 73)

Abstract. In answer to a recent article by Jauch and Baron bearing this same title, the information theory approach to thermodynamics is here upheld. After a brief historical survey and an outline of the derivation as formulated by one of us in previous publications, Jauch and Baron's critique of Szilard's argument pertaining to the 'well-informed heat engine' is discussed.

I. Introduction

In a recent paper Jauch and Baron[1] argue against the identification of the thermodynamic entropy concept as defined by Clausius and the information theory entropy concept as defined by Shannon [2]. In support of their thesis they present a new discussion of Szilard's thought experiment of the 'well-informed heat engine' [4].

We definitely belong to the other school of thought and intend to say briefly why.

While admitting with others [5] that a general mathematical definition of the entropy concept can be produced and used in many fields, Jauch and Baron do not mention the fact that the entropy concept of statistical mechanics has actually been deduced from the information concept. The corresponding papers are not quoted in their article, where Brillouin (1957) [4] is the only author mentioned as asserting the identity of the Clausius and the Shannon entropy concepts.

Jaynes (1957) [6], much inspired [7] by an article of Cox (1946) [8], later expanded in a book [9], is the recognized author of the derivation of the fundamental equations of equilibrium statistical mechanics (or 'thermostatistics' in the terminology of one of us [10]) from the inductive reasoning probability concept as introduced by Bayes [11], Laplace [12] and Hume [13]. In his two pioneering articles [6, 7] Jaynes presents his deduction in terms of, respectively, classical and quantal statistical mechanics. In the latter case he uses of course von Neumann's [14, 15] density matrix.

What is perhaps less known is that the same line of reasoning had been lucidly presented and used, also in von Neumann's quantum statistical formalism, as early as 1937 by Elsasser [16], who quotes Fisher (1929) [17] as one of his inspirers.

One point of interest in the Elsasser–Jaynes quantum information formalism is that the density matrix, and corresponding negentropy or information attached to the system under study, are calculated from the results of a set of 'macroscopic' measurements simultaneously performed, these being interpreted as the (quantum mechanical) mean values $\langle F_i \rangle$ attached to *not necessarilly commuting* operators F_i.

For the sake of completeness we mention that the history of the inductive reasoning probability concept continues beyond Fisher, Cox and Shannon; Watanabe [18], Carnap [19], Kemeny [20], Jeffreys [21] and others can be added to the list.

In statistical physics Szilard is not the only forerunner of Elsasser, Brillouin and Jaynes. Lewis (1930) [22], in a paper devoted to time symmetry, has the sentence 'Gain in entropy always means loss of information, and nothing more. It is a subjective concept.' Van der Waals (1911) [23] derives the time asymmetry in the H-theorem from the classical time asymmetric use of Bayes' conditional probabilities, an idea also expressed by Gibbs [24] in an often quoted sentence. Jaynes has followed up his pioneering articles by more comprehensive publications [25], as has also one of us [26, 27]. Among other authors using the information theoretical approach in probability theory or in statistical mechanics we quote Kinchin [28], Yaglom and Yaglom [29], Katz [30], Hobson [31], and Baierlein [32].

In Section II we outline the information-theoretical derivation of the laws of equilibrium in statistical mechanics.

As for the more special topic of Maxwell's demon and Szilard's 'well-informed heat engine' we have brief comments in Section III with a reference to Brillouin.

II. Outline of the Information Theory Basis for Physical Theory

Part of Cox's contribution may be summarized as follows: suppose we wish to inform someone else of our *incomplete* knowledge of a subject. Is there a unique code which enables us to say neither more or less than we really know? Cox saw that instead of trying to *find* such a code, it would be necessary to *design* it. To design implies generation of alternative designs and the selection among them according to criteria. But what criteria should be used for the code? Cox chose criteria equivalent to the following:

1.   Consistency
2.   Freedom from Ambiguity
3.   Universality
4.   Honesty

What is surprising is that these criteria are necessary and sufficient to develop unique functional equations (27, Chapter I). For example, one of Cox's functional equations is:

$$[AB|E] = F([A|BE], [B|E])$$
$$= F([B|AE], [A|E])$$

(1)

F is a function to be determined, [ ] is a measure. Cox's solutions are the ordinary equations of mathematical probability theory:

$$p(A|E) + p(\sim A|E) = 1 \quad 0 < p < 1 \tag{2a}$$

$$p(AB|E) = p(A|BE)\, p(B|E) \tag{2b}$$

[A and B are propositions, $\sim A$ is the denial to A, E is the evidence and p is 'a numerical encoding of what the evidence E implies'.] Equations (2a) and (2b) can be used to develop all of probability calculus [27].

Cox's approach is unique in his deliberate attempt to *design a code* for the communication of partial information. The code is constrained to obey certain functional equations, which turn out to yield the equations of the calculus of probabilities. This result sheds new light on an old controversy; namely, the 'meaning' of the concept 'probability'. Because these equations are obtained by design, the interpretation of the function p is clear.

In the notation $p(\bullet|E)$, p is 'an encoding of knowledge about $\bullet$'. E represents the knowledge to be encoded. Only a measure which obeys the above two equations can be used as an encoding to satisfy the desired criteria.

The definition of p, due to Cox, is free of two limitations. On the one hand, it is not defined by reference to physical objects such as balls in urns or frequency of numbers in the toss of dice. On the other hand, it is not developed as an 'element on a measure space', devoid of all reference to anything but mathematical context. In no sense do we wish to minimize the importance of being able to put mathematical probability properly in perspective with respect to the rest of mathematics. But if we are to say what we 'mean' by 'probability', we must go beyond merely stating the mathematical properties of the function $p(\ )$.

The interpretation 'p is a numerical encoding of what the evidence E implies' is critical to all that follows.

If we take the Cox interpretation of p as fundamental and general, the question naturally arises: What are the rules for translating a statement E (normally made in a 'natural' language) into an assignment of a set of numbers represented by p? This question is the central task of statistics.

Jaynes' principle enters as a synthesis of Cox's result, just given, and Shannon's result in communication theory. If the knowledge E has been encoded as a set of p's, the measure S indicates how much is yet left to be learned.

$$S = -k \sum P_i \ln p_i \tag{3}$$

Proofs of the uniqueness and generality of S abound [2, 4, 28].

What interests us here is that Shannon's measure uniquely measures the *incompleteness* of the knowledge represented by E. If E were *complete*, the knowledge would be *deterministic*; i.e., would leave no residue of uncertainty. When E is deterministic the calculus reduces to sets of p's which are either 0 or 1 and the logic becomes purely deductive rather than inductive. For cases in which E is incomplete, Jaynes proposed, therefore, the principle of minimum prejudice as follows [6, 7]:

The minimally prejudiced assignment of probabilities is that which maximizes the entropy

$$S = -k \sum p_i \ln p_i \tag{4}$$

subject to the given information

The particularization of this principle for any field of inquiry depends upon the information to be encoded (i.e., upon E and the set A_i). In common parlance we say the uncertainty measure has to be applied to a well-defined question (which A_i is true?) and well-defined evidence (E). Statisticians say 'define the sample space'; thermodynamicists say 'define the system'. Both are saying the same thing, i.e. define the set A_i and be explicit about the experiment (E).

The entropy of Clausius becomes a special case of Shannon's entropy if we ask the right question. The question is put in the following form: suppose an observer knows he is dealing with a system in a volume V which may be in a quantum state 'i' characterized by N_{ai} particles of type a, N_{bi} particles of type b, etc., and an energy ϵ_i. He knows his instruments are too crude to say precisely what ϵ_i, N_{ai}, N_{bi}, etc., truly are. All he can usefully observe are the repeatable measurements on ϵ_i, N_{ai}, N_{bi}, etc.

To apply Jaynes' principle requires the definition of the set of all possible answers. For the system postulated the question is therefore:

$Q =$ 'In what quantum state is the system? (V is given)'

The set of possible answers is:

$A_i =$ 'It is in the ith quantum state, for which the energy is ϵ_i, the number of particles of type a is N_{ai}, the number of particles type b is N_{bi}, etc.'

For illustration in this paper we shall confine our attention to systems in which electricity, magnetism and gravity play no part. The generalization to these phenomena has been given [6, 7, 26].

According to the Cox–Shannon–Jaynes development, the observer should 'encode' his knowledge in a probability assignment. We identify the 'repeatable measurements' with a mathematical 'expectation' for within the theory no other quantity can be so identified. The knowledge, E, therefore, is encoded by maximizing

$$S = -k \sum p_i \ln p_i \tag{4}.$$

subject to

$$\sum p_i = 1 \tag{5}$$

$$\sum p_i \epsilon_i = \langle \epsilon \rangle \tag{6}$$

$$\sum p_i N_{ci} = \langle N_c \rangle \quad c = a, b, \ldots \tag{7}$$

where p_i is the probability that the system is in state i.

By the usual mathematical methods we find

$$p_i = \exp(-\Omega - \beta \epsilon_i - \alpha_a N_{ai} - \alpha_b N_{bi} - \ldots) \tag{8}$$

which is recognized as Gibbs Grand Canonical Distribution. The application of Jaynes' principle has served to introduce three new constructs, represented by Ω, β and the set $\{\alpha_c\}$.

The system of four equations above may be used to replace the set of probabilities and thereby exhibit a set of necessary and sufficient relations among the four constructs S, Ω, β, $\{\alpha_c\}$.

$$S = \Omega + \beta \langle \epsilon \rangle + \sum_c \alpha_c \langle N_c \rangle \tag{9}$$

$$\Omega = \ln \sum_i \exp\left(-\beta \epsilon_i - \sum_c \alpha_c N_{ci}\right) \tag{10}$$

$$\partial \Omega / \partial \beta = -\langle \epsilon \rangle \tag{11}$$

$$\partial \Omega / \partial \alpha_c = -\langle N_c \rangle \tag{12}$$

Two things should be pointed out here. First, there has been no real use of physics. Thus far $\langle \epsilon \rangle$ and $\langle N_c \rangle$ have been defined only by identifying them with 'repeatable' measurements of energy and composition without saying what 'energy' and 'composition' are. The mathematical results should be familiar to all who have studied statistical mechanics and their extension to more general cases should be obvious. Since we have not introduced or made use of any of the properties of energy or the particles, the results are all due to the rules of statistical inference inherent in the Cox–Shannon–Jaynes formulation. There is no reference to ensembles, heat baths, 'thermodynamic systems of which ours is an example drawn at random', etc.

This feature of being able to separate clearly which results are due to statistics and which are due to physics is a particular advantage in the information theory approach. The statistical quantities p_i, S, $\langle \epsilon \rangle$ and $\langle N_c \rangle$ generated Lagrange multipliers Ω, β, $\{\alpha_c\}$ *independent of the physical properties* associated with $\langle \epsilon \rangle$ and $\langle N_c \rangle$; the form of the four equations given comes only from the general procedure for inference laid down by Jaynes. That principle comes from logic; not reasoning about physical systems.

To describe the physical behavior of S, Ω, β and $\{\alpha_c\}$ we have to define the rules for changes in $\langle \epsilon \rangle$ and $\langle N_c \rangle$, i.e. put physics into the description. This has been done, for example, in Ref. [26].

The detailed derivation is given in the references. We quote only some general results to illustrate that the maximum entropy encoding of knowledge about the system of volume V to which we attach expectations $\langle \epsilon \rangle$ and $\langle N_c \rangle$ leads to the concepts associated with classical thermodynamics.

In this derivation the zeroth, first, second and third laws become *consequences*, not premises. Such a conclusion is indeed far reaching and it is no wonder the idea has been resisted for the dozen years since it was first put forward [10].

The properties of the Grand Canonical Distribution were first given by Gibbs who referred to his distributions as 'analogues' [24]. Denbigh [33], in his famous textbook on thermodynamics, also makes it quite clear that his statistical descriptions are *analogies* to classical thermodynamics. All workers who have dealt with statistical mechanics without basing their work squarely upon Shannon's information theory, as used by Jaynes and Cox, have either been silent on the connection between Clausius' entropy and the statistically defined entropy or been careful to disclaim any *necessary* connection between the two.

The important clue to understanding why the results given are more than a mere analogy is the recognition that we are actually defining that elusive state called 'equilibrium'. In this treatment, the encoding and all deductions from it, are valid only for those systems for which 'repeatable' measurements on ϵ_i and N_{ci} are possible and for which knowledge of $\langle \epsilon \rangle$ and $\langle N_c \rangle$ *are sufficient to define the macrostate of the system in volume V*. We can use the derivation to describe the mathematical properties of this state, which we call 'equilibrium', i.e. how changes occur on passage from one equilibrium state to another, how two or more systems interact, etc. These results are valid for systems which satisfy the premises of the theory, i.e. for which 'equilibrium' exists. It remains for experiment to decide if there exist states of physical systems for which the premises can be met. Such a situation is quite common in physics. For example, in mechanics it is postulated that in a 'Newtonian frame': force = mass × acceleration. The question of whether Newtonian frames exist or if a particular frame of reference is Newtonian is settled by seeing if all the deductions from 'force = mass × acceleration' are satisfied.

This circularity in all physical theories is usually glossed over in the education of physicists. It is the subject of very careful scrutiny in Norwood Hanson's illuminating inquiry into theory building [34]. It is in a similar way that the general rules of inference (the maximum entropy encoding) are used to develop a description of 'equilibrium'. Mathematical relations are shown to be a consequence of the encoding process; behavior consistent with these equations proves that 'equilibrium' exists.

It is not generally understood that the concept of equilibrium is ill-defined in the literature of classical thermodynamics just as 'Newtonian frame' was glossed over in pre-relativity days. Attempts to define equilibrium, when they are made at all, are usually based on the idea of waiting for a long time. This idea of waiting a long time is not useful. Geological samples from the earth's interior have been found to be in thermodynamic disequilibrium. If substances that have been around for times comparable to the life of the earth are not in equilibrium, surely 'waiting' doesn't guarantee equilibrium. The proof of disequilibrium is the failure of the material to satisfy the phase rule. And the phase rule is, of course, a consequence of thermodynamics.

There is no way out of the dilemma that equilibrium is defined via thermodynamic constructs which constructs were in turn defined for the equilibrium state. We have no way of telling if a system is 'at equilibrium' except by making experiments which rely on the constructs which are defined by the theory of equilibrium. It is this dilemma which has inspired the comment 'there is no such thing as an immaculate perception'. What we see does depend on what we think.

This is not a special weakness of the information theory approach. It is inherent in the work of Gibbs, who defined equilibrium as the condition of maximum entropy.

The definition of 'equilibrium' thus given does not depend on the physics associated with ϵ_i and N_{ci}. Indeed, these symbols could stand for *anything* and the results would satisfy the desiderata. In references [10] and [27] it is demonstrated that the needed physics is obtained by introducing the following ideas:

1.   The ϵ_i are additive, conserved.
2.   The ϵ_i depend on i and the dimensions which determine V.

From these ideas and the previous equations we may derive all the known relations of classical thermodynamics.

Because the information theory's simplicity and freedom from such artificial constructs as ensembles, heat baths, etc., enables us to keep separate which results come from physics and which from statistics; important differences, often lost in non-information theory treatments are kept in the foreground. For example, irreversibility is traced to the difference between 'force' and 'expected (or equilibrium) force'. There is maintained a distinction between the principle of conservation of energy (a deterministic addition of energies of Newtonian systems) and the First Law of Thermodynamics (a statistical treatment of energy). The roles of $\beta(=1/RT)$ in diffusion of energy and of $\alpha(=-\mu/RT)$ in diffusion of particles are seen to be identical.

Heat is usually treated as a pre-existing idea to be 'explained' by physics. In the information theory treatment it is seen that someone who believes in the principle of conservation of energy (and who wishes to retain consistency in his ideas) *must invent* the concept of heat if he tries to make statistical descriptions. In this treatment entropy is taken as *primitive* and heat *derived* from the resulting statistical descriptions. Also, heat is introduced without the need to define it in terms of temperature or adiabatic walls (and not developed as if 'adiabatic' were understood before heat)!

The information theory treatment thus inverts the usual procedure, in which heat, temperature, and work are taken as primitive, and in which energy and entropy are derived. This break in tradition is hard to accept for those steeped in a tradition that treats the laws of thermodynamics as though they were 'discovered' by experimentalists who knew instinctively about heat, temperature, work, equilibrium and equations of state. But the laws of physics are not 'discovered', they are 'invented' or – better yet – 'designed' according to criteria such as:

1. Consistency
2. Freedom from Ambiguity
3. Universality
4. Honesty

and are, therefore, constrained to the same results as produced simply, elegantly and directly by the information theory approach.

The information theory approach tells us *why* our ancestors *had* to invent temperature, heat, and reversible processes. It elucidates the 'paradoxes' of Szilard, Gibbs and many others. But most of all, it unifies our understanding of many phenomena. And it does so by showing that the entropy of thermodynamics is but a special case of the entropy of information theory.

III. Critique of Jauch and Baron's Discussion of Szilard's Thought Experiment

We definitely do not follow Jauch and Baron in their rebuttal of Szilard's argument. We understand the question as follows:

1. *A matter of semantics.* Jauch and Baron borrow from von Neumann the statement that 'in phenomenological thermodynamics each conceivable process constitutes valid evidence, provided that it does not conflict with the two fundamental laws of thermodynamics', and then add from their own that 'If an idealization is in conflict with a law that is basic to the second law, then it cannot be used as evidence for violation of the second law'.

It is certainly obvious that a self-consistent theory (and macroscopic, phenomenological thermodynamics is a consistent theory) cannot be criticized from within. But this does not forbid the production of thought experiments based on knowledge from *outside* the domain of the theory in order to criticize it. In his criticism of Aristotelian mechanical conceptions Galileo largely used thought experiments based on information that was at hand to everybody, *but* was outside the realm of Aristotelian physics.

The very concept of bouncing point molecules, and of pressure as integrated momentum exchange per sec cm², certainly is *outside* the domain of phenomenological, macroscopic, thermodynamics – not to speak of the consideration of one single molecule, and of learning in what half of the cylinder it is found.

Therefore, let us imitate Socrates in his criticism of Zeno, and proceed.

2. With Jauch and Baron, let us not get involved in quantum subtleties, but instead use the point particle concept of classical mechanics and of the classical kinetic theory of gases.

Let us first discard Jauch and Baron's large heat reservoir; we will bring it in later on.

There is no question that if Szilard's single molecule is (nineteenth-century language) or is known to be (post Szilard and Lewis language) in one definite half of the cylinder, the entropy of the single molecule gas is smaller than when the molecule is allowed to move all through the whole cylinder. If the transition from one state to the other is secured by opening the door in the piston, then the entropy of the gas inside the cylinder increases by $k \operatorname{Ln} 2$.

Does this statement contradict the classical thermodynamical statement that (in Jauch and Baron's terms) 'The entropy of the...system piston, gas...remains constant because it is closed and the changes are reversible'? In fact it does not, because the mere (frictionless) opening of the door entails an 'irreversible' change. Though energetically isolated, our (limited) system is not informationally isolated. However, with this distinction, we are certainly stepping outside the domain of classical thermodynamics.

As a result of opening the door, the pressure inside the cylinder falls down to one-half of what it was; this is because the molecule, while retaining by hypothesis its kinetic energy, now spends only half of its time in each half of the cylinder. Whence the classical expression for the change in entropy. (Note that while the molecule is not 'aware' that the door has been opened, the observer is, hence the entropy increase is computed as of the opening of the door.)

3. Jauch and Baron write: "However, at the exact moment when the piston is in the middle of the cylinder and the opening is closed, the gas violates the law of Gay Lussac because it is compressed to half its volume without expenditure of energy. We therefore conclude that the idealizations in Szilard's experiment are inadmissible in their actual context."

Socrates' walking and walking certainly was inadmissible in the context of Zeno's arguments. Nevertheless he *could* walk. If, by definition, our single molecule is a Newtonian point particle, nothing on earth can prevent us from suddenly closing our frictionless, massless, impenetrable door, and learning afterwards in what half of the cylinder we have trapped our molecule. There is *absolutely nothing* self-contradictory in this, not even the idealized concept of the door, which can be approached at will without even contradicting *classical* thermodynamics.

Moreover, no *classical* thermodynamicist would object to the reversed procedure: opening the door. This is adiabatic expansion, the subject of an experiment by Joule.

Why then had we termed adiabatic expansion an 'irreversible' process, and are we now speaking of it as time symmetric to the process of trapping the single molecule by closing the door? Because macroscopic irreversibility is one thing, and microscopic reversibility another thing, which have to be reconciled. It would lead us too far astray to delve here in this problem; we simply refer the reader to a recent discussion of it in terms that are consonant to those we are using here [35].

4. Finally we bring in Jauch and Baron's pulleys, strings and scales, which will restore the macroscopic irreversibility of the whole process.

From now on, as soon as we suddenly close the door, we do *not* allow the (single molecule) gas to expand adiabatically: we harness it, and have it lift (reversibly) a weight. This will cause its temperature to drop down, so that the heat reservoir becomes extremely useful if we want to lift many weights. So we bring it in also.

And *now* the *whole* system, supposed to be isolated, undergoes a (macroscopically) *reversible* change, so that its entropy remains constant.

However, *potential energy has been gained at the expenditure of heat* so that, at first sight, there is something wrong in the entropy balance. What are we overlooking?

We are overlooking that the observer has to *know*, that is, to *learn* which way the piston begins moving, and *then* push a weight on the right scale. This is his *free decision*, in accord with the *general decision* he has made, to use the heat in the reservoir for lifting weights. However, we are not delving here in a discussion of the twin Aristotelian aspects of information: cognizance and will [36].

Suffice it to say that, in order to have the entropy balance right, we *must* include in it the *information* gained by the observer. But this was Szilard's statement.

5. Finally, together with Brillouin [4] and others, Jauch and Baron point out rightly that the preceding 'system' can be transformed into a 'robot', the functioning of which, however, will require drawing negentropy from an existing source, by an amount at least as large as the negentropy created by lifting the weights.

The point is that the robot does not just step out of nowhere – no more than does a refrigerator or a heat engine. This brings into the problem Brillouin's 'structural negentropy', also Brillouin's 'information contained in the expression of the physical laws' that the engineer has used, and, finally, the problem of all the thinking and decision-making on the engineer's part.

In other words, if you push information out of the door by appealing to the robot, then it will come back right through the adiabatic wall.

6. *Concluding* this section, we believe that, while it is possible, and very informative, to deduce Thermodynamics from a general theory of Information, the converse is not possible. Thermodynamics is too rooted in specifics of physics to produce a general theory of information.

But this is a mere instance of the way scientific progress goes on...

REFERENCES

[1] J. M. JAUCH and J. G. BARON, Helv. Phys. Acta *45*, 220 (1972).
[2] C. E. SHANNON, Bell Syst. Techn. Journ. *27*, 379, 623 (1948); C. E. SHANNON and W. WEAVER, *The Mathematical Theory of Communication* (Univ. of Illinois Press, Urbana 1949).
[3] L. Szilard, Zeits. für Phys. *53*, 840 (1929).
[4] L. BRILLOUIN, *Science and Information Theory* (Academic Press, New York 1957).
[5] H. GRAD, Comm. Pure Appl. Math. *14*, 323 (1971).
[6] E. T. JAYNES, Phys. Rev. *106*, 620 (1957); *108*, 171 (1957).
[7] E. T. JAYNES, Amer. Journ. Phys. *31*, 66 (1963).
[8] R. T. Cox, Amer. Journ. Phys. *14*, 1 (1946).
[9] R. T. Cox, *The Algebra of Probable Inference* (John Hopkins Press, Baltimore 1961).
[10] M. TRIBUS, J. Appl. Mech. March 1961, pp. 1–8; M. TRIBUS and R. B. Evans, Appl. Mech. Rev. *16* (10), 765–769 (1963); M. TRIBUS, P. T. SHANNON and R. B. Evans, AEChI Jour. March 1966, pp. 244–248; M. TRIBUS, Amer. Sci. *54* (2) (1966).
[11] R. T. BAYES, Philos. Trans. *53*, 370 (1763).
[12] S. P. DE LAPLACE, *Essai Philosophique sur les Probabilitiés*, 1774. See also *A Philosophical Essay on Probabilities* (Dover, New York 1951).
[13] D. HUME, *An Enquiry Concerning Human Destiny*, 1758.
[14] J. VON NEUMANN, Nachr. Akad. Wiss. Goettingen, Math.-Phys. Kl., 245 and 273 (1927).
[15] J. VON NEUMANN, *Mathematische Grundlagen der Quantenmachanik* (Springer, Berlin 1972). See also *Mathematical Foundations of Quantum Mechanics* (Princeton Univ. Press, Princeton, N.J. 1955).
[16] W. M. ELSASSER, Phys. Rev. *52*, 987 (1937).
[17] R. A. FISHER, Proc. Camb. Phil. Soc. *26*, 528 (1929); *28*, 257 (1932).
[18] S. WATANABE, Zeits. für Phys. *113*, 482 (1939).
[19] R. CARNAP, *The Continuum of Inductive Methods* (Univ. of Chicago Press 1952).
[20] J. KEMENY, Journ. Symbolic Logic *20*, 263 (1955).
[21] H. JEFFREYS, *Theory of Probability* (Oxford, Clarendon Press 1939).
[22] G. N. LEWIS, Science *71*, 569 (1939).
[23] J. D. VAN DER WAALS, Phys. Zeits. *12*, 547 (1911).
[24] J. W. GIBBS, *Elementary Principles in Statistical Mechanics* (Yale Univ. Press, New Haven, Conn. 1914), p. 150.
[25] E. T. JAYNES, *Foundations of probability theory and statistical mechanics*, in *Studies in the Foundations of Methodology and Philosophy of Science*, Vol. 1, Delaware Seminar in the Foundations of Physics (Springer, New York 1967); *Information theory and statistical mechanics*, in *Brandeis Lectures* (Benjamin, Inc., New York 1963), p. 181.

[26] M. Tribus, *Thermostatics and Thermodynamics* (D. van Nostrand Co., Princeton, N.J. 1961). See also N. Термостатnка, *Tepmoznhamnka* (Moscow 1970).

[27] M. Tribus, *Rational Descriptions, Decisions and Designs* (Pergamon, Oxford and New York 1970). See also *Decisions Rationnelles dans l'Incertain* (Masson, Paris 1972).

[28] A. I. Khinchin, *Mathematical Foundations of Information Theory* (Dover, New York 1957).

[29] A. M. Yaglom and I. M. Yaglom, *Probabilité et Information* (Dunod, Paris 1959).

[30] A. Katz, *Principles of Statistical Mechanics* (W. H. Freeman and Co., San Francisco and London 1967).

[31] A. Hobson, *Concepts in Statistical Mechanics* (Gordon and Breach, New York 1971).

[32] R. Baierlein, *Atoms and Information Theory* (W. H. Freeman and Co., San Francisco and London 1971).

[33] K. G. Denbigh, *The Principles of Chemical Equilbrium* (Cambridge University Press 1955).

[34] N. R. Hanson, *Patterns of Discovery* (Cambridge University Press 1958).

[35] O. Costa de Beauregard (reporter): *Discussion on temporal asymmetry in thermodynamics and cosmology*, in *Proceedings of the International Conference on Thermodynamics*, held in Cardiff, edited by P. T. Landsberg (Butterworths, London 1970).

[36] O. Costa de Beauregard, *Is there a paradox in the theory of time anisotropy*, in *A Critical Review of Thermodynamics*, edited by E. B. Stuart, B. Gal-Or and A. J. Brainard (Mono Book Corps., Baltimore 1970), pp. 463–472. See also Studium Generale *54*, 10 (1971).

The operation of Maxwell's demon in a low entropy system

A. F. Rex

Physics Department, University of Puget Sound, Tacoma, Washington 98416

(Received 24 October 1985; accepted for publication 28 March 1986)

The problem of Maxwell's sorting demon traditionally has been studied for the case in which the hot and cold regions differ very little in temperature. In this article a solution is presented for the case in which the temperature difference is great so that the total entropy is lower. Calculations indicate that in this case the demon must use a large number of photons to observe the proper kinds of particles. This causes an increase in entropy which more than offsets the decrease caused by an exchange of particles.

I. INTRODUCTION

The well-known sorting demon first proposed by Maxwell[1] remains one of the best examples of the wide range of applicability of the second law of thermodynamics. Maxwell was not able to reconcile the demon completely with the second law because he failed to take into account the energy (and hence the entropy) added to a system of particles by the act of observation. The necessary understanding of light quantization and black body radiation was not available at the time of Maxwell's death in 1879. Some relevant work concerning the relationship between quantum mechanics and the second law was done by Born and Green.[2,3] However, a more straightforward approach was taken by Brillouin,[4,5] who used only the "old" quantum theory of light quantization and black body radiation, along with classical thermodynamics. It is this approach to the problem of Maxwell's demon which is cited most often (although still infrequently) by thermodynamics texts and monographs.[6]

Brillouin's solution is valid over almost the entire range of classical thermodynamics. However, there are some particularly interesting examples with parameters lying outside of those allowed by Brillouin's simplifying assumptions. This article will consider some of those examples. Whenever necessary the most generous concessions will be allowed the demon. In spite of these concessions, the demon (not surprisingly) still will not be able to violate the second law.

II. THEORY

Brillouin considered two gas-filled regions A and B separated by a movable partition. The partition is controlled by the demon, who hopes to decrease the total entropy of the system by allowing only relatively fast particles to pass from the cold to the hot region. It is assumed that $T_B > T_A$, with $T_B - T_A = \Delta T$. Also, a temperature T is defined so that

$$T_A = T - \tfrac{1}{2}\Delta T \tag{1}$$

and

$$T_B = T + \tfrac{1}{2}\Delta T. \tag{2}$$

In each region j the equipartition theorem dictates that the mean energy of a particle is

$$\overline{E}_j = \tfrac{3}{2} kT_j. \tag{3}$$

Therefore the demon should select a particle from A with energy $\tfrac{3}{2} kT (1 + \epsilon_1)$ and allow it to pass into B. Similarly, a particle with energy $\tfrac{3}{2} kT (1 - \epsilon_2)$ will be allowed to pass from B into A.

In order to see those particles, one must distinguish photons scattered from them from the black body radiation.

This requires that the energy of the photon used to observe the particle is $h\nu > kT$. The entropy increase due to the act of observation is then

$$\Delta S_d = h\nu/T = kb, \qquad (4)$$

where $b = h\nu/kT > 1$. Since (at least) two photons must be used in the process described above, the net entropy increase is

$$\Delta S_d = 2kb. \qquad (5)$$

The entropy decrease effected by the demon is calculated using the energy transfer

$$Q = \tfrac{3}{2} kT \,(\epsilon_1 + \epsilon_2). \qquad (6)$$

The resulting entropy decrease is

$$\Delta S_i = (Q/T_B) - (Q/T_A) \cong -Q(\Delta T)/T^2 \qquad (7)$$

or

$$\Delta S_i \cong -\tfrac{3}{2} k(\epsilon_1 + \epsilon_2)\,(\Delta T/T). \qquad (8)$$

Now Brillouin presumes that both ϵ_1 and ϵ_2 are small and that $\Delta T \ll T$, which means that

$$\Delta S_i = -\tfrac{3}{2} k\eta, \qquad (9)$$

with $\eta \ll 1$. Therefore the net entropy change is

$$\Delta S_d + S_i \cong k(2b - \tfrac{3}{2}\eta) > 0 \qquad (10)$$

and the second law is validated.

The example just presented is not valid universally, however. Crucial to this argument is the assumption in Eq. (7) that $T_A T_B \cong T^2$. The exact expression is

$$T_A T_B = T^2 - (\Delta T)^2/4. \qquad (11)$$

The resulting entropy decrease due to energy exchange is now

$$\Delta S_i = -Q(\Delta T)/[T^2 - (\Delta T)^2/4]. \qquad (12)$$

ΔS_i is not necessarily negligible any more. In the limit as ΔT approaches T (the most favorable case from the demon's point of view),

$$\Delta S_i = -\tfrac{3}{4} k(\epsilon_1 + \epsilon_2)[\,(T_B^2 - T_A^2)/(T_A T_B)\,], \qquad (13)$$

or using Eq. (6),

$$\Delta S_i \cong -\tfrac{3}{4} k(\epsilon_1 + \epsilon_2)(T_B/T_A). \qquad (14)$$

A comparison of Eqs. (5) and (14) reveals where the difficulty lies. By definition $\epsilon_2 < 1$, but in principle ϵ_1 may be somewhat greater than unity. At first glance this would seem to be a violation of the second law, for while b must be greater than unity in order to distinguish a particle from the black body radiation, there is no clear justification for it to be greater than ϵ_1.

The resolution of this problem lies in the fact that a single photon will not be sufficient to find a particle with the desired velocity. Consider how the values of ϵ_1 relate to the physical situation. In order to obtain a relatively high value for ϵ_1 (even to obtain a value approaching unity), the demon must select a particle with exceptionally high speed compared with the mean.

$$\bar{v}_A = \sqrt{8kT_A/\pi m}, \qquad (15)$$

where m is the mass of a single particle. Particles with this desired characteristic will be found only far out on the "tail" of the Maxwell speed distribution. The fraction F of those particles with a speed greater than a given speed v_2 for a classical gas at temperature T_A is

$$F = \int_{v_2}^{\infty} f(v)\,dv, \qquad (16)$$

where $f(v)$ is the normalized Maxwell function

$$f(v) = 4(m/2\pi kT_A)^{3/2}v^2 \exp(-mv^2/2kT_A). \qquad (17)$$

This means that the number n_1 of photons normally re-

Table I. Calculated values of n_1, n_2, ϵ_1, and ϵ_2 as a function of temperatures and selected speeds for nitrogen gas. Temperatures are in K and speeds in m/s.

T_A	T_B	$\bar{v}_A$	$\bar{v}_B$	v_1	v_2	n_1	n_2	ϵ_1	ϵ_2
300	320	475	490	300	600	3.9	5.3	0.31	0.67
300	320	475	490	100	800	16	113	1.3	0.96
300	320	475	490	100	1200	1100	113	4.3	0.96
200	220	388	407	300	500	4.2	3.4	0.34	0.52
200	220	388	407	200	600	9.4	9.3	0.94	0.78
200	220	388	407	200	1000	1500	9.3	4.4	0.78
100	120	274	300	200	400	7.0	4.3	0.64	0.59
100	120	274	300	100	500	27	27	1.6	0.90
100	120	274	300	100	1000	7.2×10^6	27	9.3	0.90
600	620	672	683	600	800	3.3	2.4	0.19	0.33
600	620	672	683	400	1000	7.7	5.9	0.85	0.70
600	620	672	683	400	2000	2.4×10^4	5.9	6.4	0.70
2000	2100	1226	1256	1000	2000	13	2.9	1.2	0.45
2000	2100	1226	1256	1000	3000	670	2.9	4.0	0.45
300	500	475	612	300	800	16	9.5	0.81	0.75
300	500	475	612	300	1200	1100	7.5	3.1	0.75
300	1000	475	867	300	1200	1100	25	1.5	0.84
300	1000	475	867	200	2000	2.4×10^9	79	6.0	0.93
200	500	388	613	200	800	82	29	1.1	0.87
200	500	388	613	200	1250	6.0×10^4	29	3.7	0.87
100	500	274	613	100	800	1.6×10^4	220	1.4	0.96
100	500	274	613	100	1000	7.2×10^6	220	2.8	0.96

Table II. Calculated values of n_1, n_2, ϵ_1, and ϵ_2 as a function of temperatures and selected speeds for hydrogen gas. Temperatures are in K and speeds in m/s.

T_A	T_B	$\bar{v}_A$	$\bar{v}_B$	v_1	v_2	n_1	n_2	ϵ_1	ϵ_2
300	320	1777	1835	1500	2100	3.2	2.8	0.15	0.41
300	320	1777	1835	1000	2500	6.0	7.1	0.63	0.74
300	320	1777	1835	1000	3000	16	7.1	1.3	0.74
300	320	1777	1835	1000	3500	53	7.1	2.2	0.74
200	220	1451	1521	1200	2000	5.5	3.0	0.54	0.45
200	220	1451	1521	1000	3000	84	4.5	2.5	0.62
30	50	562	725	300	1000	23	15	1.0	0.82
30	50	562	725	300	1500	2800	15	3.5	0.82
600	620	2513	2554	2000	3000	3.3	3.0	0.19	0.47
600	620	2513	2554	2000	5000	58	3.0	2.3	0.47
2000	2100	4587	4701	4000	6000	4.5	2.5	0.42	0.37
2000	2100	4587	4701	4000	10000	150	2.5	2.9	0.37
300	1000	1777	3244	1500	3500	53	11	0.52	0.72
300	1000	1777	3244	1000	5000	7400	34	2.1	0.88
200	1000	1451	3244	1400	3500	550	13	0.65	0.74
200	1000	1451	3244	1400	5000	1.1×10^6	13	2.4	0.74
100	1000	1026	3244	1000	3300	1.6×10^5	34	0.60	0.85
100	1000	1026	3244	1000	3500	8.4×10^5	34	0.80	0.85

quired to find a particle with speed greater than v_2 will be

$$n_1 = \frac{1}{F} = \left(\int_{v_2}^{\infty} f(v)\,dv \right)^{-1}. \qquad (18)$$

Similarly the demon must select an appropriately slow particle for transfer from B to A. Clearly the number of photons needed to find such a particle (with speed less than v_1) will be

$$n_2 = \left(\int_0^{v_1} f(v)\,dv \right)^{-1}. \qquad (19)$$

Note that the temperature T_B must be used in $f(v)$ in Eq. (19). Also, it is clear that v_1 must not be more than $\bar{v}_A$ and v_2 must not be less than $\bar{v}_B$. With these constraints the net entropy change will be

$$\Delta S_d + \Delta S_i \geqslant k(n_1 b + n_2 b - 2\epsilon_1 - 2\epsilon_2), \qquad (20)$$

where the inequality is due to the nature of the approximations made to obtain Eqs. (13) and (14). The sum of n_1 and n_2 must be sufficiently large in order for (20) to satisfy the second law, i.e., so that the right-hand side of (20) is positive.

III. RESULTS

The integrals in Eqs. (18) and (19) were performed on a computer using Newtonian quadrature. The integral in Eq. (18) was calculated using limits v_2 to $10v_2$. The exponential factor in the Maxwell function ensures that these limits will be sufficient to yield a very accurate result.

Tables I and II show some results for the typical gases nitrogen and hydrogen. Since ϵ_2 is restricted to values $0 < \epsilon_2 < 1$, it is useful to concentrate on ϵ_1. As was noted in Sec. II, higher values of ϵ_1 represent a greater entropy de-

Table III. Calculated values of n_1, n_2, ϵ_1, and ϵ_2 as a function of temperatures and selected speeds for a dilute gas of electrons. Temperatures are in K and speeds in m/s.

T_A	T_B	$\bar{v}_A$	$\bar{v}_B$	v_1	v_2	n_1	n_2	ϵ_1	ϵ_2
300	320	1.08×10^5	1.12×10^5	1.0×10^5	1.2×10^5	2.7	2.3	0.01	0.30
300	320	1.08×10^5	1.12×10^5	1.0×10^5	2.0×10^5	31	2.3	1.8	0.30
300	320	1.08×10^5	1.12×10^5	1.0×10^5	3.0×10^5	5600	2.3	5.3	0.30
100	120	6.2×10^4	6.8×10^4	5.0×10^4	1.0×10^5	11	3.5	0.98	0.50
100	120	6.2×10^4	6.8×10^4	5.0×10^4	2.0×10^5	1.4×10^5	3.5	6.9	0.50
1	2	6200	8800	5000	1.5×10^4	515	6.5	2.3	0.64
1	2	6200	8800	1900	2.0×10^4	1.4×10^5	6.5	4.8	0.64
0.1	1	1974	6242	1900	6500	3.0×10^5	35	0.67	0.86
0.1	1	1974	6242	1900	1.0×10^4	9.5×10^{13}	35	3.0	0.86
1.0×10^{-6}	2.0×10^{-6}	6.2	8.8	6	10	12	4.1	0.45	0.48
1.0×10^{-6}	2.0×10^{-6}	6.2	8.8	6	20	1.4×10^5	4.1	4.8	0.48
1000	1500	2.0×10^5	2.4×10^5	1.9×10^5	2.5×10^5	4.0	3.0	0.09	0.37
1000	1500	2.0×10^5	2.4×10^5	1.9×10^5	3.0×10^5	8.6	3.0	0.57	0.37
1000	1500	2.0×10^5	2.4×10^5	1.9×10^5	4.0×10^5	69	3.0	1.8	0.37
1000	2000	1.0×10^5	2.8×10^5	1.9×10^5	3.0×10^5	8.6	4.1	0.31	0.48
1000	2000	2.0×10^5	2.8×10^5	1.9×10^5	4.0×10^5	69	4.1	1.3	0.48

crease associated with the exchange of particles between A and B. The calculations presented in Tables I and II suggest strongly that there is no adjustment of parameters which will result in a favorable outcome for the demon, i.e., a net decrease in entropy. The best strategy for increasing ϵ_1, namely to increase v_2, is precisely the thing which causes n_1 to increase most quickly. In all cases examined it is clear that n_1 increases much more rapidly than ϵ_1. This should not be unexpected considering the nature of the statistical distribution of speeds.

In order to determine whether this result is peculiar to typical gas molecules, calculations were also performed for a gas of electrons. It is assumed that the gas is dilute enough so that Coulomb forces do not adversely affect the work of the demon. This assumption also makes it reasonable to believe that classical statistics will be valid over the wide range of temperatures considered. Again the results (shown in Table III) indicate that any attempt to increase ϵ_1 results in a much greater increase in n_1. This is true for a wide range of temperatures T_A and T_B.

While these results are by no means exhaustive, they provide further insight into the problems faced by Maxwell's entropy reducing demon. Indeed it is clear that these entropy reductions can only be slight in comparison with the entropy added through the required process of observation. It is interesting to note what a crucial role this process of observation (normally important in modern quantum theory) plays in dealing with particles which obey classical statistics. This is perhaps one of the best examples of such an overlap between classical and quantum concepts.

[1] J. C. Maxwell, *Theory of Heat* (London, 1871).
[2] M. Born and H. S. Green, Proc. R. Soc. London Ser. A **192**, 166 (1948).
[3] Max Born, Ann. Phys. **3**, 107 (1948).
[4] L. Brillouin, J. Appl. Phys. **22**, 334 (1951).
[5] L. Brillouin, J. Appl. Phys. **22**, 338 (1951).
[6] See, for example, A. B. Pippard, *The Elements of Classical Thermodynamics* (Cambridge U. P., Cambridge, 1981).

CHAPTER 4

Maxwell's Demon, Information Erasure, and
Computing

Irreversibility and Heat Generation in the Computing Process

Abstract: It is argued that computing machines inevitably involve devices which perform logical functions that do not have a single-valued inverse. This logical irreversibility is associated with physical irreversibility and requires a minimal heat generation, per machine cycle, typically of the order of kT for each irreversible function. This dissipation serves the purpose of standardizing signals and making them independent of their exact logical history. Two simple, but representative, models of bistable devices are subjected to a more detailed analysis of switching kinetics to yield the relationship between speed and energy dissipation, and to estimate the effects of errors induced by thermal fluctuations.

1. Introduction

The search for faster and more compact computing circuits leads directly to the question: What are the ultimate physical limitations on the progress in this direction? In practice the limitations are likely to be set by the need for access to each logical element. At this time, however, it is still hard to understand what physical requirements this puts on the degrees of freedom which bear information. The existence of a storage medium as compact as the genetic one indicates that one can go very far in the direction of compactness, at least if we are prepared to make sacrifices in the way of speed and random access.

Without considering the question of access, however, we can show, or at least very strongly suggest, that information processing is inevitably accompanied by a certain minimum amount of heat generation. In a general way this is not surprising. Computing, like all processes proceeding at a finite rate, must involve some dissipation. Our arguments, however, are more basic than this, and show that there is a minimum heat generation, independent of the rate of the process. Naturally the amount of heat generation involved is many orders of magnitude smaller than the heat dissipation in any practically conceivable device. The relevant point, however, is that the dissipation has a real function and is not just an unnecessary nuisance. The much larger amounts of dissipation in practical devices may be serving the same function.

Our conclusion about dissipation can be anticipated in several ways, and our major contribution will be a tightening of the concepts involved, in a fashion which will give some insight into the physical requirements for logical devices. The simplest way of anticipating our conclusion is to note that a binary device must have at least one degree of freedom associated with the information. Classically a degree of freedom is associated with kT of thermal energy. Any switching signals passing between devices must therefore have this much energy to override the noise. This argument does not make it clear that the signal energy must actually be dissipated. An alternative way of anticipating our conclusions is to refer to the arguments by Brillouin and earlier authors, as summarized by Brillouin in his book, *Science and Information Theory,*[1] to the effect that the measurement process requires a dissipation of the order of kT. The computing process, where the setting of various elements depends upon the setting of other elements at previous times, is closely akin to a measurement. It is difficult, however, to argue out this connection in a more exact fashion. Furthermore, the arguments concerning the measurement process are based on the analysis of specific models (as will some of our arguments about computing), and the specific models involved in the measurement analysis are rather far from the kind of mechanisms involved in data processing. In fact the arguments dealing with the measurement process do not define *measurement* very well, and avoid the very essential question: When is a system A coupled to a system B performing a measurement? The mere fact that two physical systems are coupled does not in itself require dissipation.

Our main argument will be a refinement of the following line of thought. A simple binary device consists of a particle in a bistable potential well shown in Fig. 1. Let us arbitrarily label the particle in the left-hand well as the ZERO state. When the particle is in the right-hand well, the device is in the ONE state. Now consider the operation

RESTORE TO ONE, which leaves the particle in the ONE state, regardless of its initial location. If we are told that the particle is in the ONE state, then it is easy to leave it in the ONE state, without spending energy. If on the other hand we are told that the particle is in the ZERO state, we can apply a force to it, which will push it over the barrier, and then, when it has passed the maximum, we can apply a retarding force, so that when the particle arrives at ONE, it will have no excess kinetic energy, and we will not have expended any energy in the whole process, since we extracted energy from the particle in its downhill motion. Thus at first sight it seems possible to RESTORE TO ONE without any expenditure of energy. Note, however, that in order to avoid energy expenditure we have used two different routines, depending on the initial state of the device. This is not how a computer operates. In most instances a computer pushes information around in a manner that is independent of the exact data which are being handled, and is only a function of the physical circuit connections.

Can we then construct a single time-varying force, $F(t)$, which when applied to the conservative system of Fig. 1 will cause the particle to end up in the ONE state, if it was initially in either the ONE state or the ZERO state? Since the system is conservative, its whole history can be reversed in time, and we will still have a system satisfying the laws of motion. In the time-reversed system we then have the possibility that for a single initial condition (position in the ONE state, zero velocity) we can end up in at least two places: the ZERO state or the ONE state. This, however, is impossible. The laws of mechanics are completely deterministic and a trajectory is determined by an initial position and velocity. (An initially unstable position can, in a sense, constitute an exception. We can roll away from the unstable point in one of at least two directions. Our initial point ONE is, however, a point of stable equilibrium.) Reverting to the original direction of time development, we see then that it is not possible to invent a single $F(t)$ which causes the particle to arrive at ONE regardless of its initial state.

If, however, we permit the potential well to be lossy, this becomes easy. A very strong positive initial force applied slowly enough so that the damping prevents oscillations will push the particle to the right, past ONE, regardless of the particle's initial state. Then if the force is taken away slowly enough, so that the damping has a chance to prevent appreciable oscillations, the particle is bound to arrive at ONE. This example also illustrates a point argued elsewhere[2] in more detail: While a heavily overdamped system is obviously undesirable, since it is made sluggish, an extremely underdamped one is also not desirable for switching, since then the system may bounce back into the wrong state if the switching force is applied and removed too quickly.

2. Classification

Before proceeding to the more detailed arguments we will need to classify data processing equipment by the means used to hold information, when it is not interacting

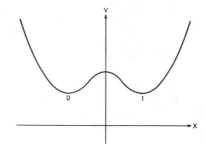

Figure 1 **Bistable potential well.**
x is a generalized coordinate representing quantity which is switched.

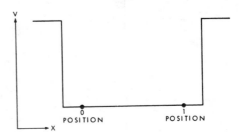

Figure 2 **Potential well in which ZERO and ONE state are not separated by barrier.**
Information is preserved because random motion is slow.

or being processed. The simplest class and the one to which all the arguments of subsequent sections will be addressed consists of devices which can hold information without dissipating energy. The system illustrated in Fig. 1 is in this class. Closely related to the mechanical example of Fig. 1 are ferrites, ferroelectrics and thin magnetic films. The latter, which can switch without domain wall motion, are particularly close to the one-dimensional device shown in Fig. 1. Cryotrons are also devices which show dissipation only when switching. They do differ, however, from the device of Fig. 1 because the ZERO and ONE states are not particularly favored energetically. A cryotron is somewhat like the mechanical device illustrated in Fig. 2, showing a particle in a box. Two particular positions in the box are chosen to represent ZERO and ONE, and the preservation of information depends on the fact that Brownian motion in the box is very slow. The reliance on the slowness of Brownian motion rather than on restoring forces is not only characteristic of cryotrons, but of most of the more familiar forms of information storage: Writing, punched cards, microgroove recording, etc. It is clear from the literature that all essential logical functions can be performed by

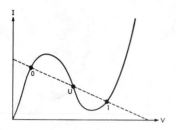

Figure 3   **Negative resistance characteristic (solid line) with load line (dashed).**
ZERO *and* ONE *are stable states,* U *is unstable.*

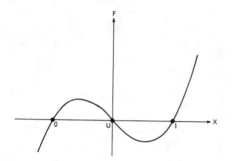

Figure 4   **Force versus distance for the bistable well of Fig. 1.**
ZERO *and* ONE *are the stable states,* U *the unstable one.*

devices in this first class. Computers can be built that contain either only cryotrons, or only magnetic cores.[3, 4]

The second class of devices consists of structures which are in a steady (time invariant) state, but in a dissipative one, while holding on to information. Electronic flip-flop circuits, relays, and tunnel diodes are in this class. The latter, whose characteristic with load line is shown in Fig. 3, typifies the behavior. Two stable points of operation are separated by an unstable position, just as for the device in Fig. 1. It is noteworthy that this class has no known representatives analogous to Fig. 2. All the active bistable devices (latches) have built-in means for restoration to the desired state. The similarity between Fig. 3 and the device of Fig. 1 becomes more conspicuous if we represent the bistable well of Fig. 1 by a diagram plotting force against distance. This is shown in Fig. 4. The line $F=0$ intersects the curve in three positions, much like the load line (or a line of constant current), in Fig. 3. This analogy leads us to expect that in the case of the dissipative device there will be transitions from the desired state, to the other stable state, resulting from thermal agitation or quantum mechanical tunneling, much like for the dissipationless case, and as has been

discussed for the latter in detail by Swanson.[5] The dissipative device, such as the single tunnel diode, will in general be an analog, strictly speaking, to an unsymmetrical potential well, rather than the symmetrical well shown in Fig. 1. We can therefore expect that of the two possible states for the negative resistance device only one is really stable, the other is metastable. An assembly of bistable tunnel diodes left alone for a sufficiently long period would eventually almost all arrive at the same state of absolute stability.

In general when using such latching devices in computing circuits one tries hard to make the dissipation in the two allowed states small, by pushing these states as closely as possible to the voltage or current axis. If one were successful in eliminating this dissipation almost completely during the steady state, the device would become a member of our first class. Our intuitive expectation is, therefore, that in the steady state dissipative device the dissipation per switching event is at least as high as in the devices of the first class, and that this dissipation per switching event is supplemented by the steady state dissipation.

The third and remaining class is a "catch-all"; namely, those devices where time variation is essential to the recognition of information. This includes delay lines, and also carrier schemes, such as the phase-bistable system of von Neumann.[6] The latter affords us a very nice illustration of the need for dissipative effects; most other members of this third class seem too complex to permit discussion in simple physical terms.

In the von Neumann scheme, which we shall not attempt to describe here in complete detail, one uses a "pump" signal of frequency ω_0, which when applied to a circuit tuned to $\omega_0/2$, containing a nonlinear reactance, will cause the spontaneous build-up of a signal at the lower frequency. The lower frequency signal has a choice of two possible phases (180° apart at the lower frequency) and this is the source of the bistability. In the von Neumann scheme the pump is turned off after the subharmonic has developed, and the subharmonic subsequently permitted to decay through circuit losses. This decay is an essential part of the scheme and controls the direction in which information is passed. Thus at first sight the circuit losses perform an essential function. It can be shown, however, that the signal reduction can be produced in a lossless nonlinear circuit, by a suitably phased pump signal. Hence it would seem adequate to use lossless nonlinear circuits, and instead of turning the pump off, change the pump phase so that it causes signal decay instead of signal growth. The directionality of information flow therefore does not really depend on the existence of losses. The losses do, however, perform another essential function.

The von Neumann system depends largely on a coupling scheme called *majority logic*, in which one couples to three subharmonic oscillators and uses the sum of their oscillations to synchronize a subharmonic oscillator whose pump will cause it to build up at a later time than the initial three. Each of the three signals which are added together can have one of two possible phases. At most two of the signals can cancel, one will always survive, and thus there will always be a phase determined for the build-up of the next oscillation. The synchronization signal can, therefore, have two possible magnitudes. If all three of the inputs agree we get a synchronization signal three times as big as in the case where only two inputs have a given phase. If the subharmonic circuit is lossless the subsequent build-up will then result in two different amplitudes, depending on the size of the initial synchronization signal. This, however, will interfere with the basic operation of the scheme at the next stage, where we will want to combine outputs of three oscillators again, and will want all three to be of equal amplitude. We thus see that the absence of the losses gives us an output amplitude from each oscillator which is too dependent on inputs at an earlier stage. While perhaps the deviation from the desired amplitudes might still be tolerable after one cycle, these deviations could build up, through a period of several machine cycles. The losses, therefore, are needed so that the unnecessary details of a signal's history will be obliterated. The losses are essential for the standardization of signals, a function which in past theoretical discussions has perhaps not received adequate recognition, but has been very explicitly described in a recent paper by A. W. Lo.[7]

3. Logical irreversibility

In the Introduction we analyzed Fig. 1 in connection with the command RESTORE TO ONE and argued that this required energy dissipation. We shall now attempt to generalize this train of thought. RESTORE TO ONE is an example of a logical truth function which we shall call *irreversible*. We shall call a device *logically irreversible* if the output of a device does not uniquely define the inputs. We believe that devices exhibiting logical irreversibility are essential to computing. Logical irreversibility, we believe, in turn implies physical irreversibility, and the latter is accompanied by dissipative effects.

We shall think of a computer as a distinctly finite array of N binary elements which can hold information, without dissipation. We will take our machine to be synchronous, so that there is a well-defined machine cycle and at the end of each cycle the N elements are a complicated function of their state at the beginning of the cycle.

Our arguments for logical irreversibility will proceed on three distinct levels. The first-level argument consists simply in the assertion that present machines do depend largely on logically irreversible steps, and that therefore any machine which copies the logical organization of present machines will exhibit logical irreversibility, and therefore by the argument of the next Section, also physical irreversibility.

The second level of our argument considers a particular class of computers, namely those using logical functions of only one or two variables. After a machine cycle each of our N binary elements is a function of the state of at most two of the binary elements before the machine cycle. Now assume that the computer is logically reversi-

ble. Then the machine cycle maps the 2^N possible initial states of the machine onto the same space of 2^N states, rather than just a subspace thereof. In the 2^N possible states each bit has a ONE and a ZERO appearing with equal frequency. Hence the reversible computer can utilize only those truth functions whose truth table exhibits equal numbers of ONES and ZEROS. The admissible truth functions then are the identity and negation, the EXCLUSIVE OR and its negation. These, however, are not a complete set[8] and do not permit a synthesis of all other truth functions.

In the third level of our argument we permit more general devices. Consider, for example, a particular three-input, three-output device, i.e., a small special purpose computer with three bit positions. Let p, q, and r be the variables before the machine cycle. The particular truth function under consideration is the one which replaces r by $p \cdot q$ if $r = 0$, and replaces r by $\overline{p \cdot q}$ if $r = 1$. The variables p and q are left unchanged during the machine cycle. We can consider r as giving us a choice of program, and p, q as the variables on which the selected program operates. This is a logically reversible device, its output always defines its input uniquely. Nevertheless it is capable of performing an operation such as AND which is not, in itself, reversible. The computer, however, saves enough of the input information so that it supplements the desired result to allow reversibility. It is interesting to note, however, that we did not "save" the program; we can only deduce what it was.

Now consider a more general purpose computer, which usually has to go through many machine cycles to carry out a program. At first sight it may seem that logical reversibility is simply obtained by saving the input in some corner of the machine. We shall, however, label a machine as being logically reversible, if and only if all its individual steps are logically reversible. This means that every single time a truth function of two variables is evaluated we must save some additional information about the quantities being operated on, whether we need it or not. Erasure, which is equivalent to RESTORE TO ONE, discussed in the Introduction, is not permitted. We will, therefore, in a long program clutter up our machine bit positions with unnecessary information about intermediate results. Furthermore if we wish to use the reversible function of three variables, which was just discussed, as an AND, then we must supply in the initial programming a separate ZERO for every AND operation which is subsequently required, since the "bias" which programs the device is not saved, when the AND is performed. The machine must therefore have a great deal of extra capacity to store both the extra "bias" bits and the extra outputs. Can it be given adequate capacity to make all intermediate steps reversible? If our machine is capable, as machines are generally understood to be, of a nonterminating program, then it is clear that the capacity for preserving all the information about all the intermediate steps cannot be there.

Let us, however, not take quite such an easy way out. Perhaps it is just possible to devise a machine, useful in the normal sense, but not capable of embarking on a nonterminating program. Let us take such a machine as it normally comes, involving logically irreversible truth functions. An irreversible truth function can be made into a reversible one, as we have illustrated, by "embedding" it in a truth function of a large number of variables. The larger truth function, however, requires extra inputs to bias it, and extra outputs to hold the information which provides the reversibility. What we now contend is that this larger machine, while it is reversible, is not a useful computing machine in the normally accepted sense of the word.

First of all, in order to provide space for the extra inputs and outputs, the embedding requires knowledge of the number of times each of the operations of the original (irreversible) machine will be required. The usefulness of a computer stems, however, from the fact that it is more than just a table look-up device; it can do many programs which were not anticipated in full detail by the designer. Our enlarged machine must have a number of bit positions, for every embedded device of the order of the number of program steps and requires a number of switching events during program loading comparable to the number that occur during the program itself. The setting of bias during program loading, which would typically consist of restoring a long row of bits to say ZERO, is just the type of nonreversible logical operation we are trying to avoid. Our unwieldy machine has therefore avoided the irreversible operations during the running of the program, only at the expense of added comparable irreversibility during the loading of the program.

4. Logical irreversibility and entropy generation

The detailed connection between logical irreversibility and entropy changes remains to be made. Consider again, as an example, the operation RESTORE TO ONE. The generalization to more complicated logical operations will be trivial.

Imagine first a situation in which the RESTORE operation has already been carried out on each member of an assembly of such bits. This is somewhat equivalent to an assembly of spins, all aligned with the positive z-axis. In thermal equilibrium the bits (or spins) have two equally favored positions. Our specially prepared collections show much more order, and therefore a lower temperature and entropy than is characteristic of the equilibrium state. In the adiabatic demagnetization method we use such a prepared spin state, and as the spins become disoriented they take up entropy from the surroundings and thereby cool off the lattice in which the spins are embedded. An assembly of ordered bits would act similarly. As the assembly thermalizes and forgets its initial state the environment would be cooled off. Note that the important point here is not that all bits in the assembly initially agree with each other, but only that there is a single, well-defined initial state for the collection of bits. The well-defined initial state corresponds, by the usual statistical mechanical definition of entropy, $S = k \log_e W$, to zero entropy. The degrees of freedom associated with the information can, through thermal relaxation, go to any

one of 2^N states (for N bits in the assembly) and therefore the entropy can increase by $kN \log_e 2$ as the initial information becomes thermalized.

Note that our argument here does not necessarily depend upon connections, frequently made in other writings, between entropy and information. We simply think of each bit as being located in a physical system, with perhaps a great many degrees of freedom, in addition to the relevant one. However, for each possible physical state which will be interpreted as a ZERO, there is a very similar possible physical state in which the physical system represents a ONE. Hence a system which is in a ONE state has only half as many physical states available to it as a system which can be in a ONE or ZERO state. (We shall ignore in this Section and in the subsequent considerations the case in which the ONE and ZERO are represented by states with different entropy. This case requires arguments of considerably greater complexity but leads to similar physical conclusions.)

In carrying out the RESTORE TO ONE operation we are doing the opposite of the thermalization. We start with each bit in one of two states and end up with a well-defined state. Let us view this operation in some detail.

Consider a statistical ensemble of bits in thermal equilibrium. If these are all reset to ONE, the number of states covered in the ensemble has been cut in half. The entropy therefore has been reduced by $k \log_e 2 = 0.6931 k$ per bit. The entropy of a closed system, e.g., a computer with its own batteries, cannot decrease; hence this entropy must appear elsewhere as a heating effect, supplying $0.6931 kT$ per restored bit to the surroundings. This is, of course, a minimum heating effect, and our method of reasoning gives no guarantee that this minimum is in fact achievable.

Our reset operation, in the preceding discussion, was applied to a thermal equilibrium ensemble. In actuality we would like to know what happens in a particular computing circuit which will work on information which has not yet been thermalized, but at any one time consists of a well-defined ZERO or a well-defined ONE. Take first the case where, as time goes on, the reset operation is applied to a random chain of ONES and ZEROS. We can, in the usual fashion, take the statistical ensemble equivalent to a time average and therefore conclude that the dissipation per reset operation is the same for the timewise succession as for the thermalized ensemble.

A computer, however, is seldom likely to operate on random data. One of the two bit possibilities may occur more often than the other, or even if the frequencies are equal, there may be a correlation between successive bits. In other words the digits which are reset may not carry the maximum possible information. Consider the extreme case, where the inputs are all ONE, and there is no need to carry out any operation. Clearly then no entropy changes occur and no heat dissipation is involved. Alternatively if the initial states are all ZERO they also carry no information, and no entropy change is involved in resetting them all to ONE. Note, however, that the reset operation which sufficed when the inputs were all ONE (doing nothing) will not suffice when the inputs are all ZERO. When the initial states are ZERO, and we wish to go to ONE, this is analogous to a phase transformation between two phases in equilibrium, and can, presumably, be done reversibly and without an entropy increase in the universe, but only by a procedure specifically designed for that task. We thus see that when the initial states do not have their fullest possible diversity, the necessary entropy increase in the RESET operation can be reduced, but only by taking advantage of our knowledge about the inputs, and tailoring the reset operation accordingly.

The generalization to other logically irreversible operations is apparent, and will be illustrated by only one additional example. Consider a very small special-purpose computer, with three binary elements p, q, and r. A machine cycle replaces p by r, replaces q by r, and replaces r by $p \cdot q$. There are eight possible initial states, and in thermal equilibrium they will occur with equal probability. How much entropy reduction will occur in a machine cycle? The initial and final machine states are shown in Fig. 5. States α and β occur with a probability of $\frac{1}{8}$ each: states γ and δ have a probability of occurrence of $\frac{3}{8}$ each. The initial entropy was

$$S_i = k \log_e W = -k \Sigma \rho \log_e \rho$$

$$= -k \Sigma \tfrac{1}{8} \log_e \tfrac{1}{8} = 3k \log_e 2 \; .$$

The final entropy is

$$S_f = -k \Sigma \rho \log_e \rho$$

$$= -k(\tfrac{1}{8} \log \tfrac{1}{8} + \tfrac{1}{8} \log \tfrac{1}{8} + \tfrac{3}{8} \log \tfrac{3}{8} + \tfrac{3}{8} \log \tfrac{3}{8}) \; .$$

The difference $S_i - S_f$ is $1.18\,k$. The minimum dissipation, if the initial state has no useful information, is therefore $1.18\,kT$.

The question arises whether the entropy is really reduced by the logically irreversible operation. If we really map the possible initial ZERO states and the possible initial ONE states into the same space, i.e., the space of ONE states, there can be no question involved. But, perhaps, after we have performed the operation there can be some small remaining difference between the systems which were originally in the ONE state already and those that had to be switched into it. There is no harm in such differences persisting for some time, but as we saw in the discussion of the dissipationless subharmonic oscillator, we cannot tolerate a cumulative process, in which differences between various possible ONE states become larger and larger according to their detailed past histories. Hence the physical "many into one" mapping, which is the source of the entropy change, need not happen in full detail during the machine cycle which performed the logical function. But it must eventually take place, and this is all that is relevant for the heat generation argument.

5. Detailed analysis of bistable well

To supplement our preceding general discussion we shall give a more detailed analysis of switching for a system representable by a bistable potential well, as illustrated, one-dimensionally, in Fig. 1, with a barrier large com-

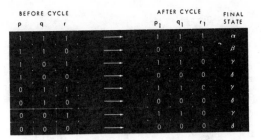

Figure 5 **Three input - three output device which maps eight possible states onto only four different states.**

pared to kT. Let us, furthermore, assume that switching is accomplished by the addition of a force which raises the energy of one well with respect to the other, but still leaves a barrier which has to be surmounted by thermal activation. (A sufficiently large force will simply eliminate one of the minima completely. Our switching forces are presumed to be smaller.) Let us now consider a statistical ensemble of double well systems with a non-equilibrium distribution and ask how rapidly equilibrium will be approached. This question has been analyzed in detail in an earlier paper,[2] and we shall therefore be satisfied here with a very simple kinetic analysis which leads to the same answer. Let n_A and n_B be the number of ensemble members in Well A and Well B respectively. Let U_A and U_B be the energies at the bottom of each well and U that of the barrier which has to be surmounted. Then the rate at which particles leave Well A to go to Well B will be of the form $\nu n_A \exp[-(U-U_A)/kT]$. The flow from B to A will be $\nu n_B \exp[-(U-U_B)/kT]$. The two frequency factors have been taken to be identical. Their differences are, at best, unimportant compared to the differences in exponents. This yields

$$\frac{dn_A}{dt} = -n_A \nu \exp[-(U-U_A)/kT]$$
$$+ n_B \nu \exp[-(U-U_B)/kT] \; ,$$

$$\frac{dn_B}{dt} = n_A \nu \exp[-(U-U_A)/kT]$$
$$- n_B \nu \exp[-(U-U_B)/kT] \; . \qquad (5.1)$$

We can view Eqs. (5.1) as representing a linear transformation on (n_A, n_B), which yields $\left(\dfrac{dn_A}{dt}, \dfrac{dn_B}{dt}\right)$. What are the characteristic values of the transformation? They are:

$$\lambda_1 = 0, \quad \lambda_2 = -\nu \exp[(U-U_A)/kT]$$
$$-\nu \exp[-(U-U_B)/kT] \; .$$

The eigenvalue $\lambda_1 = 0$ corresponds to a time-independent well population. This is the equilibrium distribution

$$n_A = n_B \exp \frac{1}{kT}[U_B - U_A].$$

The remaining negative eigenvalue must then be associated with deviations from equilibrium, and $\exp(-\lambda_2 t)$ gives the rate at which these deviations disappear. The relaxation time τ is therefore in terms of a quantity U_0, which is the average of U_A and U_B

$$\frac{1}{\tau} = \lambda_2 = \nu \exp[-(U - U_0)/kT$$
$$\cdot \{\exp[-(U_0 - U_A)kT] + \exp[(U_0 - U_B)kT]\}. \tag{5.2}$$

The quantity U_0 in Eq. (5.2) cancels out, therefore the validity of Eq. (5.2) does not depend on the definition of U_0. Letting $\Delta = \frac{1}{2}(U_A - U_B)$, Eq. (5.2) then becomes

$$\frac{1}{\tau} = 2\nu \exp[-(U - U_0)/kT]\cosh \Delta/kT. \tag{5.3}$$

To first order in the switching force which causes U_A and U_B to differ, $(U - U_0)$ will remain unaffected, and therefore Eq. (5.3) can be written

$$\frac{1}{\tau} = \frac{1}{\tau_0}\cosh \Delta/kT, \tag{5.4}$$

where τ_0 is the relaxation time for the symmetrical potential well, when $\Delta = 0$. This equation demonstrates that the device is usable. The relaxation time τ_0 is the length of time required by the bistable device to thermalize, and represents the maximum time over which the device is usable. τ on the other hand is the minimum switching time. Cosh Δ/kT therefore represents the maximum number of switching events in the lifetime of the information. Since this can be large, the device can be useful. Even if Δ is large enough so that the first-order approximation needed to keep $U - U_0$ constant breaks down, the exponential dependence of $\cosh \Delta/kT$ on Δ, in Eq. (5.3) will far outweigh the changes in $\exp[(U - U_0)kT]$, and τ_0/τ will still be a rapidly increasing function of Δ.

Note that Δ is one-half the energy which will be dissipated in the switching process. The thermal probability distribution within each well will be about the same before and after switching, the only difference is that the final well is 2Δ lower than the initial well. This energy difference is dissipated and corresponds to the one-half hysteresis loop area energy loss generally associated with switching. Equation (5.4) therefore confirms the empirically well-known fact that increases in switching speed can only be accomplished at the expense of increased dissipation per switching event. Equation (5.4) is, however, true only for a special model and has no really general significance. To show this consider an alternative model. Let us assume that information is stored by the position of a particle along a line, and that $x = \pm a$ correspond to ZERO and ONE, respectively. No barrier is assumed to exist, but the random diffusive motion of the particle is taken to be slow enough, so that positions will be preserved for an appreciable length of time. (This model is probably closer to the behavior of ferrites and ferroelectrics, when the switching occurs by domain wall motion, than our preceding bistable well model. The energy differences between a completely switched and a partially switched ferrite are rather small and it is the existence of a low domain-wall mobility which keeps the particle near its initial state, in the absence of switching forces, and this initial state can almost equally well be a partially switched state, as a completely switched one. On the other hand if one examines the domain wall mobility on a sufficiently microscopic scale it is likely to be related again to activated motion past barriers.) In that case, particles will diffuse a typical distance s in a time $\tau \sim s^2/2D$. D is the diffusion constant. The distance which corresponds to information loss is $s \sim a$, the associated relaxation time is $\tau_0 \sim a^2/2D$. In the presence of a force F the particle moves with a velocity μF, where the mobility μ is given by the Einstein relation as D/kT. To move a particle under a switching force F through a distance $2a$ requires a time τ_s given by

$$\mu F \tau_s = 2a, \tag{5.5}$$

or

$$\tau_s = 2a/\mu F. \tag{5.6}$$

The energy dissipation 2Δ, is a $2aF$. This gives us the equations

$$\tau_s = 2a^2/\mu\Delta, \tag{5.7}$$
$$\tau_s/\tau_0 = 4kT/\Delta, \tag{5.8}$$

which show the same direction of variation of τ_s with Δ as in the case with the barrier, but do not involve an exponential variation with Δ/kT. If all other considerations are ignored it is clear that the energy bistable element of Eq. (5.4) is much to be preferred to the diffusion stabilized element of Eq. (5.8).

The above examples give us some insight into the need for energy dissipation, not directly provided by the arguments involving entropy consideration. In the RESTORE TO ONE operation we want the system to settle into the ONE state regardless of its initial state. We do this by lowering the energy of the ONE state relative to the ZERO state. The particle will then go to this lowest state, and on the way dissipate any excess energy it may have had in its initial state.

6. Three sources of error

We shall in this section attempt to survey the relative importance of several possible sources of error in the computing process, all intimately connected with our preceding considerations. First of all the actual time allowed for switching is finite and the relaxation to the desired state will not have taken place completely. If T_s is the actual time during which the switching force is applied and τ_s is the relaxation time of Eq. (5.4) then $\exp(-T_s/\tau_s)$ is the probability that the switching will not have taken place. The second source of error is the one considered in detail in an earlier paper by J. A. Swanson,[1] and represents the fact that τ_0 is finite and information will decay while it is supposed to be sitting quietly in its initial state. The relative importance of these two errors is a matter of design compromises. The time T_s, allowed for switching, can always be made longer, thus making the switching relaxation more complete. The total time available for a program is, however, less than τ_0, the relaxation time for stored information, and therefore increasing the time allowed for switching decreases the number of steps in the maximum possible program.

A third source of error consists of the fact that even if the system is allowed to relax completely during switching there would still be a fraction of the ensemble of the order $\exp(-2\Delta/kT)$ left in the unfavored initial state. (Assuming $\Delta \gg kT$.) For the purpose of the subsequent discussion let us call this Boltzmann error. We shall show that no matter how the design compromise between the first two kinds of errors is made, Boltzmann error will never be dominant. We shall compare the errors in a rough fashion, without becoming involved in an enumeration of the various possible exact histories of information.

To carry out this analysis, we shall overestimate Boltzmann error by assuming that switching has occurred in every machine cycle in the history of every bit. It is this upper bound on the Boltzmann error which will be shown to be negligible, when compared to other errors. The Boltzmann error probability, per switching event is $\exp(-2\Delta/kT)$. During the same switching time bits which are not being switched are decaying away at the rate $\exp(-t/\tau_0)$. In the switching time T_s, therefore, unswitched bits have a probability T_s/τ_0 of losing their information. If the Boltzmann error is to be dominant

$$T_s/\tau_0 < \exp(-2\Delta/kT) . \tag{6.1}$$

Let us specialize to the bistable well of Eq. (5.4). This latter equation takes (6.1) into the form

$$\frac{2T_s}{\tau_s} \exp(-\Delta/kT) < \exp(-2\Delta/kT) , \tag{6.2}$$

or equivalently

$$\frac{T_s}{\tau_s} < \tfrac{1}{2}\exp(-\Delta/kT) . \tag{6.3}$$

Now consider the relaxation to the switched state. The error incurred due to incomplete relaxation is $\exp(-T_s/\tau_s)$, which according to Eq. (6.3) satisfies

$$\exp(-T_s/\tau_s) > \exp[-\tfrac{1}{2}\exp(-\Delta/kT)] . \tag{6.4}$$

The right-hand side of this inequality has as its argument $\tfrac{1}{2}\exp(-\Delta/kT)$ which is less than $\tfrac{1}{2}$. Therefore the right-hand side is large compared to $\exp(-2\Delta/kT)$, the Boltzmann error, whose exponent is certainly larger than unity. We have thus shown that if the Boltzmann error dominates over the information decay, it must in turn be dominated by the incomplete relaxation during switching.

A somewhat alternate way of arguing the same point consists in showing that the accumulated Boltzmann error, due to the maximum number of switching events permitted by Eq. (5.4), is small compared to unity.

Consider now, instead, the diffusion stabilized element of Eq. (5.8). For it, we can find instead of Eq. (6.4) the relationship

$$\exp(-T_s/\tau_s) > \exp[(-\Delta/4kT)\exp(-2\Delta/kT)] , \tag{6.5}$$

and the right-hand side is again large compared to the Boltzmann error, $\exp(-2\Delta/kT)$. The alternative argument in terms of the accumulated Boltzmann error exists also in this case.

When we attempt to consider a more realistic machine model, in which switching forces are applied to coupled devices, as is done for example in diodeless magnetic core logic,[4] it becomes difficult to maintain analytically a clean-cut breakdown of error types, as we have done here. Nevertheless we believe that there is still a somewhat similar separation which is manifested.

Summary

The information-bearing degrees of freedom of a computer interact with the thermal reservoir represented by the remaining degrees of freedom. This interaction plays two roles. First of all, it acts as a sink for the energy dissipation involved in the computation. This energy dissipation has an unavoidable minimum arising from the fact that the computer performs irreversible operations. Secondly, the interaction acts as a source of noise causing errors. In particular thermal fluctuations give a supposedly switched element a small probability of remaining in its initial state, even after the switching force has been applied for a long time. It is shown, in terms of two simple models, that this source of error is dominated by one of two other error sources:

1) Incomplete switching due to inadequate time allowed for switching.

2) Decay of stored information due to thermal fluctuations.

It is, of course, apparent that both the thermal noise and the requirements for energy dissipation are on a scale which is entirely negligible in present-day computer components. The dissipation as calculated, however, is an absolute minimum. Actual devices which are far from minimal in size and operate at high speeds will be likely to require a much larger energy dissipation to serve the purpose of erasing the unnecessary details of the computer's past history.

Acknowledgments

Some of these questions were first posed by E. R. Piore a number of years ago. In its early stages[2,5] this project was carried forward primarily by the late John Swanson. Conversations with Gordon Lasher were essential to the development of the ideas presented in the paper.

References

1. L. Brillouin, *Science and Information Theory*, Academic Press Inc., New York, New York, 1956.

2. R. Landauer and J. A. Swanson, *Phys. Rev.*, **121,** 1668 (1961).

3. K. Mendelssohn, *Progress in Cyrogenics*, Vol. 1, Academic Press Inc., New York, New York, 1959. Chapter I by D. R. Young, p. 1.

4. L. B. Russell, *IRE Convention Record*, p. 106 (1957).

5. J. A. Swanson, *IBM Journal*, **4,** 305 (1960).

We would like to take this opportunity to amplify two points in Swanson's paper which perhaps were not adequately stressed in the published version.

(1) The large number of particles (~ 100) in the optimum element are a result of the small energies per particle (or cell) involved in the typical cooperative phenomenon used in computer storage. There is no question that information can be stored in the position of a single particle, at room temperature, if the activation energy for its motion is sufficiently large ($\sim$ several electron volts).

(2) Swanson's optimum volume is, generally, not very different from the common sense requirement on U, namely: $\nu t \exp(-U/kT) \ll 1$, which would be found without the use of information theory. This indicates that the use of redundancy and complicated coding methods does not permit much additional information to be stored. It is obviously preferable to eliminate these complications, since by making each element only slightly larger than the "optimum" value, the element becomes reliable enough to carry information without the use of redundancy.

6. R. L. Wigington, *Proceedings of the IRE*, **47,** 516 (1959).

7. A. W. Lo, Paper to appear in *IRE Transactions on Electronic Computers*.

8. D. Hilbert and W. Ackermann, *Principles of Mathematical Logic*, Chelsea Publishing Co., New York, 1950, p. 10.

Received October 5, 1960

Logical Reversibility of Computation*

Abstract: The usual general-purpose computing automaton (e.g., a Turing machine) is logically irreversible – its transition function lacks a single-valued inverse. Here it is shown that such machines may be made logically reversible at every step, while retaining their simplicity and their ability to do general computations. This result is of great physical interest because it makes plausible the existence of thermodynamically reversible computers which could perform useful computations at useful speed while dissipating considerably less than kT of energy per logical step. In the first stage of its computation the logically reversible automaton parallels the corresponding irreversible automaton, except that it saves all intermediate results, thereby avoiding the irreversible operation of erasure. The second stage consists of printing out the desired output. The third stage then reversibly disposes of all the undesired intermediate results by retracing the steps of the first stage in backward order (a process which is only possible because the first stage has been carried out reversibly), thereby restoring the machine (except for the now-written output tape) to its original condition. The final machine configuration thus contains the desired output and a reconstructed copy of the input, but no other undesired data. The foregoing results are demonstrated explicitly using a type of three-tape Turing machine. The biosynthesis of messenger RNA is discussed as a physical example of reversible computation.

Introduction

The usual digital computer program frequently performs operations that seem to throw away information about the computer's history, leaving the machine in a state whose immediate predecessor is ambiguous. Such operations include erasure or overwriting of data, and entry into a portion of the program addressed by several different transfer instructions. In other words, the typical computer is logically irreversible – its transition function (the partial function that maps each whole-machine state onto its successor, if the state has a successor) lacks a single-valued inverse.

Landauer [1] has posed the question of whether logical irreversibility is an unavoidable feature of useful computers, arguing that it is, and has demonstrated the physical and philosophical importance of this question by showing that whenever a physical computer throws away information about its previous state it must generate a corresponding amount of entropy. Therefore, a computer must dissipate at least $kT \ln 2$ of energy (about 3×10^{-21} joule at room temperature) for each bit of information it erases or otherwise throws away.

An irreversible computer can always be made reversible by having it save all the information it would otherwise throw away. For example, the machine might be given an extra tape (initially blank) on which it could record each operation as it was being performed, in

sufficient detail that the preceding state would be uniquely determined by the present state and the last record on the tape. However, as Landauer pointed out, this would merely postpone the problem of throwing away unwanted information, since the tape would have to be erased before it could be reused. It is therefore reasonable to demand of a useful reversible computer that, if it halts, it should have erased all its intermediate results, leaving behind only the desired output and the originally furnished input. (The machine must be allowed to save its input – otherwise it could not be reversible and still carry out computations in which the input was not uniquely determined by the output.) We will show that general-purpose reversible computers (Turing machines) satisfying these requirements indeed exist, and that they need not be much more complicated than the irreversible computers on which they are patterned. Computations on a reversible computer take about twice as many steps as on an ordinary one and may require a large amount of temporary storage. Before proceeding with the formal demonstration, the argument will be carried through at the present heuristic level.

---
*Much of the work on physical reversibility reported in this paper was done under the auspices of the U.S. Atomic Energy Commission while the author was employed by the Argonne National Laboratory, Argonne, Illinois.

We begin with the reversible but untidy computer mentioned earlier, which has produced, and failed to erase, a long history of its activity. Now, a tape full of random data cannot be erased except by an irreversible process; however, the history tape is not random — there exists a subtle mutual redundancy between it and the machine that produced it, which may be exploited to erase it reversibly. For example, if at the end of the computation a new stage of computation were begun using the inverse of the original transition function, the machine would begin carrying out the entire computation backward, eventually returning the history tape to its original blank condition[2]. Since the forward computation was deterministic and reversible, the backward stage would be also. Unfortunately, the backward stage would transform the output back into the original input, rendering the overall computation completely useless. Destruction of the desired output can be prevented simply by making an extra copy of it on a separate tape, after the forward stage, but before the backward stage. During this copying operation (which can be done reversibly if the tape used for the copy is initially blank), the recording of the history tape is suspended. The backward stage will then destroy only the original and not the copy. At the end of the computation, the computer will contain the (reconstructed) original input plus the intact copy of the output; all other storage will have been restored to its original blank condition. Even though no history remains, the computation is reversible and deterministic, because each of its stages has been so.

One disadvantage of the reversible machine would appear to be the large amount of temporary storage needed for the history — for a ν-step first stage, ν records of history would have to be written. In a later section it will be argued that by performing a job in many stages rather than just three, the required amount of temporary storage can often be greatly reduced. The final section discusses the possibility of reversible physical computers, capable of dissipating less than kT of energy per step, using examples from the biochemical apparatus of the genetic code.

Logically reversible Turing machines

This section formalizes the argument of the preceding section by showing that, given an ordinary Turing machine S, one can construct a reversible three-tape Turing machine R, which emulates S on any standard input, and which leaves behind, at the end of its computation, only that input and the desired output. The R machine's computation proceeds by three stages as described above, the third stage serving to dispose of the history produced by the first. The remainder of this section may be skipped by those uninterested in the details of the proof.

The ordinary type of one-tape Turing machine [3] consists of a control unit, a read/write head, and an infinite tape divided into squares. Its behavior is governed by a finite set of transition formulas (commonly called quintuples) of the read-write-shift type. The quintuples have the form

$$AT \rightarrow T' \sigma A', \tag{1}$$

meaning that if the control unit is in state A and the head scans the tape symbol T, the head will first write T' in place of T; then it will shift left one square, right one square, or remain where it is, according to the value of σ ($-$, $+$, or 0, respectively); finally the control unit will revert to state A'. In the usual generalization to n-tape machines, T, T', and σ are all n-tuples within the quintuple.

Each quintuple defines a (partial) one-to-one mapping of the present whole-machine state (i.e., tape contents, head positions, and control state) onto its successor and, as such, is deterministic and reversible. Therefore a Turing machine will be deterministic if and only if its quintuples have non-overlapping domains, and will be reversible if and only if they have non-overlapping ranges. The former is customarily guaranteed by requiring that the portion to the left of the arrow be different for each quintuple. On the other hand, the usual Turing machine is not reversible.

In making a Turing machine reversible, we will need to add transitions that closely resemble the inverses of the transitions it already has. However, because the write and shift operations do not commute, the inverse of a read-write-shift quintuple, though it exists, is of a different type; namely, shift-read-write. In constructing a reversible machine it is necessary to include quintuples of both types, or else to use a formalism in which transitions and their inverses have the same form. Here the latter approach is taken — the reversible machine will use a simpler type of transition formula in which, during a given transition, each tape is subjected to a read-write or to a shift operation but no tape is subjected to both.

Definition: A *quadruple* (for an n-tape Turing machine having one head per tape) is an expression of the form

$$A[t_1, t_2, \cdots, t_n] \rightarrow [t_1', t_2', \cdots, t_n']A', \tag{2}$$

where A and A' are positive integers (denoting internal states of the control unit before and after the transition, respectively); each t_k may be either a positive integer denoting a symbol that must be read on the kth tape or a solidus ($/$), indicating that the kth tape is not read during the transition; each t_k' is either a positive integer denoting the symbol to be written on the kth tape or a member of the set ($-$, 0, $+$) denoting a left, null, or right shift of the kth tape head. For each tape k, $t_k' \in (-, 0, +)$ if and only if

$t_k = /$. Thus the machine writes on a tape if and only if it has just read it, and shifts a tape only if it has not just read it.

Like quintuples, quadruples define mappings of the whole-machine state which are one-to-one. Any read-write-shift quintuple can be split into a read-write and a shift, both expressible as quadruples. For example, the quintuple (1) is equivalent to the pair of quadruples

$$AT \rightarrow T' A'' \tag{3}$$

$$A''[/ / \cdots /] \rightarrow \sigma A', \tag{4}$$

where A'' is a new control-unit state different from A and A'. When several quintuples are so split, a different connecting state A'' must be used for each, to avoid introducing indeterminacy.

Quadruples have the following additional important properties, which can be verified by inspection. Let

$$\alpha \equiv A[t_1, \cdots, t_n] \rightarrow [t_1', \cdots, t_n']A' \tag{5}$$

and

$$\beta \equiv B[u_1, \cdots, u_n] \rightarrow [u_1', \cdots, u_n']B' \tag{6}$$

be two n-tape quadruples.

1) α and β are mutually inverse (define inverse mappings of the whole-machine state) if and only if $A = B'$ and $B = A'$ and, for every k, either ($t_k = u_k = /$ and $t_k' = -u_k'$) or ($t_k \neq /$ and $t_k' = u_k$ and $t_k = u_k'$). The inverse of a quadruple, in other words, is obtained by interchanging the initial control state with the final, the read tape symbols with the written, and changing the signs of all the shifts.
2) The domains of α and β overlap if and only if $A = B$ and, for every k, ($t_k = /$ or $u_k = /$ or $t_k = u_k$). Non-overlapping of the domains requires a differing initial control state or a differing scanned symbol on some tape read by both quadruples.
3) The ranges of α and β overlap if and only if $A' = B'$ and, for every k, ($t_k = /$ or $u_k = /$ or $t_k' = u_k'$). The property is analogous to the previous one, but depends on the final control state and the written tape symbols.

A *reversible, deterministic n-tape Turing machine* may now be defined as a finite set of n-tape quadruples, no two of which overlap either in domain or range. We now wish to show that such machines can be made to emulate ordinary (irreversible) Turing machines. It is convenient to impose on the machines to be emulated certain format-standardization requirements, which, however, do not significantly limit their computing power [4].

Definition: An input or output is said to be *standard* when it is on otherwise blank tape and contains no embedded blanks, when the tape head scans the blank square immediately to the left of it, and when it includes only letters belonging to the tape alphabet of the machine scanning it.

Definition: A standard Turing machine is a finite set of one-tape quintuples

$$AT \rightarrow T' \sigma A' \tag{1}$$

satisfying the following requirements:

1) Determinism: No two quintuples agree in both A and T.
2) Format: If started in control state A_1 on any standard input, the machine, if it halts, will halt in control state A_f (f being the number of control states), leaving its output in standard format.
3) Special quintuples: The machine includes the following quintuples

$$A_1 b \rightarrow b + A_2 \tag{7}$$

$$A_{f-1} b \rightarrow b \, 0 \, A_f, \tag{8}$$

and control states A_1 and A_f appear in no other quintuple. These two are thus the first and last executed respectively in any terminating computation on a standard input. The letter b represents a blank.

The phrase "machine **M**, given standard input string I, computes standard output string P" will be abbreviated **M:** $I \rightarrow P$. For an n-tape machine this will become **M:** $(I_1; I_2; \cdots; I_n) \rightarrow (P_1; P_2; \cdots; P_n)$, where I_k and P_k are the standard input and the standard output on the kth tape. A blank tape will be abbreviated B.

The main theorem can now be stated:

Theorem: For every standard one-tape Turing machine **S**, there exists a three-tape reversible, deterministic Turing machine **R** such that if I and P are strings on the alphabet of **S**, containing no embedded blanks, then **S** halts on I if and only if **R** halts on $(I; B; B)$, and **S:** $I \rightarrow P$ if and only if **R:** $(I; B; B) \rightarrow (I; B; P)$.

Furthermore, if **S** has f control states, N quintuples and a tape alphabet of z letters, including the blank, **R** will have $2f + 2N + 4$ states, $4N + 2z + 3$ quadruples and tape alphabets of z, $N + 1$, and z letters, respectively. Finally, if in a particular computation **S** requires ν steps and uses s squares of tape, producing an output of length λ, then **R** will require $4\nu + 4\lambda + 5$ steps, and use s, $\nu + 1$, and $\lambda + 2$ squares on its three tapes, respectively. (It will later be argued that where $\nu \gg s$, the total space requirement can be reduced to less than $2\sqrt{\nu s}$.)

Proof: To construct the machine **R** we begin by arranging the N quintuples of **S** in some order with the standard quintuples first and last:

$$1) \qquad A_1 b \to b + A_2$$
$$\vdots$$
$$m) \qquad A_j T \to T' \sigma A_k$$
$$\vdots$$
$$N) \qquad A_{f-1} b \to b \, 0 \, A_f. \tag{9}$$

Each quintuple is now broken into a pair of quadruples as described earlier. The mth quintuple becomes

$$\begin{cases} A_j T \to T' A_m' \\ A_m' \, / \to \sigma A_k. \end{cases} \tag{10}$$

The newly added states A_m' are different from the old states and from each other; each A' appears in only one pair of quadruples.

Table 1 Structure and operation of a three-tape reversible Turing machine. The computation proceeds in three stages using different sets of quadruples and control states, linkage occurring through states A_f and C_f. On the right the contents of the tapes are shown symbolically at the beginning and end of each stage. The underbar denotes the position of the head. The initial state is A_1 and, for a terminating computation, C_1 is the final state.

Stage	Quadruples		Working tape	History tape	Output tape
			_INPUT	_•	_
	1)	$\begin{cases} A_1[b \mid b] \to [b+b]A_1' \\ A_1'[/ \, b \mid] \to [+1 \, 0]A_2 \end{cases}$			
		$\vdots$			
Compute[a]	$m)$	$\begin{cases} A_j[T \mid b] \to [T'+b]A_m' \\ A_m'[/ \, b \mid] \to [\sigma \, m \, 0]A_k \end{cases}$			
		$\vdots$			
	$N)$	$\begin{cases} A_{f-1}[b \mid b] \to [b+b]A_N' \\ A_N'[/ \, b \mid] \to [0 \, N \, 0]A_f \end{cases}$			
			_OUTPUT	HISTOR_Y	_
		$A_f[b \, N \, b] \to [b \, N \, b]B_1'$			
		$B_1'[/ \, / \, /] \to [+0+]B_1$			
	$x \ne b: \{$	$B_1[x \, N \, b] \to [x \, N \, x]B_1' \;\}$			
Copy output[b]		$B_1[b \, N \, b] \to [b \, N \, b]B_2'$			
		$B_2'[/ \, / \, /] \to [-0-]B_2$			
	$x \ne b: \{$	$B_2[x \, N \, x] \to [x \, N \, x]B_2' \;\}$			
		$B_2[b \, N \, b] \to [b \, N \, b]C_f$			
			_OUTPUT	HISTOR_Y	_OUTPUT
	$N)$	$\begin{cases} C_f[/ \, N \, /] \to [0 \, b \, 0]C_N' \\ C_N'[b \mid b] \to [b-b]C_{f-1} \end{cases}$			
		$\vdots$			
Retrace	$m)$	$\begin{cases} C_k[/ \, m \, /] \to [-\sigma \, b \, 0]C_m' \\ C_m'[T' \mid b] \to [T-b]C_j \end{cases}$			
		$\vdots$			
	1)	$\begin{cases} C_2[/ \, 1 \, /] \to [-b \, 0]C_1' \\ C_1'[b \mid b] \to [b-b]C_1 \end{cases}$			
			_INPUT	_	_OUTPUT

[a] The labels 1) . . . m) . . . N) are not part of the machine. They indicate correspondence to the quintuples of the original irreversible machine, which the reversible machine emulates.

[b] In the second stage the small braces indicate sets of quadruples, with one quadruple for each nonblank tape letter x.

Two extra tapes are then added, one for the history and one for the duplicate copy of the output. The ouput (third) tape is left blank and null-shifted for the present, but the history (second) tape is used to record the index m as each transition pair is executed.

The mth pair of quadruples now has the form

$$\begin{cases} A_j[T\,/\,b] \to [T'+b]A_m{}' \\ A_m{}'[/\,b\,/] \to [\sigma\,m\,0]A_k. \end{cases} \quad (11)$$

Notice that the history (second) tape is out of phase with the other two — it is written on while they are being shifted and vice versa. This phasing is necessary to assure reversibility — it serves to capture the information that would otherwise be thrown away when the specific control state $A_m{}'$ passes to the more general state A_k. The + shifting of the history tape assures that a blank square will always be ready to receive the next m value. If the computation of S does not halt, neither will that of **R**, and the machine will continue printing on the history tape indefinitely. On the other hand, if (on a standard input) S halts, **R** will eventually execute the Nth pair of quadruples, finding itself in state A_f, with the output in standard format on tape 1. The history head will be scanning the number N which it has just written at the extreme right end of the history on tape 2. Control then passes to the second stage of computation, which copies the output onto tape 3 (see Table 1). The control states for this stage are denoted by B's and are distinct from all the A-type control states. Notice that the copying process can be done reversibly without writing anything more on the history tape. This shows that the generation (or erasure) of a duplicate copy of data requires no throwing away of information.

The third stage undoes the work of the first and consists of the inverses of all first-stage transitions with C's substituted for A's. In the final state C_1, the history tape is again blank and the other tapes contain the reconstructed input and the desired output.

As Table 1 shows, the total number of control states is $2N + 2f + 4$, the number of quadruples $4N + 2z + 3$, and the space and time requirements are as stated at the beginning of the proof. The non-overlapping of the domains and ranges of all the quadruples assures determinism and reversibility of the machine **R**. In the first stage, the upper transitions of each pair do not overlap in their domains because of the postulated determinacy of the original Turing machine S, whose quintuples also began $A_jT \to$. The ranges of the upper quadruples (as well as the domains of the lower) are kept from overlapping by the uniqueness of the states $A_m{}'$. Finally, the ranges of the lower quadruples are saved from overlapping by the unique output m on the history tape. The state A_f causes no trouble, even though it occurs in both stage 1 and

stage 2, because by the definition of the machine S it does not occur on the left in stage 1; similarly for state C_f. The non-overlapping of the stage 2 quadruples can be verified by inspection, while the determinism and reversibility of stage 3 follow from those of stage 1.

Discussion

The argument developed above is not limited to three-tape Turing machines, but can be applied to any sort of deterministic automaton, finite or infinite, provided it has sufficient temporary storage to record the history. One-tape reversible machines exist, but their frequent shifting between the working and history regions on the tape necessitates as many as ν^2 steps to emulate a ν-step irreversible computation.

In the case that S is a universal Turing machine, **R** becomes a machine for executing any computer program reversibly. For such a general-purpose machine it seems highly unlikely that we can avoid having to include the input as part of the final output. However, there are many calculations in which the output uniquely determines the input, and for such a problem one might hope to build a specific reversible computer that would simply map inputs onto outputs, erasing everything else. This is indeed possible, provided we have access to an ordinary Turing machine which, given an output, computes the corresponding input. Let S_1 be the (irreversible) Turing machine that computes the output from the input and S_2 be the one that computes the input from the output. The reversible computation proceeds by seven stages as shown in Table 2, of which the first three employ a reversible form of the S_1 computer and, as in Table 1, serve to map the input onto the input and output. Stage four interchanges input and output. Stages five and seven use a reversible realization of the S_2 computer; stage five has the sole purpose of producing a history of the S_2 computation (i.e., of the input from the output) which, after the extra copy of the input has been erased in stage six, is used in stage seven to destroy itself and the remaining copy of the input, while producing only the desired output.

We shall now return to the more usual situation, in which the input must be saved because it is not a known, computable function of the output. Performing a computation reversibly entails only a modest increase in computing time and machine complexity; the main drawback of reversible computers appears thus to be the large amount of temporary storage they require for the history in any long, compute-bound job (i.e., one whose number of steps, ν, greatly exceeds the number of squares of memory used, s). Fortunately, the temporary storage requirement can be cut down by breaking the job into a sequence of n segments, each one of which would be performed and retraced (and the history tape thereby erased and made ready for reuse) before proceeding to

Table 2   Reversible computer for a specific problem in which the input is a known, computable function of the output.

Stage	Action	Tape 1	Tape 2	Tape 3
		INPUT	—	—
1.	Forward S_1 computation			
		OUTPUT	HISTORY 1	—
2.	Copy output			
		OUTPUT	HISTORY 1	OUTPUT
3.	Retraced S_1 computation			
		INPUT	—	OUTPUT
4.	Interchange output with input			
		OUTPUT	—	INPUT
5.	Forward S_2 computation			
		INPUT	HISTORY 2	INPUT
6.	Reversible erasure of extra copy of input			
		INPUT	HISTORY 2	—
7.	Retraced S_2 computation			
		OUTPUT	—	—

the next. Each segment would leave on the working tape (tape 1) a restart dump that would be used as the input of the next segment; but to preserve reversibility it would also have to leave (on tape 3, say) a copy of its own input, which would in most cases simply be the preceding restart dump. At the end of the computation we would have, in addition to the original input and desired output, all the $n - 1$ intermediate dumps (concatenated, e.g., on tape 3). These intermediate results, which would not have been produced had the job not been segmented, either can be accepted as permanent (but unwanted) output, in exchange for the n-fold reduction of the history tape, or can themselves be reversibly erased by first making an extra copy of the desired final output (putting it, say, on a previously unused part of tape 3), then *reversing the whole n-segment computation*. This reversal is possible because each segment has been performed reversibly. The sequence of restart dumps thus functions as a kind of higher-level history, and it is erased by a higher-level application of the same technique used to erase the primary histories. At the end of the computation, the machine will contain only the original input and the desired nth segment output, and every step of the original irreversible computation will have been performed twice forward and twice backward. For a job with v steps and a restart dump of size s, the total temporary storage requirement (minimized by choosing $n = \sqrt{v/s}$) is $2\sqrt{vs}$ squares, half on the history

tape and half on the dump tape. A $(\frac{1}{2}\sqrt{v/s})$-fold reduction in space can thus be bought by a twofold increase in time (ignoring the time required to write and read restart dumps) without any unwanted output. By a systematic reversal of progressively larger nested sequences of segments one might hope to reach an absolute minimum temporary storage requirement growing only as $\log v$, for sufficiently large v, with the time increasing perhaps as v^2, because of the linearly increasing number of times each segment would have to be retraced.

It thus appears that every job of computation can be done in a logically reversible manner, without inordinate increases in machine complexity, number of steps, unwanted output, or temporary storage capacity.

Physical reversibility

The existence of logically reversible automata suggests that physical computers might be made thermodynamically reversible, and hence capable of dissipating an arbitrarily small amount of energy per step if operated sufficiently slowly. A full treatment of physically reversible computers is beyond the scope of the present paper [5], but it is worthwhile to give a brief and non-rigorous introduction to how they might work.

An obvious approach to the minimizing the energy dissipation is to design the computer so that it can operate near thermodynamic equilibrium. All moving parts would then, at any instant, have near-thermal velocity, and the desired logical transitions would necessarily be accomplished by spontaneous thermally activated motion over free energy barriers not much higher than kT. At first sight this might seem impossible — in existing electronic computers, for example, even when a component being switched is itself nondissipative (e.g., a magnetic core), the switching process depends on temporarily applying a strong external force to push the component irreversibly over a high free energy barrier. However, nature provides a beautiful example of a thermally activated "computer" in the biochemical apparatus responsible for the replication, transcription and translation of the genetic code [6]. Each of these processes involves a long, deterministic sequence of manipulations of coded information, quite analogous to a computation, and yet, so far as is known, each is simply a sequence of coupled, thermally activated chemical reactions. In biochemical systems, enzymes play the essential role of selectively lowering the activation barriers for the desired transitions while leaving high barriers to obstruct all undesired transitions — those which in a computer would correspond to errors. Although the environment in which enzymes normally function is not at chemical equilibrium, many enzyme-catalyzed reactions are freely reversible, and one can find a set of equilibrium reactant concentrations at which both forward and reverse reactions occur equally rapidly, while competing uncatalyzed reactions have negligible rates. It is thus not unreasonable to postulate a thermally activated computer in which, at equilibrium, every logically allowed transition occurs equally often forward and backward, while illogical transitions hardly ever occur. In the following discussion chemical terminology will be used, without implying that thermally activated computers must be chemical systems.

The chemical realization of a logically reversible computation is a chain of reactions, each coupled only to the preceding one and the following one. It is helpful to think of the computing system as comprising a major reactant (analogous to DNA) that encodes the logical state, and minor reactants that react with the major one to change the logical state. Only one molecule of the major reactant is present, but the minor reactants are all present at definite concentrations, which may be manipulated to drive the computation forward or backward. If the minor reactants are in equilibrium, and the major reactant initially corresponds to the initial state of a ν-step computation, the system will begin a random walk through the chain of reactions, and after about ν^2 steps will briefly visit the final state. This does not deserve to be called a computation; it would be legitimate to insist that the system proceed through the chain of reactions with some positive drift velocity and, after sufficient time, have a high probability of being in the final state (if

the computation has one). The former requirement can be met by adjusting the chemical potentials of the minor reactants so that each forward step dissipates a little energy ε; the latter can be met by dissipating a trivial extra amount during the last step. (If all steps had equal dissipation, $\varepsilon < kT$, the final state occupation probability would be only about ε/kT. By dissipating an extra $kT \ln (3\ kT/\varepsilon)$ of energy during the last step, this probability is increased to about 95%.) Given a uniform rate Γ for all forward reactions, an energy dissipation $\varepsilon < kT$ per step will buy a drift velocity (i.e., computation speed) of $\Gamma\varepsilon/kT$ steps per second. On the other hand, for $\varepsilon > kT$, backward steps will be effectively suppressed and the computation speed will approach the forward reaction rate Γ. The chemical system is thus a thermodynamically reversible computer of the type we have been seeking.

If we attempt to apply the preceding argument to a logically irreversible computer, we can see that here the reactions form a branching structure, with a main trunk corresponding to the desired computation path, and side branches corresponding to incorrect or "extraneous" reverse computations. The states on the side branches are valid predecessors of the final state but not valid successors of the initial state. A few such extraneous states would pose no problem — a small driving force would still suffice to push the system into the desired final state. Temporary backward excursions onto the side branches would occur, but would not lead to errors, contrary to what one might expect. Since no state of a deterministic computer can have more than one logical successor, the erroneously reversed operations would be corrected as soon as the computation proceeded forward again, and the desired path would be rejoined. The real problem comes from the enormous number of extraneous predecessors; typically they outnumber the states on the intended computation path by hundreds of orders of magnitude. This is because, in irreversibly programmed computations, one can usually proceed backward along an extraneous path for many steps, making further wrong choices along the way, before arriving at a state that has no predecessors.

If a thermally activated computer with many extraneous states is operated close to equilibrium, the system will spend only a minuscule fraction of its time on the desired path of computation, let alone in the desired final state. An acceptable computation rate requires 1) that finite (but time-consuming) backward excursions be largely suppressed, and 2) that infinite ones be completely suppressed. This in turn means (roughly speaking) that the dissipation per step must exceed kT ln m, where m is the mean number of immediate predecessors 1) averaged over states near the intended path, or 2) averaged over all accessible states, whichever is greater. For a typical irreversible computer, which throws away about one bit per logical operation, m is approximately two, and thus $kT \ln 2$ is, as Landauer has argued [1], an approximate lower bound on the energy dissipation of such machines. For a logically reversible computer, however, m is exactly one by construction.

The biosynthesis and biodegradation of messenger RNA may be viewed as convenient examples of logically reversible and irreversible computation, respectively. Messenger RNA, a linear polymeric informational macromolecule like DNA, carries the genetic information from one or more genes of a DNA molecule, and serves to direct the synthesis of the proteins encoded by those genes. Messenger RNA is synthesized by the enzyme RNA polymerase in the presence of a double-stranded DNA molecule and a supply of RNA monomers (the four nucleotide pyrophosphates ATP, GTP, CTP, and UTP) [7]. The enzyme attaches to a specific site on the DNA molecule and moves along, sequentially incorporating the RNA monomers into a single-stranded RNA molecule whose nucleotide sequence exactly matches that of the DNA. The pyrophosphate groups are released into the surrounding solution as free pyrophosphate molecules. The enzyme may thus be compared to a simple tape-copying Turing machine that manufactures its output tape rather than merely writing on it. Tape copying is a logically reversible operation, and RNA polymerase is both thermodynamically and logically reversible. In the cellular environment the reaction is driven in the intended forward direction of RNA synthesis by other reactions, which maintain a low concentration of free pyrophosphate, relative to the concentrations of nucleotide pyrophosphates [8]. A high pyrophosphate concentration would drive the reaction backward, and the enzyme would carry out a sequence-specific degradation of the RNA, comparing each nucleotide with the corresponding DNA nucleotide before splitting it off. This process, which may be termed logically reversible erasure of RNA, does not normally occur in biological systems—instead, RNA is degraded by other enzymes, such as polynucleotide phosphorylase [9], in a logically irreversible manner (i.e., without checking its sequence against DNA). Polynucleotide phosphorylase catalyzes the reaction of RNA with free phosphate (maintained at high concentration) to form nucleotide phosphate monomers. Like the polymerase reaction, this reaction is thermodynamically reversible; however, because of its logical irreversibility, a fourfold greater phosphate concentration is needed to drive it forward than would be required for a logically reversible

phosphorolytic degradation. The extra driving force is necessary to suppress the undesired synthesis of nonsense RNA by random polymerization.

In biological systems, apparently, the speed and flexibility of irreversible erasure outweigh its extra cost in free energy ($kT \ln 4$ per nucleotide in this case). Indeed, throughout the genetic apparatus, energy is dissipated at a rate of roughly 5 to 50 kT per step; while this is ten orders of magnitude lower than in an electronic computer, it is considerably higher than what would theoretically be possible if biochemical systems did not need to run at speeds close to the kinetic maximum—presumably to escape the harmful effects of radiation, uncatalyzed reactions, and competition from other organisms.

Acknowledgment
I thank Rolf Landauer for raising the question of reversibility of computation in the first place and for stimulating discussions of my models.

References and notes
1. R. Landauer, *IBM J. Res. Develop.* **3**, 183 (1961). R. W. Keyes and R. Landauer, *IBM J. Res. Develop.* **14**, 152 (1970), investigate a specific model computer whose energy dissipation per step is about kT.
2. R. W. Keyes [*Science* **168**, 796 (1970)], in summarizing Landauer's argument [1], commented that a saved history might be used to reverse the steps of the original computation, but that this was not practical in a general purpose computer. He did not explicitly point out that a reversible machine can be made to erase its own history (an ability which, we have argued, allows it to be useful as a general purpose computer).
3. For a good informal exposition of Turing machines see Chapter 6 of M. L. Minsky, *Computation: Finite and Infinite Machines*, Prentice-Hall, Inc., Englewood Cliffs, N. J., 1967.
4. By the addition of a few extra tape symbols and quintuples, an arbitrary Turing machine can be made to obey these format requirements while computing essentially the same function as it did before. See M. Davis, *Computability and Unsolvability*, McGraw-Hill Book Co., Inc., New York, 1958, pp. 25–26.
5. The author is currently preparing a paper on physically reversible model computers.
6. For a good introduction to this subject see James D. Watson *Molecular Biology of the Gene* (2nd ed.), W. A. Benjamin, Inc., New York, 1970.
7. Ibid., p. 336 ff.
8. Ibid., p. 155 ff.
9. Ibid., p. 403.

Received April 12, 1973

C. H. Bennett is located at the IBM Thomas J. Watson Research Center, Yorktown Heights, New York 10598.

MAXWELL'S DEMON AND COMPUTATION*

RICHARD LAING†

University of Michigan

In this paper we show how a form of Maxwellian Demon can be interpreted as a computing automaton. We then point out some ways in which the Demon systems can be generalized, and briefly describe and discuss the properties of some of the corresponding automata. It is shown that a generalized Maxwell Demon system can carry out arbitrary Turing computations.

Finally, the association developed between classes of thermodynamic systems and classes of computational systems is employed to suggest approaches to some fundamental problems of the relationships between computation, the information obtained by computation, and energy.

1. Maxwell's Demon. A Maxwellian Demon system, in its most familiar form, consists of an "intelligent mechanism" (the Demon Proper) posted in the enclosed connecting passage between two finite chambers. The two chambers contain initially a sparse, uniformly distributed population of molecules moving at various speeds. The Demon is capable of observing the contents of the two chambers and can detect, of individual molecules approaching his position in the connecting passage, whether the particle is (relative to a standard imposed by the Demon) fast or slow moving.

The Demon can act selectively so as to permit a molecule of either the fast or slow type to pass from one of the chambers to the next, or can bar the transit of the particle, thus forcing it to remain in its original chamber. The Demon may thus impose a segregation of the molecules so that eventually all the molecules judged fast are in one chamber, and all the molecules judged slow are in the opposite chamber. It is clear that the Demon Proper requires only a small number of distinct different internal states in order to bring about that final desired state of affairs.

Once the desired final situation is reached, the chamber containing only fast molecules will be hotter than the chamber containing only slow molecules, and the temperature difference so created can be harnessed to yield energy. This problem of putative violation of the Second Law of Thermodynamics (the entropy of the entire system under consideration seemingly having been decreased) was analyzed and resolved by Szilard [3] who pointed out that an amount of energy at least as great as whatever amount of energy can be gained, must necessarily have been expended by the intelligent Demon in his detection, inspection, and routing activities.

2. Maxwell's Demon as Computing Automaton. We will now show how ordinary Maxwellian Demon systems (as well as some related thermodynamic systems) may be rigorously interpreted as computing automata.

* Received September, 1973.

† This research was supported in part through a grant from the National Science Foundation.

In automaton terms, the above described ordinary Maxwell Demon system can be viewed as an automaton system consisting of two counters, each of finite capacity, under the control of a finite state mechanism. A counter, in the sense in which we shall use it here, is a device which stores a positive integer or zero and which can be increased or decreased one unit at a time. We shall require that the control mechanism, which determines the increment or decrement, be able to detect (in this case of a finite capacity counter) three significant counter states: that the counter is empty, that the counter contains some positive integer, and that the counter is at maximum capacity. (This last property of course has no significance for counters of indefinitely large capacity.)

We now show how a Maxwell Demon system can be interpreted as a computing automaton, in particular, as a finite state automaton equipped with two finite capacity counters. The Demon Proper will act as the finite state control unit, while the two Demon system chambers along with the finite numbers of two distinguishable types of particles will act as the two finite capacity counters. One of the chambers will serve as a *register* chamber, the other as a *reservoir* chamber. The numbers of fast (slow) particles in the register chamber will represent the position of the first (second) counter. If one of the two counters is to be incremented, then a corresponding fast or slow molecule is permitted to pass from the reservoir to the register chamber, while decrement is accomplished by directing the passage of molecules back from the register to the reservoir chamber. Since the Demon, as we have described its properties, is capable of detecting whether all molecules of a particular type have exited from a chamber, the zero, positive, and maximum tests required of finite capacity counters can also be made.

The "classic" computation of the customary Maxwell Demon system might thus be viewed as one in which, starting from any initial setting of the two counters, the control automaton Demon acts so as to increase the "fast" molecule counter in the register chamber to its maximum value, while decreasing the "slow" molecule counter to zero. When this desired situation has been reached the Demon may enter a special "halt" state, thus signalling to an outside observer successful completion of activity. In this example, of course, the register is the "hot" chamber, while the reservoir is the "cold" chamber.

3. Generalizations of the Maxwellian Demon System.

We now wish to describe and to discuss some generalizations of the basic Maxwellian Demon system. Of the many possible generalizations we will mainly focus our attention on the following:

1. *Enlarged Demon Memory*; instead of restricting the Demon to the few internal states by which the classic Maxwell paradox behavior is implemented, a Demon can assume any fixed number of states. This will permit much more sophisticated control automaton behavior.
2. *Increased Numbers of Chambers and of Distinguishable Particle Types*; The number of chambers as well as the numbers of distinguishable particle types can be increased to any finite number. This will permit the representation of any desired fixed finite number of counter registers or reservoirs.
3. *Indefinitely Large Chambers and Indefinitely Many Numbers of Particles*; indefinitely many particles (of each type) may be employed, the chambers becoming indefinitely

large so as to accommodate the particles. This will permit the representation of indefinite capacity counter registers and reservoirs.
4. *Increased Demon Observational Scope*; a Demon will be able to inspect the contents of finite but indefinitely large chambers and note whether the chamber is empty of molecules of any particular type. This will allow us to employ indefinitely large reservoir and register chambers as indefinite capacity counters.

These generalizations yield many different Demon systems and there can be many corresponding kinds of automata. Indeed, as we will show in a moment, such Demon systems can carry out *any* effective (algorithmic) procedure. This is so because appropriately generalized Demon systems can simulate the computations of an arbitrary Turing machine. Indeed, a Maxwellian Demon system, embracing our first and second generalizations, consisting of a finite state control automaton and two infinite or indefinitely expansible chambers containing indefinitely large numbers of two kinds of particles is sufficient to simulate an arbitrary Turing machine, including the so-called *Universal* Turing machine. (A universal Turing machine is a Turing machine which, if supplied on its tape with both the description of an arbitrary Turing machine and a problem, will simulate the computation of the arbitrary machine acting upon the problem and will produce the answer if such is computable.)

This result—that a Demon system consisting of a fixed finite control automaton to which is appended two chambers of two kinds of particles is sufficient to simulate the computation of an arbitrary Turing machine—is obtained as follows.

Shannon [2] showed that there is a universal Turing machine which consists of a fixed finite control automaton, and an indefinitely extendible two-way, read-write tape (a "Turing" tape) employing only two tape symbols. Minsky [1] showed that a machine consisting of a fixed finite control automaton and two counters each of indefinitely large capacity can simulate an arbitrary Turing machine of the Shannon type. (See **Appendix**.) We will show that the Demon system consisting of a fixed finite control automaton manipulating indefinitely large numbers of particles of two types, in two indefinitely large chambers, is sufficient to simulate an arbitrary machine of the Minsky type.

We need only show that our chambers and particles can simulate two indefinite capacity counters. One of our chambers will serve as counter register for indefinite numbers of two kinds of particles. The other chamber will serve as a reservoir (both source and sink) for particles of both types. We can begin with all the particles of both types in the reservoir chamber. (The register chamber will never hold more than a finite number of particles, so that this chamber can always be emptied in a finite amount of time.) As with the fixed capacity counters discussed earlier, the register is increased by permitting passage from the reservoir to the register chamber, and decreased by the opposite action.

Although the Demon is not required to detect emptiness in the reservoir chamber, he must be able to detect, in the register chamber, when no particles of a given type remain. Our increased observational scope generalization explicitly permits this, and so we can simulate two unbounded counters, and thus also the Minsky machine, and the desired result is obtained.

Although such conceptually rather simple Demon system machines can carry out arbitrary computations, these particular Demon automata are (like Turing machines themselves) not necessarily very realistic models of actual physical computation or of actual parts of the physical universe. The indefinitely extendible tape of the Turing machine system and the indefinitely large chambers and numbers of particles of our Demon system, if viewed as physically existing, presuppose a particular conception of material reality, namely, that it contains indefinitely large numbers of particles, etc. Recall also that for our particle and chamber system to work as counters in the intended manner, the control Demon must be able to detect whether there are particles of a particular type remaining in a register counter (that is, whether a chamber is exhausted of particles of a particular type). If the chambers must be indefinitely large (to hold indefinitely large numbers of particles) then the "observational scope" of the control Demon must be indefinitely large (and this may impose an indefinitely high operating cost on the Demon).

Another important point: There is nothing essential about our use of *two* distinguishable sorts of particles, such as the fast and slow particles of the original Maxwell Demon paradox. For example, if we permit outselves an inexhaustible reservoir chamber and *two* indefinite capacity register chambers, then, while distinguishing only a *single* kind of particle, we can still simulate the action of two indefinite capacity counters (the number of particles in each of the two separated register chambers representing the position of a counter) and obtain the desired result.

Notice also that if an arbitrary Turing machine is embeddable in the physical universe, then the familiar halting problem, word problem, etc., characteristic of the set of arbitrary Turing machines may carry over to become possible properties of the universe.

4. Models of Bounded Computation. The indefinitely large chambers, and the indefinitely large numbers of particles required in the Turing machine model (depending as they do on special properties of the physical universe for their real implementation) make them a poor model of practical computation. We will now therefore consider some *bounded* Demon systems and discuss their computational properties. Let us focus attention on the Demon systems obtained by enlarging the Demon memory and increasing the numbers of finite capacity chambers and particle types. In particular let us consider Demon systems in which the Demon proper has some fixed finite number of states, the Demon can distinguish some fixed finite number of particle kinds, there is a fixed finite number of each particle kind, and a fixed finite number of chambers to which the Demon has access in sorting particles.

In carrying out computations by such systems, clearly we might expand the finite automaton Demon proper itself to any desired size, so that a task of any size, "loaded" into the system in terms of kinds and locations of particles, could be carried out. However, this unnecessarily exaggerates the role of the finite state control Demon. Turing machine theory tells us that the finite automaton control Demon need not itself become indefinitely large in handling an indefinitely large task but only large enough to incorporate the properties of the universal imitator of other control automata.

Thus the finite state control automaton need not be arbitrarily large, but rather, after attaining a certain degree of complexity, need only interact with the auxiliary storage available to it in its chamber and particle systems in order to carry out its tasks.

The situation for both Turing machines (apart from their unbounded capacity) and especially for our bounded chamber automata is thus in many ways quite analogous to ordinary computation, with its division of roles between a fixed finite state control unit of considerable structural complexity, and a (largely) uniform storage medium (tapes, cores) which (theoretically, at least) can be readily and indefinitely expanded in a straightforward manner to accommodate problems of increasing size and complexity.

5. Reformulating the Paradox. We shall now consider the state of affairs if we should actually attempt to carry out practical computation by Demon and chamber particle manipulating systems. Let us for the moment adopt a naive point of view, where we, in particular, are ignorant of Szilard's analysis and resolution of the Demon paradox. In such a state of mind we might come to believe that such particle manipulating systems might provide us with unlimited amounts of expense-free computing power. We can, for example, imagine designing a Demon which can distinguish some number of kinds of particles and to which is appended some fixed finite number of finite chambers containing some fixed finite number of particle kinds. As in a real computer we begin by having the control clear the record of past computations, placing the machine in a standard initial condition. In our chamber automaton this would be accomplished by the Demon placing all the particles of all types in a reservoir chamber, thus clearing all register chambers. We then submit some practical computer problems to the Demon machine. In a real computing machine we do this by inserting a program (including data to be operated on) into the computer storage. Such program loading into our Demon system might be handled in various ways. We might for example "bleed" into the register chambers the proper number of particles to represent the program and the data. This loading Demon could of course be made part of the control Demon itself.

We now permit the Demon to direct the flow of particle movement produced by thermal agitation, according to his internal program (as well as any additional instructions which may be represented in the initial contents of the register-chamber-counter). Eventually (for the sort of total functions computed in practical situations) the Demon will halt, and the number represented in one of our chamber-counters (or in some defined subset of chambers, depending on the particular operation) will be the desired answer.

As with the original problem of Maxwell's Demon, we seem to be getting something for nothing. Such "free" computation offends our understanding about physical systems in general, as well as all practical experience of the properties of computing machinery.

This difficulty can of course be resolved by calling upon Szilard's analysis of the original Maxwell Demon paradox. By this analysis computation will clearly cost us at least as much as whatever energy is necessary for the Demon to carry out his particle detecting and routing activities.

6. Conclusions. We have shown that "practical" computations (indeed all Turing computations) can be expressed as the behavior of a very simple thermodynamic system, the (generalized) Maxwell Demon system. Szilard has analyzed the Maxwell Demon system, and its properties are well known. As the "classic" thermodynamic behavior imposed by an "intelligent" Demon on a uniform distribution of particles is constrained to obey fundamental thermodynamic laws, so also must the more sophisticated behavior we have imposed.

This association between computational and thermodynamical behavior suggests the possibility that convenient methods might be devised for expressing arbitrary computational procedures (in whatever form—Turing table, Algol program, etc.— they may arise) as the behavior of some single, standard, easily analyzable thermodynamic system, so that, furthermore, the *cost* of any computation in terms of energy consumption in the standard thermodynamic system might be ascertained. Such a reduction of arbitrary computations to a common energy-measurable form would make possible precise comparisons of the efficiency of alternative methods for computing the same function, or perhaps even permit establishing accurate, useful measures of maximum efficiency of particular practical computations.

This association between computational and thermodynamical behavior also holds out the more general possibility that a new and fruitful exchange between computer science and physics can be established; in particular, the concepts and techniques of thermodynamical systems analysis may prove applicable to problems of computational complexity, while the recently developed (and still rapidly growing) body of results in computational complexity theory may prove useful in studying thermodynamic efficiency.[1]

APPENDIX

We briefly outline a proof of Minsky's result that a finite state control automaton equipped with two indefinite capacity counters can simulate the computation of an arbitrary Turing machine. We will first show how the simulation can be carried out by employing *three* counters, and then show how this may be reduced to two counters.

At any instant a Turing machine configuration consists of the internal state of the control automaton, the location of the automaton on the tape, and the contents of the tape. The central problem of carrying out Turing computations by means of a finite state control automaton plus counters, is that of representing by counters the tape contents, change in tape contents, and change of read-head position.

Shannon [2] showed that the computations of an arbitrary Turing machine can be simulated

---

[1] J. von Neumann ([4], pp. 59–63) comments on applications of thermodynamic concepts to information processing systems, and makes the point that efficiency in information processing may depend on avoiding excessive speed and size imbalances between system parts, just as efficiency of a heat engine often depends on avoiding excessively large temperature differences between parts. In the next section ([4], pp. 66–67) von Neumann briefly considers the problem of the thermodynamical minimum cost of elementary information processing acts, that is, "per elementary decision of a two way alternative and per elementary transmittal of 1 unit of information."

by a Turing machine employing only two tape symbols. For a Shannon two tape symbol machine, at any given moment, the tape contents to the left and to the right of the read-head can be represented as two separate strings of zeroes and ones. These two separate, right and left strings can be interpreted as binary numerals. The numeral to the left of the read-head position will be read in the usual fashion, least significant digit to the far right (next to the square occupied by the read-head). We will interpret the numeral to the right of the read-head sequence as having its least significant digit to the far *left* (again closest to the read-head-occupied square), reversing the ordinary positional convention.

If a leftward read-head move is called for, the binary numeral to the left will become one digit shorter (the least significant digit having moved under the read-head), and the binary numeral to the right will become one digit longer (the square originally under the read-head now being exposed and becoming the new least significant digit). The result of such a move is to halve the *significance* of each original digit position to the left, while *doubling* the significance of each original digit position to the right.

We will now show how three counters may be employed to represent tape configurations and their changes. Counter 1 will store the number, which in binary notation is the string of zeroes and ones to the left of the read-head position, while counter 2 will store the number which in binary notation is the string of zeroes and ones to the right of the read-head position. We will show how to alter the numbers in the counters so as to represent a leftward read-head shift. We do this by halving the number in counter 1, while doubling the number in counter 2. For this doubling and halving we will require the assistance of our third counter. To halve counter 1 we decrease it in steps of two, while increasing counter 3 in steps of one. When counter 2 has reached zero, counter 3 will register half the original contents of counter 1. Counter 3 is then decreased in single steps, while counter 1 is increased in tandem. When counter 3 is empty, counter 1 will register half its original contents. To double counter 2, we decrease it by single steps, while increasing counter 3 by two steps. Counter 3 will end with twice the original contents of counter 2 and this revised (doubled) contents is transferred by tandem action back to counter 2.

We must now consider how the automaton read-head comes to read its counters to gain the "tape" input information which will determine its next state, and how it "writes" into its counter storage. In our example, when the read-head is to move left it does so by halving the number representing the sequence of zeroes and ones to its left. If the halving comes out even, then the least significant digit must necessarily have been a zero, if the halving came out odd, the least significant digit was a 1; in either case, the read-head can tell the contents of the next square and can then take the required action called for in its internal program.

Writing into a counter is effected as follows: the read-head is cognizant of the intended contents of the tape square it is abandoning. If it is a zero, then simple doubling of counter 2 will be sufficient to indicate this fact. If it is a one, then in addition to doubling counter 2, the read-head control automaton will increase counter 2 by one additional step.

We have indicated how a leftward move on the tape is represented in a counter system; rightward moves are carried out, *mutatis mutandis*, in the same fashion. Our finite control automaton is capable of directing all these actions.

This completes our description of how three indefinite capacity counters may be employed to represent the actions of a Turing tape: one counter for each right and left tape segment, and one counter for manipulating the contents of the first two. In order to reduce this to *two* counters, we will store *both* numbers representing tape segments in a *single* counter, reserving the remaining counter for our manipulations. In order to represent two distinct numbers as a single number we employ Gödelization. A description of a part of the process employed should make the technique clear. We begin with the number $G = 2^k \cdot 3^l \cdot 5^0 \cdot 7^0$ in counter 1, where k and l are numbers which (as before) in binary notation are the left and right hand Turing binary tape segments. Let us show how to divide k in half, so as (as before) to represent a leftward shift of the read-head. We do this by repeatedly dividing G by two, *and* each two times we are successful in this division, we multiply once by 5 (employing our remaining counter, counter 2, to assist us in this). Thus after twice dividing G by two and multiplying once by 5, the number in counter 1 will be $2^{k-2} \cdot 3^l \cdot 5^1 \cdot 7^0$. At the conclusion of *all* successful divisions by two, the number in counter 1 will be $2^0 \cdot 3^l \cdot 5^{k/2} \cdot 7^0$. We can now revise our Gödelization to reflect the doubling of the significance of the positions of the right hand tape sequence, by doubling its representing number l.

We do this by successive divisions by 3 and for each successful division by three we multiply by 7 *twice*. We will thus eventually end with $2^0 \cdot 3^0 \cdot 5^{k/2} \cdot 7^{2l}$, which is the desired transformation on k and l

We have thus managed to carry out the desired tape transformations employing only two counters and (save for matters of bookkeeping detail of the sort as indicated earlier) the Minsky result can be obtained.

REFERENCES

[1] Minsky, M. "Recursive Unsolvability of Post's Problem of Tag and Other Topics in Theory of Turing Machines." *Annals of Mathematics* 74 (1961): 437–454

[2] Shannon, C. E. "A Universal Turing Machine with Two Internal States." In *Automata Studies*. Edited by C. E. Shannon and J. McCarthy. Princeton: Princeton University Press, 1956. Pages 157–165.

[3] Szilard, L. "*Über die Entropieverminderung in einem Thermodynamischen System bei Eingriffen intelligenter Wesen.*" *Zeitschrift für Physik* 53 (1929) 840–852. (A translation of this paper, under the title "On the Decrease of Entropy in a Thermodynamic System by the Intervention of Intelligent Beings" appeared in *Behavioral Science* 9 (1964): 301–310).

[4] Von Neumann, J. *Theory of Self-Reproducing Automata*. Edited and completed by A. W. Burks. Urbana, Illinois: University of Illinois Press, 1966.

The Thermodynamics of Computation—a Review

Charles H. Bennett

IBM Watson Research Center, Yorktown Heights, New York 10598

Received May 8, 1981

Computers may be thought of as engines for transforming free energy into waste heat and mathematical work. Existing electronic computers dissipate energy vastly in excess of the mean thermal energy kT, for purposes such as maintaining volatile storage devices in a bistable condition, synchronizing and standardizing signals, and maximizing switching speed. On the other hand, recent models due to Fredkin and Toffoli show that in principle a computer could compute at finite speed with zero energy dissipation and zero error. In these models, a simple assemblage of simple but idealized mechanical parts (e.g., hard spheres and flat plates) determines a ballistic trajectory isomorphic with the desired computation, a trajectory therefore not foreseen in detail by the builder of the computer. In a classical or semiclassical setting, ballistic models are unrealistic because they require the parts to be assembled with perfect precision and isolated from thermal noise, which would eventually randomize the trajectory and lead to errors. Possibly quantum effects could be exploited to prevent this undesired equipartition of the kinetic energy. Another family of models may be called Brownian computers, because they allow thermal noise to influence the trajectory so strongly that it becomes a random walk through the entire accessible (low-potential-energy) portion of the computer's configuration space. In these computers, a simple assemblage of simple parts determines a low-energy labyrinth isomorphic to the desired computation, through which the system executes its random walk, with a slight drift velocity due to a weak driving force in the direction of forward computation. In return for their greater realism, Brownian models are more dissipative than ballistic ones: the drift velocity is proportional to the driving force, and hence the energy dissipated approaches zero only in the limit of zero speed. In this regard Brownian models resemble the traditional apparatus of thermodynamic thought experiments, where reversibility is also typically only attainable in the limit of zero speed. The enzymatic apparatus of DNA replication, transcription, and translation appear to be nature's closest approach to a Brownian computer, dissipating 20–$100kT$ per step. Both the ballistic and Brownian computers require a change in programming style: computations must be rendered *logically* reversible, so that no machine state has more than one logical predecessor. In a ballistic computer, the merging of two trajectories clearly cannot be brought about by purely conservative forces; in a Brownian computer, any extensive amount of merging of computation paths would cause the Brownian computer to spend most of its time bogged down in extraneous predecessors of states on the intended path, unless an extra driving force of $kT\ln 2$ were applied (and dissipated) at each merge point. The mathematical means of rendering a computation logically reversible (e.g., creation and annihilation of a history file) will be discussed. The old Maxwell's demon problem is discussed in the light of the relation between logical and thermodynamic reversibility: the essential irreversible step, which prevents the demon from breaking the second law, is not the making of a measurement (which in principle can be done reversibly) but rather the logically irreversible act of erasing the record of one measurement to make room for the next. Converse to the rule that logically irreversible operations on data require an entropy increase elsewhere in the computer is the fact that a tape full of zeros, or one containing some computable pseudorandom sequence such as pi, has fuel value and can be made to do useful thermodynamic work as it randomizes itself. A tape containing an algorithmically random sequence lacks this ability.

1. INTRODUCTION

The digital computer may be thought of as an engine that dissipates energy in order to perform mathematical work. Early workers naturally wondered whether there might be a fundamental thermodynamic limit to the efficiency of such engines, independent of hardware. Typical of early thinking in this area was the assertion by von Neumann, quoted from a 1949 lecture (von Neumann, 1966), that a computer operating at temperature T must dissipate at least $kT\ln 2$ (about 3×10^{-21} J at room temperature), "per elementary act of information, that is per elementary decision of a two-way alternative and per elementary transmittal of one unit of information." Brillouin (1962) came to a similar conclusion by analyzing a thought experiment involving detection of holes in a punched tape by photons, and argued further that the energy dissipation must increase with the reliability of the measurement, being approximately $kT\ln(1/\eta)$ for a measurement with error probability η. These conjectures have a certain plausibility, in view of the quantitative relation between entropy and information exemplified by Maxwell's demon (Szilard, 1929), and the fact that each classical degree of freedom used to store a bit of information, e.g., the charge in a capacitor, suffers from kT of thermal noise energy, which seemingly would have to be overcome in order to read or manipulate the bit reliably. However, it is now known that computers can in principle do an arbitrarily large amount of reliable computation per kT of energy dissipated. In retrospect, it is hardly surprising that computation, like a complex, multistep industrial process, can in principle be accomplished with arbitrarily little waste, i.e., at thermodynamic cost only marginally greater than the difference in thermodynamic potential (if any) between its input and output. The belief that computation has an irreducible entropy cost per step may have been due to a failure to distinguish sufficiently between dissipation (an irreversible net increase in entropy) and reversible transfers of entropy.

Though they are several orders of magnitude more efficient than the first electronic computers, today's computers still dissipate vast amounts of energy compared to kT. Probably the most conspicuous waste occurs in volatile memory devices, such as TTL flip-flops, which dissipate energy continuously even when the information in them is not being used. Dissipative storage is a convenience rather than a necessity: magnetic cores, CMOS, and Josephson junctions exemplify devices that dissipate only or chiefly when they are being switched. A more basic reason for the inefficiency of existing computers is the macroscopic size and inertia of their components, which therefore require macroscopic amounts of energy to switch quickly. This energy (e.g., the energy in an electrical pulse sent from one component to another) could in principle be saved and reused, but in practice it is easier to dissipate it and form the next pulse from new energy, just as it is usually more practical to stop a moving vehicle with brakes than by saving its kinetic energy in a flywheel. Macroscopic size also explains the poor efficiency of neurons, which dissipate about $10^{11}kT$ per discharge. On the other hand, the molecular apparatus of DNA replication, transcription, and protein synthesis, whose components are truly microscopic, has a relatively high energy efficiency, dissipating $20-100kT$ per nucleotide or amino acid inserted under physiological conditions.

Several models of thermodynamically reversible computation have been proposed. The most spectacular are the ballistic models of Fredkin and Toffoli (1982), which can compute at finite speed with zero energy dissipation. Less spectacular but perhaps more physically realistic are the Brownian models developed by Bennett (1973; see also below) following earlier work of Landauer and Keyes (1970), which approach zero dissipation only in the limit of zero speed. Likharev (1982) describes a scheme for reversible Brownian computing using Josephson devices.

Mathematically, the notion of a computer is well characterized. A large class of reasonable models of serial or parallel step-by-step computation, including Turing machines, random access machines, cellular automata, and tree automata, has been shown to be capable of simulating one another and therefore to define the same class of computable functions. In order to permit arbitrarily large computations, certain parts of these models (e.g., memory) are allowed to be infinite or indefinitely extendable, but the machine state must remain finitely describable throughout the computation. This requirement excludes "computers" whose memories contain prestored answers to infinitely many questions. An analogous requirement for a strictly finite computer, e.g, a logic net constructed of finitely many gates, would be that it be able to perform computations more complex than those that went into designing it. Models that are reasonable in the further sense of not allowing exponentially growing parallelism (e.g., in a d-dimensional cellular automaton, the effective degree of parallelism is bounded by the dth power of time) can generally simulate one another in polynomial time and linear space (in the jargon of computational complexity, time means number of machine cycles and space means number of bits of memory used). For this class of models, not only the computability of functions, but their rough level of difficulty (e.g., polynomial vs. exponential time in the size of the argument) are therefore model independent. Figure 1 reviews the Turing machine model of computation, on which several physical models of Section 3 will be based.

For time development of a physical system to be used for digital computation, there must be a reasonable mapping between the discrete logical states of the computation and the generally continuous mechanical states of the apparatus. In particular, as Toffoli suggests (1981), distinct logical variables describing the computer's mathematical state (i.e., the contents of a bit of memory, the location of a Turing machine's read/write head) ought to be embedded in distinct dynamical variables of the computer's physical state.

2. BALLISTIC COMPUTERS

The recent "ballistic" computation model of Fredkin and Toffoli (1982), shows that, in principle, a somewhat idealized apparatus can compute without dissipating the kinetic energy of its signals. In this model, a simple assemblage of simple but idealized mechanical parts (hard spheres colliding with each other and with fixed reflective barriers) determines a ballistic trajectory isomorphic with the desired computation. In more detail (Figure 2), the input end of a ballistic computer consists of a "starting line," like the starting line of a horse race, across which a number of hard spheres ("balls") are simultaneously fired straight forward into the computer with precisely equal velocity. There is a ball at each position in the starting line corresponding to a binary 1 in the input; at each position corresponding to a 0, no ball is fired. The computer itself has no moving parts, but contains a number of fixed barriers ("mirrors") with which the balls collide and which cause the balls to collide with each other. The collisions are elastic, and between collisions the balls travel in straight lines with constant velocity, in accord with Newton's second law. After a certain time, all the balls simultaneously emerge across a "finish line" similar to the starting line, with the presence or absence of balls again signifying the digits of the output. Within the computer, the mirrors perform the role of the logic gates of a conventional electronic computer, with the balls serving as signals.

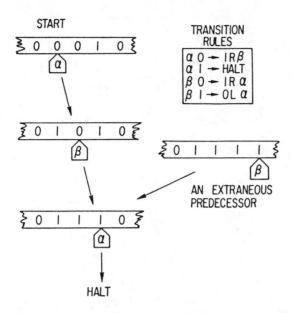

Fig. 1. An elementary mathematical model of computation, the Turing machine, consists of an infinite tape scanned by a movable finite automaton or "head," that can read or write one bit at a time, and shift a unit distance left or right along the tape. In order to remember what it is doing from one machine cycle to the next, the Turing machine head has a finite number of distinct internal states (here two: α and β). The Turing machine's behavior is governed by a fixed set of transition rules that indicate, for each combination of head state and scanned tape symbol, the new tape symbol to be written, the shift direction, and a new head state. The figure shows a short computation in which the machine has converted the input 00010, originally furnished on its tape, into the output 01110, and then halted. This Turing machine, because of its limited number of head states, can do only trivial computations; however, slightly more complicated machines, with a few dozen head states and correspondingly more transition rules, are "universal," i.e., capable of simulating any computer, even one much larger and more complicated than themselves. They do this by using the unlimited tape to store a coded representation of the larger machine's complete logical state, and breaking down each of the larger machine's machine cycles into many small steps, each simple enough to be performed by the Turing machine head. The configuration labeled "extraneous predecessor" is not part of the computation, but illustrates the fact that typical Turing machines, like other computers, often throw away information about their past, by making a transition into a logical state whose predecessor is ambiguous. This so-called "logical irreversibility" has an important bearing on the thermodynamics of computation, discussed in Section 4.

It is clear that such an apparatus cannot implement all Boolean functions: only functions that are conservative (the number of ones in the output equals the number of ones in the input) and bijective (to each output there corresponds one and only one input) can be implemented; but as Fredkin and Toffoli (1982) and Toffoli (1981) show, an arbitrarily Boolean function can be embedded in a conservative, bijective function without too much trouble.

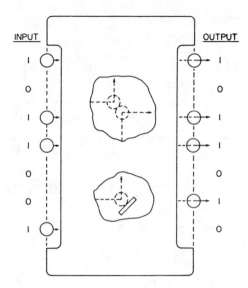

Fig. 2. Ballistic computer of Fredkin and Toffoli. In this example, the arrangement of mirrors inside the box is such that, when any five-bit number (here 13) is presented in the first five input positions, followed by 01 in the last two, the same five-bit number will appear in the first five output positions, followed by 01 if the number is composite, or 10 if the number is prime. The inclusion of the input as part of the output, and the use of two unlike bits to encode the desired answer, illustrate the embedding of an irreversible Boolean function into one that is reversible and conservative.

The two chief drawbacks of the ballistic computer are the sensitivity of its trajectory to small perturbations, and difficulty of making the collisions truly elastic. Because the balls are convex, small errors in their initial positions and velocities, or errors introduced later (e.g., by imperfect alignment of the mirrors) are amplified by roughly a factor of 2 at each collision between balls. Thus an initial random error of one part in 10^{15} in position and velocity, roughly what one would expect for billiard balls on the basis of the uncertainty principle, would cause the trajectory to become unpredictable after a few dozen collisions. Eventually the balls would degenerate into a gas, spread throughout the apparatus, with a Maxwell distribution of velocities. Even if classical balls could be shot with perfect accuracy into a perfect apparatus, fluctuating tidal forces from turbulence in the atmospheres of nearby stars would be enough to randomize their motion within a few hundred collisions. Needless to say, the trajectory would be spoiled much sooner if stronger nearby noise sources (e.g., thermal radiation and conduction) were not eliminated.

Practically, this dynamical instability means that the balls' velocities and positions would have to be corrected after every few collisions. The resulting computer, although no longer thermodynamically reversible, might still be of some practical interest, since energy cost per step of restoring the trajectory might be far less than the kinetic energy accounting for the computation's speed.

One way of making the trajectory insensitive to noise would be to use square balls, holonomically constrained to remain always parallel to each other and to the fixed walls. Errors would then no longer grow exponentially, and small perturbations could simply be ignored. Although this system is consistent with the laws of classical mechanics it is a bit unnatural, since there are no square atoms in nature. A macroscopic square particle would not do, because a fraction of its kinetic energy would be converted into heat at each collision. On the other hand, a square molecule might work, if it were stiff enough to require considerably more than kT of energy to excite it out of its vibrational ground state. To prevent the molecule from rotating, it might be aligned in an external field strong enough to make the energy of the first librational excited state similarly greater than kT. One would still have to worry about losses when the molecules collided with the mirrors. A molecule scattering off even a very stiff crystal has sizable probability of exciting long-wavelength phonons, thereby transferring energy as well as momentum. This loss could be minimized by reflecting the particles from the mirrors by long-range electrostatic repulsion, but that would interfere with the use of short-range forces for collisions between molecules, not to mention spoiling the uniform electric field used to align the molecules.

Although quantum effects might possibly help stabilize a ballistic computer against external noise, they introduce a new source of internal instability in the form of wave-packet spreading. Benioff's discussion (1982) of quantum ballistic models shows how wave packet spreading can be prevented by employing a periodically varying Hamiltonian, but not apparently by any reasonably simple time-independent Hamiltonian.

In summary, although ballistic computation is consistent with the laws of classical and quantum mechanics, there is no evident way to prevent the signals' kinetic energy from spreading into the computer's other degrees of freedom. If this spread is combatted by restoring the signals, the computer becomes dissipative; if it is allowed to proceed unchecked, the initially ballistic trajectory degenerates into random Brownian motion.

3. BROWNIAN COMPUTERS

If thermal randomization of the kinetic energy cannot be avoided, perhaps it can be exploited. Another family of models may be called Brownian computers, because they allow thermal noise to influence the

trajectory so strongly that all moving parts have nearly Maxwellian velocities, and the trajectory becomes a random walk. Despite this lack of
discipline, the Brownian computer can still perform useful computations
because its parts interlock in such a way as to create a labyrinth in
configuration space, isomorphic to the desired computation, from which the
trajectory is prevented from escaping by high-potential-energy barriers on
all sides. Within this labyrinth the system executes a random walk, with a
slight drift velocity in the intended direction of forward computation
imparted by coupling the system to a weak external driving force.

In more concrete terms, the Brownian computer makes logical state
transitions only as the accidental result of the random thermal jiggling of its
information-bearing parts, and is about as likely to proceed backward along
the computation path, undoing the most recent transition, as to proceed
forward. The chaotic, asynchronous operation of a Brownian computer is
unlike anything in the macroscopic world, and it may at first appear
inconceivable that such an apparatus could work; however, this style of
operation is quite common in the microscopic world of chemical reactions,
were the trial and error action of Brownian motion suffices to bring reactant
molecules into contact, orient and bend them into a specific conformation
("transition state") that may be required for reaction, and separate the
product molecules after reaction. It is well known that all chemical reactions
are in principle reversible: the same Brownian motion that accomplishes the
forward reaction also sometimes brings product molecules together, pushes
them backward through the transition state, and lets them emerge as
reactant molecules. Though Brownian motion is scarcely noticeable in
macroscopic bodies (e.g., $(kT/m)^{1/2} \approx 10^{-6}$ cm/sec for a 1-g mass at room
temperature), it enables even rather large molecules, in a fraction of a
second, to accomplish quite complicated chemical reactions, involving a
great deal of trial and error and the surmounting of potential energy
barriers of several kT in order to arrive at the transition state. On the other
hand, potential energy barriers of order 100 kT, the typical strength of
covalent bonds, effectively obstruct chemical reactions. Such barriers, for
example, prevent DNA from undergoing random rearrangements of its base
sequence at room temperature.

To see how a molecular Brownian computer might work, we first
consider a simpler apparatus: a Brownian tape-copying machine. Such an
apparatus already exists in nature, in the form of RNA polymerase, the
enzyme that synthesizes a complementary RNA copy of one or more genes
of a DNA molecule. The RNA then serves to direct the synthesis of the
proteins encoded by those genes (Watson, 1970). A schematic snapshot of
RNA polymerase in action is given in Figure 3. In each cycle of operation,
the enzyme takes a small molecule (one of the four nucleotide pyrophos-

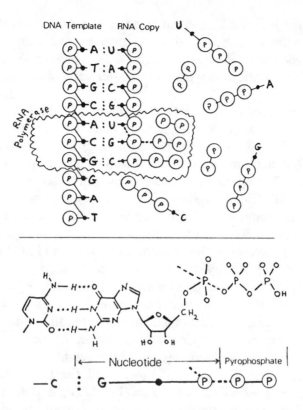

Fig. 3. RNA Polymerase synthesizing a complementary RNA strand on a single-strand DNA "template." Double and triple dots between DNA and RNA bases indicate base-pairing interaction; dashed lines indicate covalent bonds being formed and broken by RNA polymerase. Below, in more detail, the arriving GTP monomer about to lose its pyrophosphate group and be attached to the growing RNA strand.

phates, ATP, GTP, CTP, or UTP, whose base is complementary to the base about to be copied on the DNA strand) from the surrounding solution, forms a covalent bond between the nucleotide part of the small molecule and the existing uncompleted RNA strand, and releases the pyrophosphate part into the surrounding solution as a free pyrophosphate molecule (PP). The enzyme then shifts forward one notch along the DNA in preparation for copying the next nucleotide. In the absence of the enzyme, this reaction would occur with a negligible rate and with very poor specificity for selecting bases correctly complementary to those on the DNA strand. Assuming RNA polymerase to be similar to other enzymes whose mechanisms have been studied in detail, the enzyme works by forming many weak (e.g., van der Waals and hydrogen) bonds to the DNA, RNA, and incoming nucleotide pyrophosphate, in such a way that if the incoming nucleotide is correctly base-paired with the DNA, it is held in the correct transition state conformation for forming a covalent bond to the end of the RNA strand, while breaking the covalent bond to its own pyrophosphate group. The transition state is presumably further stabilized (its potential energy lowered) by favorable electrostatic interaction with strategically placed charged groups on the enzyme.

The reaction catalyzed by RNA polymerase is reversible: sometimes the enzyme takes up a free pyrophosphate molecule, combines it with the end nucleotide of the RNA, and releases the resulting nucleotide pyrophosphate into the surrounding solution, meanwhile backing up one notch along the DNA strand. The operation of the enzyme thus resembles a one-dimensional random walk (Figure 4), in which both forward and backward steps are possible, and would indeed occur equally often at equilibrium. Under biological conditions, RNA polymerase is kept away from equilibrium by other metabolic processes, which continually supply ATP, GTP, UTP, and CTP and remove PP, thereby driving the chain of reactions strongly in the direction of RNA synthesis. In domesticated bacteria, RNA polymerase runs forward at about 30 nucleotides per second, dissipating about $20kT$ per nucleotide, and making less than one mistake per ten thousand nucleotides.

In the laboratory, the speed and direction of operation of RNA polymerase can be varied by adjusting the reactant concentrations. The closer these are to equilibrium, the slower and the less dissipatively the enzyme works. For example, if ATP, GTP, UTP, and CTP were each present in 10% excess over the concentration that would be in equilibrium with a given ambient PP concentration, RNA synthesis would drift slowly forward, the enzyme on average making 11 forward steps for each 10 backward steps. These backward steps do not constitute errors, since they are undone by subsequent forward steps. The energy dissipation would be $kT \ln(11/10) \approx 0.1kT$ per (net) forward step, the difference in chemical potential between reactants and products under the given conditions. More

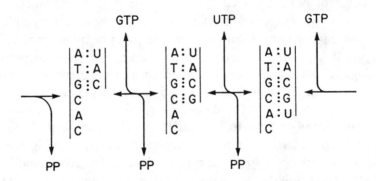

Fig. 4. RNA polymerase reaction viewed as a one-dimensional random walk.

generally, a dissipation of ϵ per step results in forward/backward step ratio of $e^{+\epsilon/kT}$, and for small ϵ, a net copying speed proportional to ϵ.

The analysis so far has ignored true errors, due to uncatalyzed reactions. Because these occur in some fixed, hardware-dependent ratio η_0 to the gross (rather than the net) number of catalyzed transitions, they set a limit on how slowly the copying system can be driven and still achieve reasonable accuracy. For example, if a copying system with an intrinsic error rate of 10^{-4} were driven at $0.1kT$ per step, its error rate would be about 10^{-3}; but if it were driven at $10^{-4}kT$ or less, near total infidelity would result. Because the intrinsic error rate is determined by the difference in barriers opposing correct and incorrect transitions, it is a function of the particular chemical hardware, and does not represent a fundamental thermodynamic limit. In principle it can be made arbitrarily small by increasing the size and complexity of the recognition sites (to increase the potential energy difference ΔE between correct and incorrect reaction paths), by lowering the temperature (to increase the Boltzmann ratio $e^{\Delta E/kT}$ of correct to error transitions without changing ΔE) and by making the apparatus larger and more massive (to reduce tunneling). In situations calling for very high accuracy (e.g., DNA copying), the genetic apparatus apparently uses another strategem for reducing errors: dissipative error correction or proofreading (Hopfield, 1974; Ninio, 1975), depicted in Figure 5. The dissipation-error tradeoff for model nonproofreading and proofreading copying systems is discussed by Bennett (1979). An amusing if impractical feature of this tradeoff is that when a copying system is operated at very low speed (and therefore high error rate), the errors themselves serve as a thermodynamic driving force, and can push the copying slowly forward even in the presence of a small reverse bias in the driving reaction. Of course, in obediance to the second law, the entropy of the incorporated errors more than makes up for the work done against the external reactants.

A true chemical Turing machine is not difficult to imagine (Figure 6). The tape might be a linear informational macromolecule analogous to RNA, with an additional chemical group attached at one site to encode the head state (α) and location. Several hypothetical enzymes (one for each of the Turing machine's transition rules) would catalyze reactions of the macromolecule with small molecules in the surrounding solution, transforming the macromolecule into its logical successor. The transition $\alpha 0 \to 1R\beta$, for example, would be carried out by an enzyme that brings with it the groups 1 and β that must be added during the transition, and has additional specific affinities allowing it to temporarily bind to groups 0 and α that must be removed. (Real enzymes with multiple, highly specific binding sites are well known, e.g., the acylating enzymes of protein synthesis.) In Figure 6, the hypothetical enzyme binds on the right, since its transition rule calls

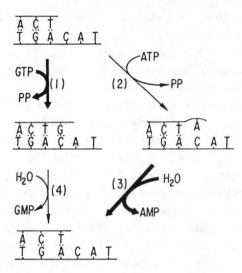

Fig. 5. Proofreading in DNA replication. The enzyme responsible for copying DNA usually inserts the correct nucleotide (1), but occasionally inserts an incorrect one (2). To counter this, another enzyme (or another active site on the same enzyme) catalyzes a proofreading reaction (3), which preferentially removes incorrectly paired nucleotides from the end of an uncompleted DNA strand. The proofreading enzyme also occasionally makes mistakes, removing a nucleotide even though it is correct (4). After either a correct or an incorrect nucleotide has been removed, the copying enzyme gets another chance to try to insert it correctly, and the proofreading enzyme gets another chance to proofread, etc. It is important to note that the proofreading reaction is not simply the thermodynamic reverse of the copying reaction: it uses different reactants, and has a different specificity (favoring incorrect nucleotides, while the copying reaction favors correct nucleotides). The minimum error rate (equal to the product of the error rates of the writing and proofreading steps) is obtained when both reactions are driven strongly forward, as they are under physiological conditions. Proofreading is an interesting example of the use of thermodynamic irreversibility to perform the logically irreversible operation of error correction.

for a right shift. After the requisite changes have been made, it drops off and is readied for reuse. At some point in their cycle of use the hypothetical enzymes are made to catalyze a reaction involving external reactants (here ATP:ADP), whose concentrations can be adjusted to provide a variable driving force.

Assume for the moment that the enzymatic Turing machine is *logically reversible*, i.e., that no whole-machine state has more than one logical predecessor (this mathematical requirement on the structure of the computation will be discussed in the next section). Then the net computation speed will be linear in the driving force, as was the case with RNA polymerase, because the logically accessible states (i.e., configurations of the macromolecule accessible by forward and backward operation of the enzymes) form a one-dimensional chain, along which the executes a random walk with drift velocity proportional to ϵ/kT.

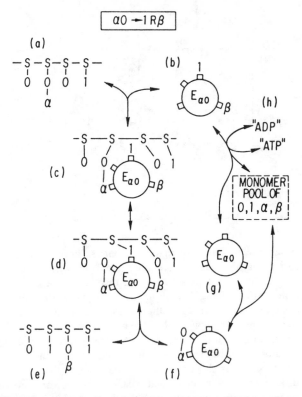

Fig. 6. Hypothetical enzymatic Turing machine. Macromolecular tape (a) consists of a structural backbone S–S–S bearing tape symbols 1,0 and head marker α. Macromolecule reacts (c,d) with enzyme (b) that catalyzes the transition $\alpha 0 \rightarrow 1 R \beta$, via specific binding sites (tabs), thereby resulting in logical successor configuration (e). Enzyme is then prepared for reuse (f,g,h). Coupling to external reaction (h) drives the reactions, which would otherwise drift indifferently forward and backward, in the intended forward direction.

It is also possible to imagine an error-free Brownian Turing machine made of rigid, frictionless clockwork. This model (Figure 7) lies between the billiard-ball computer and the enzymatic computer in realism because, on the one hand, no material body is perfectly hard; but on the other hand, the clockwork model's parts need not be machined perfectly, they may be fit together with some backlash, and they will function reliably even in the presence of environmental noise. A similar model has been considered by Reif (1979) in connection with the **P = PSPACE** question in computational complexity.

The baroque appearance of the clockwork Turing machine reflects the need to make all its parts interlock in such a way that, although they are free to jiggle locally at all times, no part can move an appreciable distance except when it is supposed to be making a logical transition. In this respect it resembles a well worn one of those wooden cube puzzles that must be

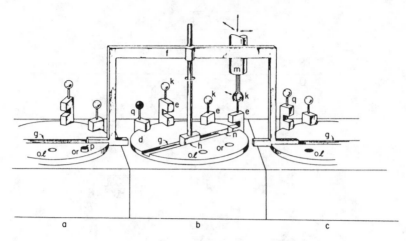

Fig. 7. Brownian Turing machine made of rigid, frictionless, loosely fitting clockwork. This figure shows the Turing machine tape (a,b,c) and the read–write–shift equipment. The machine is scanning square b. Each tape square has a disk (d) which interlocks with several E-shaped bit-storage blocks (e), holding them in the up (1) or down (0) position. A framework (f) fits over the scanned tape square, engaging the disks of the two adjacent squares (via their grooves g), to keep them from rotating when they are not supposed to. After the bits are read (cf. next figure) they must in general be changed. In order to change a bit, its knob (k) is first grasped by the manipulator (m), then the notch (n) is rotated into alignment by the screwdriver (h) and the bit storage block (e) is slid up or down. The block is then locked into place by further rotating the disk, after which the manipulator can safely let go and proceed to grasp the next bit's knob. Each tape square has a special knob (q) that is used to help constrain the disks on nonscanned tape squares. In principle these might all be constrained by the framework (f), but that would require making it infinitely large and aligning it with perfect angular accuracy. To avoid this, the framework (f) is used only to constrain the two adjacent tape squares. All the remaining tape squares are indirectly constrained by pegs (p) coupled to the special knob (q) of an adjacent square. The coupling (a lever arrangement hidden under the disk) is such that, when any square's q knob is down, a peg (p) engages the rightmost of two openings (o r) on the next tape square to the left, and another peg disengages the leftmost (o l) of two openings on the next tape square to the right. A q knob in the up position does the opposite: it frees the tape square to its left and locks the tape square to its right. To provide an outward-propagating chain of constraints on each side of the scanned square, all the q knobs to its right must be up, and all the q knobs to its left must be down. The q knob on the scanned square can be in either position, but just before a right shift it is lowered, and just before a left shift it is raised. To perform the shift, the screwdriver rotates the scanned square's groove (g) into alignment with the framework, then the manipulator (m), by grasping some convenient knob, pulls the whole head apparatus (including m itself, as well as f, h, and parts not shown) one square to the left or right.

solved by moving one part a small distance, which allows another to move in such a way as to free a third part, etc. The design differs from conventional clockwork in that parts are held in place only by the hard constraints of their loosely fitting neighbors, never by friction or by spring pressure. Therefore, when any part is about to be moved (e.g., when one of the E-shaped blocks used to store a bit of information is moved by the manipulator **m**), it must be grasped in its current position before local constraints on its motion are removed, and, after the move, local constraints must be reimposed before the part can safely be let go of.

Perhaps the most noteworthy feature of the machine's operation is the "obstructive read" depicted in Figure 8. In general, the coordinated motion of the screwdriver **h** and manipulator **m**, by which the Turing machine control unit acts on the tape, can be described as a deterministic un-branched path in the five-dimensional configuration space spanning the screwdriver's rotation and the manipulator's translation and grasp (because of backlash, this path is not single trajectory, but a zero-potential-energy channel of finite width surrounded by infinite potential energy barriers, within which the system performs a Brownian random walk, with a slight forward drift velocity). However, before it can know what to write or which way to shift, the control unit must ascertain the current contents of the scanned tape square. To do this, during the read stage of the machine cycle, the path of the manipulator branches nondeterministically into two paths, one of which is obstructed (due to collision with the knob **k**) by a bit in the up position, the other by the same bit in the down position. This bifurcation followed by obstruction is repeated for each additional bit stored on the tape square, so that, by the time the manipulator has negotiated all the

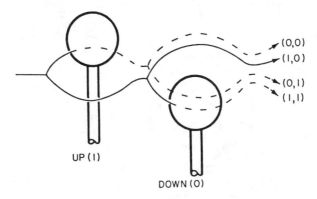

Fig. 8. Obstructive read. The clockwork Turing machine's control unit guides the manipulator along a branching path, one of whose branches is obstructed by a knob in the up position, the other by the same knob in the down position.

bifurcations and obstructions, it is again on a single path determined by the contents of the scanned tape square. If the manipulator by chance wanders into the wrong path at a bifurcation and encounters an obstruction, the forward progress of the computation is delayed until Brownian motion jiggles the manipulator back to the bifurcation and forward again along the right path.

Figure 9 suggests how the manipulator and screwdriver might be driven through their paces by the main control unit. A master camshaft, similar to a stereophonic phonograph record, would contain a network of tunnels isomorphic with the Turing machine's finite state transition graph. A weak spring (the only spring in the whole apparatus) biases the camshaft's Brownian motion, causing it to revolve on average in the direction corresponding to forward computation. Revolution of the camshaft imposes certain motions on a captive cam follower, which in turn are translated by appropriate mechanical linkages into synchronous motions of the manipulator and screwdriver in Figure 7, required to perform read, write, and shift operations on the Turing machine tape. During the read phase, the cam follower passes through a bifurcation in its tunnel for each bit to be read, causing the manipulator to perform an obstructive read, and delaying the

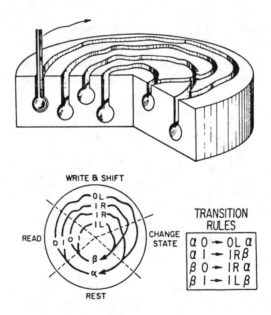

Fig. 9. Above: master camshaft of the clockwork Turing machine's control unit. Below: top view of camshaft, and the transition rules to which its tunnels are isomorphic.

computation until the cam follower, by Brownian trial and error, chooses the right tunnel. The obstructive read places the cam follower at the beginning of a specific tunnel segment corresponding to the current head state and tape symbol, and the rest of this tunnel segment drives the manipulator and screwdriver through the coordinated motions necessary to accomplish the write and shift operations. The obstructive read also serves another, less obvious purpose: it prevents the machine from wandering backward into states that are not logical predecessors of the present state. If the machine is logically reversible as supposed, this means that the only unobstructed path for the camshaft to rotate backwards one full revolution is the path leading to the present state's unique logical predecessor.

As in the case of the enzymatic Turing machine, the drift velocity is linear in the dissipation per step. Because the clockwork Turing machine cannot make illogical transitions, the only kind of error it is susceptible to is failure to be in the final logical state of its computation. Indeed, if the driving force ϵ is less than kT, any Brownian computer will at equilibrium spend most of its time in the last few predecessors of the final state, spending only about ϵ/kT of its time in the final state itself. However, the final state occupation probability can be made arbitrarily large, independent of the number of steps in the computation, by dissipating a little extra energy during the final step, a "latching energy" of $kT\ln(kT/\epsilon)+kT\ln(1/\eta)$ sufficing to raise the equilibrium final state occupation probability to $1-\eta$.

Quantum mechanics probably does not have a major qualitative effect on Brownian computers: in an enzymatic computer, tunneling and zero-point effects would modify transition rates for both catalyzed and uncatalyzed reactions; a quantum clockwork computer could be viewed as a particle propagating in a multidimensional labyrinth in configuration space (since the clockwork computer's parts are assumed to be perfectly hard, the wave function could not escape from this labyrinth by tunneling). Both models would exhibit the same sort of diffusive behavior as their classical versions.

[It should perhaps be remarked that, although energy transfers between a quantum system and its environment occur via quanta (e.g., photons of black body radiation) of typical magnitude about kT, this fact does not by itself imply any corresponding coarseness in the energy cost per step: a net energy transfer of $0.01kT$ between a Brownian computer and its environment could for example be achieved by emitting a thermal photon of $1.00kT$ and absorbing one of $0.99kT$. The only limitation on this kind of spontaneous thermal fine tuning of a quantum system's energy comes from its energy level spacing, which is less than kT except for systems so cold that the system as a whole is frozen into its quantum ground state.]

4. LOGICAL REVERSIBILITY

Both the ballistic and Brownian computers require a change in programming style: *logically irreversible* operations (Landauer, 1961) such as
erasure, which throw away information about the computer's preceding
logical state, must be avoided. These operations are quite numerous in
computer programs as ordinarily written; besides erasure, they include
overwriting of data by other data, and entry into a portion of the program
addressed by several different transfer instructions. In the case of Turing
machines, although the individual transition rules (quintuples) are reversible, they often have overlapping ranges, so that from a given instantaneous
description it is not generally possible to infer the immediately preceding
instantaneous description (Figure 1). In the case of combinational logic, the
very gates out of which logic functions are traditionally constructed are for
the most part logically irreversible (e.g., AND, OR, NAND), though NOT is
reversible.

Logically irreversible operations must be avoided entirely in a ballistic
computer, and for a very simple reason: the merging of two trajectories into
one cannot be brought about by conservative forces. In a Brownian computer, a small amount of logical irreversibility can be tolerated (Figure 10),
but a large amount will greatly retard the computation or cause it to fail
completely, unless a finite driving force (approximately $kT \ln 2$ per bit of
information thrown away) is applied to combat the computer's tendency to
drift backward into extraneous branches of the computation. Thus driven,
the Brownian computer is no longer thermodynamically reversible, since its
dissipation per step no longer approaches zero in the limit of zero speed.

In spite of their ubiquity, logically irreversible operations can be
avoided without seriously limiting the power of computers. A means of
simulating arbitrary irreversible computations reversibly is given by Bennett
(1973) using Turing machines, was independently discovered by Fredkin,
using reversible Boolean logic (Toffoli, 1980), and is outlined below.

We begin by noting that it is easy to render any computer reversible in
a rather trivial sense, by having it save all the information it would
otherwise have thrown away. For example the computer could be given an
extra "history" tape, initially blank, on which to record enough about each
transition (e.g., for a Turing machine, which quintuple was being used) that
the preceding state would be uniquely determined by the present state and
the last record on the history tape. From a practical viewpoint this does not
look like much of an improvement, since the computer has only postponed
the problem of throwing away unwanted information by using the extra
tape as a garbage dump. To be usefully reversible, a computer ought to be
required to clean up after itself, so that at the end of the computation the

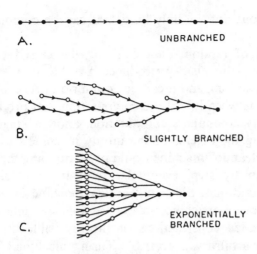

A. UNBRANCHED

B. SLIGHTLY BRANCHED

C. EXPONENTIALLY BRANCHED

Fig. 10. Various kinds of computation graph, with black nodes denoting logical states (instantaneous descriptions, in Turing machine terminology) on the intended computation path, and open nodes denoting extraneous predecessors. Arrows indicate intended direction of transitions, but if the driving force is weak, backward transitions occur nearly as often as forward ones. In a strictly reversible computation (A), the graph is unbranched, and an arbitrarily small driving force ϵ suffices to drive the computation forward with drift velocity proportional to ϵ. An arbitrarily small driving force still suffices for a slightly branched graph (B), with a few extraneous predecessors per state on the intended path, but the computation proceeds more slowly, due to temporary detours onto the extraneous branches. Slightly branching trees occur, for example when the same variable is assigned several times in succession: at any point in the computation, the most recent assignment can be randomly undone (giving the variable any value at all), but the result is typically a "garden-of-Eden" state with no predecessor, because this random value is inconsistent with the forward result of the previous assignment. Exponentially branching trees (C) also occur, for example, in loops that assign a succession of different variables. If such a tree is infinite, then a small driving force is insufficient to keep the computation from wandering onto an extraneous branch never to return; to drive the computation forward in such a tree, the dissipation per step must exceed kT times the mean number of immediate predecessors per state. Even if the exponential backward branching is eventually stopped by garden-of-Eden states, as is commonly the case, extraneous states may outnumber states on the intended path by factors of 2^{100} or so, slowing down the computation by that much unless backward excursions are again suppressed by dissipating about kT times the logarithm of the mean number of immediate predecessors of states near the intended computation path.

only data remaining are the desired output and the originally furnished input. [A general-purpose reversible computer must be allowed to save its input, or some equivalent information; otherwise it could not perform computations in which the input was not uniquely determined by the output. Formally this amounts to embedding the partial recursive function $x \to \varphi(x)$, computed by the original irreversible machine, in a $1:1$ partial recursive function $x \to \langle x, \varphi(x) \rangle$, to be computed by the reversible machine;

since 1:1 functions are the only kind that can be computed by reversible machines.]

A tape full of random data can only be erased by an irreversible process. However, the history produced by the above untidy reversible computer is not random, and it can be gotten rid of reversibly, by exploiting the redundancy between it and the computation that produced it. If, at the end of the untidy computer's computation, another stage of computation were begun, using the inverse of the untidy machine's transition function, the inverse, or "cleanup" machine would begin undoing the untidy machine's computation step by step, eventually returning the history tape to its original blank condition. Since the untidy machine is reversible and deterministic, its cleanup machine is also reversible and deterministic. [Bennett (1973) gives detailed constructions of the reversible untidy and cleanup machines for an arbitrary irreversible Turing machine.] The cleanup machine, of course, is not a general-purpose garbage disposer: the only garbage it can erase is the garbage produced by the untidy machine of which it is the inverse.

Putting the untidy and cleanup machines together, one obtains a machine that reversibly does, then undoes, the original irreversible computation. This machine is still useless because the desired output, produced during the untidy first stage of computation, will have been eaten up along with the undesired history during the second cleanup stage, leaving behind only a reconstructed copy of the original input. Destruction of the desired output can be easily prevented, by introducing still another stage of computation, after the untidy stage but before the cleanup stage. During this stage the computer makes an extra copy of the output on a separate, formerly blank tape. No additional history is recorded during this stage, and none needs to be, since copying onto blank tape is already a 1:1 operation. The subsequent cleanup stage therefore destroys only the original of the output but not the copy. At the end of its three-stage computation, the computer contains the (reconstructed) original input plus the intact copy of the output. All other storage will have been restored to its original blank condition. Even though no history remains, the computation is reversible and deterministic, because each of its stages has been so. The use of separate tapes for output and history is not necessary; blank portions of the work tape may be used instead, at the cost of making the simulation run more slowly (quadratic rather than linear time). Figure 11A summarizes the three-stage computation.

The argument just outlined shows how an arbitrary Turing machine can be simulated in not much more time by a reversible Turing machine, at the cost of including the input as part of the output, and perhaps using a lot of temporary storage for the history. By cleaning up the history more often

A

Computation Stage	Contents of		
	Work area	History area	Output area
	_INPUT	-	-
Untidy	WO_RK	HISTO_	-
	_OUTPUT	HISTORY_	-
	OUTP_UT	HISTORY_	OUT_
Copy output	OUTPUT_	HISTORY_	OUTPUT_
	_OUTPUT	HISTORY_	_OUTPUT
Cleanup	WO_RK	HISTO_	_OUTPUT
	_INPUT	-	_OUTPUT

B

Computation Stage	Contents of		
	Work area	Hist. area	Output area
	INPUT	-	-
1. Untidy φ comp.			
	OUTPUT	φ HISTORY	-
2. Copy output			
	OUTPUT.	φ HISTORY	OUTPUT
3. Cleanup φ comp.			
	INPUT	-	OUTPUT
4. Interchange data			
	OUTPUT	-	INPUT
5. Untidy φ^{-1} comp.			
	INPUT	φ^{-1} HISTORY	INPUT
6. Cancel extra input			
	INPUT	φ^{-1} HISTORY	-
7. Cleanup φ^{-1} comp.			
	OUTPUT	-	-

Fig. 11. (A) Reversible simulation of an irreversible computation. The reversible computer has three storage areas (e.g., tapes): a work area in which the simulation takes place; a history area in which garbage generated by the irreversible computation is saved temporarily, thereby rendering the computation reversible; and an output area. The work area initially contains the input; the history and output areas are initially blank. The computation takes place in three stages, representative snapshots of which are shown. The underbars represent the locations of read/write heads for a three-tape machine, or analogous place markers for other machines. (B) Reversible computation of an arbitrary 1:1 function φ with no extra output, given irreversible algorithms for φ and φ^{-1}. The computation proceeds by seven stages as shown. Stage 5 has the sole purpose of producing the φ^{-1} history, which, after the extra input has been reversibly erased in stage 6, serves in stage 7 to destroy itself and the remaining copy of the input, leaving only the desired output.

(Bennett, 1973), space on the history tape may be traded off against time or additional garbage output. This tradeoff, the details of which remain to be worked out, provides an upper bound on the cost of making computations reversible. However, it has been observed in practice that many computations (e.g., numerical integration of differential equations) can be performed by reversible algorithms with *no* penalty in time, storage, or extra output.

In cases where the original irreversible Turing machine computes a $1:1$ function, it can be simulated reversibly with no additional output, but with perhaps an exponential increase in run time. This is done by combining McCarthy's (1956) trial-and-error procedure for effectively computing the inverse of a $1:1$ partial recursive function [given an algorithm φ for the original function and an argument y, $\varphi^{-1}(y)$ is defined as the first element of the first ordered pair $\langle x, s \rangle$ such that $\varphi(x) = y$ in less than s steps] with Bennett's procedure (1973; Figure 11B] for synthesizing a reversible Turing machine with no extra output from two mutually inverse irreversible Turing machines. These results imply that the reversible Turing machines provide a Gödel numbering of $1:1$ partial recursive functions (i.e., every $1:1$ partially reversible function is computable by a reversible TM and vice versa). The construction of a reversible machine from an irreversible machine and its inverse implies that the open question, of whether there exists a $1:1$ function much easier to compute by an irreversible machine than by any reversible machine, is equivalent to the question of whether there is an easy $1:1$ function with a hard inverse.

Simulation of irreversible logic functions by reversible gates is analogous (Toffoli, 1980) to the constructions for Turing machines. The desired function is first embedded in a one-to-one function (e.g., by extending the output to include a copy of the input) which is then computed by reversible gates, such as the three-input, three-output AND/NAND gate. The first two inputs of this gate simply pass through unchanged to become the first two outputs; the third output is obtained by taking the EXCLUSIVE-OR of the third input with the AND of the first two inputs. The resulting mapping from three bits onto three bits (which is its own inverse) can be used together with constant inputs to compute any logic function computable by conventional gates, but in so doing, may produce extra "garbage" bits analogous to the reversible Turing machine's history. If the function being computed is $1:1$, these bits need not appear in the final output, because they can be disposed of by a process analogous to the reversible Turing machine's cleanup stage, e.g., by feeding them into a mirror image of the reversible logic net that produced them in the first place. The "interaction gate" used in the ballistic computer (Fredkin and Toffoli, 1981) may be regarded as having two inputs and four outputs (respectively, x & y, y & ¬ x, x & ¬ y, and x & y) for the four possible exit paths from the collision zone between balls **x** and **y**. The interaction gate is about as simple as can be imagined in its physical realization, yet it suffices (with the help of mirrors to redirect and synchronize the balls) to synthesize all conservative Boolean functions, within which all Boolean functions can be easily embedded. The rather late realization that logical irreversibility is not an essential feature of computation is probably due in part to the fact that reversible gates require somewhat more inputs and outputs (e.g., $3:3$ or $2:4$) to provide a basis for nontrivial computation than irreversible gates do (e.g., $2:1$ for NAND).

5. REVERSIBLE MEASUREMENT AND MAXWELL'S DEMON

This section further explores the relation between logical and thermo-dynamic irreversibility and points out the connection between logical irreversibility and the Maxwell's demon problem.

Various forms of Maxwell's demon have been described; a typical one would be an organism or apparatus that, by opening a door between two equal gas cylinders whenever a molecule approached from the right, and closing it whenever a molecule approached from the left, would effortlessly concentrate all the gas on the left, thereby reducing the gas's entropy by $Nk\ln 2$. The second law forbids any apparatus from doing this reliably, even for a gas consisting of a single molecule, without producing a corresponding entropy increase elsewhere in the universe.

It is often supposed that *measurement* (e.g., the measurement the demon must make to determine whether the molecule is approaching from the left or the right) is an unavoidably irreversible act, requiring an entropy generation of at least $k\ln 2$ per bit of information obtained, and that this is what prevents the demon from violating the second law. In fact, as will be shown below, measurements of the sort required by Maxwell's demon can be made reversibly, provided the measuring apparatus (e.g., the demon's internal mechanism) is in a standard state before the measurement, so that measurement, like the copying of a bit onto previously blank tape, does not overwrite information previously stored there. Under these conditions, the essential irreversible act, which prevents the demon from violating the second law, is not the measurement itself but rather the subsequent restoration of the measuring apparatus to a standard state in preparation for the next measurement. This forgetting of a previous logical state, like the erasure or overwriting of a bit of intermediate data generated in the course of a computation, entails a many-to-one mapping of the demon's physical state, which cannot be accomplished without a corresponding entropy increase elsewhere.

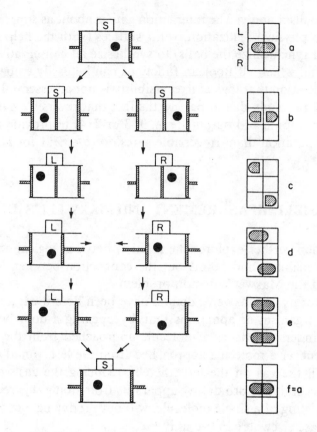

Fig. 12. A one-molecule Maxwell's demon apparatus.

Figure 12 shows the cycle of operation of a one-molecule Maxwell's demon apparatus. The left side of the figure shows the apparatus, and the right side shows the sequence changes in its phase space, depicted schematically as a product of a horizontal coordinate representing the location of the molecule and a vertical coordinate representing the physical state of the demon's "mind." The demon's mind has three states: its standard state S before a measurement, and two states L and R denoting the result of a measurement in which the molecule has been found on the left or right, respectively. At first (a) the molecule wanders freely throughout the apparatus and the demon is in the standard state S, indicating that it does not know where the molecule is. In (b) the demon has inserted a thin partition trapping the molecule on one side or the other. Next the demon performs a reversible measurement to learn (c) whether the molecule is on the left or the right. The demon then uses this information to extract $kT \ln 2$ of isothermal work from the molecule, by inserting a piston on the side not containing the molecule and allowing the molecule to expand (d) against the piston to fill the whole apparatus again (e). Notice that a different manipulation is required to extract work from the molecule depending on which side it is on; this is why the demon must make a measurement, and why at (d) the demon will be in one of two distinct parts of its own phase space depending on the result of that measurement. At (e) the molecule again fills the whole apparatus and the piston is in its original position. The only record of which side the molecule came from is the demon's record of the measurement, which must be erased to put the demon back into a standard state. This erasure (e–f) entails a twofold compression of the occupied volume of the demon's phase space, and therefore cannot be made to occur spontaneously except in conjunction with a corresponding entropy increase elsewhere. In other words, all the work obtained by letting the molecule expand in stage (d) must be converted into heat again in order to compress the demon's mind back into its standard state.

In the case of a measuring apparatus which is *not* in a standard state before the measurement, the compression of the demon's state, and the compensating entropy increase elsewhere, occur at the same time as the measurement. However, I feel it important even in this case to attribute the entropy cost to logical irreversibility, rather than to measurement, because in doing the latter one is apt to jump to the erroneous conclusion that all transfers of information, e.g., the synthesis of RNA, or reversible copying onto blank tape, have an irreducible entropy cost of order $kT \ln 2$ per bit.

As a further example of reversible copying and measurement, it may be instructive to consider a system simpler and more familiar than RNA polymerase, viz., a one-bit memory element consisting of a Brownian particle in a potential well that can be continuously modulated between bistability (two minima separated by a barrier considerably higher than kT) and monostability (one minimum), as well as being able to be biased to favor one well or the other. Such systems have been analyzed in detail in Landauer (1961) and Keyes and Landauer (1970); a physical example (Figure 13) would be an ellipsoidal piece of ferromagnetic material so small that in the absence of a field it consists of a single domain, magnetized parallel or antiparallel to the ellipse axis (alternatively, a round piece of magnetically anisotropic material could be used). Such a system can be modulated between bistability and monostability by a transverse magnetic field, and biased in favor of one minimum or the other by a longitudinal magnetic field. When the transverse field just barely abolishes the central minimum, the longitudinal magnetization becomes a "soft mode," very sensitive to small longitudinal components of the magnetic field.

This sensitivity can be exploited to copy information reversibly from one memory element to another, provided the memory element destined to

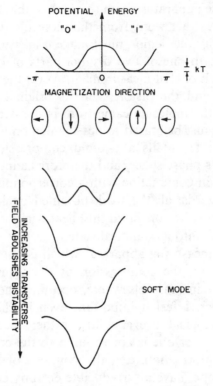

Fig. 13. A bistable potential well, realized by a one-domain ferromagnet. Increasing transverse magnetic field abolishes the bistability, resulting in a "soft mode," very sensitive to small longitudinal fields.

receive the information is in a standard state initially, so that the copying is logically reversible. Figure 14 shows how this reversible copying might be done. The apparatus contains two fixed memory elements, one (top) containing a zero for reference and the other (bottom) containing the data bit to be copied. A third memory element is movable and will be used to receive the copy. It is initially located next to the reference element and also contains a zero. To begin the copying operation, this element is slowly moved away from the reference bit and into a transverse field strong enough to abolish its bistability. This manipulation serves to smoothly and continuously change the element from its initial zero state to a unistable state. The element is then gradually moved out of the transverse field toward the data bit. As the movable bit leaves the region of strong transverse field, its soft mode is biased by the weak longitudinal field from the data bit, thereby making it choose the same direction of magnetization as the data bit. [The region of strong transverse field is assumed to be wide enough that by the time the movable bit reaches its bottom edge, the longitudinal bias field is

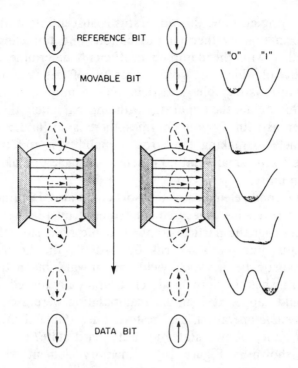

Fig. 14. Reversible copying using a one-domain ferromagnet. The movable bit, initially zero, is mapped into the same state as the data bit (zero in left column; one in center column). Right column shows how the probability density of the movable bit's magnetization, initially concentrated in the "0" minimum, is deformed continuously until it occupies the "1" minimum, in agreement with a "1" data bit.

due almost entirely to the data bit, with only a negligible perturbation (small compared to kT) from the more distant reference bit.] The overall effect has been to smoothly change the movable element's magnetization direction from agreeing with the reference bit at the top (i.e., zero) to agreeing with the data bit on the bottom. Throughout the manipulation, the movable element's magnetization remains a continuous, single-valued function of its position, and the forces exerted by the various fields on the movable element during the second half of the manipulation are equal and opposite to those exerted during the first half, except for the negligible long-range perturbation of the bias field mentioned earlier, and a viscous damping force (reflecting the finite relaxation time of spontaneous magnetization fluctuations) proportional to the speed of motion. The copying operation can therefore be performed with arbitrarily small dissipation. If carried out in reverse, the manipulation would serve to reversibly erase one of two bits known to be identical, which is the logical inverse of copying onto blank tape.

Like a copying enzyme, this apparatus is susceptible to degradation of its stored information by thermal fluctuations and tunneling. These phenomena, together with the damping coefficient, determine the minimum error probability of which any given apparatus of this type, operating at a given temperature, is capable, and determine a minimum dissipation per step required to operate the apparatus with approximately this error probability. However, as with copying enzymes, there is no fundamental thermodynamic obstacle to making the error probability η and the dissipation ϵ/kT both arbitrarily small, and no practical obstacle to making them both much less than unity.

Bistable magnetic elements of this sort could also, in principle, be used to perform the reversible measurement required by Maxwell's demon. In Figure 15 a diamagnetic particle trapped in the right side of a Maxwell's demon apparatus introduces a weak upward bias in the mode-softening horizontal magnetic field, which yields an upward magnetization of the bistable element when the horizontal field is gradually turned off.

What would happen if a similar manipulation were used to perform a logically *irreversible* operation, e.g., restoring a bistable element that might initially be in either of two states to a standard state? An apparatus for doing this is shown in Figure 16: a memory element which might be magnetized either up or down is moved gradually into a transverse field, rotated slightly counterclockwise to bias the magnetization downward, moved out of the field, and rotated back again, leaving it in the down or zero state.

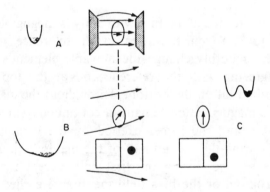

Fig. 15. A one-domain ferromagnet used to make measurements for Maxwell's demon: The bistable element has been moved out of strong transverse field (A) just far enough to create a soft mode (B), which is biased by the perturbation of the field by a diamagnetic Brownian particle in the right side of a Maxwell's demon apparatus. Slowly turning the field off (C) completes the measurement. Peripheral diagrams show potential energy and probability density of the ferromagnetic element's magnetization direction.

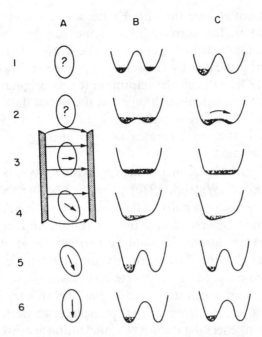

Fig. 16. Erasure of a bistable one-domain ferromagnet. Column A: the bistable element, which may be magnetized either up or down (1), is moved gradually (2) into a transverse field that abolishes its bistability symmetrically (3). It is then rotated slightly counterclockwise (4), to bias the soft mode downward, removed from the field (5), and rotated back again, leaving it in the down or zero state (6). Column B: Evolution of the probability density when the manipulation just described is used to erase a random, unknown bit. Column C: Behavior of the probability density when the manipulation is applied to a known bit (here zero). An irreversible entropy increase of $k \ln 2$ occurs at stage 2, when the probability density leaks out of the initially occupied minimum.

Although such many-to-one mappings have been called logically irreversible, in a subtler sense they may be reversible or not depending on the data to which they are applied. If the initial state in Figure 16 is truly unknown, and properly describable by a probability equidistributed between the two minima (Figure 16B), then undoing the manipulation of Figure 16 exactly restores the initial state of ignorance, and the operation can be viewed as reversible. It is also thermodynamically reversible: the $kT \ln 2$ of work required to carry out the manipulation is compensated by a decrease of $k \ln 2$ in the bistable element's entropy. This expenditure of external work to decrease a system's entropy is analogous to the isothermal compression of a gas to half its volume.

If, on the other hand, the initial state of the memory element were known (e.g., by virtue of its having been set during some intermediate stage of computation with known initial data) the operation would be irreversible:

undoing it would not restore the initial state, and the conversion of $kT \ln 2$ of work into heat in the surroundings would not be compensated by a decrease in the bistable element's entropy. The irreversible entropy increase occurs at the point indicated by the arrow in Figure 16C, when the system's probability density leaks from the minimum it was originally in to fill both minima (as it could have done all along had the initial data been unknown). This is analogous to the free expansion of gas into a previously evacuated container, in which the gas increases its own entropy without doing any work on its environment.

The normal biochemical mechanism by which RNA is destroyed when it is no longer needed (Watson, 1970) provides another example of logical irreversibility. As indicated before, the synthesis of RNA by RNA polymerase is a logically reversible copying operation, and under appropriate (nonphysiological) conditions, it could be carried out at an energy cost of less than kT per nucleotide. The thermodynamically efficient way to get rid of an RNA molecule would be to reverse this process, i.e., to take the RNA back to the DNA from which it was made, and use an enzyme such as RNA polymerase with a slight excess of pyrophosphate to perform a sequence-specific degradation, checking each RNA nucleotide against the corresponding DNA nucleotide before splitting it off. This process does not occur in nature; instead RNA is degraded in a nonspecific and logically irreversible manner by other enzymes, such as polynucleotide phosphorylase. This enzyme catalyzes a reversible reaction between an RNA strand and free phosphate (maintained at high concentration) to split off successive nucleotides of the RNA as nucleotide phosphate monomers. Because the enzyme functions in the absence of a complementary DNA strand, the removal of each nucleotide is logically irreversible, and when running backwards (in the direction of RNA synthesis) the enzyme is about as likely to insert any of the three incorrect nucelotides as it is to reinsert the correct one. This logical irreversibility means that a fourfold higher phosphate concentration is needed to drive the reaction forward than would be required by a sequence-specific degradation. The excess phosphate keeps the enzyme from running backwards and synthesizing random RNA, but it also means that the cycle of specific synthesis followed by nonspecific degradation must waste about $kT \ln 4$ per nucleotide even in the limit of zero speed. For an organism that has already spent around $20kT$ per nucleotide to produce the RNA with near maximal speed and accuracy, the extra $1.4kT$ is obviously a small price to pay for being able to dispose of the RNA in a summary manner, without taking it back to its birthplace.

Corollary to the principle that erasing a random tape entails an entropy increase in the environment is the fact that a physical system of low entropy (e.g., a gas at high pressure, a collection of magnetic domains or individual atomic spins, all pointing "down," or more symbolically, a tape full of zeros) can act as a "fuel," doing useful thermodynamic or mechanical work as it randomizes itself. For example, a compressed gas expanding isothermally against a piston increases its own entropy, meanwhile converting waste heat from its surroundings into an equivalent amount of mechanical work. In an adiabatic demagnetization experiment, the randomization of a set of aligned spins allows them to pump heat from a cold body into warmer surroundings. A tape containing N zeros would similarly serve as a fuel to do $NkT \ln 2$ of useful work as it randomized itself.

What about a tape containing a computable pseudorandom sequence like the first N digits of the binary expansion of pi? Although the pattern of digits in pi looks random to begin with, and would not accomplish any useful work if allowed to truly randomize itself in an adiabatic demagnetization apparatus of the usual sort, it could be exploited by a slightly more complicated apparatus. Since the mapping (N zeros)$\leftrightarrow$(first N bits of pi) is one-to-one, it is possible in principle to construct a reversible computer that would execute this mapping physically, in either direction, at an arbitrarily small thermodynamic cost per digit. Thus, given a pi tape, we could convert it into a tape full of zeros, then use that as fuel by allowing it to truly randomize itself at the expense of waste heat in the surroundings.

What about a tape containing N bits generated by coin tossing? Of course coin tossing might accidentally yield a tape of N consecutive zeros, which could be used as fuel; however, the typical result would be a sequence with no such unusual features. Since the tape, after all, contains a specific sequence, $NkT \ln 2$ of work ought to be made available when it is mapped, in a one-to-many manner, onto a uniform distribution over all 2^N N-bit sequences. However, because there is no concise description of the way in which this specific sequence differs from the bulk of other sequences, no simple apparatus could extract this work. A complicated apparatus, containing a verbose description or verbatim copy of the specific sequence, could extract the work, but in doing so it would be doing no more than canceling the specific random sequence against the apparatus's copy of it to produce a blank tape, then using that as fuel. Of course there is a concise procedure for converting a random tape into a blank tape: erase it. But this procedure is not logically reversible, and so would require an input of energy equal to the fuel value of the blank tape it produced.

Finally, suppose we had seven identical copies of a typical random tape. Six of these could be converted into blank tapes by a logically and thermodynamically reversible process, e.g., subtracting one copy from another, digit by digit, to produce a tape full of zeros. The last copy could not be so canceled, because there would be nothing left to cancel it against. Thus the seven identical random tapes are interconvertible to six blank tapes and one random tape, and would have a fuel value equal to that of six blank tapes. The result of their exploitation as fuel, of course, would be seven *different* random tapes.

6. ALGORITHMIC ENTROPY AND THERMODYNAMICS

The above ideas may be generalized and expressed more precisely using algorithmic information theory, described in an introductory article by Chaitin (1975a), and review articles by Zvonkin and Levin (1970), and Chaitin (1977).

Ordinary information theory offers no solid grounds for calling one N-bit string "more random" than another, since all are equally likely to be produced by a random process such as coin tossing. Thus, in particular, it cannot distinguish bit strings with fuel value from those without. This inability reflects the fact that entropy is an inherently statistical concept, applicable to ensembles but not to the individual events comprising them. In equilibrium statistical mechanics, this fact manifests itself as the well-known impossibility of expressing macroscopic entropy as the ensemble average of some microscopic variable, the way temperature can be expressed as the average of $mv^2/2$: since the entropy of a distribution $\mathbf{p}$ is defined as

$$S[\mathbf{p}] = \sum_x p(x) \log[1/p(x)]$$

obviously there can be no one function $f(x)$, such that for all $\mathbf{p}$,

$$S[\mathbf{p}] = \sum_x p(x) f(x)$$

The absence of a microscopic quantity corresponding to entropy is a nuisance both practically and conceptually, requiring that entropy always be measured by indirect calorimetric methods, both in the laboratory and in Monte Carlo and molecular-dynamics "computer experiments" (Bennett, 1975), and frustrating the natural desire of molecular model builders to regard an individual molecular configuration as having an entropy.

Though it does not help the practical problem, the notion of algorithmic entropy resolves the conceptual problem by providing a microstate function, $H(x)$, whose average is very nearly equal to the macroscopic entropy $S[\mathbf{p}]$, not for all distributions $\mathbf{p}$ (which would be impossible) but rather for a large class of distributions including most of those relevant to statistical mechanics. Algorithmic entropy is a measure, not of any obvious physical property of the microstate x, but rather of the number of bits required to describe x in an absolute mathematical sense, as the output of a universal computer. Algorithmic entropy is small for sequences such as the first million digits of pi, which can be computed from a small description, but large for typical sequences produced by coin tossing, which have no concise description. Sequences with large algorithmic entropy cannot be erased except by an irreversible process; conversely, those with small algorithmic entropy can do thermodynamic work as they randomize themselves.

Several slightly different definitions of algorithmic entropy have been proposed; for definiteness we adopt the definition of Levin (Gacs, 1974; Levin, 1976) and Chaitin (1975b) in terms of self-delimiting program size: the algorithmic entropy $H(x)$ of a binary string x is the number of bits in the smallest self-delimiting program causing a standard computer to embark on a halting computation with x as its output. (A program is self-delimiting if it needs no special symbol, other than the digits 0 and 1 of which it is composed, to mark its end.) The algorithmic entropy of discrete objects other than binary strings, e.g., integers, or coarse-grained cells in a continuous phase space, may be defined by indexing them by binary strings in a standard way. A string is called "algorithmically random" if it is not expressible as the output of a program much shorter than the string itself. A simple counting argument shows that, for any length N, most N-bit strings are algorithmically random (e.g., there are only enough $N - 10$ bit programs to describe at most $1/1024$ of all the N-bit strings).

At first it might appear that the definition of H is extremely machine dependent. However, it is well known that there exist computers which are universal in the strong sense of being able to simulate any other computer with at most an additive constant increase in program size. The algorithmic entropy functions defined by any two such machines therefore differ by at most $O(1)$, and algorithmic entropy, like classical thermodynamic entropy, may be regarded as well defined up to an additive constant.

A further noteworthy fact about $H(x)$ is that it is not an effectively computable function of x: there is no uniform procedure for computing $H(x)$ given x. Although this means that $H(x)$ cannot be routinely evaluated the way $x!$ and $\sin(x)$ can, it is not a severe limitation in the present context, where we wish chiefly to prove theorems about the relation between H and other entropy functions. From a more practical viewpoint, the molecular model builder, formerly told that the question "what is its entropy?" was meaningless, is now told that the question is meaningful but its answer cannot generally be determined by looking at the model.

It is easy to see that simply describable deterministic transformations cannot increase a system's algorithmic entropy very much (i.e., by more than the number of bits required to describe the transformation). This follows because the final state can always be described indirectly by describing the initial state and the transformation. Therefore, for a system to increase its algorithmic entropy, it must behave probabilistically, increasing its statistical entropy at the same time. By the same token, simply describable reversible transformations (1 : 1 mappings) leave algorithmic entropy approximately unchanged.

Algorithmic entropy is a microscopic analog of ordinary statistical entropy in the following sense: if a macrostate **p** is *concisely describable*, e.g., if it is determined by equations of motion and boundary conditions describable in a small number of bits, then its statistical entropy is nearly equal to the ensemble average of the microstates' algorithmic entropy. In more detail, the relation between algorithmic and statistical entropy of a macrostate is as follows:

$$S_2[\mathbf{p}] < \sum_x p(x)H(x) \leq S_2[\mathbf{p}] + H(\mathbf{p}) + O(1) \tag{1}$$

Here $S_2[\mathbf{p}] = \sum_x p(x)\log_2[1/p(x)]$, the macrostate's statistical entropy in binary units, measures the extent to which the distribution **p** is spread out over many microstates; $H(x)$, the microstate's algorithmic entropy, measures the extent to which a particular microstate x is not concisely describable; and $H(\mathbf{p})$, the algorithmic entropy of **p**, is the number of bits required to describe the distribution **p**.

We need to say in more detail what it means to describe a distribution. Strictly construed, a description of **p** would be a program to compute a tabulation of the components of the vector **p**, to arbitrarily great precision in case any of the components were irrational numbers. In fact, equation (1) remains true for a much weaker kind of description: a Monte Carlo program for sampling some distribution **q** not too different from **p**. In this context, a Monte Carlo program means a fixed program, which, when given to the machine on its input tape, causes the machine to ask from time to time for additional bits of input; and if these are furnished probabilistically by tossing a fair coin, the machine eventually halts, yielding an output distributed according to the distribution **q**. For **q** not to be too different from **p** means that $\sum_x p(x)\log_2[p(x)/q(x)]$ is of order unity.

For typical macrostates considered in statistical mechanics, the equality between statistical entropy and the ensemble average of algorithmic entropy holds with negligible error, since the statistical entropy is typically of order 10^{23} bits, while the error term $H(\mathbf{p})$ is typically only the few thousand bits required to describe the macrostate's determining equations of motion, boundary conditions, etc. Macrostates occurring in nature (e.g., a gas in a box with irregular walls) may not be so concisely describable, but the traditional approach of statistical mechanics has been to approximate nature by simple models.

We now sketch the proof of equation (1). The left inequality follows from the convexity of the log function and the fact that, when algorithmic entropy is defined by self-delimiting programs, $\sum_x 2^{-H(x)}$ is less than 1. The right inequality is obtained from the following inequality, which holds for all x:

$$H(x) \leqslant H(\mathbf{q}) + \log_2[1/q(x)] + O(1) \tag{2}$$

Here $\mathbf{q}$ is a distribution approximating $\mathbf{p}$ that can be exactly sampled by a Monte Carlo program of size $H(\mathbf{q})$. The additive $O(1)$ constant again depends on the universal computer but not on $\mathbf{q}$ or x. Equation (2) follows from the fact that one way of algorithmically describing x is to first describe the distribution $\mathbf{q}$ and then describe how to locate x within this distribution. The proof that a self-delimiting program of size $\log_2[1/q(x)] + O(1)$ bits suffices to compute x, given a Monte Carlo routine for sampling $\mathbf{q}$, is given by Chaitin (1975b, Theorem 3.2); slightly weaker versions of the idea are easy to understand intuitively. Equation (1) is finally obtained by summing equation (2) over the distribution $\mathbf{p}$, and applying the criterion of closeness of approximation of $\mathbf{p}$ by $\mathbf{q}$.

In conjunction with the second law, equation (1) implies that when a physical system increases its algorithmic entropy by N bits (which it can only do by behaving probabilistically), it has the capacity to convert about $NkT \ln 2$ of waste heat into useful work in its surroundings. Conversely, the conversion of about $NkT \ln 2$ of work into heat in the surroundings is necessary to decrease a system's algorithmic entropy by N bits. These statements are classical truisms when entropy is interpreted statistically, as a property of ensembles. The novelty here is in using algorithmic entropy, a property of microstates. No property of the ensembles need be assumed, beyond that they be concisely describable.

ACKNOWLEDGMENTS

The work on enzymatic and clockwork Turing machines was done in 1970–72, at Argonne National Laboratory (Solid State Science Division), under the auspices of the U.S. Atomic Energy Commission. I wish to thank Rolf Landauer and Gregory Chaitin for years of stimulating discussions of reversibility and entropy, Michael Chamberlain for background information on polymerases, and John Slonczewski for background information on ferromagnets.

REFERENCES

Benioff, Paul (1982) to appear in *Journal of Statistical Mechanics.*

Bennett, C. H. (1973). "Logical Reversibility of Computation", *IBM Journal of Research and Development*, **17**, 525–532.

Bennett, C. H. (1975). "Efficient Estimation of Free Energy Differences from Monte Carlo Data," *Journal of Computational Physics*, **22**, 245–268.

Bennett, C. H. (1979). "Dissipation-Error Tradeoff in Proofreading," *BioSystems*, **11**, 85–90.

Chaitin, G. (1975a). "Randomness and Mathematical Proof," *Scientific American*, **232**, No. 5, 46–52.

Chaitin, G. (1975b). "A Theory of Program Size Formally Identical to Information Theory," *Journal of the Association for Computing Machinery*, **22**, 329–340.

Chaitin, G. (1977). "Algorithmic Information Theory," *IBM Journal of Research and Development*, **21**, 350–359, 496.

Brillouin, L. (1956). *Science and Information Theory* (2nd edition, 1962), pp. 261–264, 194–196. Academic Press, London.

Fredkin, Edward, and Toffoli, Tommaso, (1982). "Conservative Logic," MIT Report MIT/LCS/TM-197; *International Journal of Theoretical Physics*, **21**, 219.

Gacs, P. (1974). "On the Symmetry of Algorithmic Information," *Soviet Mathematics Doklady*, **15**, 1477.

Hopfield, J. J. (1974). *Proceedings of the National Academy of Science USA*, **71**, 4135–4139.

Keyes, R. W., and Landuer, R. (1970). *IBM Journal of Research and Development*, **14**, 152.

Landauer, R. (1961). "Irreversibility and Heat Generation in the Computing Process," *IBM Journal of Research and Development*, **3**, 183–191.

Levin, L. A. (1976). "Various Measures of Complexity for Finite Objects (Axiomatic Description)," *Soviet Mathematics Doklady*, **17**, 522–526.

Likharev, K. (1982). "Classical and Quantum Limitations on Energy Consumption in Computation," *International Journal of Theoretical Physics*, **21**, 311.

McCarthy, John (1956). "The Inversion of Functions Defined by Turing Machines," in *Automata Studies*, C. E. Shannon and J. McCarthy, eds. Princeton Univ. Press, New Jersey.

Ninio, J. (1975). *Biochimie*, **57**, 587–595.

Reif, John H. (1979). "Complexity of the Mover's Problem and Generalizations," Proc. 20'th IEEE Symp. Found. Comp. Sci., San Juan, Puerto Rico, pp. 421–427.

Szilard, L. (1929). *Zeitschrift für Physik*, **53**, 840–856.

Toffoli, Tommaso (1980). "Reversible Computing," MIT Report MIT/LCS/TM-151.

Toffoli, Tommaso (1981). "Bicontinuous Extensions of Invertible Combinatorial Functions," *Mathematical and Systems Theory*, **14**, 13–23.

von Neumann, J. (1966). Fourth University of Illinois lecture, in *Theory of Self-Reproducing Automata*, A. W. Burks, ed., p. 66. Univ. of Illinois Press, Urbana.

Watson, J. D. (1970). *Molecular Biology of the Gene* (2nd edition). W. A. Benjamin, New York.

Zvonkin, A. K., and Levin, L. A. (1970). "The Complexity of Finite Objects and the Development of the Concepts of Information and Randomness by Means of the Theory of Algorithms," *Russian Mathematical Surveys*, **25**, 83–124.

MAXWELL'S DEMON, SZILARD'S ENGINE AND QUANTUM MEASUREMENTS

W.H. Zurek

Theoretical Astrophysics
Los Alamos National Laboratory
Los Alamos, New Mexico 87545

and

Institute for Theoretical Physics
University of California
Santa Barbara, California 93106

ABSTRACT

We propose and analyze a quantum version of Szilard's "one-molecule engine." In particular, we recover, in the quantum context, Szilard's conclusion concerning the free energy "cost" of measurements: $\Delta F \geqslant k_B T \ln 2$ per bit of information.

I.   INTRODUCTION

In 1929 Leo Szilard wrote a path-breaking paper entitled "On the Decrease of Entropy in a Thermodynamic System by the Intervention of Intelligent Beings."[1] There, on the basis of a thermodynamic "gedanken experiment" involving "Maxwell's demon," he argued that an observer, in order to learn, through a measurement, which of the two equally probable alternatives is realized, must use up at least

$$\Delta F = k_B T \ln 2 \qquad\qquad (1)$$

of free energy. Szilard's paper not only correctly defines the quantity known today as information, which has found a wide use in the work of Claude Shannon and others in the field of communication science.[3] It also formulates physical connection between thermodynamic entropy and information-theoretic entropy by establishing "Szilard's limit," the least price which must be paid in terms of free energy for the information gain.

The purpose of this paper is to translate Szilard's classical thought experiment into a quantum one, and to explore its consequences for quantum theory of measurements. A "one-molecule gas" is a "microscopic" system and one may wonder whether conclusions of Szilard's classical analysis remain valid in the quantum domain. In particular, one may argue, following Jauch and Baron,[4] that Szilard's analysis is inconsistent, because it employs two different, incompatible classical idealizations of the one-

mclecule gas--dynamical and thermodynamical--to arrive at Eq. (1). We
shall show that the apparent inconsistency pointed out by Jauch and Baron
is removed by quantum treatment. This is not too surprising, for, after
all, thermodynamic entropy which is central in this discussion is incompatible with classical mechanics, as it becomes infinite in the limit
$\hbar \to 0$. Indeed, information--theoretic analysis of the operation of Szilard's
engine allows one to understand, in a very natural way, his thermodynamical
conclusion, Eq.(1), as a consequence of the conservation of information in
a closed quantum system.

The quantum version of Szilard's engine will be considered in the
following section. Implications of Szilard's reasoning for quantum theory
and for thermodynamics will be explored in Sec. III--where we shall assume
that "Maxwell's Demon" is classical, and in Sec. IV, where it will be a
quantum system.

II. QUANTUM VERSION OF SZILARD'S ENGINE

A complete cycle of Szilard's classical engine is presented in Fig. 1.
The work it can perform in the course of one cycle is

$$\Delta W = \int_{V/2}^{V} p(v)dv = k_B T \int_{V/2}^{V} dv/v = k_B T \ln 2 \tag{2}$$

Above, we have used the law of Gay-Lussac, p=kT/V, for one-molecule gas.
This work gain per cycle can be maintained in spite of the fact that the
whole system is at the same constant temperature T. If Szilard's model
engine could indeed generate useful work, in the way described above at no
additional expense of free energy, it would constitute a perpetuum mobile,
as it delivers mechanical work from an (infinite) heat reservoir with no
apparent temperature difference. To fend off this threat to the thermodynamic irreversibility, Szilard has noted that, "If we do not wish to admit that the Second Law has been violated, we must conclude that...the
measurement...must be accompanied by a production of entropy." Szilard's
conclusion has far-reaching consequences, which have not yet been fully
explored. If it is indeed correct, it can provide an operational link
between the concepts of "entropy" and "information." Moreover, it forces
one to admit that a measuring apparatus can be used to gain information
only if measurements are essentially irreversible.

Before accepting Szilard's conclusion one must realize that it is
based on a very idealized model. In particular, two of the key issues have
not been explored in the original paper. The first, obvious one concerns
fluctuations. One may argue that the one-molecule engine cannot be analyzed
by means of thermodynamics, because it is nowhere near the thermodynamic
limit. This objection is overruled by noting that arbitrarily many
"Szilard's engines" can be linked together to get a "many-cylinder" version
of the original design. This will cut down fluctuations and allow one to
apply thermodynamic concepts without difficulty.

A more subtle objection against the one-molecule engine has been advanced by Jauch and Baron.[*] They note that "Even the single-molecule gas
is admissible as long as it satisfies the gas laws. However, at the exact moment when the piston is in the middle of the cylinder and the opening is closed, the gas violates the law of Gay-Lussac because gas is compressed to half its volume without expenditure of energy." Jauch and
Baron "...therefore conclude that the idealizations in Szilard's experiment are inadmissible in their actual context..." This objection is not
easy to refute for the classical one-molecule gas. Its molecule should
behave as a billiard ball. Therefore, it is difficult to maintain that

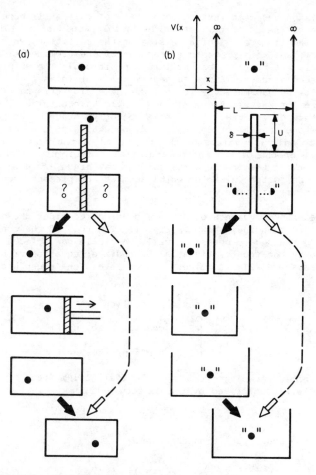

Figure 1.   A cycle of Szilard's engine.
  a)   Original, classical version
  b)   Quantum version discussed here. The measurement of the location of
       the molecule is essential in the process of extracting work in both
       classical and quantum design.

after the piston has been inserted, the gas molecule still occupies the whole volume of the container. More defensible would be a claim that while the molecule is on a definite side of the partition, we do not know on which side, and this prevents extraction of the promised k_BT ln 2 of energy. (This was more or less Szilard's position.) The suspicious feature of such argument is its subjectivity: Our (classical) intuition tells us that the gas molecule is on a definite side of a partition. Moreover, what we (or Maxwell's demon) know should have nothing to do with the objective state of the gas. It is this objective state of the gas which should allow one to extract energy. And, objectively, the gas has been compressed to half its volume by the insertion of the partition no matter on which side of the piston the molecule is. The eventual "observation" may help in making the engine work, but one may argue, as do Jauch and Baron, that the "potential to do work" seems to be present even before such a measurement is performed.

To re-examine arguments of Jauch and Baron, consider the quantum version of Szilard's engine, shown in Fig. 1. The role of the container is now played by the square potential well. A single gas molecule of mass m is described by the (nonrelativistic) Schrödinger equation with the boundary conditions $\psi(-L/2)=\psi(L/2)=0$. Energy levels and eigenfunctions are given by;

$$E_n = n^2\pi^2\hbar^2/(2mL^2) = \epsilon n^2 \qquad (2a)$$

$$<x|\psi_n> = \begin{cases} (2/L)^{\frac{1}{2}}\cos 2\pi nx/L & \text{for } n=2k+1 \qquad (2b) \\ (2/L)^{\frac{1}{2}}\sin 2\pi nx/L & \text{for } n=2k \qquad (2c) \end{cases}$$

At a finite temperature $T=\beta^{-1}k_B^{-1}$ the equilibrium state of the system will be completely described by the density matrix:

$$\rho = Z^{-1}\sum_n \exp(-\beta E_n)|\psi_n><\psi_n|. \qquad (3)$$

Above, Z is the usual partition function:

$$Z = \sum_{n=1}^{\infty}\exp(-\beta\epsilon n^2) = \sum_{n=1}^{\infty}\zeta^{n^2} \qquad (4)$$

For $1/2<\zeta< 1$, Z can be adequately approximated by:

$$Z = \frac{1}{2}(\sqrt{\pi}/|\ln\zeta| -1). \qquad (5)$$

For our purposes a still simpler, high-temperature approximation

$$Z = (\pi/\epsilon\beta)^{\frac{1}{2}}/2 = L(h^2/2\ mk_BT)^{\frac{1}{2}} . \qquad (6)$$

valid for $\epsilon\ll k_BT$, will be sufficient most of the time. This is, of course, the familiar Boltzmann gas partition function. It can be readily generalized to the three-dimensional box

$$Z = L_xL_yL_z/(h^2/2\pi mk_BT)^{3/2} , \qquad (7)$$

as well as to the case when there are N "classically" indistinguishable particles. The point of this elementary calculation is to demonstrate that, in the further analysis, we can rely on classical estimates of pressure, internal energy, entropy, etc...for one molecule gas which were used by Szilard[1]: A partition function completely determines thermodynamic behavior of the system.

Consider now a "piston," slowly inserted in the middle of the potential well "box". This can be done either (1) while the engine is coupled with the reservoir, or (2) when it is isolated. In either case, it must be done slowly, so that the process remains either (1) thermodynamically or (2) adiabatically reversible. We shall imagine the piston as a potential barrier of width $d \ll L$ and height that eventually attains $U \gg k_B T$. The presence of this barrier will alter the structure of the energy levels: these associated with even n will be shifted "upwards" so that the new eigenvalues are:

$$E'_{2k} = \epsilon'(2k)^2 + \Delta_k = E_k + \Delta_k \qquad (8)$$

where

$$\epsilon' = \epsilon\, L^2/(L-d)^2 \qquad (9)$$

and

$$\Delta_k \cong (4\epsilon'/\pi)\exp(-d\sqrt{2m(U-E_k)}/\hbar). \qquad (10)$$

Energy levels corresponding to the odd values of n are shifted upwards by $\Delta E_n \sim (2n+1)\epsilon'$ so that

$$E'_{2k-1} = \epsilon'(2k)^2 - \Delta_k = E_k - \Delta_k \qquad (11)$$

A pair of the eigenvalues E'_{2k}, E'_{2k-1} can be alternatively regarded as the kth doubly degenerate eigenstate of the newly created two-well potential with degeneracy broken for finite values of U.

For $U \to \infty$ exact eigenfunctions can be given for each well separately. For finite U, for these levels where $\Delta_k \ll E_k$, eigenfunctions of the complete potential can be reconstructed from the kth eigenfuctions of the left ($|L_k\rangle$) and right ($|R_k\rangle$) wells:

$$E_k + \Delta_k \quad \leftrightarrow |\psi_k^+\rangle = (|L_k\rangle - |R_k\rangle)/\sqrt{2}$$

$$E_k - \Delta_k \quad \leftrightarrow |\psi_k^-\rangle = (|L_k\rangle + |R_k\rangle)/\sqrt{2}$$

Alternatively, eigenfunctions of the left and right wells can be expressed in terms of energy eigenfunctions of the complete Hamiltonian

$$|L_k\rangle = (|\psi_k^+\rangle + |\psi_k^-\rangle)/\sqrt{2} \qquad (12c)$$

$$|R_k\rangle = (|\psi_k^-\rangle - |\psi_k^+\rangle)/\sqrt{2} \qquad (12d)$$

III. MEASUREMENTS BY THE CLASSICAL MAXWELL'S DEMON

Consider a measuring apparatus which, when inserted into Szilard's engine, determines on which side of the partition the molecule is. Formally, this can be accomplished by the measurement of the observable

$$\hat{n} = \lambda\,(|L\rangle\langle L| - |R\rangle\langle R|). \qquad (13)$$

Here $\lambda > 0$ is an arbitrary eigenvalue, while

$$|L\rangle = \left(\sum_{k=1}^{N} |L_k\rangle\right)/N^{1/2} \qquad (13a)$$

$$|R> = \left(\sum_{k=1}^{N} |R_k>\right) /N^{1/2} \tag{13b}$$

and N is sufficiently large, $N^2 \varepsilon \beta \gg 1$.

The density matrix before the measurement, but after piston is inserted, is given by

$$\tilde{\rho} = \tilde{z}^{-1} \sum_{k=1}^{\infty} \exp(-\beta E_k) \{\exp(-\beta \Delta_k) |\psi_k^+><\psi_k^+| + \exp(\beta \Delta_k) |\psi_k^-><\psi_k^-|\} \tag{14}$$

$$= \tilde{z}^{-1} \sum_{k=1}^{\infty} \exp(-\beta E_k) \{\cosh\beta\Delta_k (|L_k><L_k| + |R_k><R_k|) + \sinh\beta\Delta_k (|L_k><R_k| + |R_k><L_k|)\}$$

Depending on the outcome of the observation, the density matrix becomes either ρ_L or ρ_R where;

$$\rho_L = Z_L^{-1} \sum_{k=1}^{\infty} \exp(-\beta E_k)\cosh\beta\Delta_k |L_k><L_k|, \tag{15a}$$

$$\rho_R = Z_R^{-1} \sum_{k=1}^{\infty} \exp(-\beta E_k)\cosh\beta\Delta_k |R_k><R_k|. \tag{15b}$$

Both of these options are chosen with the same probability. The classical "demon" "knows" the outcome of the measurement. This information can be used to extract energy in the way described by Szilard.

We are now in a position to return to the objection of Jauch and Baron. The "potential to do work" is measured by the free energy A(T,L)   which can be readily calculated from the partition function

$$A(T,L) \quad = -k_B T \ln Z(T,L) \quad .$$

For the one-molecule engine this free energy is simply

$$A = -k_B T \ln[L/(h^2/2\pi m k_B T)^{\frac{1}{2}}] \tag{16}$$

before the partition is inserted. It becomes

$$\tilde{A} = -k_B T \ln[(L-d)/(h^2/2\pi m k_B T)^{\frac{1}{2}}] \tag{17}$$

after the insertion of the partition. Finally, as a result of the measurement, free energy increases regardless of the outcome

$$A_L = A_R = -k_B T \ln[((L-d)/2)/h^2/2\pi m k_B T)^{\frac{1}{2}}]$$

$$= -k_B T(\tilde{A} - \ln 2) \tag{18}$$

Let us also note that the change of A as a result of the insertion of the partition is negligible:

$$\tilde{A} - A = k_B T \ln(L/(L-d)) \sim 0(d/L). \tag{19}$$

However, the change of the free energy because of the measurement is precisely such as to account for the $W = k_B T \ln 2$ during the subsequent expansion of the piston:

$$A_L - \tilde{A} = k_B T \ln 2. \tag{20}$$

It is now difficult to argue against the conclusion of Szilard. The formalism of quantum mechanics confirms the key role of the measurement in the operation of the one-molecule engine. And the objection of Jauch and Baron, based on a classical intuition, is overruled.

The classical gas molecule, considered by Szilard, as well as by Jauch and Baron, may be on the unknown side of the piston, but cannot be on "both" sides of the piston. Therefore, intuitive arguments concerning the potential to do useful work could not be unambiguously settled in the context of classical dynamics and thermodynamics. Quantum molecule, on the other hand, can be on "both" sides of the potential barrier, even if its energy is far below the energy of the barrier top, and it will "collapse" to one of the two potential wells only if $\hat{\Pi}$ is "measured."

It is perhaps worth pointing out that the density matrix $\tilde{\rho}$, Eq. (15), has a form which is consistent with the "classical" statement that " a molecule is on a definite, but unknown side of the piston" almost equally well as with the statement that "the molecule in in a thermal mixture of the energy eigenstates of the two-well potential." This second statement is rigorously true in the limit of weak coupling with the resevoir: gas is in contact with the heat bath and therefore is in thermal equilibrium. On the other hand, the off-diagonal terms of the very same density matrix in the $|L_k>, |R_k>$ representation are negligible ($\sim \sinh\beta\Delta_k$). Therefore, one can almost equally well maintain that this density matrix describes a molecule which is on an "unknown, but definite" side of the partition. The phase between $|R_n>$ and $|L_n>$ is lost.

The above discussion leads us to conclude that the key element needed to extract useful work is the <u>correlation</u> between the state of the gas and the state of the demon. This point can be analyzed further if we allow, in the next section, the "demon" to be a quantum system.

IV. MEASUREMENT BY "QUANTUM MAXWELL'S DEMON"

Analysis of the measurement process in the previous section was very schematic. Measuring appartus, which has played the role of the "demon" simply acquired the information about the location of the gas molecule, and this was enough to describe the molecule by ρ_L or ρ_R. The second law demanded the entropy of the apparatus to increase in the process of measurement, but, in the absence of a more concrete model for the apparatus it was hard to tell why this entropy increase was essential and how did it come about. The purpose of this section is to introduce a more detailed model of the apparatus, which makes such an analysis possible.

We shall use as an apparatus a two-state quantum system. We assume that it is initially prepared by some external agency -- we shall refer to it below as an "external observer" -- in the "ready to measure" state $|D_0\rangle$. The first stage of the measurement will be accomplished by the transition:

$$|L_n>|D_0> \rightarrow |L_n> |D_L>$$ (21a)

$$|R_n>|D_0> \rightarrow |R_n>|D_R>$$ (21b)

for all levels n. Here, $|D_R>$ and $|D_L>$ must be orthogonal if the measurement is to be reliable. This will be the case when the gas and the demon interact via an appropriate coupling Hamiltonian, e.g.:

$$H_{int} = i\delta \left(|L_n><L_n| - |R_n><R_n| \right) \left(|D_L><D_R| - |D_R><D_L| \right)$$ (22)

for the time interval $\Delta t = \Pi\hbar/(4\delta)$ [5,6], and the initial state of the demon is:

$$|D_0\rangle = (|D_L\rangle + |D_R\rangle)/\sqrt{2} \qquad (23)$$

For, in this case the complete density matrix becomes:

$$P = \exp(-iH_{int}\,\Delta t/\hbar)\,\tilde{\rho}\,|D_0\rangle\langle D_0| =$$

$$\cong (\rho_L\,|D_L\rangle\langle D_L| + \rho_R\,|D_R\rangle\langle D_R|)/2 \qquad (24)$$

Here and below we have omitted small off-diagonal terms ($\sim\beta\Delta_n$) present in $\tilde{\rho}$, Eq. (14) and, by the same token, we shall drop corrections ($\sim\beta^2\Delta_n^2$) from the diagonal of ρ_L and ρ_R. As it was pointed out at the end of the last section, for the equilibrium there is no need for the "reduction of the state vector." The measured system -- one molecule gas -- is already in the mixture of being on the left and right-hand side of the divided well.

To study the relation of the information gain and entropy increase in course of the measurement, we employ the usual definition of entropy in terms of the density matrix [3, 6, 7, 8]

$$S(\rho) = -k_B \mathrm{Tr}\,\rho\ln\rho \qquad (25)$$

The information is then:

$$I(\rho) = \ln(\mathrm{Dim}(H)) - S(\rho)/k_B, \qquad (26)$$

where H is the Hilbert space of the system in question. Essential in our further discussion will be the mutual information $I_\mu(P_{AB})$ defined for two subsystems, A and B, which are described jointly by the density matrix P_{AB}, while their individual density matrices are ρ_A and ρ_B: '

$$I_\mu(P_{AB}) = I(P_{AB}) - (I(\rho_A) + I(\rho_B)). \qquad (27)$$

In words, mutual information is the difference between the information needed to specify A and B are not correlated, $P_{AB} = \rho_A\rho_B$, then $I_\mu(P_{AB}) = 0$.

The readoff of the location of the gas molecule by the demon will be described by an external observer not aware of the outcome by the transition:

$$\tilde{\rho}\,|D_0\rangle\langle D_0| \rightarrow (\rho_L\,|D_L\rangle\langle D_L| + \rho_R\,|D_R\rangle\langle D_R|)/2 \qquad (28)$$

The density matrix of the gas is then:

$$\tilde{\rho} = \tilde{z}^{-1}\sum_{n=1}\exp(-\beta\epsilon n^2)(|L_n\rangle\langle L_n| + |R_n\rangle\langle R_n|) = (\rho_L + \rho_R)/2 \qquad (29)$$

Thus, even after the measurement by the demon, the density matrix of the gas, ρ_G will be still :

$$\rho_G = \langle D_L|P|D_L\rangle + \langle D_R|P|D_R\rangle = \tilde{\rho} \qquad (30)$$

The state of the demon will, on the other hand, change from the initial pure state $|D_0\rangle\langle D_0|$ into a mixture:

$$\rho_D = \sum_n(\langle L_n|P|L_n\rangle + \langle R_n|P|R_n\rangle) = (|D_L\rangle\langle D_L| + |D_R\rangle\langle D_R|)/2 \qquad (31)$$

Entropy of the gas viewed by the external observer remains constant:

$$S(\rho_G)=S(\tilde{\rho})= \partial(\beta\ln\tilde{Z})/\partial\beta \qquad (32)$$

Entropy of the demon has however <u>increased</u>:

$$S(\rho_D)-S(\,|D_0\!><\!D_0|\,)=k_B\ln2 \qquad (33)$$

Nevertheless, the combined entropy of the gas-demon system could not have
changed: In our model evolution during the read-off was dynamical, and
the gas-demon system was isolated. Yet, the sum of the entropies of the two
subsystems -- the gas and the demon -- has increased by $k_B\ln2$. The obvious
question is then: where is the "lost information" $\Delta I=I(P)-(I(\tilde{\rho})+I(\rho_D))$?
The very form of this expression and its similarity to the right-hand side
of Eq. (27) suggests the answer: The loss of the information by the demon
is compensated for by an equal increase of the mutual information:

$$\Delta I_\mu=I_\mu(P)-I_\mu(\tilde{\rho}\,|D_0\!><\!D_0|\,). \qquad (34)$$

Mutual infromation can be regarded as the information gained by the demon.
From the conservation of entropy during dynamical evolutions it follows that
an increase of the mutual information must be compensated for by an equal
increase of the entropy.

$$\Delta I_\mu-\Delta S/k_B=0 \qquad (35)$$

This last equation is the basis of Szilard's formula, Eq. (1).

At this stage readoff of the location of the gas molecule is reversible.
To undo it, one can apply the inverse of the unitary operation which has produced the correlation. This would allow one to erase the increase of entropy
of the demon, but only at a price of the loss of mutual information.

One can now easily picture further stages of the operation of Szilard's
engine. The state of the demon can be used to decide which well is "empty"
and can be "discarded."[6] The molecule in the other well contains twice as
much energy as it would if the well were <u>adiabatically</u> (i.e. after decoupling
it from the heat reservoir) expanded from its present size $\sim L/2$ to L.
Adiabatic expansion conserves entropy. Therefore, one can immediately gain
$\Delta W=\frac{1}{2}<E>=k_BT/4$ without any additional entropy increases. One can also gain
$\Delta W=k_BT\ln2$, Eq. (2), by allowing adiabatic expansion to occur in small increments, inbetween which one molecule gas is reheated by the re-established
contact with the reservoir. In the limit of infinitesimally small increments
this leads, of course, to the isothermal expansion. At the end the state
of the gas is precisely the same as it was at the beginning of the cycle, and
we are ΔW "richer" in energy. If Szilard's engine could repeat this cycle,
this would be a violation of the second law of thermodynamics. We would have
a working model of a <u>perpetuum mobile</u>, which extracts energy in a cyclic process from an infinite reservoir <u>without</u> the temperature difference.

Fortunately for the second law, there is an essential gap in our above
design: The demon is still in the mixed state, ρ_D, Eq. (31). To perform the
next cycle, the observer must "reset" the state of the demon to the initial
$|D_0>$. This means that the entropy $dS=k_B\ln2$ must be somehow removed from the
system. If we were to leave demon in the mixed state, coupling it with the
gas through H_{int} will not result in the increase of their mutual information:
The one-bit memory of the demon is still filled by the outcome of the past
measurement of the gas. Moreover, this measurement cannot any longer be reversed by allowing the gas and the demon to interact. For, even though the
density matrix of each of these two systems has remained the same, their joint

density matrix is now very different:

$$\tilde{\rho}\rho_D = \{(\rho_L|D_L><D_L| + \rho_R|D_R><D_R|)/2 + (\rho_L|D_R><D_R| + \rho_R|D_L><D_L|)/2\}/2 \quad (36)$$

One could, presumably, still accomplish the reversal using the work gained in course of the cycle. This would, however, defy the purpose of the engine. The only other way to get the demon into the working order must be executed by an "external observer" or by its automated equivalent: The demon must be reset to the "ready-to-measure" state $|D_0>$.

As it was pointed out by Bennett in his classic analysis, this operation of memory erasure is the true reason for irreversibility, and the ultimate reason why the free energy, Eq. (1), must be expended.[9] Short of reversing the cycle, any procedure which resets the state of the demon to $|D_0>$ must involve a measurement. For instance, a possible algorithm could begin with the measurement whether the demon is in the state $|D_L>$ or in the orthogonal state $|D_R>$. Once this is established then, depending on the outcome, the demon may be rotated either "rightward" from $|D_L>$, or "leftward" from $|D_R>$, so that its state returns to $|D_0>$. The measurement by some external agency -- some "environment" -- is an essential and unavoidable ingredient of any resetting algorithm. In its course entropy is "passed on" from the demon to the environment.

V. SUMMARY

The prupose of our discussion was to analyze a process which converts thermodynamic energy into useful work. Our analysis was quantum, which removed ambiguities pointed out by Jauch and Baron in the original discussion by Szilard. We have concluded, that validity of the second law of thermodynamics can be satisfied only if the process of measurement is accompanied by the increase of entropy of the measuring apparatus by the amount no less than the amount of gained information. Our analysis confirms therefore conclusions of Szilard (and earlier discussion of Smoluchowski [10], which has inspired Szilard's paper). Moreover, we show that the ultimate reason for the entropy increase can be traced back to the necessity to "reset" the state of the measuring apparatus[9] , which, in turn, must involve a measurement. This necessity of the "readoff" of the outcome by some external agency -- the "environment" of the measuring apparatus has been already invoked to settle some of the problems of quantum theory of measurements.[11] Its role in the context of the above example is to determine what was the outcome of the measurement, so that the apparatus can be reset. In the context of quantum measurements its role is very similar: it forces one of the outcomes of the measurement to be definite, and, therefore, causes the "collapse of the wavepacket."

In view of the title of Szilard's paper, it is perhaps worthwhile to point out that we did not have to invoke "intelligence" at any stage of our analysis: all the systems could be presumably unanimated. However, one can imagine that the ability to measure, and make the environment "pay" the entropic cost of the measurement is also one of the essential attributes of animated beings.

ACKNOWLEDGMENTS

I would like to thank Charles Bennett and John Archibald Wheeler for many enjoyable and stimulating discussions on the subject of this paper. The research was supported in part by the National Science Foundation under Grant No. PHY77-27084, supplemented by funds from the National Aeronautics and Space Administration.

REFERENCES

1. L. Szilard,"On the Decrease of Entropy in a Thermodynamic System by the Intervention of Intelligent Beings," Z. Phys. 53:840 (1929); English translation reprinted in Behavioral Science 9:301 (1964), as well as in Ref. 2, p. 539.
2. J.A. Wheeler and W.H. Zurek, eds., Quantum Theory and Measurement (Princeton University Press, Princeton, 1983).
3. C.E. Shannon and W. Weaver, The Mathematical Theory of Communication, (University of Illinois Press, Urbana, 1949).
4. J.M. Jauch and J.G. Baron, "Entropy, Information, and Szilard's Paradox," Helv. Phys. Acta, 45:220 (1972).
5. W.H. Zurek, "Pointer Basis of Quantum Apparatus: Into What Mixture Does the Wavepacket Collapse?" Phys. Rev. D24:1516 (1981).
6. W.H. Zurek, "Information Transfer in Quantum Measurements: Irreversibility and Amplification," Quantum Optics, Experimental Gravitation and Measurement Theory, eds. P. Meystre and M.O. Scully (Plenum Press, New York, 1983).
7. J.R. Pierce and E.C. Rosner, Introduction to Communication Science and Systems (Plenum Press, New York, 1980).
8. H. Everett III, Dissertation, reprinted in B.S. DeWitt and N. Graham, eds., The Many -- Worlds Interpretation of Quantum Mechanics (Princeton University Press, Princeton, 1973).
9. C.H. Bennett, "The Thermodynamics of Computation" Int. J. Theor. Phys. 21:305 (1982).
10. M. Smoluchowski, "Vorträge über die Kinetische Theorie der Materie und Elktrizitat," Leipzig 1914.
11. W.H. Zurek, "Environment-Induced Superselection Rules," Phys. Rev. D26:]862 (1982).

Computation: A Fundamental Physical View

Rolf Landauer

IBM Thomas J. Watson Research Center, P.O. Box 218, Yorktown Heights, New York 10598, U.S.A.

Received September 3, 1986; accepted September 12, 1986

Abstract

Attempts to understand the fundamental physical limits of computation have been under way for over a quarter century. We discuss this field, with emphasis on the central notion of reversible computation, and emphasis on the relationship to the ultimate nature of physical law. A brief discussion of the generation of information is included. In ordinary computation, noise is a source of error, to be offset to the maximum possible extent. This can be done via reversible computation. Alternatively, there are situations in which noise controls the transitions in a system between many competing states of local stability, and can be used to explore this manifold. In the general case, where the noise depends on the state of the system, relative stability can only be determined by the kinetics along the *whole* pathway from one state of local stability to another one. Examination of the two terminal states to be compared cannot tell us which is the more likely state.

1. Introduction; reversible computation

The search for the fundamental physical limits of the computational process has been under way for more than a quarter century. The important notion of reversible computation, which came out of that search, was published in 1973 [1]. It is not our purpose, here, to review and explain this whole field. For an introduction to the area, and clues to the citation trail, see Refs. [2] and [3]. We will, instead, take the opportunity to make or emphasize some subsidiary points, which may not have had the same frequent exposure to public view.

First of all, let us explain why this field deserves attention. It is not for technological reasons. Reversible computation, which consists of a sequence of logical 1:1 mappings, is illustrated in Fig. 1. Each possible initial program defines a separate track in Fig. 1, with no merging or splitting. Such a computation resembles the motion of a particle through a periodic lattice, which − under a small driving force − will move diffusively over a short time scale, but will exhibit a drift velocity and predictable progress, over a longer time scale. Reversible computation can be carried out with energy dissipation proportional to the driving force and, therefore, to the computational velocity. That means that there is no minimal energy dissipation per step. But even if we ask for predictable computation, which does not act diffusively, a driving force corresponding to an expenditure of a few kT per step will accomplish that. Note that this will be kT per step of the total computer, and may correspond to the action of many simultaneous logic events. By comparison, low powered real circuits consume of the order of $10^9 kT$ per logic event. When reality is so far from the fundamental limits, the limits do not serve as guide to the technologist.

Then why are we in this business? *Because it is at the very core of science.* Science, and physics most particularly, is expressed in terms of mathematics, i.e. in terms of rules for handling numbers. Information, numerical or otherwise, is not an abstraction, but is inevitably tied to a physical repre-

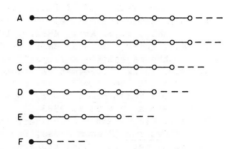

Fig. 1. The left-hand end of a horizontal chain represents the initial state, and forward computation represents motion to the right, through a sequence of states represented by successive circles. Different letters correspond to different initial states, i.e., different programs.

sentation. The representation can be a hole in a punched card, an electron spin up or down, the state of a neuron, or a DNA configuration. There really is no software, in the strict sense of disembodied information, but only inactive and relatively static hardware. Thus, the handling of information is inevitably tied to the physical universe, its content and its laws. This is illustrated by the right hand arrow of Fig. 2. We have all been indoctrinated by the mathematicians and their sense of values. Given ε, $\exists N$, such that −−−−−−−. Now we come back and ask, "Does this arbitrarily large N, this implied unlimited sequence of *infallible* operations, *really exist*?" If not, then the continuum mathematics of our early education can have no relationship to executable algorithms and physical

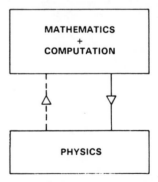

Fig. 2. Information handling, shown at the top, is dependent on that which the real physical universe permits, through available "parts," and through the laws of physics. This dependency is indicated by the right arrow. But the laws of physics are directions for processing information and, therefore, dependent on executable algorithms. This is indicated by the dashed arrow at left.

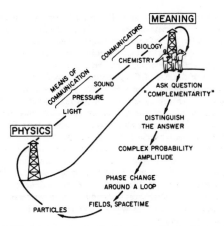

Fig. 3. Wheeler's "meaning circuit". According to Wheeler, Physics gives light and sound and pressure, tools of communication. It gives biology and chemistry and, through them, communicators. Communication between communicators gives meaning. Meaning calls for the asking of questions, but the asking of one question stands in a complementary relation to the asking of another.

law. This brings us to the left hand arrow of Fig. 2, which states that physical law requires operations which, at least in principle, are executable. Thus, ultimately, we need a self-consistent formulation of the laws of physics, as suggested in Fig. 2. The laws describing our universe must be restricted to algorithms which are executable in our actual universe; what is executable will, in turn, depend on the contents of that universe (i.e. the storehouse of possible parts) and to the laws describing the interaction of these parts.

The self-consistency invoked in Fig. 2 is reminiscent of Wheeler's Meaning Circuit, shown in Fig. 3, and adapted from Ref. [4]. John Wheeler has pointed us toward Era III of physics, in which, ". . . we have to seek nothing less than the foundation of physical law itself." Wheeler contrasts this to Era II, which commenced with Newton, where the laws of physics were to be discovered, but their origin was not a fit subject for discussion. Wheeler has given us a specific proposal for Era III, the "meaning circuit". In this, physics gives rise to all the phenomena whose study has usually occupied us. These phenomena, in turn, give rise to biology, communicators, and their questions, and these lead to measurement and the laws of physics. Our typical view in science has been one under which the laws of physics were there at the beginning; the laws are a process control program which steers the evolution of the universe. Wheeler reminds us that the discovery of laws is, or involves, quantum mechanical measurement. The results of measurement are not independent of the act of measurement, and the outcome of the measurement was not there, all along, to be revealed in its finally measured form. If I can be presumptuous enough to differ from Wheeler, it is related to his stress on human observers and their posing of questions. Measurement does not require intelligent beings, the environment is continually acting on a system, and making measurements [5]. Incidentally, that is the most elementary way in which Schrödinger's famous cat paradox is misleading. Long before the human observer looks at the cat, the air molecules bouncing into the cat have measured its temperature, or its breathing motion.

All along, parts of the cat had made measurements on each other, e.g., the state of the brain cells depends on the continued blood flow. In fact, long before the bullet has left its barrel, there have been interactions of that sort. *I* do not really know what constitutes a *measurement*, though *others* are likely to have the answer to that [6, 7]. Most particularly, I do not know what constitutes a set of measurements leading to a physical law. It is not clear that this has to involve complex organisms that publish conference papers. Perhaps the universe, like Schrödinger's cat, is asking questions about the laws of physics all along. I do not assert that Wheeler, in Fig. 3, is wrong. Rather: I am not sure he is right, *perhaps* the circuit can close at a lower level.

While this author admits that he is uncertain about the exact character of a "measurement", others are less squeamish. Some of the critics of reversible computation [8–12] invoke a simple recipe which goes like this: Computation continually requires measurement on the existing state of the computer. Measurement requires energy dissipation, as is known from Szilard's analysis of Maxwell's demon [13], and requires energy dissipation related to the number of possibilities between which the measurement discriminates, even if done slowly. This criticism of reversible computation, based on a *perception* of *applicable principles*, has been refuted [14], in general terms. But there is a more cogent counterargument. Reversible computation has been described in terms of a number of detailed embodiments, listed in Ref. [3]. One of these [15] invokes Josephson junction circuitry, and could actually be made. The critics of reversible computation need to show us where such proposals err; otherwise, we are dependent upon their particular notion of what constitutes a measurement. Simply coupling two systems together, for a period, so that there is a cross-influence in their time evolution, does not require energy dissipation. This was already stated, in connection with the computational process, in 1961 [16]. Then why does measurement require energy dissipation? Because, after the measurement (or before the first measurement) the measurement apparatus has to be reset. This represents the erasure of information, and it is the erasure of information which in measurement [17], just as in computation [16], requires energy dissipation. Unfortunately, the literature on the energy requirements of the classical measurement process, while correct, manages to obscure this simple and central point. Reversible computation is, of course, a process that avoids erasure; Fig. 1 consists of a sequence of 1 : 1 mappings. It was the brilliant insight of Bennett [1] that universal computation can actually be carried out reversibly.

In connection with the continuing occasional objections to reversible computation [8–12], I take the liberty of including some editorial remarks, more personal and subjective in character than is typical for a scientific paper. When I was first exposed to Bennett's notion of reversible computation I was very skeptical, despite the fact that my own work had, in some ways, come very close. It took me months to become fully convinced that Bennett was right. Since then I have seen many colleagues, in a first exposure, struggle with this perhaps counter-intuitive idea. But it is now many years and many papers later. Reversible computation has been explored and expounded by a good many authors from a variety of veiwpoints, and it should not longer be that hard to understand. Remarkably enough, some of the critics [11, 12] refer to my work, but do not actually cite me.

The study of the physical limits of the computational process, so far, has served primarily to dispel limits that might have been expected on the basis of superficial speculation. *kT* is not a minimal energy dissipation, per step, nor does the uncertainty principle help to set energy dissipation requirements. Noise immunity, in the intentionally used degrees of freedom (in contrast to fluctuations which actually cause equipment deterioration) is available to any required degree. Then where are the real limits? They are, presumably, related to more cosmological questions, and unlikely to be answered by those of us who started the field. How many degrees of freedom, for example, can be kept together effectively, to constitute a computer? If we cannot have an unlimited memory, then can we really calculate π to as many placed as desired. A start toward such cosmological questions has been made by several investigators [18]. We will not try to evaluate or summarize these attempts; the important point: They are a thrust in the right general direction.

There are, of course, others who are concerned with the fact that our actual universe is not really characterized by a continuum. T. D. Lee [19] has proposed a "discrete mechanics". Feynman has stated [20], "... *everything* that happens in a finite volume of space and time would have to be exactly analyzable with a finite number of logical operations. The present theory of physics is not that way, apparently. It allows space to go down into infinitesimal distances, wavelengths to get infinitely great, terms to be summed in infinite order, and so forth; and, therefore, if this proposition is right, physical law is wrong". That statement clearly has a resemblance to our exposition. Ross [21] has invoked a model of the real number line based on probabilistic considerations. Woo [22] discusses the relation between discrete field theory and Turing machines. None of these, however, seem to go as far as we do, and none of them point out that the correct physical law must be based on algorithms whose nature is still to be found, rather than on classical mathematical analysis [23].

Mathematicians declared their independence of the real physical universe, about a century ago, and explained that they were really describing abstract objects and spaces. If some of these modelled real events, all right, but . . . . They ignored the question which we have emphasized. Mathematicians may be describing abstract spaces, but the actual information manipulation is still in the real physical universe. By and large, mathematicians do not welcome the points we have made, and scorn questions about physical executability, even though the mathematics community occasionally arrives at its own reasons for questioning the continuum. There are exceptions, however. One is found in the work of Bremermann [24]. A particularly clear version occurs in the work of Herman Weyl. Wheeler [25] quotes Weyl, . . . *belief in this transcendental world [of mathematical ideals, of propositions of infinite length, and of a continuum of natural numbers] taxes the strength of our faith hardly less than the doctrines of the early Fathers of the Church or of the scholastic philosophers of the Middle Ages.* Wheeler then goes on with his own statement: *Then how can physics in good conscience go on using in its description of existence a number system that does not even exist?*

The noise immunity in reversible computation is obtained by invoking large potentials, which act as barriers to noise in the undesired processes. In Bennett's original springless clockwork Turing machine [1] "hard" parts are assumed, which are not penetrable by each other, and which do not fall apart under the influence of thermal fluctuatións. Similar assumptions underlie other reversible computer proposals. It is important to understand that the immunity is bought at the expense of the size of the potentials involved, or − mor or less equivalently − the size of the parts, and not at the expense of energy dissipation. In the real universe, with a limited selection of parts, arbitrary immunity may not be available. Noise immunity, however, which lasts for the lifetime of the universe should be adequate. The many real pressures, however, for continued miniaturization in computers, are likely to take us in the opposite direction. Techniques for improving the reliability of computation have been discussed in Ref. [3]. We stress, here, the undesirability of noise induced disturbances in computation, in anticipation of a subsequent section in which noise is viewed in a more constructive way.

2. Generation of information

Reference [16] pointed to the association between information destruction and physical irreversibility. The prevalence of friction and information loss leads to the questions: Are there counterbalancing processes? Does information get generated, or does it only disappear? We will try to give a very partial answer adapted from Ref. [26]. The generation of information must be the opposite of its destruction. Systems that are initially indistinguishable must develop a recognizable difference. There are several possible causes for the development of such differences. The most commonly cited one will be invoked later in this paper; noise that reaches our system from external sources (or from any degrees of freedom not explicitly described in the system's equations of motion) causes ensemble members, which were initially together, to diffuse apart. One can then go on, of course, to argue that the information did not really arise, but reflects information originally in the noise sources, and is transferred to the system of concern. In a universe with limited precision, however, the noise cannot be followed back in time and space to any desired accuracy. Thus, the distinctions in behaviour produced by noise can be considered to be "generated".

In the last decade it has become acceptable to invoke chaotic processes, instead [27]. These are processes in deterministic nonlinear systems, possibly systems with only a few degrees of freedom, which are not periodic or quasi-periodic. Nearby trajectories diverge exponentially in time, instead of the typical diffusive $t^{1/2}$ divergence caused by noise [28]. Once again, that exponential divergence, by itself, does not really produce information. We must also claim that two systems that originally were very close, but not identical, are nevertheless in some "in principle" sense indistinguishable. Furthermore it is possible, as discussed in the paper by Swinney in this set of proceedings, to distinguish between the effects of external noise and the effects of deterministic chaos. Amplifiers can also serve to push signals apart that are close together, initially. Amplifiers need not have the form of transistor circuits with a spatially separate input and output. In parametric amplifiers, to cite one example [28], we can utilize a departure from the neighbourhood of an unstable state and can achieve exponential growth in time. The growing separation of these signals will be accompanied by dissipative effects, i.e. by a compression of phase space for other degrees of freedom.

It is not clear whether one of the mechanisms cited above has to be regarded as the most fundamental. If a choice is necessary, then our preference lies with the direct effects of noise. After all noise clearly exists, and is pervasive, whereas noiseless dynamic systems do not exist. We add a cautionary note. Quantum mechanics, despite an intimate relationship to probabilities, contains no built in noise sources. It does not provide for a growing spread in nearby systems; entropy is conserved in quantum mechanics just as in the classical case.

Arbitrarily reliable computation, with unlimited precision, is unlikely to be available in our real worl. Thus, the very question discussed in the preceding paragraph, whether two initially identical states become separated with time, does not really have a very clear meaning. After all, in a world with limited precision, we can never be absolutely certain about the initial identity of two very close-lying states. Thus, the likely limited precision of our number handling introduces something like noise into our basic laws of dynamics. It is not necessarily an artifact which requires supplementary explanation.

3. What is computation?

We have equated the computational process with a universal Turing machine, essentially that which a real and practical computer can do if it had access to unlimited memory? This is a process in which branching is possible. Intermediate results are invoked as the basis for decisions about subsequent steps. As pointed out by Keyes [29], many otherwise interesting physical processes proposed for computational purposes do not allow such an unlimited chain of steps, but only a limited sequence chosen by the apparatus designer.

A good many physical processes, involving cellular automata rules, or other ways of coupling large arrays of elements in a relatively uncomplicated geometrical way, and without a great deal of detailed design, have been proposed as potentially useful tools for pattern recognition, as associative memories, and for other similar purposes. We can cite only a small proportion of this extensive literature [30]. It is not our purpose here to evaluate or explain these proposals. Our key point: Many of these proposals are unrelated to universal computation. Cellular automata can, of course, be chosen so as to be capable of universal computation, and even to do computation which is logically reversible [31], but many of the cellular automata discussed in the literature are more limited than that. Motion toward one of many attractors, in a system with competing states of local stability, is *not* universal computation. That does not mean that the processes are uninteresting, or that they have no utility. Nevertheless, I will insert here, a somewhat conservative reaction. Proposals for computer simulations of networks which learn, are unstructured or randomly structured initially, and mimic neuron interaction, date from the early 1950's and the beginning of large electronic computers. At IBM, this project carried out by N. Rochester and collaborators, on the engineering model of the 701, was called the "Conceptor". Such proposals have become more sophisticated with time, but have never achieved major practical success. Some of the enthusiasm, in the current audience, comes from physical scientists who have

not asked: How can (and have) some of these goals been achieved through more conventional software techniques, and more conventionally organized hardware? For example, we do know how to build content-addressable memories out of silicon technology. Pattern recognition is a hard process for digital computers; nevertheless, it has been done in *real* applications. Over the decades, for example, a good deal of progress has been made toward the recognition of continuous speech. The hard part is not the motion toward an attractor, within a basis, but is the *definition* of the basin of attraction. In an associative memory, which can respond to slightly faulty patterns, one has to learn about the likely errors. "Hopfield," entered by keystroke, is quite likely to turn out "opfield", it is unlikely to be inverted to "Dleifpoh". A successful recognition system must take such statistics into account. If it is a system that learns, then it must be able to apply the experience with the name "Hopfield" to the name "Smith". Some of the recent physical literature on neural networks can, perhaps, be justified as a model of biological functions, rather than as a useful technique for man-made devices. This author is not qualified to judge that realm. I cannot help, however, noticing the unqualified assertions in the physics literature, exemplified by [32]:

> It is generally expected that the essential characteristics of the dynamics [of a neural network] are captured by a Hamiltonian of the form
>
> $$H_N = -\tfrac{1}{2} \sum_{i,j} J_{ij} S(i) S(j). \qquad (1)$$
>
> The N neurons are described by Ising spin variables . . .

Others [33], publishing in the same journal of neurophysiology and computer science, are a little more cautious and point out that they are analyzing a particular *model*. The biologists, as exemplified by a recent review of neuronal circuits [34], have paid little attention, though that − by itself − leads us to no clear conclusion.

The relationship between physical processes and computation has become widely appreciated in recent years [35], and once again we can only cite some illustrative items. A computer, however, even a special purpose analog computer, needs places where input is entered and output collected, in a standardized representation. An electronic analog computer had dials to set the input. A slide rule had numbers and a scale printed on its surface; in fact, it was the very choice of representation which gave the slide rule its utility for multiplication. To call any physical evolution with time an analog computation seems a little strained, though we cannot say it is clearly wrong.

In connection with our reference to input and output, it is appropriate to discuss this in connection with reversible computation. It is sometimes assumed that, even if information transfer within the computer can be done without a mimimal dissipation [11, 12], this does not apply to the input and output; a *measurement* at that point becomes essential. It is true, of course, that these input-output processes can be made more dissipative than the computational steps but they do not have to be more dissipative. Why should information transfer into the system or out of the system *have* to be more dissipative than that within the system? Bennett [17] has pointed out that a magnetic tape can be copied slowly without minimal dissipation. The same point is already implicit in the work of Keyes and Landauer [36].

Do we need a dissipative measurement to signal the completion of a program? That, most certainly, is one possibility. We can, also, give ourselves lots of time to do whatever it is we want to do upon program completion, if we dissipate several kT so that the computer cannot fluctuate right back out of the final state into an earlier state, as is likely in the diffusive behavior of reversible computers. But once again we must ask if the transfer of information out of whatever it is we call the computer, to another set of digital registers, is really very different from transfer within the so-called computer? It is, because reversible computation has to be undone, and if we also reverse the information transfer out of the computer prematurely, our computation will have been useless. The easiest answer to that, but not necessarily the optimum answer, is to perform occasonal dissipative measurements on the computer, to see if the "Task Completion Bit" is in its 1 status. When it is, the reversible computer can go into a long idling cycle, in which only an internal computer clock advances to give us a time to copy the output register with very little dissipation. After that the computer reverses itself, clearing out its own output register and restoring its initial state.

4. Fluctuations

In the preceding discussion noise has been a potential source of error in otherwise predictable computations. This is in accord with the historical interest in noise as a source of confusion and error in measurement and communication. In more recent times there has been a growing awareness that noise can be *a controlling qualitative influence on the development of systems*. In systems which are multistable, i.e., have two or more competing states of local stability, noise determines the motion of the system between these competing states. Small systems, as found in molecular biology, and in the drive toward miniaturization of computer components, can show a strong susceptibility to noise. Furthermore such noise induced transitions may be of utility, as invoked in the simulated annealing technique for optimization in the presence of complex constraints [37]. A similar application occurs in a model for the mechanism of perception and visual recognition [38] in which fluctuations are invoked to allow escape from premature fixation. First order phase transitions, in ordinary thermodynamic systems, can occur by homogeneous nucleation, and the formation of a critical nucleus is a fluctuation which takes the system from one state of local stability (i.e., the original metastable phase) to a new state of local stability. Evolution and the origin of life can be viewed as an optimization process, in which fluctuations (e.g., mutations) take us from one metastable ecology, to a new one [39, 40]. In contrast to the discussions in Ref. [40], some of which represent a longstanding orientation in ecology, physical scientists have been inclined to use the word *self-organization* very loosely. To apply this expression to the Benard instability, for example, to the Zhabotinskii reaction, or to the oscillations of a laser, under conditions where these temporal and spatial patterns are the only allowed behavior, seems strained. We might, with equal justice, refer to the revolution of an electron around a hydrogen nucleus, or the rotation of a water wheel, as *self-organization* [41].

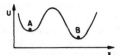

Fig. 4. Damped potential with metastable state A and state of lowest energy at B.

Questions about relative stability, e.g., is A or B of Fig. 4, the more likely state, are statistical questions. In the absence of fluctuations a particle will simply stay at a local minimum; it can escape from a well only with the assistance of noise. Let us discuss the type of situation shown in Fig. 4, but invoke greater generality than suggested by Fig. 4. Consider a law of motion along x which is not necessarily that of a particle in a potential, but can represent a broader class of systems. x could, for example, be the charge on a capacitor in an electrically excited bistable circuit, or represent the chemical composition in an open and driven chemical reactor. Without noise, the flux of probability ϱ

$$j = \varrho v(x) \tag{4.1}$$

is determined by the noiseless macroscopic velocity $v(x)$, determined by the system's kinetics. Equation (4.1) would cause the density to accumulate at the points of local stability, where $v(x) = 0$. In the presence of noise different ensemble members, which start together, subsequently diffuse apart from each other and also away from the deterministic trajectory defined by $\dot{x} = v(x)$. In the simplest cases this can be represented by an additional diffusion term in eq. (4.1), leading to

$$j = \varrho v(x) - D \frac{\partial p}{\partial x}. \tag{4.2}$$

In the steady state j is independent of x. Unless current is introduced at $x = \pm \infty$ we will have $j = 0$ for all x. In that case, eq. (4.2) can readily be integrated to yield

$$\varrho(x) \simeq \exp \int (v/D) \, dx, \tag{4.3}$$

showing that the steady state represents a balance between the deterministic velocity v, restoring the system to points of local stability, and D which represents the noise, permitting departure from such points of local stability. As pointed out elsewhere [28], eq. (4.3) is a generalization of the Boltzmann factor, $\exp(-U/kT)$. If we compare the population between two points of local stability, we find

$$\varrho(B)/\varrho(A) = \exp \int_A^B (v/D) \, dx. \tag{4.4}$$

Equation (4.4) shows the dependence on $D(x)$ between A and B. The kinetics along the connecting path matters, we cannot just inspect the end points A and B. We cannot expect, in general, some analog to Maxwell's equal area rule, which will predict relative stability on the basis of $\int_A^B v(x) \, dx$. This was pointed out by this author [42] in 1962, is implicit in the work of R. L. Stratonovich [43] and was again emphasized [44] in 1975. The first version of the argument to be given subsequently in this paper [45] appeared in 1975, and was elaborated and repeated on a number of subsequent occasions. The point is frequently ascribed to later authors, and associated

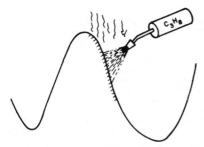

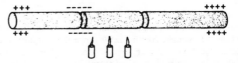

Fig. 6. Particle in an insulating tube, or series of tubes, subject to force field maintained by charges on the outside of the tube. The tube is heated nonuniformly.

Fig. 5. A bistable potential in which the top right-hand side of the barrier has been brought to a temperature well above the adjacent portions. Particles escaping from the right-hand well can now get through the heated zone much more easily, leading to a smaller effective barrier.

with the labels *multiplicative noise, noise induced phase transitions,* and *external noise.*

In equilibrium, noise is defined by the temperature, and cannot be made an arbitrary function of the state of the system, i.e., of x in our one-dimensional examples. It is this property which leads to the Maxwell equal area rule. More generally, however, the noise sources can be tailored to be almost any function of the state of the system. Our subsequent example will emphasize this. Consider a potential, as shown in Fig. 4. The right hand well is lower; in thermal equilibrium $\varrho(x)$ will be larger there. Let us now deviate from equilibrium in a very simple way. We heat up part of the right hand well, as illustrated in Fig. 5. We assume this is a heavily damped well; particles crossing the temperature boundary come to their new temperature very quickly.

To clarify the physical situation sketched in Fig. 5, we provide one possible embodiment in Fig. 6. This shows a sequence of insulating tubes with a particle. The particle is charged and the force-field is maintained by charges deposited on the outside of the tube. Different sections of the tube are maintained at different temperatures. The particle incident on a tube wall is assumed to bounce off without change in charge, but bounce off with the local tube temperature.

In Fig. 5 the particles entering the hot section from the right gain the energy needed for escape much more easily than without the elevated temperature. The particles in the right hand well, therefore, escape much more easily than without the blow-torch. The particles in the left hand well have an unmodified escape problem. In the steady state the two escape rates must balance. Therefore, the population in the right-hand well is depleted by the blow torch. If the temperature elevation is made large enough, most of the effect of the barrier in the hot section is eliminated. If the hot section is also made to extend over enough of the right-hand barrier shoulder, then the right-hand well which originally was more densely populated, becomes less densely occupied. The key point of this example: Relative stability can be controlled through the kinetics in parts of the system space which are rarely occupied. Therefore no amount of concern related to the neighborhood of the states of local stability can tell us which is the more likely neighborhood. This tells us that many of the favored principles in the physical chemistry literature, related to entropy, entropy production, excess entropy production, etc., cannot be applied to multistable systems. There are no short cuts for such systems; the detailed

kinetics along the transition paths must be taken into account. The relevance of this to discussions of evolution and the origin of life have been emphasized elsewhere [39, 46].

The lack of available short cuts, in predicting the noise-activated exploration of many competing states of local stability, relates to questions of complexity which have been discussed in the literature. As an introduction to this part of our discussion, let us first consider chaos. Multiply periodic motion, e.g., $y = \cos [\omega_0 t + (\delta \sin \omega_m t) t]$ may look a little complex, but does not present any unusual difficulty in the calculation of y at a much later time; we do not need to follow the motion, in detail, over the intervening period. Chaos is usually more complex than that, in a genuine way. To predict a position a great many "cycles" later on, in the typical chaotic case, requires that we follow the motion very precisely. The program that directs such a calculation need not be complex, it is not a matter of great algorithmic complexity [47]. It is rather the detailed execution of the calculation which is long, i.e., the number of steps involved. This is a complexity measure which Bennett has proposed, discussed, and called "depth" [48].

The noise-activated search for likely states of local stability presents us with a similar dichotomy. If we are dealing with a multistable potential, and thermal equilibrium noise, then the depth of a set of wells allows us to compute their eventual (long-term) relative probability densities. (If we are concerned with the integrated probability of finding a particle *near* a minimum, rather than the probability *density*, then we must also take the well potential curvature into account, or equivalently compare free energies, rather than energies. That is not a significant distinction for our purposes.) If, however, we are dealing with a system which is not in thermal equilibrium, then it becomes more difficult. The additional difficulty relates to our discussion of the kinetics of Fig. 5, but of also the fact that in this more general case we can have circulation present in the steady state. The kinetics along the various pathways must then be taken into account. To predict the probability distribution at a much later time, from a given initial state, we *must* follow the motion in detail. (The italicized word *must* in the preceding sentence represents an intuitive assessment, and is not a result of a proof.) Such a measure of complexity, counting the number of states of local stability which have to be explored along the way, has been proposed by Kuhn [49]. He has called it *knowledge gained*, in connection with his discussions of the origin of life and the time-development of biological evolution. In general we can expect that there will be situations in which both of the above mentioned complexities are present simultaneously, and are not separable. We can start with a deterministic law of system motion, which is already chaotic, and the modify the system to make it stochastic.

The analogy between complexity in chaos and that in stochastic multistability is not meant to be carried too far.

Chaos was only used as an introduction to a complexity measure which characterizes program execution time. Chaotic motion, for example, does not settle down. The solution to a master equation, however, typically approaches a steady solution. In a space of unlimited extent, however, containing always more remote states of local stability, population changes *can* continue indefinitely.

This discussion of complexity in the presence of multistability is a first rough thrust in a direction which seems to deserve more thought, but is likely to demand more formal skills than this author can easily supply. The preceding discussion, for example, has only mentioned the possibility of circulation, without detailed consideration of it. Circulation can be present in purely deterministic motion; it can also be introduced by noise terms added to a deterministic equation.

References

1. Bennett, C. H., IBM J. Res. Dev. **17**, 525 (1973).
2. Bennett, C. H. and Landauer, R., Sci. Am. **253**, No. 1, 48 (1985); **253**, No. 4, 9 (1985); Landauer, R. and Büttiker, M., Physica Scripta **T9**, 155 (1985); Landauer, R., in Computer Culture, The Scientific Intellectual and Social Impact of the Computer (Edited by H. R. Pagels), Ann. N. Y. Acad. Sci. **426**, 161 (1984); Landauer, R., Found. Phys. **16**, 551 (1986).
3. Landauer, R., in Der Informationsbegriff in Technik und Wissenschaft (Edited by O. G. Folberth and C. Hackl), p. 139, Oldenbourg, Munich (1986).
4. Wheeler, J. A., in Problems in Theoretical Physics (Edited by A. Giovannini, F. Mancini and M. Marinaro), p. 121, Univ. Salerno Press (1984); Wheeler, J. A., in Frontiers of Nonequilibrium Statistical Physics (Edited by G. T. Moore and M. O. Scully), Plenum, New York (1986).
5. Zurek, W. H., in Foundations of Quantum Mechanics in the Light of New Technology (Edited by S. Kamefuchi), p. 181, Physical Soc., Japan (1983). See also a number of papers in New Techniques and Ideas in Quantum Measurement Theory (Edited by D. Greenberger), N. Y. Acad. Sci. (in press).
6. Wheeler, J. A. and Zurek, W. H., Quantum Theory and Measurement, Princeton University Press (1983).
7. New Techniques and Ideas in Quantum Measurement Theory (Edited by D. Greenberger), N. Y. Acad. Sci. (in press).
8. Hastings, H. M. and Waner, S., Bio Systems **17**, 241 (1985).
9. Robinson, A. L., Science **223**, 1164 (1984).
10. Porod, W., Grondin, R. O., Ferry, D. K. and Porod, G., Phys. Rev. Lett. **52**, 232 (1984); Phys. Rev. Lett. **53**, 1206 (1984).
11. Rothstein, J., On Ultimate Thermodynamic Limitations in Communication and Computation, in Proceedings of the conference on Performance Limits in Communication Theory and Practice (Edited by J. K. Skwirzynski) Martinus Nijhoff, Dordrecht (in press).
12. Drogin, E. M., Defense Electronics, p. 31 (March, 1986).
13. Szilard, L., in Z. Phys. **53**, 840 (1929), English translation in Ref. [6], p. 539.
14. Benioff, P., Phys. Rev. Lett. **53**, 1203 (1984); ibid. Bennett, C. H., p. 1202, Landauer, R., p. 1205; Toffoli, T., p. 1204.
15. Likharev, K. K., Int. J. Theor. Phys. **21**, 311 (1982); Likharev, K. K., Tylov, S. V. and Semenov, V. K., IEEE Trans. Magn. **21**, 947 (1985).
16. Landauer, R., IBM J. Res. Dev. **5**, 183 (1961).
17. Bennett, C. H., Int. J. Theor. Phys. **21**, 905 (1982); Sci. Am. (to be published).
18. Barrow, J. D. and Tipler, F. J., The Anthropic Cosmological Principle, Ch. 10, p. 613, Clarendon, Oxford (1986); Dyson, F. J., Rev. Mod. Phys. **51**, 447 (1979); Tippler, F. J., Int. J. Theor. Phys. **25**, 617 (1986).
19. Friedberg, R. and Lee, T. D., Nucl. Phys. **B225**, 1 (1983); Lee, T. D., Difference Equations as the Basis of Fundamental Physical Theories, given at symposium, Old and New Problems in Fundamental Physics, held in honor of Wick, G. C. (Pisa, Italy, October 25, 1984).
20. Feynman, R. P., Int. J. Theor. Phys. **21**, 467 (1982).
21. Ross, D. K., Int. J. Theor. Phys. **23**, 1207 (1984).
22. Woo, C. H., Phys. Lett. **168B**, 376 (1986).
23. Landauer, R., IEEE Spectrum **4**, 105 (1967).
24. Bremermann, H. J., in The Encyclopedia of Ignorance (Edited by R. Duncan and M. Weston-Smith), p. 167, Pergamon, New York (1977).
25. Wheeler, J. A., Am. Sci. **74**, 366 (1986).
26. Landauer, R., in Computer Culture: The Scientific, Intellectual and Social Impact of the Computer, (Edited by H. R. Pagels), p. 167, Ann. N. Y. Acad. Sci. **426**, 161 (1984).
27. Shaw, R., Z. Naturforsch. **36a**, 80 (1981); Ford, J., Phys. Today **36**, 40 (1983).
28. Landauer, R., in Nonlinearity in Condensed Matter (Edited by A. R. Bishop, D. K. Campbell, P. Kumar and S. E. Trullinger), Springer (in press).
29. Keyes, R. W., Science **230**, 138 (1985).
30. Hopfield, J. J. and Tank, D. W., Science **233**, 625 (1986), includes an extensive list of earlier citations; Choi, M. Y. and Huberman, B. A., Phys. Rev. **B31**, 2862 (1985); Cooper, L. N., in J. C. Maxwell, the Sesquicentennial Symposium (Edited by M. S. Berger), Elsevier, Lausanne (1984); Ebeling, W., Pattern Processing and Optimization by Reaction Diffusion Systems (preprint); Edelman, G. M. and Reeke, G. N., Proc. Natl. Acad. Sci. USA **79**, 2091 (1982); Frumkin, A. and Moses, E., Phys. Rev. **A34**, 714 (1986); Huberman, B. A. and Hogg, T., Physica Scripta **32**, 271 (1985); Little, W. A. and Shaw, G. L., Behavioral Biology **14**, 115 (1975); Parisi, G., J. Phys. **A19**, L617 (1986); See also Ref. [38], and Kinzel, W. (in this issue).
31. Margolus, N., in Physica D, Cellular Automata. (Edited by D. Farmer, T. Toffoli and S. Wolfram), p. 81, North-Holland, Amsterdam (1984).
32. van Hemmen, J. L. and Kühn, R., Phys. Rev. Lett. **57**, 913 (1986).
33. Amit, D. J., Gutfreund, H. and Sompolinsky, H., Phys. Rev. Lett. **55**, 1530 (1985).
34. Dumont, J. P. C. and Robertson, R. Meldrum, Science **233**, 849 (1986); See also Thompson, R. F., Science **233**, 941 (1986) for more generous citation practices. Even here, however, the physics based papers are included in a peripheral and supplementary citation.
35. Albert, D. Z., Phys. Lett. **98A**, 249 (1983); Geroch, R. and Hartle, J. B., Found. Phys. **16**, 533 1986; Kantor, F. W., Information Mechanics, Wiley, New York (1977); Kantor, F. W., Int. J. Theor. Phys. **21**, 525 (1982); Manthey, M. J. and Moret, B. M. E., Commun. ACM **26**, 137 (1983); Noyes, H. P., Gefwert, C. and Manthey, M. J., in New Techniques and Ideas in Quantum Measurement Theory (Edited by D. Greenberger), N. Y. Acad. Sci. (in press); Steiglitz, K., Two Non-Standard Paradigms for Computation: Analog Machines and Cellular Automata, in Performance Limits in Communication Theory and Practice (Edited by J. K. Skwirzynski) Martinus Nijhoff, Dordrecht (in press); Vichniac, G. Y., Physica **10D**, 96 (1984); Wolfram, S., Phys. Rev. Lett. **54**, 735 (1985); Yates, F. E., Am. J. Physiol. **238**, R277 (1980); Marcer, P. J., The Church-Turing Hypothesis, Artificial Intelligence and Cybernetics, presented at International Cybernetics Congress, Namur, Aug. 1986.
36. Keyes, R. W. and Landauer, R., IBM J. Res. Dev. **14**, 152 (1970).
37. Kirkpatrick, S. and Toulouse, G., J. Physique **46**, 1277 (1985).
38. Ackley, D. H., Hinton, G. E. and Sejnowski, T. J., Cognitive Science **9**, 147 (1985); Kienker, P. K., Sejnowski, T. J., Hinton, G. E. and Schumacher, L. E., Separating figure from ground with a parallel network, Perception (in press); Sejnowski, T. J., Kienker, P. K. and Hinton, G. E., Learning symmetry groups with hidden units: Beyond the perceptron, Physica D (in press).
39. Landauer, R., Helv. Phys. Acta **56**, 847 (1983).
40. Anderson, P. W., Proc. Nat. Acad. Sci. **80**, 3386 (1983); Anderson, P. W. and Stein, D. L., in Self-Organizing Systems: The Emergence of Order (Edited by F. E. Yates, D. O. Walter and G. B. Yates) Plenum, New York (in press); Ebeling, in Strukturbildung Bei Irreversiblen Prozёssen, p. 168, Teubner, Leipzig (1976); see also Ebeling, W. and Feistel, R., Physik der Selbstorganisation und Evolution, Akademie-Verlag, Berlin (1982); Kirkpatrick, M., Am. Nat. **119**, 833 (1982); Kuhn, H. and Kuhn, C., Origins of Life **9**, 137 (1978); Küppers, B.-O., in Der Informationsbegriff in Technik und Wissenschaft (Edited by O. G. Folberth and C. Hackl), p. 181, Oldenbourg, Munich (1986); Lande, R., Proc. Natl. Acad. Sci. **82**, 7641 (1985); Levinton, J., Science **231**, 1490 (1986); Lewin, R., Science **231**, 672 (1986); Newman, C. M., Cohen, J. E. and Kipnis, C., Nature **315**, 399 (1985); Schuster, P., Physica Scripta, this issue; Wright, S., in Evolution and the Genetics of Populations, Vol. 3, p. 443, Univ. Chicago Press (1977).
41. Remarks adapted from Landauer, R., Am. J. Physiol. **241**, R107

(1981).

42. Landauer, R., J. Appl. Phys. **33**, 2209 (1962).
43. Stratonovich, R. L., Topics in the Theory of Random Noise, Gordon and Breach, New York, Vol. 1 (1963), Vol. II (1967).
44. Landauer, R., J. Stat. Phys. **13**, 1 (1975).
45. Landauer, R., Phys. Rev. **A12**, 636 (1975).
46. Landauer, R., in Self-Organizing Systems: The Emergence of Order (Edited by F. E. Yates, D. O. Walter and G. B. Yates), Plenum, N. Y.

(in press).

47. Chaitin, G. J., IBM J. Res. Dev. **21**, 350 (1977).
48. Wright, R., The Sciences **25**, 10, No. 2 (1985). Bennett, C. H., Found. Phys. **16**, 585 (1986).
49. Kuhn, H. and Waser, J., in Biophysics (Edited by W. Hoppe, W. Lohmann, H. Markl and H. Ziegler), p. 830, Springer, Heidelberg (1983).

Keeping the Entropy of Measurement: Szilard Revisited

Elihu Lubkin[1]

Received January 13, 1987

What happens to von Neumann's entropy of measurement after we get the outcome? It becomes entropy of erasure. This is cribbed from Szilard (1929). Also, two errors in that celebrated paper are corrected.

1. INTRODUCTION

The Second Law of Thermodynamics forbids a net gain of information. Yet a measurement "provides information." Measurement itself thus becomes paradoxical, until one reflects that the gain in information about the system of interest might be offset by a gain in entropy of some "garbage can" gc. Indeed, it *must* be so offset to save the bookkeeping of the Second Law. This apparent and paradoxical gain in information attendant upon observation, presumably due to neglect of some dissipant gc, has long prompted aberrant speculation that intelligent beings and even life in general somehow indeed violate the Second Law, an erroneous view I cite only for perspective. For some time I have fallen prey to a version of this paradox, developed in the context of standard quantum theory of measurement as delineated by von Neumann (1955), a trap I have recently been able to escape with the help of Szilard (1929), the celebrated paper in which the related paradox of Maxwell's demon is broken. Here I describe a precise formulation, then resolution of my paradox of information through measurement.

2. REVIEW OF VON NEUMANN

Von Neumann finds *no* paradoxical loss of entropy through measurement, but rather a *gain* of entropy quite in conformity with the Second

[1]Department of Physics, University of Wisconsin-Milwaukee, Milwaukee, Wisconsin 53201.

Law. I go over this well-known ground to explore the paradox of the *missing* paradox!

Indeed, if we start with a pure state vector $|x\rangle = \sum a_i |e_i\rangle$ resolved on the orthonormal basis of states $|e_i\rangle$ separated by distinct outcomes of the measurement, then the $p_i = |a_i|^2$ are the probabilities of the various outcomes, or, in an early way of saying it, the probabilities of the different possible "quantum jumps." Interaction with the measuring device makes the system "jump" with probabilities p_i, which introduce nonnegative entropy

$$\sum p_i \ln \frac{1}{p_i} \equiv \left\langle \ln \frac{1}{p} \right\rangle \equiv vN \tag{1}$$

(in Boltzmen or e-folds). Perhaps I should attribute this notion of production of entropy to Dirac (1938–39), who noted that the quantum jumps not only introduce entropy, but might account for *all* production of entropy, a thesis with ancient roots (Lucretius ∼55 B.C.; see Latham, 1951, p. 66) that I also long ago found support for in a calculation (Lubkin, 1978).

Von Neumann makes this already familiar production of entropy vN unambiguous by dealing with very concrete ensembles. Thus, the pure state $|x\rangle$ before the measurement is presented as some large number N of copies of an $|x\rangle$-prepared system. After measurement, $p_i N$ estimates the number of copies cast into state $|e_i\rangle$, hence the originally pure ensemble $|x\rangle\langle x| = P$ gets replaced by the mixture $\sum |e_i\rangle p_i \langle e_i| = Y$. The entropy per copy of P is 0, the entropy per copy of Y is quite unambiguously the vN attributable to measurement, or to "quantum jumps."

The clarity of this mixing of the multicopy ensemble unfortunately reaches its resulting increase vN of entropy by so well bypassing the phenomenon of *gain* of information through measurement that we simply do not learn enough about our paradox from it. Of course, more generally, the original ensemble P need not be pure, and the mutually orthogonal outcome spaces E_i [of a sharp test (Lubkin, 1979b), definition on p. 550; also Lubkin (1974)] need not be one-dimensional, yet the final ensemble $Y = \sum_i E_i P E_i$ if distinct from P is of greater entropy than P, which happens if any E_i fails to commute with P, this greater generality being, however, equally useless to us in regard to our paradox.

3. THE PARADOX

So, to formulate the paradox, as it were to look for trouble, I focus attention as before upon the *individual* trial, rather than on the statistical behavior of the very many trials dealt with by von Neumann. We still have the probabilities $p_i = |a_i|^2$ (in the case of initial pure state x) as predictions of the likelihoods of our single outcome for our individual trial. Indeed, after the trial is over, *but before we look* at the outcome, the original state matrix P is replaced by the new state matrix Y. Yet when we do learn the outcome, Y is in turn replaced by $E_i Y E_i$ (unnormalized), with i the index of the single observed outcome, or more simply (and normalized) by E_i itself if E_i is one-dimensional (dimension of its image space). The threefold sequence

$$P \to Y \to E_i \tag{2}$$

(to keep to the simple one-dimensional case, which illustrates the point nicely), with recognition of a state Y after the essential interaction of measurement but before transition of the answer "i" to the observer, emphasizes the increase in entropy in the first step $P \to Y$, so that we may be properly shocked at the loss of this entropy in the second step, $Y \to E_i$. Also, the $P \to Y$ increase in entropy is of course precisely the $\langle \ln (1/p) \rangle$ entropy of measurement vN of von Neumann, which we bet is the "right answer." We are now in the uncomfortable position of betting on a "right answer" for an entropy of measurement provided that we do not look at the outcome, yet getting zero if we do look, as if a proper measurement does not involve looking at the result, which is surely an unhappy state of affairs!

4. DEBATE ON THE SINGLE TRIAL

Some may fault the notion of probability without an ensemble as the root of my trouble; to relate the probabilities p_i to experience, we must run many trials, not one, and so the probabilities, to be physically meaningful, *must* refer only to the very many trials. Yet let us run our N trials one by one. If *each* time we generate no entropy, then we will not have generated any entropy in the *string* of N trials, either. And the per-trial "entropy" vN of the "N-ensemble" of N trials in my above version of von Neumann appears only in describing the *nonuniformity* of the ensemble. Our knowledge of each outcome after it happens is replaced by the randomness of entropy in the amount vN only if the state we produce for a next experiment is *randomly* chosen from that ensemble. To repeat, the generation of entropy by measurement, if nil in the particular trial, is nil in the N trials together, and entropy of the ensemble for a subsequent test is produced only by the possible policy of disregarding the separation into cases provided by the particular outcomes, and using the whole ensemble in a future experiment *with no regard for the known sorting into cases of the earlier individual outcomes*.

Is there, then, no true entropy of measurement, but just entropy from a refusal to accept the sorting provided? No, there must be more to it than that, because of the $P \to Y \to E_i$ paradox; Y, the situation before we look, but after the measurement has taken place, already possesses entropy of measurement vN, which cannot be lost in the $Y \to E_i$ phase; *therefore, there must be a garbage can gc.*

5. BOHREAN DOUBTS

Or is the situation too vague? Increase of entropy is, after all, not universal. Define your system of interest to shrink to nothing, then its entropy of course goes to zero. If, as another but less trivial case, the system is so well isolated as to obey a law of unitary motion, its entropy remains constant, and frustratingly for Boltzmann, will not increase. The Second Law is for situations in which the system is imperfectly isolated, so that it tends to develop new correlations with the outside, yet where somehow the gross content of the system remains fixed, on the average, so that shrinking to nothing, for example, is forbidden. Then the density matrix of the system of interest, in having the increasing external correlations lopped off through Landau tracing over externalities (Lubkin 1978), becomes increasingly mixed. Another reason that having "the system" perfectly isolated is suspicious is that specification of a precise value of some observable forces a detailed correlation of the system with the outside in regard to complementary observables (e.g., Lubkin, 1979b, p. 537). Perhaps these various philosophical demands attending definition of the type of "system" that should indeed obey the Second Law engender an incompatibility with the "systems" in a paradigm of measurement; perhaps "systems" for clear Second-Law bookkeeping and "systems" in measurement are complementary. But I feel that these Bohrean misgivings anent the clarity of my paradox are mooted by finding gc with the help of Szilard's example. More strongly, it *must* be that the Second Law and measurement *go together*, because they both refer to the empiricism of everyday life, the particularization of definite outcomes in everyday measurement serving as the injector of randomness that drives the Second Law, as noted already by Lucretius and Dirac.

6. AMPLITUDES IN SUPPORT OF THE SINGLE TRIAL

Having drawn attention to the philosophical objection to probabilities for a single trial, I should make it clear why I nevertheless regard the $P \to Y$ phase to be meaningful for a single trial, again for the clear pure case $P = |x\rangle\langle x|$. We may regard state x times the equipment's original state y_0 to evolve, $\sum a_i |e_i\rangle \otimes |y_0\rangle \to \sum a_i |e_i\rangle \otimes |y_i\rangle$, to a new *pure* state, with density matrix

$$\bar{Y} = \sum_{ij} a_i a_j^* |e_i\rangle \otimes |y_i\rangle\langle e_j| \otimes \langle y_j|$$

with $Y = \sum_i |a_i|^2 |e_i\rangle\langle e_i|$ obtained from $\bar{Y}$ by the Landau tracing-out of the equipment. That is, the various *amplitudes* for different "outcomes" are in principle capable of subsequent interference, and our option to disregard this by confining attention to the x-system subsequently is what reduces the amplitudes to probabilities and engenders entropy. So the branching into distinct channels is there, physically, in the Schrödinger equation, which gives us $\bar{Y}$, even before the neglect or approximation that limits our attention to Y. And this Y already formally has entropy $vN = \mathrm{Tr}\, Y \ln(1/Y)$, even though operator Y acts on the Hilbert space appropriate to *one* trial, *not* on a tensor product of N copies of that Hilbert space. The fact that entropy vN times N is most easily *displayed* by the scatter in an N-copy ensemble *associated* to Y should not be used to obscure the fact that the entropy vN times 1 is already there without any such display. Of course, to emphasize the already physical qualities of this amplitudinous branching has become known as the "many-worlds" point of view; the reader will follow better if I say that for me, this is the *right* view.

7. PLURAL REALITIES

Indeed for clarity I restate the paradox in grossly multiworldly language.

First Multiworldly Statement: $vN = \sum p_i \ln(1/p_i)$ explicitly contemplates the multiplicity of branches issuing from a node of measurement, hence is obviously appropriate for a contemplator of that multiplicity, say, for an early observer who has not yet read the outcome, or for an outer observer or friend outside the laboratory. But in the reality relative to an inner or late observer who *has* read the outcome, the other branches are excluded, and the entropy expression vN in seeming to yet take those other branches seriously seems no longer appropriate.

Preliminary Resolution. Now, the amount of entropy vN or more must nevertheless yet be there, even in the bookkeeping of an inner observer, because the reality of experienece is the steady progress "inward" of an observer, through a series of particularized outcomes, and it is to this common experience or *stream* of consciousness that the Second Law and indeed the notion of time applies, else the Second Law could not have been found out in the 19th century. So while vN for the *outer* or early observer is simply a feature of multitudinous branching, there must also be a vN *inner* to each branch harbored in a gc in each branch.

Second Multiworldly Statement. Branching realities might be feared inconsistent with laws framed in a philosophy of one unique reality, hence inconsistent with all the traditional "*First*" laws of conservation, and inconsistent, too, with the Second Law. Since "each branch has all the baryons" (Lubkin, 1979a, p. 174), laws of conservation are fine—of course such laws are also tied to symmetry, and enough symmetries will remain. The present investigation may be taken to deal with the scare that the *Second* Law might fail.

Resolution Again. But it must not fail. When the probabilities are swept away by a specific outcome, their entropy must yet be swept into a gc, not actually annulled. This is the usual caution, in an entropic embarrassment, that one may not have been sufficiently careful in defining the problem's thermodynamically relevant "universe."

8. THE ANSWER, gc

Where, then, is the garbage can? Szilard (1929) finds it for me: gc is the damper on the register that receives the outcome, the damper that allows that register to get rid of its former configuration. I call this dissipation *entropy of erasure* (er), and argue that $er \geq vN$.

Lemma. Let the k-labeled orthogonal states of the register reg occur with Boltzmann's probabilities

$$q_k \propto \exp(-\varepsilon_k/T_0) \tag{3}$$

in the mixed state of reg at temperature T_0 that is to correspond to "erasure"; note that by choosing the energies ε_k of the levels, one can adjust the q_k at will. Outcome k of a measurement is assumed to set reg instead to pure energy level k. Then, if the probability of this outcome is p_k, the entropy of erasure is given by the "cross entropy" expression

$$er = -\sum p_k \ln q_k \tag{4}$$

Proof. Suppose that, due to the outcome having been k, the reg starts at pure state E_k before erasure to T_0; to calculate the entropy of that erasure "er_k" from such a start: er_k is a sum of two terms.

$$er_k = \Delta S_{reg} + \Delta S_{res} \tag{5}$$

The part ΔS_{reg} is S_{reg} at T_0 minus S_{reg} at E_k. As the latter is pure, its entropy S_{reg} is 0, whereas S_{reg} at $T_0 = -\sum q_j \ln q_j$. So also $\Delta S_{reg} = -\sum q_j \ln q_j$. The other term ΔS_{res} is the heat gained by the T_0 reservoir used for the quenching, divided by T_0. If the thermodynamic internal energy of reg after quenching is U_0, then the heat gained by reg is $U_0 - \varepsilon_k$, whence the heat gained by res is $-(U_0 - \varepsilon_k)$; so

$$er_k = -\sum q_j \ln q_j - (U_0 - \varepsilon_k)/T_0 \tag{6}$$

is the result for the entropy er_k of erasure from the definite outcome k. Of course,

$$U_0 = \sum q_j \varepsilon_j \tag{7}$$

Finally, the expected value er for the entropy of erasure if reg starts from an unknown setting k but with probability p_k is

$$er \equiv \sum p_k \cdot er_k \tag{8}$$

This convex combination alters (6) only in replacing ε_k by $\sum p_k \varepsilon_k$, giving

$$er = -\sum q_j \ln q_j + \sum (p_j - q_j)\varepsilon_j / T_0 \tag{9}$$

Let

$$z \equiv \sum \exp(-\varepsilon_k / T_0) \tag{10}$$

Then $\varepsilon_k / T_0 = -\ln q_k - \ln z$ eliminates the ε's, to give

$$er = -\sum q_j \ln q_j + \sum (p_j - q_j)(-\ln q_j - \ln z) \tag{11}$$

which indeed simplifies to $-\sum p_j \ln q_j$, hence to (4). ∎

Theorem:

$$er \geq vN \tag{12}$$

Proof. It is to be shown that $-\sum p_k \ln q_k \geq -\sum p_k \ln p_k$, that is, that $-\sum p_k \ln q_k$ considered as a function of the arbitrarily assignable quenching probabilities q_k for fixed values of the experiment's own probabilities p_k is minimum at $q_k = p_k$. This is immediately verified, using a Lagrangian multiplier λ for the constraint $\sum q_k = 1$. Thus, $d(-\sum p_k \ln q_k) = \lambda d \sum q_k$, $-\sum p_k \, dq_k / q_k = \lambda \sum dq_k$, $-p_k / q_k = \lambda$, hence $q_k \propto p_k$, hence $q_k = p_k$ since both p's and q's must sum to 1. It is also easy to check that this stationary point is indeed a minimum, e.g., $-\sum p_k \ln q_k \to +\infty$ at the $q_k = 0$ boundaries. ∎

Varying instead on the p's for fixed q's produces no interesting result.

Significance of the Theorem. The reservoir that quenches reg, thereby erasing its old contents, indeed is an adquate gc for upholding the Second Law, in that quenching the outcome of a former trial of the same experiment in that gc produces enough entropy to compensate for the loss of entropy vN upon learning the outcome of a new trial. Quenching indeed produces *more* than enough entropy, unless the quenched or erased mixed state of reg is selected to have the same probabilities as the experiment's own. In this way each trial of a long sequence needed to establish empirical probabilities will indeed contribute in the mean at least its proper share vN to increase the entropy of the universe, and will do that by dissipation in the gc cribbed from Szilard.

9. CONTEMPLATION OF SZILARD (1929), WITH MINOR CORRECTIONS

Erasure in Szilard. I first explain wherein lies my debt to Szilard (1929). Szilard is exorcising the Maxwell's demon. This demon is an entity "who" by observing molecules can operate an engine in a way that reduces the entropy of the universe, or equivalently, extracts work from a single heat reservoir, in violation of Kelvin's principle. Szilard argues convincingly that the essence of the demon is the storage of information about one dynamical variable x in another one y, and concentrates on cases where the set of possible values for y has two elements: in modern jargon, y is embodied in a one-bit register. Szilard gives examples to show that if such writing of x on y could be done without producing entropy, then the demon would work, and the Second Law would fail, but that if each such writing somehow entails the production of one bit of entropy, the demon fails. (In 1929, "amount $k_B \ln 2$ of entropy, where k_B is Boltzmann's constant.") He concludes abstractly from the Second Law that such writing must produce the required bit of entropy to compensate the deficit, but he is not satisfied with that, and he accordingly builds a model of a one-bit register, to see precisely where entropy gets produced. He is so careful not to produce entropy unnecessarily that he frighteningly manages to write demonically on his register *without* producing entropy, if reg is in a known state before writing. This disaster is avoided when he does find the requisite production of entropy upon *erasing* back to a known state, for the next cycle. His known state is equilibrium at some temperature T_0; the erasure is effected by plunging reg into a reservoir at T_0. (Szilard does not use the word "erase," but that is the idea.) Since I also find my gc through entropy of erasure, I have now explained my debt to Szilard; I note that for a two-state register er $= -p_1 \ln q_1 - p_2 \ln q_2 \leq \ln 2$ and is $\ln 2$, one bit, only when $p_1 = p_2 = q_1 = q_2$, and that the more general expression appears also in Szilard; I have simplified for readability.

I will now attempt to discharge my debts to Szilard and to the patient reader by correcting some mistakes; the excitement of discovery carried the brilliant author past some fine points.

Degeneracy g. Szilard uses a two-level quantum system or atom for his register. To record one answer "0," the atom is to be cooled to its ground state, which is unobjectionable; cool (near to) absolute zero, $1/T \to +\infty$. To record the other answer "1," the atom should be heated to its *nondegenerate* excited state. The easy way to do that is to heat to $1/T \to -\infty$, or $T \to 0^-$, the "other absolute zero" of negative temperature, but Szilard refuses to anticipate the discovery (Purcell and Pound, 1951) of negative temperature. He instead makes his excited state *highly degenerate*, giving it a multiplicity

$g \gg 1$. Then a large, positive temperature, $1/T \approx 0$, which is really only halfway to $-\infty$, seems to work, as the odds of occupation of the upper level are g times the odds for the lower. Unfortunately, the hot mixed state has large entropy $\ln(g+1)$, and will produce entropy more than the one bit $\ln 2$ on being plunged into the resetting reservoir at T_0. (Or if T_0 is near ∞, resetting the *cold* state will produce excessive entropy.) As Szilard wishes to show that it is possible to *just* compensate the deficit of entropy, such excessive production of entropy would contradict his point about that. To see how the g-foldness of the upper level actually leads to the trouble of excessive heat/temperature upon cooling, note that although the energy ("heat") transferred is independent of g, the T_0 denominator does involve g: In the easy case, $q_k = p_k = 1/2$, and in particular is $1/2$ for the ground state, we have $e^0 = 1 = g e^{-\varepsilon/T_0}$, where ε is the step between levels, hence $T_0 = \varepsilon/\ln g$ is indeed depressed by the largeness of g, and entropy $\sim \varepsilon/T_0$ is enhanced and excessive.

If one does not like my glib repair with negative temperature, one may instead write upon a nondegenerate upper level as follows: First cool to the lower level. Then apply a causal Hamiltonian motion to "rotate" that to the upper level.

I of course wish to extend optimal management of a two-level reg to an n-level reg. For writing, I must be able to set reg to one of these n levels, not only to the ground state (by cooling to 0^+) or to the top state (by heating to 0^-). There are enough *other* absolute zeros available (Lubkin, 1984) through chemical potentials to indeed select any level, approximately, by direct Gibbsian equilibrium. Here the alternative method of causal Hamiltonian motions subsequent to cooling to the ground state is much plainer.

Bits and Pieces. Szilard tries so hard to avoid unnecessary production of entropy that he unwittingly lets his crucial bit slip by even in erasure, and so seemingly *creates* a demon: I erase by plunging reg directly into a T_0-bath, which may seem a gratuitous crudeness, to be replaced by a more quasistatic scheme . . . but which would, if possible, reinstate the demon! Szilard at first tries to avoid this seeming crudeness. His equipment is a cold T_A-bath, a hot T_B-bath, the erasing T_0-bath, body K that is the register, but also extra pieces A and B, and a large number of other reservoirs for implementing quasistatic non-entropy-producing processes. After having been written on, K is either at T_A, signifying one of the two y values, or at T_B, signifiying the other. If it were generally known which of these, T_A or T_B, was K's temperature, then K could indeed be reset to T_0 quasistatistically, hence without producing entropy. Szilard wishes to convince us that when it is, however, *not* known which of T_A, T_B is K's temperature, *then* erasure does entail the production of entropy demanded by the Second

Law: *indeed this is his essential and correct contribution.* Unfortunately, he has used his pieces *A* and *B* "too well." One of *A*, *B* is in contact with *K*. Piece *A* is at T_A, *B* is at T_B, and *K* is at the temperature of the piece touching it, but we do not know which that is. Yet in order to bring *K* to T_0 *without* producing entropy, we need only to move quasistatically *both A and B* to T_0 separately! Then *K* will go to T_0 automatically and gradually, by conduction of heat through whichever piece it touches.

Having thus seemingly exploded Szilard's central point, I must somehow patch it up: It seems to me that the shifting of contact of *K*, sometimes with piece *A* but sometimes *B*, *itself* requires a lever with two settings, and it is exclusion of this lever's budget of entropy from the discussion that allows a bit to escape scrutiny. Indeed, Szilard's *first* contraption instructs me about levers. It is a cylinder of volume $V_1 + V_2$ containing one ideal-gas molecule, the volume being then split into V_1, V_2 by slipping in a piston sideways. Then if the molecule is in V_1, its pressure will force the piston in one direction; if the molecule is in V_2, however, the force will be oppositely directed. *A lever* is provided, to in either case cause the force to *raise* a weight, thus seemingly achieving a demonic engine—if we forget to bookkeep entropy for the lever, which Szilard does not let us do in this case.

But adding *detailed* consideration of a lever, except to fend off Szilard's unwitting *A-B-K* demon, is *not* instructive. The purpose of Szilard's body *K* is to see the dissipation happen: If that dissipation instead happens elsewhere, in some extra lever, then that will involve another body *K'*, and we will have made no progress at all! So I got rid of pieces *A* and *B*, and let *K* (or reg) itself touch the dissipant entity. Indeed Szilard's *mathematics* pays no attention to his pieces *A* and *B*. The strategy is to refuse to complicate with extra registers, and so to show the fallacy of simple demons. Then the Second Law itself, having survived Maxwell's assault, gains our confidence, and so causes us to lose interest in building other demons.

10. CLASSICAL DEMONS AND ORTHOGONALITY IN HILBERT SPACE

Is it possible to revive the paradoxical disappearance of entropy by changing the construction of reg to make er smaller? No; to have unambiguous separation of cases, the different outcomes must write reg into mutually *orthogonal* states, which already fixes the model. It would be silly to go on for my original problem, the statement of which stems from a quantum mechanical context. But the problem of Maxwell's demon antedates quantum mechanics, which may make us wonder whether Szilard's solution is as essentially quantal as it seems to be, from his use of a register with two energy levels. Indeed, if classical logic is allowed (Birkhoff and von Neumann, 1936; Jauch, 1968; Finkelstein *et al.*, 1962), er can be made arbitrarily small, thus breaking Szilard's solution: Just let the several pure recording states of reg all make arbitrarily *small* angles in Hilbert space with one common pure state vector y_0, and erase to y_0. E.g., have Szilard's two settings of y be two linear polarizations of a photon, but separated by only a small angle. If we think about this classically, the electric vector will have slightly distinct directions, and that is classically enough to cause unambiguously distinct consequences. The demon does work classically. I leave conversion of my blend of Hilbert space with "classical logic" into a thoroughly engineered classically mechanical demon as an "exercise"!

From the Second Law to Wigner's Principle. Contrapositively, we may choose to assume the Second Law, which demands that er $\geq vN$, and so reach a denial of the usefulness of a set of nonorthogonal states as a register. This, then, is a *thermodynamic* foundation for Wigner's familiar principle (Wigner, 1952) that if a measurement unambiguously separates states in always leading to distinct settings of some dial, those states must not only be distinct, they must be orthogonal. Of course, Wigner's argument from unitarity of the overall process in time is undoubtedly clearer . . . unless you set out to *build* time from observation.

11. NOT LANDAU TRACING?

The entropy of any single mixed state Y may be imagined found from Landau tracing of an encompassing pure state: Diagonalize $Y = \sum p_i |x_i\rangle\langle x_i|$, and use $\psi = \sum p_i^{1/2} x_i \otimes y_i$ for an encompassing pure state's vector, where the y_i are orthonormal and orthogonal to all the x's. Is the entropy of erasure er also of this character?

It has *not* been so computed: The computations of separate er_k were done first, *then* convexly combined to er $= \sum p_k \cdot er_k$. The nonlinearity of $x \to -x \ln x$ in Boltzmann's definition of entropy guarantees that if the convex combination were done first, the result would be wrong. In particular, for the optimum case $q_k = p_k$, one would "get" *no* production of entropy upon quenching to T_0 were the wrong order used. The computation of er did not investigate one single density matrix Y; indeed, naively replacing the separate E_k by the single density matrix $Y = \sum p_k E_k$ just gave a wrong answer.

Yet there *is* in a sense an "encompassing" pure state ψ: the wave function of the system and reg, in interaction together. Nevertheless, the analysis of details within ψ was *not* done by selecting some factor Hilbert space to be Landau-traced out. The physical analogue of such Landau-ignoring of a factor space is subdividing a system into a system of interest and a complementary part to be ignored. This Landau philosophy may, however, not be general, in that *reality* is not subdivided. In the calculation of er, we instead used a *different* simple reality for each outcome k, namely reg set at E_k, we T_0-quenched *that*, and then convexly combined the produced entropies er_k on the excuse of calculating a mean entropy over a long run: a time average rather than an ensemble average. This is also what Szilard does. Hence, since 1929 we have had a calculation of entropy production outside the scope of Landau tracing, and based upon relative reality, albeit disguised as an old-fashioned averaging over time.

It should be noted that Landau tracing does implicitly play its part here: If, in contemplating any single $E_k \rightarrow T_0$ quench, we imagine following the detailed unitary motion of reg in interaction with a T_0-reservoir, then no entropy will be produced until we Landau-neglect that reservoir; and that will get you er_k. What I suspect may *not* be attainable by Landau tracing is a unified derivation of er, as distinct from er_k.

A related trouble—for reviving my paradox, not Maxwell's—is the thought that you need never erase if you have enough "clean paper" to write on. My answer to this is that the entropic debt is then paid in advance, when you manufacture all that clean paper. It is roughly if not precisely analogous to "getting work from heat without a cold reservoir" by letting cylinders of ideal gas expand without restoring their original condition.

ACKNOWLEDGMENTS

Thanks to Leonard Parker for pointing out the old-fashioned nature of the time-averaging, and the possible gap separating this from Landau tracing; to Thelma Lubkin for the objection of "clean paper"; to Atsushi Higuchi for the thought of a possibly *thoroughly* classical demon; and to Ming-Lap Chow for pressing me to look at Wheeler and Zurek (1983).

REFERENCES

Birkhoff, G., and von Neumann, J. (1936). *Annals of Mathematics*, **37**, 823.
Dirac, P. A. M. (1938-39). *Proceedings of the Royal Society of Edinburgh*, **59**, 2, 122.
Finkelstein, D., Jauch, J. M., Schiminovich, S., and Speiser, D. (1962). *Journal of Mathematical Physics*, **3**, 207.
Jauch, J. M. (1968). *Foundations of Quantum Mechanics*. Addison-Wesley, Reading, Massachusetts.
Latham, R. E. (1951). *On the Nature of the Universe, A translation of Lucretius* (~ 55 B.C.), Penguin Books, Baltimore, Maryland.
Lubkin, E. (1974). *Journal of Mathematical Physics*, **15**, 663.
Lubkin, E. (1978). *Journal of Mathematical Physics*, **19**, 1028.
Lubkin, E. (1979a). *International Journal of Theoretical Physics*, **18**, 165-177.
Lubkin, E. (1979b). *International Journal of Theoretical Physics*, **18**, 519-600.

Lubkin, E. (1984). Lie algebras of first laws of thermodynamics for physics without time,
    XIIIth International Colloquium on Group Theoretical Methods in Physics, W. W. Zachary,
    ed., pp. 275–278, World Scientific, Singapore.

Purcell, E. M., and Pound, R. V. (1951). *Physical Review*, **81**, 279–280.

Szilard, L. (1929). *Zeitschrift für Physik*, **53**, 840–56 [Translation in Wheeler and Zurek (1983).]

Von Neumann, J. (1955). *Mathematical Foundations of Quantum Mechanics*, Princeton Univer-
    sity Press, Princeton, New Jersey [Reprinted in Wheeler and Zurek (1983).]

Wheeler, J. A., and Zurek, W. H. eds. (1983). *Quantum Theory and Measurement*, Princeton
    University Press, Princeton, New Jersey.

Wigner, E. P. (1952). *Zeitschrift für Physik*, **133**, 101.

Notes on the history of reversible computation

by Charles H. Bennett

We review the history of the thermodynamics of information processing, beginning with the paradox of Maxwell's demon; continuing through the efforts of Szilard, Brillouin, and others to demonstrate a thermodynamic cost of information acquisition; the discovery by Landauer of the thermodynamic cost of information destruction; the development of the theory of and classical models for reversible computation; and ending with a brief survey of recent work on quantum reversible computation.

Concern with the thermodynamic limits of computation was preceded historically by the paradox of Maxwell's demon [1] and the realization that one bit of information is somehow equivalent to $k \ln 2$ units of entropy, or about 2.3×10^{-24} cal/Kelvin. This equivalence was implicit in the work of Szilard [2] and became explicit in Shannon's use [3] of the term "entropy" and the formula

$$H = -\sum_i P_i \log P_i$$

to describe the self-information of a message source.

The history of this subject is noteworthy because it offers an example of how ideas that are strikingly successful in one

area of science (in this case the uncertainty principle and the theory of black-body radiation) can stimulate unconscious false analogies, and so impede progress in other areas of science (thermodynamics of measurement and computation).

In the nineteenth century, despite the vision of Babbage, computation was thought of as a mental process, not a mechanical one. Accordingly, the thermodynamics of computation, if anyone had stopped to wonder about it, would probably have seemed no more urgent as a topic of scientific inquiry than, say, the thermodynamics of love. However, the need to think seriously about the thermodynamics of perceptual and mental processes was thrust upon science by the famous paradox of "Maxwell's demon," described as follows by its inventor, in a passage of admirable clarity and foresight [1]:

"One of the best established facts in thermodynamics is that it is impossible in a system enclosed in an envelope which permits neither change of volume nor passage of heat, and in which both the temperature and the pressure are everywhere the same, to produce any inequality of temperature or pressure without the expenditure of work. This is the second law of thermodynamics, and it is undoubtedly true as long as we can deal with bodies only in mass, and have no power of perceiving or handling the separate molecules of which they are made up. But if we conceive a being whose faculties are so sharpened that he can follow every molecule in its course, such a being, whose attributes are still as essentially finite as our own, would be able to do what is at present impossible to us. For we have seen that the molecules in a vessel full of air at uniform temperature are moving with velocities by no means uniform, though the mean velocity of any great number of them, arbitrarily selected, is almost exactly uniform. Now let us suppose that such a vessel is divided into two portions, A and B, by a division in which there is a small hole, and that a being, who can see the individual molecules, opens and closes this hole, so as to allow only the swifter molecules to pass from A to B, and only the slower ones to pass from B to A. He will thus, without expenditure of work, raise the temperature of B and lower that of A, in contradiction to the second law of thermodynamics.

"This is only one of the instances in which conclusions we have drawn from our experience of bodies consisting of an immense number of molecules may be found not to be applicable to the more delicate observations and experiments which we may suppose made by one who can perceive and handle the individual molecules which we deal with only in large masses.

"In dealing with masses of matter, while we do not perceive the individual molecules, we are compelled to adopt what I have described as the statistical method of calculation, and to abandon the strict dynamical method, in which we follow every motion by the calculus.

"It would be interesting to enquire how far those ideas about the nature and methods of science which have been derived from examples of scientific investigation in which the dynamical method is followed are applicable to our actual knowledge of concrete things, which, as we have seen, is of an essentially statistical nature, because no one has yet discovered any practical method of tracing the path of a molecule, or of identifying it at different times.

"I do not think, however, that the perfect identity which we observe between different portions of the same kind of matter can be explained on the statistical principle of the stability of averages of large numbers of quantities each of which may differ from the mean. For if of the molecules of some substance such as hydrogen, some were of sensibly greater mass than others, we have the means of producing a separation between molecules of different masses, and in this way we should be able to produce two kinds of hydrogen, one of which would be somewhat denser than the other. As this cannot be done, we must admit that the equality which we assert to exist between the molecules of hydrogen applies to each individual molecule, and not merely to the average of groups of millions of molecules."

Maxwell offered no definitive refutation of the demon, beyond saying that we lack its ability to see and handle individual molecules. In subsequent years Smoluchowski [4] partly solved the problem by pointing out that a simple automatic apparatus, such as a trap door, would be prevented by its own Brownian motion from functioning as an effective demon. He also remarked [5],

"As far as we know today, there is no automatic, permanently effective perpetual motion machine, in spite of molecular fluctuations, but such a device might, perhaps, function regularly if it were appropriately operated by intelligent beings. . . ."

This apparent ability of intelligent beings to violate the second law called into question the accepted belief that such beings obey the same laws as other material systems. Szilard, in his famous paper [2], "On the Decrease of Entropy in a Thermodynamic System by the Intervention of Intelligent Beings," attempted to escape from this predicament by arguing that the act of measurement, by which the demon determines the molecule's speed (or, in Szilard's version of the apparatus, determines which side of the partition it is on) is necessarily accompanied by an entropy increase sufficient to compensate the entropy decrease obtained later by exploiting the result of the measurement. Szilard was somewhat vague about the nature and location of this entropy increase, but a widely held interpretation of the situation, ever since his paper appeared, has been that measurement is an inevitably irreversible process, attended by an increase of entropy in the universe as a whole by at least $k \ln 2$ per bit of information acquired by the measurement. Later we shall see this is not quite correct: The measurement itself can be performed reversibly, but an unavoidable entropy increase, which prevents the demon from violating the second law, occurs when the demon erases the result of one measurement to make room for the next. The existence of an irreducible thermodynamic cost for information destruction (as opposed to information acquisition) was only clearly recognized three decades later by Landauer [6], and another two decades elapsed before Landauer's insight was applied to explain the demon without invoking any thermodynamic cost of measurement [7–9].

Ironically, Szilard came quite close to understanding the thermodynamic cost of information destruction. At the end of his paper, where he followed one version of his demon apparatus through a complete cycle of operation, he found that resetting the demon in preparation for the next measurement generated $k \ln 2$ of entropy. Unfortunately, he did not pursue this finding to the point of recognizing that information destruction is always thermodynamically costly, and that therefore no thermodynamic cost need be postulated for information acquisition.

Szilard's partial insight was lost as subsequent workers neglected resetting, and instead attempted to prove in detail the irreversibility of various measurement processes, particularly those in which the demon observes the molecule with light. The emphasis on measurement and neglect of resetting probably represented unconscious biases from everyday experience, where information is thought of as valuable or at worst neutral, and from quantum mechanics, which strikingly demonstrated the nontriviality of the measurement process. The influence of quantum mechanics, particularly the quantum theory of black-body radiation, can be seen in a discussion of Maxwell's demon in Brillouin's influential 1956 book *Science and Information Theory* [10]:

"The essential question is . . . *Is it actually possible for the demon to see the individual atoms?* . . . The demon is in an enclosure at equilibrium at constant temperature, where the radiation must be black body radiation, and it is impossible to see anything in the interior of a black body. . . . The demon would see thermal radiation and its fluctuations, but he would never see the molecules.

"It is not surprising that Maxwell did not think of including radiation in the system in equilibrium at temperature *T*. Black body radiation was hardly known in 1871, and it was thirty years before the thermodynamics of radiation was clearly understood and Planck's theory was developed."

Brillouin goes on to consider a dissipative measurement scheme in which the demon observes the molecules by photons from a non-equilibrium source such as a hot lamp filament, concluding that to see the molecule, the demon must use at least one photon more energetic than the photons comprising the thermal background, thereby dissipating an energy of order kT in the process of measurement.

By the 1950s the development of the theory of computation by Turing and others had made it commonplace to think of computation as a mechanical process. Meanwhile the development of electronic digital computers had naturally raised the question of the ultimate thermodynamic cost of computation, especially since heat removal has always been a major engineering consideration in the design of computers, limiting the density with which active components can be packed.

The general folklore belief at this time, descended from Szilard's and Brillouin's analyses, is expressed in a remark [11] from a 1949 lecture by von Neumann, to the effect that a computer operating at temperature T must dissipate at least $kT \ln 2$ of energy "per elementary act of information, that is, per elementary decision of a two-way alternative and per elementary transmittal of one unit of information."

A major turning point in understanding the thermodynamics of computation took place when Landauer [6] attempted to prove this folklore belief and found he couldn't. He was able to prove a lower bound of order kT for some data operations, but not for others. Specifically, he showed that "logically irreversible" operations—those that throw away information about the previous logical state of the computer—necessarily generate in the surroundings an amount of entropy equal to the information thrown away. The essence of Landauer's argument was that such operations compress the phase space spanned by the computer's information-bearing degrees of freedom, and so, in order to occur spontaneously, they must allow a corresponding expansion, in other words, an entropy increase, in other degrees of freedom.

[This argument is not without its subtleties; for example, a many-to-one operation such as erasure may be thermodynamically reversible or not, depending on the data to which it is applied. When truly *random* data (e.g., a bit equally likely to be 0 or 1) is erased, the entropy increase of the surroundings is compensated by an entropy decrease of the data, so the operation as a whole is thermodynamically reversible. This is the case in resetting Maxwell's demon, where two equiprobable states of the demon's mind must be compressed onto one. By contrast, in computations, logically irreversible operations are usually applied to nonrandom data deterministically generated by the computation. When erasure is applied to such data, the entropy increase of the environment is not compensated by an entropy decrease of the data, and the operation is thermodynamically irreversible [7].]

About 1970, having read Landauer's paper and heard him talk, I began thinking about the thermodynamics of computation. Initially I assumed, as he that, at least some logically irreversible operations were necessary to nontrivial computation. However, as a side project, I experimented with simple computations that could be done without them. For example, I wrote a reversible program that used repeated subtraction to test whether one integer is divisible by another. Such experiments revealed a common pattern: The computation consisted of two halves, the second of which almost exactly undid the work of the first. The first half would generate the desired answer (e.g., divisible or not) as well as, typically, some other information (e.g., remainder and quotient). The second half would dispose of the extraneous information by reversing the process that generated it, but would keep the desired answer. This led me to realize [12] that any computation could be rendered into this reversible format by accumulating a history of all information that would normally be thrown away, then disposing of this history by the reverse of the process that created it. To prevent the reverse stage from destroying the desired output along with the undesired history, it suffices, before beginning the reverse stage, to copy the output on blank tape. No history is recorded during this copying operation, and none needs to be, since copying onto blank tape is already logically reversible; the reverse stage of computation then destroys only the original of the output, leaving the copy intact. My technique for performing an arbitrary computation reversibly is illustrated in **Table 1**, with underbars indicating the positions of the tape heads.

A proof of the thermodynamic reversibility of computation requires not only showing that logically irreversible operations can be avoided, but also showing that, once the computation has been rendered into the logically reversible format, some actual hardware, or some physically reasonable theoretical model, can perform the resulting chain of logically reversible operations in a thermodynamically reversible fashion. Approaching the problem with a background of prior interests in biochemistry and computability theory, I saw an analogy between DNA and RNA and the tapes of a Turing machine. The notion of an informational macromolecule, undergoing transitions of its logical state by highly specific (e.g., enzyme-catalyzed) reversible chemical reactions, offered a felicitous model within which thermodynamic questions about information processing could be asked and rigorously answered. Within this theoretical framework it is easy to design an "enzymatic Turing machine" [7, 12] which would execute logically reversible computations with a dissipation per step proportional to the speed of computation. Near equilibrium, the machine would execute a slightly biased random walk, making backward steps nearly as often as forward ones. The backward steps would not result in errors, since they would be undone by subsequent forward steps. True errors—transitions to logically unrelated states—would also occur in any system with finite potential energy barriers, but their rate could be made small (in principle arbitrarily small) compared to the rate of logically correct forward and backward transitions. The enzymatic Turing machine is an example of a "Brownian" reversible computer, in which the non-information-bearing degrees of freedom are strongly coupled to, and exert a viscous drag on, the information-bearing ones, resulting in a dissipation per step proportional to the speed of computation.

Although there are no known general-purpose (i.e., universal) enzymatic Turing machines in nature, there are enzymes analogous to special-purpose Turing machines, notably RNA polymerase. This enzyme, whose function is to make an RNA transcript of the genetic information in one or more DNA genes, may be viewed as a special-purpose tape-copying Turing machine. Under physiological conditions the enzyme is driven hard forward, and dissipates about 20 kT per step; however, the operation of RNA polymerase is both logically and thermodynamically reversible, and it is routinely operated both forward and backward in the laboratory by varying the relative concentrations of reactants (nucleoside triphosphates) and product (pyrophosphate) [13, 14]. When operating backward the enzyme performs the logical inverse of copying: It removes bases one by one from the RNA strand, checking each one for complementarity with the DNA before removing it.

Edward Fredkin, at MIT, independently arrived at similar conclusions concerning reversible computation. Fredkin was motivated by a conviction that computers and physics should be more like each other. On one hand he was dissatisfied with a theoretical physics based on partial differential equations and continuous space-time. He felt it

Table 1   Scheme for reversible computation.

Stage	Contents of		
	Work tape	History tape	Output tape
Forward	_INPUT	_	_
	WORK	HIST_	_
	_OUTPUT	HISTORY_	_
Copy	_OUTPUT	HISTORY_	_
output	OUTPUT	HISTORY_	OUT_
	_OUTPUT	HISTORY_	_OUTPUT
Reverse	_OUTPUT	HISTORY_	_OUTPUT
	WORK	HIST_	_OUTPUT
	_INPUT	_	_OUTPUT

unreasonable to invoke an infinite number of bits of information to encode the state of one cubic centimeter of nature, and an infinite number of digital operations to exactly simulate one second of its evolution. By the same token he felt it wrong to base the theory of computation on irreversible primitives, not found in physics. To remedy this he found a reversible three-input three-output logic function, the "conservative logic gate" able to simulate all other logic operations, including the standard ones AND, OR, and NOT [15, 16]. He showed that conservative logic circuits can perform arbitrary computations by essentially the same programming trick I had used with reversible Turing machines: Do the computation, temporarily saving the extra information generated in the course of obtaining the desired answer, then dispose of this information by the reverse of the process by which it was created.

Fredkin's displeasure with continuum models resembles Landauer's well-known displeasure [17] with mathematical operations that have no physical way of being performed, e.g., calculating the 10^{100}th digit of pi. These doubts, however, led Fredkin to pursue the radical goal of finding a fully discrete basis for physics, whereas in Landauer they merely inspired a certain aesthetic indifference toward nonconstructive mathematics.

Fredkin was joined by T. Toffoli (who in his doctoral thesis [18] had refuted, by counterexample, an accepted but erroneous proof that reversible cellular automata cannot be computationally universal), and later by Gerard Vichniac and Norman Margolus to form the Information Mechanics group at MIT. The activities of this group are largely responsible for stimulating the current interest in reversible cellular automata with direct physical significance, notably deterministic Ising models [19–21] and momentum-conserving lattice gases that support a macroscopic hydrodynamics [22].

A major step toward Fredkin's goal of finding a reversible physical basis for computation was his discovery of the billiard-ball model of computation [16]. This takes

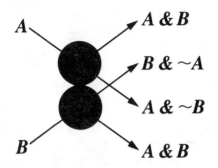

A

$A \& B$

$B \& \sim A$

$A \& \sim B$

B

$A \& B$

Figure 1

Use of a billiard-ball collision to realize a two-input, four-output logic function; data (1 or 0) represented by the presence or absence of a billiard ball on a given trajectory.

advantage of the fact that a collision between two classical hard spheres ("balls") diverts each one from the path it would have followed had the other been absent; thus a collision can be thought of as a two-input, four-output logic function whose outputs, for inputs A and B, are, respectively (cf. **Figure 1**),

A and B,
B and not A,
A and not B,
A and B.

Fredkin showed that, with the addition of "mirrors" to redirect the balls, such collisions can simulate any conservative logic function, and therefore any ordinary logic function. This implies that an infinite two-dimensional hard sphere gas, in an appropriate periodic potential (i.e., a periodic array of mirrors), is *computationally universal*—capable of being programmed through its initial condition to simulate any digital computation.

The billiard-ball computer is the prime example of a ballistic reversible computer. In contrast to the Brownian computers described earlier, ballistic computers operate with zero dissipation at finite speed, but they depend on isolating the information-bearing degrees of freedom from all sources of thermal noise, such as internal degrees of freedom of the balls or mirrors. Another way of characterizing the difference between Brownian and ballistic computers is to say that the former work by creating a low-potential energy labyrinth in configuration space, isomorphic to the desired computation, through which the system drifts despite thermal noise; the latter instead work by creating a dynamical trajectory

isomorphic to the desired computation, which the system follows exactly in the absence of noise.

A number of other classical-mechanical models of reversible computation can be characterized as clocked Brownian models: The information-bearing degrees of freedom are locked to and driven by a master "clock" degree of freedom, with dissipation proportional to speed. These include the early coupled-potential-well models of Landauer and Keyes [6, 23], which were invented before the trick of reversible programming was known, but would function as Brownian reversible computers if reversibly programmed; the author's clockwork Turing machine [7], which invokes infinitely hard potentials to achieve zero error in a Brownian setting; Likharev's reversible computer based on Josephson junctions [24], which could probably be built, and Landauer's ball-and-pipe model [15, 25].

Returning to the question of Maxwell's demon, we can now give a detailed entropy accounting of the demon's cycle of operation. We refer to Szilard's [2] version of the demon, which uses a gas consisting of a single molecule. The demon first inserts a partition trapping the molecule on one side or the other, next performs a measurement to learn which side the molecule is on, then extracts $kT \ln 2$ of work by allowing the molecule to expand isothermally to fill the whole container again, and finally clears its mind in preparation for the next measurement. The discussion below of the classical Szilard engine follows [7]; an analogous quantum analysis has been given by Zurek [26].

According to our current understanding, each step of the cycle is thermodynamically reversible if we make the usual idealization that operations are carried out quasistatically. In particular, the measurement is reversible and does not increase the entropy of the universe. What the measurement does do, however, is to establish a correlation between the state of the demon's mind and the position of the molecule. This correlation means that after the measurement the entropy of the combined system (demon + molecule) is no longer equal to the sum of the entropies of its parts. Adopting a convenient origin for the entropy scale, the entropy of the molecule is one bit (since it may be, equiprobably, on either side of the partition), the entropy of the demon's mind is one bit (since it may think, equiprobably, that the molecule is on either side of the partition), but the entropy of the combined system is only one bit, because the system as a whole, owing to the correlation, has only two equiprobable states, not four.

The next phase of the cycle, the isothermal expansion, reduces the entropy of the environment by one bit while increasing the entropy of the demon + molecule system from one bit to two bits. Because the expansion destroys the correlation between demon and molecule (rendering the information obtained by the measurement obsolete), the entropy of the demon + molecule system is now equal to the sum of the entropies of its parts, one bit each.

The last phase of the cycle, resetting the demon's mind, reduces the entropy of the demon from one bit to zero, and accordingly, by Landauer's argument, must increase the entropy of the environment by one bit. This increase cancels the decrease brought about during the expansion phase, bringing the cycle to a close with no net entropy change of demon, molecule, or environment.

One may wonder how, in view of the arguments of Brillouin and others, the demon can make its measurement without dissipation. Though plausible, these arguments only demonstrated the dissipativeness of certain particular mechanisms of measurement, not of all measurements. In a sense, the existence of copying mechanisms such as RNA polymerase demonstrates the reversibility of measurement, if one is willing to call RNA synthesis a measurement of the DNA. More traditional reversible-measurement schemes can also be devised which are ideal in the sense of having no other effect than to establish the desired correlation between the measuring apparatus and the system being measured. Such a measurement begins with the measuring apparatus in a standard dynamical or thermodynamic state and ends with it in one of several states depending on the initial state of the system being measured, meanwhile having produced no change either in the environment or in the system being measured. **Figure 2**, for example, shows a classical billiard-ball mechanism based on the ideas of Fredkin that uses one billiard ball (dark) to test the presence of another (light) without disturbing the dynamical state of the latter. The apparatus consists of a number of fixed mirrors (dark rectangles) which reflect the billiard balls. First assume that the dark ball is absent. Then a light ball injected into the apparatus at X will follow the closed diamond-shaped trajectory $ABCDEFA$ forever, representing the value 1; conversely, the absence of the light ball (i.e., no balls in the apparatus at all) represents the value 0. The goal of the measurement is to inject another ball (dark color) into the apparatus in such a way that it tests whether the light ball is present without altering the light ball's state. By injecting the dark ball at Y at the appropriate time, the light ball (if present) is diverted from, but then returned to, its original path (following BGD instead of BCD), while the dark ball leaves the apparatus at M if the light ball was present and at N if it was absent.

One can design analogous mechanisms [7, 8] for reversibly measuring which side of Szilard's engine the molecule is on without otherwise disturbing the thermodynamic state of the engine or the environment. Such reversible nondemolition measurement schemes in general exist for classical systems, and for quantum systems in which the goal of the measurement is to distinguish among orthogonal states of the system, since these states may in principle be made eigenstates of an appropriate observable. Of course a quantum measurement cannot avoid disturbing a system which is presented to it in a superposition of eigenstates the

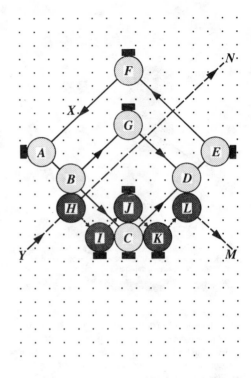

Reversible measurement in the billiard-ball model of computation.

measuring apparatus is designed to measure. The relation of irreversibility to quantum measurement has been considered by many authors (cf. the concise discussion in [27] and references therein).

An active research area recently has been the theory of quantum reversible computation. Chemical Brownian computers such as RNA polymerase are of course quantum systems, but because of the high temperature and short thermal de Broglie wavelength, quantum effects are subtle and quantitative (e.g., zero-point and tunneling corrections to reaction rates) rather than qualitative.

More distinctively quantum models have been considered by a number of authors [28–35]. These models are somewhat abstract by comparison with classical models, consisting typically of an array of two-state spins (each representing one bit) and a time evolution operator or Hamiltonian designed to make the spins pass through a sequence of states corresponding to the desired computation. The computationally relevant states are generally a subset of a set of orthonormal "basis states," in which each spin is either up or down.

One of the earliest quantum models, by Benioff [28], used a Hamiltonian such that a basis state corresponding to the initial logical state of a reversible Turing machine would be transformed, at integer times, to basis states corresponding to successive logical successors. In other words, the Hamiltonian H was chosen so that the unitary operator U, representing evolution under the Hamiltonian for unit time, mapped each computationally relevant basis state onto its logical successor. Casting the logical time evolution of a Turing machine into the form of a unitary operator requires that all basis states have successors. Thus there can be no halt states, and all computations must be either infinite or cyclic. Since the Hamiltonian represents, albeit in an abstract form, the actual interactions among parts of the quantum computer that the designer is able to choose and control, Benioff considered it important for the Hamiltonian to be simple, and in particular not to depend explicitly on the global structure of the computation being performed. In order to achieve this, he found it necessary to make H time-dependent, in effect using a three-phase clock (two phases would also have sufficed) to turn on three Hamiltonians one after another, and making U the product of three non-commuting unitary operators $U = U_3 U_2 U_1$. In each of the clock phases, some of the spins (bits) in the computer flip conditionally on the state of others.

Feynman [29] found a way to define a simple, time-independent Hamiltonian for quantum computations: Instead of incorporating the direction of the computation (forward as opposed to backward) in the Hamiltonian, he incorporated it into the initial condition, which was now not a single basis state but rather a wave-packet-like superposition of basis states. The Feynman Hamiltonian for a given unitary transition operator U is of the form $H = U + U^+$, analogous to the Hamiltonian for a one-dimensional crystal in which spin waves can propagate either forward or backward according to their initial momentum. Feynman also noted that quantum computers can exhibit behavior intermediate between Brownian and ballistic: Thermal fluctuations in the Hamiltonian scatter the propagating computation wave like phonons in a crystal, so that under appropriate conditions the mean free path between scattering events is finite but much larger than one computation step. The computation then proceeds with net velocity proportional to the driving force, as in a Brownian computer, but with a proportionality constant that varies inversely with the mean free path, like electrical conductivity.

Zurek [30] compares the dynamical stability of quantum and classical ballistic computers with respect to errors in the initial condition ("software") and the Hamiltonian ("hardware"). In the billiard-ball model either type of error produces an exponentially growing error in the trajectory, whereas for quantum computers hardware-induced errors increase only quadratically with time and software errors do not increase at all.

Margolus [33] and Benioff [34] considered the problem of finding a universal quantum computer (with infinite memory) whose Feynman-type Hamiltonian nevertheless would have a finite range of interaction. For a serial computer such as a Turing machine, in which only one part is active at a time, this is not difficult; but when an analogous construction is attempted for a parallel machine such as a cellular automaton, Margolus found, on the one hand, that the finite range of interaction forbade synchronous updating of all the sites, and, on the other hand, that with asynchronous updating the computation no longer proceeded ballistically.

Deutsch [32] considered a more general kind of quantum computer that could be programmed to perform distinctively quantum operations such as generating two bits in an Einstein–Podolsky–Rosen superposition state. With Deutsch's computer it is possible to split a computation into two (or more) subtasks, perform the subtasks simultaneously in different Everett worlds, and then allow the results of the subtasks to interfere. An appropriate measurement on the final superposed state of the computer produces a probabilistic behavior of the output, which sometimes yields the desired answer (e.g., the exclusive-or, or some other linear function of the results of the two subtasks), and sometimes yields a "failure," an eigenstate of the output operator which says nothing about the results of the subtasks. Because of the probability of failure, quantum parallelization does not reduce the average time required to complete a parallelizable computation.

Landauer [35] has reviewed several quantum computation models in more detail than given here, pointing out some of the unphysical idealizations in existing models and the importance of specifying a quantum computer more concretely than by merely inventing a Hamiltonian.

Acknowledgments

I would like to acknowledge my early mentors Berni Alder and the late Aneesur Rahman, who had no direct interest in the theory of computation, but who taught me to think clearly about reversibility in statistical physics, resisting deception by common sense and discouragement by apparent paradoxes. I would also like to thank Rolf Landauer, under whose kind influence my interest in this subject took form nearly twenty years ago. Since then I have been inspired and assisted continually by many, especially Landauer, Gregory Chaitin, Edward Fredkin, Tom Toffoli, Paul Benioff, Norman Margolus, and David Deutsch.

References

1. J. C. Maxwell, *Theory of Heat*, 4th Ed., Longmans, Green & Co., London, 1875 (1st Ed. 1871), pp. 328–329.

2. L. Szilard, *Z. Phys.* **53**, 840–856 (1929).
3. C. E. Shannon and W. Weaver, *The Mathematical Theory of Communication*, University of Illinois Press, Urbana-Champaign, IL, 1949.
4. M. von Smoluchowski, *Z. Phys.* (1912).
5. M. von Smoluchowski, lecture notes, Leipzig, 1914 (as quoted by Szilard [2]).
6. R. Landauer, *IBM J. Res. Develop.* **3**, 183–191 (1961).
7. C. H. Bennett, *Int. J. Theor. Phys.* **21**, 905–940 (1982).
8. C. H. Bennett, *Research Report RC-12526*, IBM Thomas J. Watson Research Center, Yorktown Heights, NY 10598; edited version in *Sci. Amer.* (November 1987).
9. E. Lubkin, *Int. J. Theor. Phys.* **16**, 523–535 (1987).
10. L. Brillouin, *Science and Information Theory*, 2nd Ed., Academic Press, London, 1962.
11. J. von Neumann, *Theory of Self-Reproducing Automata*, Arthur Burks, Ed., University of Illinois Press, Urbana-Champaign, IL, 1966, p. 66.
12. C. H. Bennett, *IBM J. Res. Develop.* **17**, 525–532 (1973).
13. Judith Levin, Doctoral Dissertation, Biochemistry Department, University of California, Berkeley, CA, 1985.
14. George Kassaveties, *J. Biol. Chem.* **261**, 14256–14265 (1986).
15. R. Landauer, *Ber. Bunsenges.* **80**, 1048 (1976).
16. E. Fredkin and T. Toffoli, *Int. J. Theor. Phys.* **21**, 219–253 (1982).
17. R. L. Landauer, *IEEE Spectrum* **4**, 105 (1967).
18. T. Toffoli, *J. Comp. Syst. Sci.* **15**, 213–231 (1977).
19. G. Vichniac, *Physica* **10D**, 96 (1984).
20. Y. Pomeau, *J. Phys. A* **17**, 415 (1984).
21. M. Creutz, *Ann. Phys.* **167**, 62 (1986).
22. L. Kadanoff, *Physics Today* **39**, 7 (September 1986).
23. R. W. Keyes and R. Landauer, *IBM J. Res. Develop.* **14**, 152 (1970).
24. K. K. Likharev, *Int. J. Theor. Phys.* **21**, 311 (1982).
25. R. L. Landauer, *Int. J. Theor. Phys.* **21**, 283 (1982).
26. W. Zurek, *Frontiers of Nonequilibrium Statistical Physics*, G. T. Moore and M. O. Scully, Eds., Plenum Publishing Co., New York, 1986, pp. 15–161.
27. W. Zurek, *Ann. N.Y. Acad. Sci.* **480**, 89–97 (1986).
28. P. Benioff, *Phys. Rev. Lett.* **48**, 1581–1585 (1982); *J. Stat. Phys.* **29**, 515–545 (1982).
29. R. P. Feynman, *Opt. News* **11**, 11–20 (1985).
30. W. H. Zurek, *Phys. Rev. Lett.* **53**, 391–394 (1984).
31. A. Peres, *Phys. Rev.* **32A**, 3266–3276 (1985).
32. D. Deutsch, *Proc. Roy. Soc. Lond. A* **400**, 97–117 (1985).
33. N. Margolus, *Ann. N.Y. Acad. Sci.* **480**, 487–497 (1986).
34. P. Benioff, *Ann. N.Y. Acad. Sci.* **480**, 475–486 (1986).
35. R. Landauer, *Found. Phys.* **16**, 551–564 (1986).

Received April 8, 1987; accepted for publication October 5, 1987

Charles H. Bennett *IBM Thomas J. Watson Research Center, P.O. Box 218, Yorktown Heights, New York 10598.* Dr. Bennett earned his Ph.D. from Harvard University in 1970 for molecular dynamics studies (computer simulation of molecular motion) under David Turnbull and Berni Alder. For the next two years he continued this research under the late Aneesur Rahman at Argonne Laboratories, Argonne, Illinois, coming to IBM Research in 1972. In 1973, building on the work of IBM Fellow Rolf Landauer, Dr. Bennett showed that general-purpose computation can be performed by a logically and thermodynamically reversible apparatus, one which is able to operate with arbitrarily little energy dissipation per step because it avoids throwing away information about past logical states. In 1982 he proposed a reinterpretation of Maxwell's demon, attributing its inability to break the second law to an irreducible thermodynamic cost of destroying, rather than acquiring, information. Aside from the thermodynamics of information processing, Dr. Bennett's research interests include the mathematical theory of randomness, probabilistic computation, and error-correction; the cryptographic applications of the uncertainty principle; and the characterization of the conditions under which statistical-mechanical systems evolve spontaneously toward states of high computational complexity. In 1983–85, as visiting professor of computer science at Boston University, he taught courses on cryptography and the physics of computation, and in 1986 was co-organizer of a conference on cellular automata held at MIT.

Chronological Bibliography with Annotations and Selected Quotations

This chronological bibliography contains references dealing directly or indirectly with the Maxwell's demon puzzle. It includes background references on entropy, irreversibility, quantum theory, and related topics. Annotations and quotations illustrate the diverse viewpoints, proposed resolutions, and debates that have emerged regarding Maxwell's demon and related matters. Date, author and title are shown for each entry; full bibliographic information is in the separate Alphabetical Bibliography.

<table>
<tr><td>1867</td><td>Maxwell, J. C., Letter to P. G. Tait. This famous 1867 letter bears the seminal idea for what is now called Maxwell's demon.</td></tr>
</table>

> *Or in short if heat is the motion of finite portions of matter and if we can apply tools to such portions of matter so as to deal with them separately, then we can take advantage of the different motion of different proportions to restore a uniformly hot system to unequal temperatures or to motions of large masses. Only we can't, not being clever enough.*

<table>
<tr><td>1870</td><td>Maxwell, J. C., Letter to J. W. Strutt, 6 December 1870. This letter to Lord Rayleigh is the second prepublication notice of the Maxwell's demon concept.</td></tr>
</table>

> *Moral. The 2nd law of thermodynamics has the same degree of truth as the statement that if you throw a tumblerful of water into the sea, you cannot get the same tumblerful of water out again.*

<table>
<tr><td>1871</td><td>Maxwell, J. C., *Theory of Heat*. Maxwell's public presentation of the demon in his classic thermodynamics book. See quotation in Section 1.2.1.</td></tr>
<tr><td>1874</td><td>Thomson, W., 'The Kinetic Theory of the Dissipation of Energy.' Thomson introduces the term 'demon'. Reprinted here as Article 2.1.</td></tr>
<tr><td>1876</td><td>Loschmidt, J., 'Über den Zustand des Wärmegleichgewichtes eines System von Körpern mit Rücksicht auf die Schwerkraft.' The second law cannot be a purely mechanical principle because Newtonian mechanics allows the same sequence of motions backwards as forwards. Loschmidt's work challenged Boltzmann and helped him develop his statistical definition of entropy.</td></tr>
<tr><td>1878</td><td>Maxwell, J. C., 'Diffusion.'</td></tr>
</table>

> *... the idea of dissipation of energy depends on the extent of our knowledge. Available energy is energy which we can direct into any desired channel. Dissipated energy is energy which we cannot lay hold of and direct at pleasure, such as the energy of the confused agitation of molecules ... the notion of dissipated energy could not occur to a being who could not turn any of the energies of nature to his own account, or to one who could trace the motion of every molecule and seize it at the right moment. It is only to a being in the intermediate stage, who can lay hold of some*

forms of energy while others elude his grasp, that energy appears to be
passing inevitably from the available to the dissipated state.

1878   Maxwell, J. C., 'Tait's thermodynamics.'

Hence we have only to suppose our senses sharpened to such a degree that
we could trace the motions of molecules as easily as we now trace those
of large bodies, and the distinction between work and heat would vanish,
for the communication of heat would be seen to be a communication of
energy of the same kind as that which we call work.

1879   Thomson, W., 'The Sorting Demon of Maxwell.' Thomson gives
        a detailed description of the characteristics of a Maxwell demon.
        See Section 1.2.1.

The conception of the 'sorting demon' is purely mechanical, and is of
great value in purely physical science. It was not invented to help us deal
with questions regarding the influence of life and of mind on the motions
of matter, questions essentially beyond the range of mere dynamics.

1885   Whiting, H., 'Maxwell's demons.' Whiting compares the sorting of
        a temperature-demon and the escape of high speed molecules from
        the Earth's atmosphere.

It seems to me of interest to point out that what, as Maxwell has shown,
could be done by the agency of these imaginary beings, can be and often
is actually accomplished by the aid of a sort of natural selection.

1893   Poincaré, J., 'Mechanism and experience.' Poincaré contrasts the
        irreversibility of 'real experience' with the reversibility of mechan-
        ics. He refers to Maxwell's demon as an idea that gave rise to
        the kinetic theory of gases. Alluding to the famous Recurrence
        Theorem that now bears his name:

... to see heat pass from a cold body to a warm one, it will not be
necessary to have the acute vision, the intelligence, and the dexterity of
Maxwell's demon; it will suffice to have a little patience.

1904   Boynton, W. P., *Applications of the Kinetic Theory.* One of the
        earliest textbook references to Maxwell's demon, coming in a dis-
        cussion of ideal gases, just after the Clausius and Kelvin statements
        of the second law.

The validity of the Second Law is a matter of experience, and is not
restricted to any particular substances. The reason seems to be that
we are not able to deal individually with the motions of molecules, and
discriminate between those with more and those with less energy, but
have to deal with them in a lump. Hence it is that our treatment of the
Kinetic Theory, dealing as it does with averages, presents the Second
Law as a matter of course.

1911   Knott, C. G., *Life and Scientific Work of Peter Guthrie Tait*. This
            contains Maxwell's 1867 letter and his 'Concerning demons' letter
            to Tait. See Section 1.2.1.

1912   Smoluchowski, M. von, 'Experimentell nachweisbare der üblichen
            Thermodynamik widersprechende Molekular-phänomene.' A study
            of the validity of the second law of thermodynamics within the
            framework of kinetic theory and statistical mechanics.

1914   Smoluchowski, M. von, 'Gültigkeitsgrenzen des zweiten Haupt-
            satzes der Wärmtheorie.'

1922   Planck, M., *Treatise on Thermodynamics*. Planck discusses the
            impossibility of perpetual motion, referring only indirectly to the
            demon.

1923   Lewis, G. N. and Randall, M., *Thermodynamics and the Free En-
            ergy of Chemical Substances*. These authors focus on the entropy
            of the demon itself.

            Of course even in this hypothetical case one might maintain the law of
            entropy increase by asserting an increase of entropy within the demon,
            more than sufficient to compensate for the decrease in question. Before
            conceding this point it might be well to know something more of the de-
            mon's metabolism. Indeed a suggestion of Helmholtz raises a serious sci-
            entific question of this character. He inquires whether micro-organisms
            may not possess the faculty of choice which characterizes the hypothetical
            demon of Maxwell. If so, it is conceivable that systems might be found
            in which these micro-organisms would produce chemical reactions where
            the entropy of the whole system, including the substances of the organ-
            isms themselves, would diminish. Such systems have not as yet been
            discovered, but it would be dogmatic to assert that they do not exist.

1924   Nyquist, H., 'Certain factors affecting telegraph speed.' The rate
            per character at which 'intelligence' can be transmitted is taken to
            be $K \log m$, where m is the number of possible distinct characters
            and K is a constant. Nyquist's use of 'intelligence' seems consistent
            with the modern term 'information.'

1925   Jeans, J. H., *Dynamical Theory of Gases*

            Thus Maxwell's sorting demon could effect in a very short time what
            would probably take a very long time to come about if left to the play of
            chance. There would, however be nothing contrary to natural laws in the
            one case any more than in the other.

1925   Szilard, L., 'On the extension of phenomenological thermodynam-
            ics to fluctuation phenomena,' This is Szilard's doctoral disserta-
            tion at the University of Berlin, a precursor to his seminal 1929
            paper on Maxwell's demon.

1927   Costa, J. L., Smyth, H. D. and Compton, K. T. 'A mechanical Maxwell demon.' A 'mechanical' Maxwell's demon is used to effect an experimental measurement of Maxwell's speed distribution.

1928   Hartley, R. V. L., 'Transmission of information.' A very cogent discussion, proposing a quantitative measure of information, $H = n \log s$, where s is the number of possible distinct symbols and n is the number of symbols in a message.

1929   Szilard, L., 'On the decrease of entropy in a thermodynamic system by the intervention of intelligent beings', Reprinted as Article 3.1.

1929   Clausing, P., 'Über die Entropieverminderung in einem thermodynamischen System bei Eingriffen intelligenter Wesen.' This early criticism of Szilard's 1929 paper contains an unsupported allegation that Szilard's membrane model analysis is in error.

1929   Preston, T., *The Theory of Heat*. The author discusses Maxwell's 'ingenious but illusory violation' of the second law.

> *It must be remembered, however, that to this being the gas is by no means a uniformly heated mass. The faster-moving molecules are hot and the slower cold, and the whole mass to him is made up of discrete parts at very different temperatures, and this sifting of the molecules is no more a violation of the Second law than would be the collection by an ordinary being of the warmer members of a system of bodies into one region of space and colder into another.*

1930   Lewis, G. N., 'The symmetry of time in physics.' Maxwell's demon is introduced in connection with a simple model system of three distinguishable molecules in a cylinder with a partition that has a controllable shutter. Lewis finds that entropy increases when 'a known distribution goes over into an unknown distribution', supporting the view that entropy is a subjective entity.

> *Gain in entropy always means loss of information, and nothing more. It is a subjective concept, but we can express it in its least subjective form, as follows. If, on a page, we read the description of a physico-chemical system, together with certain data which help to specify the system, the entropy of the system is determined by these specifications. If any of the essential data are erased, the entropy becomes greater; if any essential data are added, the entropy becomes less. Nothing further is needed to show that the irreversible process neither implies one-way time, nor has any other temporal implications. Time is not one of the variables of pure thermodynamics.*

1932   Neumann, J. von, *Mathematical Foundations of Quantum Mechanics*. In contrast with most books on quantum theory, von Neumann devotes a significant effort to thermodynamic considerations and macroscopic applications of quantum mechanics, particularly to measurement theory and Szilard's heat engine. See quotation in Section 1.5.

1939   Allen, H. S. and Maxwell, R. S., *A Text-Book of Heat.* The authors seem to accept the view enunciated by Lewis (1930) that entropy is subjective.

1939   Slater, J. C., *Introduction to Chemical Physics.*

Is it possible, we may well ask, to imagine demons of any desired degree of refinement? If it is, we can make any arbitrary process reversible, keep its entropy from increasing, and the Second law of thermodynamics will cease to have any significance. The answer to this question given by the quantum theory is No. An improvement in technique can carry us only a certain distance, a distance practically reached in plenty of modern experiments with single atoms and electrons, and no conceivable demon, operating according to the laws of nature, could carry us further. The quantum theory gives us a fundamental size of cell in the phase space, such that we cannot regulate the initial conditions of an assembly on any smaller scale. And this fundamental cell furnishes us with a unique way of defining entropy and of judging whether a given process is reversible or irreversible.

1939   Weber, H. C., *Thermodynamics for Chemical Engineers.* Weber alludes to a technique, which he attributes to Boltzmann, that avoids any necessity for intelligence in the demon's operation.

Assume a cell containing an extremely dilute solution of colloidal iron. Place this between the poles of a permanent magnet having poles of dimensions approximating those of the iron particles. The magnet is provided with a coil from which a current developed by the Brownian movement of the iron particles past the magnet poles can be drawn. To maintain the colloidal motion (hold the temperature constant) the whole may be immersed in the ocean, which serves as a reservoir from which to draw heat energy. The sole net result of operating this system would be the conversion of a quantity of heat to work—an impossible result according to the second law. In all such cases we are either enlisting the aid of conscious choice to differentiate between particles of molecular dimensions or dealing with a number of particles so limited that the law of probability does not hold.

1940   Jeans, J. H., *An Introduction to the Kinetic Theory of Gases.* See Jeans, 1925.

1941   Steiner, L. E., *Introduction to Chemical Thermodynamics.*

The presence of fluctuations does not permit us to violate the second law of thermodynamics. If we wished to 'compress' the gas into V_1 ... without doing work, we should have to recognize the rare moments when all the molecules are in V_1 and place a retaining wall between V_1 and V_1' before any of the molecules left V_1. Such recognition and action seem to *be reserved for Maxwell's 'demon' although the possibility is not barred that living organisms can perform the necessary selectivity to produce separations which represent less probable states.*

1944   Darrow, K. K., 'The concept of entropy.' A cogent nonmathematical review of entropy.

1944   Demers, P., 'Les demons de Maxwell et le Second principe de la thermodynamique.'

(Maxwell's demon) ... cannot be completely resolved by application of the uncertainty principle as proposed by Slater. In this regard, G. N. Lewis has made some thermodynamics remarks of interest that agree with our conclusions. One cannot however admit that an infinitesimal energy is sufficient to open a shutter between two compartments. It is necessary to expend an energy comparable to kT. The solution of this problem is based upon the existence of blackbody radiation and on the quantum nature of the emission. One might say that the kinetic theory and the Second law demand blackbody radiation and quantum theory.

1944   Dodge, B. F., *Chemical Engineering Thermodynamics.*

Maxwell was one of the first to perceive that the reason for irreversibility is our inability to deal with individual molecules. He imagined a being, known commonly as 'Maxwell's demon,' who was small enough to deal with individual molecules and who could therefore readily violate the second law. If such a demon controlled the opening and closing of a very small aperture between two vessels containing gas at a uniform temperature, he could cause a temperature difference to develop by unshuffling the 'hot' and 'cold' molecules through proper manipulation of the shutter, or he could separate a mixture of two gases. Certain bacteria are able to assume a role approaching that of Maxwell's demon when they bring about the separation of racemic mixtures.

1944   Gamow, G., *Mr. Tompkins in Paperback.* A delightful introduction to Maxwell's demon, originally published in *Mr. Tompkins Explores the Atom.* Gamow uses gambling schemes and fantasy to illustrate statistical physics. A human, temporarily shrunk to molecular size, witnesses a demon make part of an ice-filled drink boil!

1944   Schrödinger, E., *What is Life?* Though somewhat outdated, this is a good general background reference on the role of thermodynamics in biology.

1945   Demers, P., 'Le Second principe et la theorie des quanta.' This is a continuation of Demers' 1944 paper.

1948a   Born, M., 'Die Quantenmchanik und der Zweite Hauptsatz der Thermodynamik.' This paper and the following one by Born and

Green helped establish the connection between quantum theory and thermodynamics.

1948b   Born, M. and Green, H. S., 'The kinetic basis of thermodynamics.'

1949   Brillouin, L., 'Life, thermodynamics, and cybernetics.' Reprinted as Article 2.5.

1949   Jordan, P., 'On the process of measurement in quantum mechanics.'

It is generally thought that the concepts of thermodynamics are strictly macrophysical ones—that a single atom never has a temperature, and never contains a definite amount of entropy. But the tendency of Szilard's views is to acknowledge also a microphysical applicability of thermodynamics. Let us again think of our photon—it may now be in such a state as can be represented by an unpolarised beam: The two wave functions ϕ and ψ are incoherent and of the same intensity. According to Szilard this means that the photon possesses the entropy $k \ln 2$ ... According to v. Neumann this entropy is the result of a mental process of the observer: By forgetting the coherence between ϕ and ψ ... he creates the entropy $k \ln 2$. Therefore for another observer, who did not forget, the photon has the entropy 0; the notion of entropy becomes a relative one, different for different observers or different memories. In my opinion—assuming the conversion of a polarised photon into an unpolarised one to be a real physical process—this entropy too has an objective meaning, independently of the mental processes of any observer. Therefore we are forced to acknowledge a new, hitherto not recognised type of physical uncertainty.

1949   Shannon, C. E. and Weaver, W., *The Mathematical Theory of Communication* This contains Claude Shannon's 1948 landmark paper on information theory and an introduction by Warren Weaver.

1950a   Brillouin, L., 'Can the rectifier become a thermodynamical demon?' Brillouin shows that a resistor at temperature T, connected to a rectifier, generates zero rectified current and zero voltage across the rectifier. Thermal noise cannot be rectified to transform heat to electric work.

1950b   Brillouin, L., 'Thermodynamics and information theory.' A relatively nonmathematical article in which Brillouin describes his ideas on information, thermodynamics and computation.

Whether he be a Maxwell's demon or a physicist, the observer can obtain a bit of information only when a certain quantity of negentropy is lost. Information gain means an increase of entropy in the laboratory. Vice versa, with the help of this information the observer may be in a position to make an appropriate decision, which decreases the entropy of the laboratory. In other words, he may use the information to recuperate part of the loss in negentropy, but the overall balance is always an increase in entropy (a loss in negentropy).

1950   Raymond, R. C., 'Communication, entropy, and life.'

It is the purpose of this paper to suggest that the entropy of a system may be defined quite generally as the sum of the positive thermodynamic entropy which the constituents of the system would have at thermodynamic equilibrium and a negative term proportional to the information necessary to build the actual system from its equilibrium state. This definition may be applied to open systems by closing them momentarily …

1950   Wiener, N., 'Entropy and information.'

The Maxwell demon is able to lower the entropy of the mechanical output compared with the mechanical input because the demon itself possesses a negative entropy of information. This negative entropy must give information of the momentum and position of particles approaching the gateway operated by the demon in such a way that when the particle collides with the gateway, the gateway is either open or locked shut, so that no absorption of energy appears. This involves a mode of transmission more rapid than the motion of the particles to be separated, and a mode which is probably light. This light itself has a negative entropy which decreases whenever the frequency of the light is lowered by a Compton effect or similar cause. Thus the Maxwell demon gives at least one way for comparing entropy of light with mechanical entropy … This whole point of view suggests that one place to look for Maxwell demons may be in the phenomena of photosynthesis.

1951   Bohm, D., *Quantum Theory*. Brief discussion of the irreversibility of quantum measurement, with mention of Maxwell's demon.

1951a   Brillouin, L., 'Maxwell's demon cannot operate: Information and entropy. I.' Reprinted here as Article 3.2.

1951b   Brillouin, L., 'Physical entropy and information. II.'

1951   Jacobson, H., 'The role of information theory in the inactivation of Maxwell's demon.' Jacobson outlines how Brillouin's 'excellent, but not entirely general arguments' exorcising Maxwell's demon can be extended. He uses probability arguments to effect this extension for both 'pressure' and 'temperature' demons, obtaining estimates for: (1) the information needed to achieve a given entropy decrease; and (2) the entropy increase necessary to acquire that information. In (2) he assumes the demon has no need for a central nervous system, and avoids any discussion of how the demon gets its information. Rather, he focuses on the energy needed to operate the trap door reliably, given the existence of thermal fluctuations. Some of Jacobson's ideas were incorporated by Brillouin in his *Science and Information Theory*.

1951   Raymond, R. C., 'The well-informed heat engine.' Reprinted here
                as Article 3.3.

1951   Rothstein, J., 'Information, measurement, and quantum mechan-
                ics.' Reprinted here as Article 2.6.

1952a   Rothstein, J., 'Information and Thermodynamics.' Rothstein sug-
                gests informational interpretations of the laws of thermodynamics.

                *To sum up, the laws of thermodynamics can be stated as: (a) The conser-
                vation of energy. (b) The existence of modes of energy transfer incapable
                of mechanical description. In a sense (b) is implied in (a), for (a) with-
                out (b) is a mechanical theorem devoid of thermodynamic content. (c)
                The third law is true by definition, for in a perfectly ordered state at
                absolute zero there is no missing information, i.e., the entropy is zero
                (pure case).*

1952b   Rothstein, J., 'Organization and entropy.' Organization is charac-
                terized as a type of negative entropy that takes the form of encoded
                information. Theory is viewed as organization of observation.

1952c   Rothstein, J., 'A phenomenological uncertainty principle.'

                *The existence of a thermodynamic limit to the precision of any mea-
                surement follows from the facts that: (a) information is conveyed by
                making choices from an ensemble of alternatives for which an 'entropy'
                is definable ... ; (b) measurement chooses from an ensemble of possible
                results, thus yielding 'physical' information; (c) either the informational
                entropy of physical information multiplied by Boltzmann's constant must
                be a lower bound to the thermodynamic entropy generated in acquiring
                it or the second law can be violated. Example: A quantity equiprobably
                between 0 and u is measured to fall within Δu. Then choice from $u/\Delta u$
                alternatives was made at entropy cost ΔS not less than $k\ln(u/\Delta u)$.
                For preassigned experimental conditions maximum ΔS is well defined
                and $\Delta u \geq u\exp(-\Delta S/k)$. ...*

1952   Wiener, N., 'Cybernetics.' Wiener defines cybernetics as 'the em-
                ployment of communication and of the notion of the quantity of
                information for the control of artificial and natural systems', and
                uses these ideas to study Maxwell's demon.

                *... in a system like that of the Maxwell demon involving both light and
                matter, the supposed perpetual motion machine is not in reality perpet-
                ual. The light in it is degraded and exhausted by its use to operate the
                machine ...*

1953a   Balazs, N. L. 'Les relations d'incertitude d'Heisenberg empechent-
                elle le démon de Maxwell d'opérer?' It is found that Maxwell's
                demon is not restricted by the uncertainty principle if the system
                chosen is not degenerate. This agrees with, and was evidently done
                independently of, the work of Demers (1944).

1953b   Balazs, N. L., 'L'effet des statistiques sur le démon de Maxwell.' If a Bose–Einstein gas is not degenerate, Maxwell's demon is found to be free of restrictions from the uncertainty principle. In contrast, no corresponding conditions whatsoever are imposed on Maxwell's demon for a gas obeying Fermi–Dirac statistics.

1953   Klein, M. J., 'Order, Organisation, and Entropy.'

One can say that the entropy is low when the number of energy states, in which there is a non-negligible probability of finding the system is small. The entropy does not depend explicitly upon the nature of the wave functions for the system which are associated with these energy states. It is in the wave function, however, that the structure of the system is reflected, and it is this structure which is associated with the concept of organisation ... We conclude that the degree or order in a system which is measured by the entropy (low entropy corresponding to high order) is not the same thing as the degree of organisation of the system in the sense used by the biologist.

1955   Darling, L. and Hulburt, E. O., 'On Maxwell's demon.' The authors describe a situation encountered when a small dog entered a fenced area holding a hen turkey and her chicks. The resulting pandemonium and the authors' difficulties catching the dog and counting the chicks are likened to the challenge faced by a Maxwell's demon. They conclude, 'As a result of this experience we feel sure that the demon could not possibly do his molecule job, and that two demons would probably do worse than one.'

1956   Brillouin, L., *Science and Information Theory*. A clear, concise exposition of Brillouin's contributions to Maxwell's demon and information theory.

Every physical measurement requires a corresponding entropy increase, and there is a lower limit, below which the measurement becomes impossible. This limit corresponds to change in entropy of ... $k \ln 2$, or approximately $0.7k$ for one bit of information obtained ... It is very surprising that such a general result escaped attention until very recently ... A general feature of all this discussion is that the quantum conditions were used in the reasoning, but Planck's constant h is eliminated in the final results, which depend only on Boltzmann's constant k. This proves that the results are independent of quanta and of the uncertainty principle, and, in fact, a discussion can be given along classical lines without the introduction of quantum conditions ...

1956   Lotka, A. J., *Elements of Mathematical Biology* (Originally published as *Elements of Physical Biology*). Lotka references Maxwell, 'who remarked that a demon capable of dealing with individual molecules would be able to cheat the second law of thermodynamics.'

1956   Neumann, J. von, 'Probabilistic logics from unreliable components.' In a lengthy article dealing with automata, von Neumann gives a brief but notable reference to the similarity between the information theory and statistical mechanical entropy functions.

> *That information theory should thus reveal itself as an essentially thermodynamical discipline, is not at all surprising: The closeness and the nature of the connection between information and entropy is inherent in L. Boltzmann's classical definition of entropy . . .*

1957a   Jaynes, E. T. 'Information theory and statistical mechanics.' Equilibrium statistical mechanics is developed using the maximum-entropy principle of information theory, and subjectivity in statistical mechanics is discussed.

> *The essential point . . . is that we accept the von Neumann–Shannon expression for entropy, very literally, as a measure of the amount of uncertainty represented by a probability distribution; thus entropy becomes the primitive concept with which we work, more fundamental even than energy. If in addition we reinterpret the prediction problem of statistical mechanics in the subjective sense, we can derive the usual relations in a very elementary way without any consideration of ensembles or appeal to the usual arguments concerning ergodicity or equal a priori probabilities.*

1957b   Jaynes, E. T., 'Information theory and statistical mechanics. II.' Jaynes extends his development of statistical mechanics via information theory to time-dependent phenomena and irreversibility.

1957   Popper, K., 'Irreversibility; or, entropy since 1905.' Popper believes that the interpretation of the second law of thermodynamics as a statistical law became untenable once Brownian movement was observed, because the latter represents deviations from that law. He criticizes Szilard's work on entropy decrease via intervention by an intelligent being, arguing that the logic is circular.

> *(Szilard) first gives four non-equivalent formulations of the entropy law clearly implying that they are all equivalent . . . (b) Szilard then assumes the axiomatic validity of the entropy law so defined. (c) He then proves that a Maxwell demon . . . would have to pay for his information concerning the oncoming molecules by an increase of entropy; which is a trivial consequence if any form of the entropy law is to be preserved intact; and which therefore follows if the entropy law is assumed as a premiss. (d) He thereby shows that information or knowledge can be measured in terms of negative entropy, or entropy in terms of negative knowledge; which immediately leads to the interpretation of statistical probability in terms of subjective ignorance . . . But I think that hot air would continue to escape entropically even if there were no intelligent beings about to provide the corresponding amount of nescience.*

1957   Rothstein, J., 'Nuclear spin echo experiments and the foundations of statistical mechanics.'

The problem of reconciling the irreversibility of thermodynamics with the completely reversible mechanics of the ultimate constituents of the thermodynamical system is examined from an operational viewpoint. The informational nature of entropy is demonstrated, and the famous paradoxes of statistical mechanics, due to Loschmidt and Zermelo, are resolved with its aid. Spin echo experiments are shown to realize the conditions of Loschmidt's reflection paradox, and used to illustrate how reversibility occurs only with perfect 'memory' or information storage, while 'forgetting' or loss of information implies irreversibility.

1958   Elsasser, W. M., *The Physical Foundation of Biology*. A detailed nonmathematical discourse on entropy and information, including Maxwell's demon.

*... the observer must **have** knowledge of the approaching molecules in order to operate the shutter at the proper times ... This process of seeing constitutes a **physical interaction** with the system observed ... The simplest way to see a molecule is by means of ordinary light, and we may assume that in the idealized case one light quantum suffices to locate the molecule ... It is hardly necessary to say that the use of light quanta to detect molecules is somewhat arbitrary and that the same general result would obtain if some other elementary particle was used for detection.*

1958   Haar, D. ter, *Elements of Statistical Mechanics*. A brief discussion of the work of Maxwell, Szilard and Wiener, mainly useful as background information.

*... proofs of the general validity of the second law are different from the proofs of the general validity of the Heisenberg relations in quantum mechanics. In both cases one sets up an idealized experiment which should be suited to get around the theoretical limitations, but while in quantum mechanics one proves that it is **never** possible to break the limitations, in the thermodynamical case one can prove only that **on the average** it is not possible to violate the second law.*

1958   Saha, M. N. and Srivastava, B. N., *A Treatise on Heat*.

*... to Maxwell's demon the gas does not appear as a homogeneous mass but as a system composed of discrete molecules. The law of entropy does not hold for individual molecules, but is a **statistical law** and is valid only when we are compelled to deal with matter in bulk, and are unable to direct or control the motion of individual molecules. Furthermore, ... there is always a chance, though a very meagre one, that the entropy may decrease.*

1958   Rapoport, A., in Yockey, Platzman and Quastler, *Symposium on Information Theory in Biology*.

*It is noteworthy that the greatest discoveries of the physicists are stated in 'pessimistic' terms. They are statements about what **cannot** be done. For example the First Law of Thermodynamics ... says in effect that* *the perpetual motion machine cannot be constructed. But is also holds out a hope of a machine that will keep on working provided only that a large supply of heat is available—the so-called perpetual motion machine of the Second kind. The Second Law of Thermodynamics puts an end to that dream ... Yet it would be a mistake to consider these discoveries as admissions of defeat only. Each has brought a broadened understanding; the First Law of Thermodynamics by revealing heat as a source of energy; the Second Law by revealing the role of entropy. Szilard's investigation rests on quantum-theoretical principles and so provides an important juncture between thermodynamics, information theory, and quantum theory. It appears, therefore, that the grand discoveries of physics have a sobering effect. I think the principles of information theory are of a similar kind. Typically they are statements of limitations. Their constructive side is in defining the framework in which the search for new knowledge or for new means of prediction and control must be confined.*

1959   Rothstein, J., 'Physical demonology.' The idea of demons such as Maxwell's and Laplace's is generalized, showing that any law can be formulated as a principle of impotence—i.e., in terms of the non-existence of some type of demon.

1960   Finfgeld, C. and Machlup, S., 'Well-informed heat engine: efficiency and maximum power.' Reprinted here as Article 3.4.

1961   Bridgman, P. W., *The Nature of Thermodynamics*.

If the Maxwell demon had been invented yesterday instead of in the last century I believe he would not have caused as much consternation. There are too many vital points that must be cleared up. In the first place, what is this 'intelligence' that must be presupposed? ... Another doubtful feature is the method by which the demon would learn of the approach of the individual molecules. The only method would appear to be by light signals; these must come in quanta and must react with the molecule. The reaction is uncontrollable, and may be sufficiently large to divert the molecule by so much as to vitiate the manipulations of the trap door. Then there is the question of the legitimacy of assuming that 'information' can be propagated in any purely thermodynamic system ... Again, there is the question of the details of operation of the trap door; if the door is a mechanical system in the proper sense it must be perfectly elastic, and this means that its motion cannot be stopped, or is at most periodic ... when the mechanism gets small, the mechanism itself and its controls (including in the controls the brain of the demon) become subject to temperature fluctuations which are proportionally large the smaller the mechanism. How do we know that this will not vitiate the entire program? These are serious questions, and so far as I know have received no adequate discussion.

1961   Grad, H., 'The many faces of entropy.' Various 'faces' of entropy are examined in this mathematical review, including the H function, irreversibility, and statistical and classical thermodynamics.

1961   Landauer, R., 'Irreversibility and heat generation in the computing process.' Reprinted here as Article 4.1.

1961   Pierce, J. R., *Symbols, Signals and Noise.* The author introduces Maxwell's demon as 'one of the most famous perpetual-motion machines of the second kind', and analyzes a version of Szilard's one-molecule engine with suitable pulleys and weights.

1961   Wiener, N., *Cybernetics.*

It is simpler to repel the question posed by the Maxwell demon than to answer it. Nothing is easier than to deny the possibility of such beings or structures. We shall actually find that Maxwell demons in the strictest sense cannot exist in a system in equilibrium, but if we accept this from the beginning, and so not try to demonstrate it, we shall miss an admirable opportunity to learn something about entropy and about possible physical, chemical, and biological systems ... For a Maxwell demon to act, it must receive information from approaching particles concerning their velocity and point of impact on the wall. Whether these impulses involve a transfer of energy or not, they must involve a coupling of the demon and the gas ... the only entropy which concerns us is that of the system gas-demon, and not that of the gas alone ... The demon can only act on information received, and this information ... represents a negative entropy. However, under the quantum mechanics, it is impossible to obtain any information giving the position or the momentum of a particle, much less the two together, without a positive effect on the energy of the particle examined, exceeding a minimum dependent on the frequency of the light used for examination. In the long run, the Maxwell demon is itself subject to a random motion corresponding to the temperature of its environment ... In fact, it ceases to act as a Maxwell demon.

1962   Bell, D. A., *Intelligent Machines: An Introduction to Cybernetics.* Maxwell's demon is described along the lines of Raymond and Brillouin.

1962   Rothstein, J., 'Discussion: Information and organization as the language of the operational viewpoint.' It is argued that the concepts and terminology of information theory correspond to physical measurement, and that the concept of organization corresponds to laws and to operations as used in physics.

1963   Feynman, R. P., Leighton, R. B. and Sands, M., *The Feynman Lectures on Physics – Vol. 1.* Feynman investigates whether the ratchet and pawl can be operated as a heat engine that violates the second law. Using statistical arguments, he shows that by carefully choosing the weight attached to the ratchet and pawl, the engine can either just barely be driven by the weight or it can just barely lift the weight; this approaches reversibility. He estimates how the ratchet's angular velocity varies with torque, getting a curve reminiscent of an electrical rectifier. Like a rectifier, a ratchet works in reverse under certain temperature conditions. Feynman introduces Maxwell's demon, which:

> *... is nothing but our ratchet and pawl in another form, and ultimately the mechanism will heat up. If we assume that the specific heat of the demon is not infinite, it must heat up. It has but a finite number of internal gears and wheels, so it cannot get rid of the extra heat that it gets from observing the molecules. Soon it is shaking from Brownian motion so much that it cannot tell whether it is coming or going, much less whether the molecules are coming or going, so it does not work.*

1963   Jaynes, E. T., 'Information Theory and Statistical Mechanics.' A concise, readable description of how statistical mechanics can be developed via information theory.

1964   Gabor, D., 'Light and Information.' Reprinted here as Article 3.6.

1964   Rodd, P., 'Some comments on entropy and information.' Reprinted here as Article 3.5.

1965   Asimov, I., *Life and Energy*. A readable elementary discussion of molecules and molecular motion that introduces Maxwell's demon as a tool to dramatize the statistical nature of molecular motion.

1965   Bent, H. A., *The Second Law*.

> *Obituary: Maxwell's Demon (1871–c.1949) The paradox posed by Maxwell's demon bothered generations of physicists. In 1912 Smoluchowski noted that Brownian agitation of the trap door, which would result in a random opening and closing of the door, would render ineffective the long range operation of any automatic device, such as a spring valve or a ratchet and pawl. In 1939 Slater suggested that the uncertainty principle might play a role in the problem. Later it was shown that this would not be the case for heavy atoms at low pressures. Not until 1944–51, however, did two physicists, Demers and Brillouin, call attention to the fact that in an isolated enclosure in internal thermal equilibrium* **it would be impossible for the demon to see the individual molecules.** *To make the molecules visible against the background black-body radiation, the demon would have to use a torch. Happily, as Demers and Brillouin showed, the entropy produced in the irreversible operation of the torch would always exceed the entropy destroyed by the demon's sorting procedure. A real demon could not produce a violation of the second law.*

1965   Hatsopoulos, G. N. and Keenan, J. H., *Principles of General Thermodynamics*. The authors of this popular engineering thermodynamics text discuss Maxwell's demon in the book's foreword, giving a good historical account of thermodynamics and statistical mechanics. The MD is discussed again later in connection with the definition of a thermodynamic system.

1965   Jaynes, E. T., 'Gibbs vs. Boltzmann entropies.' The Gibbs and
            Boltzmann entropies are compared, and the anthropomorphic na-
            ture of entropy is emphasized.

1965   Kubo, R., *Statistical Mechanics*.

            *You may be able to find a demon who starts to do an extremely fine job
            of selecting molecules passing through the window. But he will never be
            able to continue the work indefinitely. Soon he will become dazzled and
            get sick and lose his control. Then the whole system, the gas molecules
            and the demon himself, will again approach a final equilibrium, where the
            temperature difference the demon once succeeded in building up disap-
            pears and the demon will run a fever at a temperature equal to that of the
            gas. A living organism may look like a Maxwell's demon, but it is not.
            A living organism is an open system, through which material, energy,
            and entropy are flowing. But life itself cannot violate thermodynamic
            laws.*

1965   Lehninger, A. L., *Bioenergetics: The Molecular Basis of Biological
            Energy Transformations*. Lehninger observes that that about 10^{23}
            bits of information are required to reduce the entropy of a system
            by $1\,\mathrm{cal\,mol^{-1}K^{-1}}$, showing how energetically inexpensive infor-
            mation storage and communication are. Living cells store large
            amounts of information whose energy 'equivalent' is significant.

1966   Dugdale, J. S., *Entropy and Low Temperature Physics*.

            *... Maxwell sought to demonstrate that the second law of thermodynam-
            ics has only statistical certainty. However, Brillouin, following earlier
            work by Szilard, has shown that if the demon himself is subject to the
            laws of physics (in particular the quantum theory) the operations neces-
            sary to detect the fast molecules cause an increase in entropy sufficient
            to offset the decrease in entropy which the demon is trying to bring about
            in the gas.*

1966   Feyerabend, P. K., 'On the possibility of a perpetuum mobile of
            the Second kind.' The author provides an addendum to Popper's
            1957 paper, 'Irreversibility; or, entropy since 1905.' He analyzes
            a variant of Szilard's one-molecule gas, finding (as did Popper)
            that it violates the second law without the need for information.
            Criticizing Smoluchowski's and Szilard's efforts, he concludes 'the
            attempt to save the second law from systematic deviations, apart
            from being circular and based upon an ambiguous use of the term
            'information', is also ill-conceived, for such deviations are in prin-
            ciple possible.' See the discussion of memory resetting in Section
            1.5.

1966   Frisch, D. H. 'The microscopic interpretation of entropy.' Boltz-
            mann's entropy formula is deduced from the definition $dS = dQ/T$
            and the quantum mechanical heat and work expressions.

1966   Singh, J., *Great Ideas in Information Theory, Language and Cybernetics*. Singh describes Maxwell's demon using Brillouin's information theory approach, following some of the ideas advanced by Wiener in his book *Cybernetics* (1961).

1967   Angrist, S. W. and Hepler, L. G., *Order & Chaos*. A literate, colourful treatise on thermodynamics for the lay science reader, with a chapter on 'Demons, poetry, and life.'

1967   Ehrenberg, W., 'Maxwell's demon.' A good historical overview through Brillouin's work.

> *How seriously Maxwell took his demon is hard to say. In any case, he neither carried out nor promoted experiments to test his hypothesis. His almost offhand remark has nonetheless intrigued many prominent physicist, because it holds out the possibility of a perpetual-motion machine deriving its mechanical effect from the temperature difference between the two portions of the vessel ... Szilard's analysis of Smoluchowski's proposal that intelligent man could operate a perpetual-motion machine that violated the second law of thermodynamics led him neither to a working model nor to a proof that the proposal is unworkable but rather to a postulate relating entropy to information. One may therefore praise or blame Szilard for having opened the path leading to information theory and its mysteries. I am sure, however, that this was not his intention. He believed his paper put the final seal on half a century of argument.*

1967   Kauzmann, W., *Thermal Properties of Matter – Vol. II – Thermodynamics and Statistics: With Applications to Gases*. Kauzmann describes the demon's operation, giving a sorting strategy and a formula for the time it takes a demon to generate a temperature difference (time $\approx 4V/u_{med}A$, where A = opening area, V = container volume, and u_{med} = median molecular speed). He introduces a model where a pressure demon lets molecules through the shutter from the right to left sides but not vice versa, lowering the gas entropy. He adopts Szilard's view that each demon decision requires conversion of nonthermal energy into heat, keeping the second law intact. No calculations are done with the above time formula, but for $V = 100\text{m}^3$ (big room), $A = 10^{-16}\text{m}^2$ (tiny trap door, to assure serial processing), and $u_{med} = 500 \text{ m s}^{-1}$ (room temperature), it implies a time 8×10^{15} Seconds, or 2.5×10^8 years.

1968   Bell, D. A., *Information Theory*. Bell reviews Maxwell's demon, combining Szilard's one-molecule heat engine and a variant of Brillouin's negentropy argument. He also uses an information-theoretic argument to show that the rate of entropy increase can be vanishingly small in an information channel when the power level approaches zero, in analogy with reversible heat transfer.

1968   Dutta, M., 'A hundred years of entropy.' The first one hundred years of entropy are reviewed, covering thermodynamics, statistical mechanics, communication theory and other aspects.

1968   Morowitz, H. J., *Energy Flow in Biology.*

Our current concepts of thermodynamics are rooted in the industrial revolution and the attempts to determine how much mechanical work is available from heat engines. Entropy provides a measure of the work that is unavailable because of our lack of knowledge of the detailed state of the system. The whole structure acquires consistency only because it requires work to obtain information. If this were not true, a Maxwellian demon could indeed continuously violate the Second law of thermodynamics. The Second law and the entropy measure tell us as much about the observer as about the system ... In steam-engine thermodynamics we do not require very detailed knowledge of the state of the system; however, in biology the case is entirely different as the phenomena depend on molecular detail. A misplaced methyl group can eventually kill a whale. The relationship between the observer and the system may thus achieve considerably more importance in biological thermodynamics than in previous considerations of a more coarse-grained type.

1969   Holman, J. P., *Thermodynamics.*

The conclusion of a considerable body of opinion is that either (a) the demon will be unable to distinguish between fast and slow molecules because he is subjected to a random molecular bombardment or (b) the entropy of the demon must change to account for the 'information' he receives in the measurement process. This latter argument pertaining to information has led to the use of the term entropy in the science of information theory, and has even prompted some authors to develop the entire subject of thermodynamics on the basis of concepts from information theory. In this development entropy is taken to be a measure of our increasing lack of information.

1969   Watanabe, S., *Knowing and Guessing: A Quantitative Study of Inference and Information.* A section on negentropy and thermodynamics contains a critical discussion of Brillouin's arguments. Watanabe finds that 'Brillouin's principle does not seem to be rigorously tenable although it reflects a great deal of valid insight into the difficult problem.'

1970   Daub, E. E., 'Maxwell's demon.' Reprinted here as Article 2.2.

1970   Heimann, P. M., 'Molecular forces, statistical representation and Maxwell's demon.' Reprinted here as Article 2.3.

1970   Klein, M. J., 'Maxwell, his demon, and the second law of thermodynamics.' Reprinted here as Article 2.4.

1970   Morowitz, H. J., *Entropy for Biologists.* Morowitz calls entropy a measure (regarding microstates) of the system, while information is a measure that relates to the observer. He considers this an artificial distinction, because an observer—manipulating constraints on the system—is a necessary part of thermodynamics.

1970   Penrose, O., *Foundations of Statistical Mechanics*. See the quotation in Section 1.5 herein.

1970   Wright, P. G., 'Entropy and Disorder.' Connections between entropy and intuitive qualitative ideas concerning disorder are explored. Wright warns that viewing entropy as a quantitative measure of disorder represents ' ... not the received doctrine of physical science, but ... a highly contentious opinion.'

1971   Brush, S. G., 'James Clerk Maxwell and the kinetic theory of gases: A review based on recent historical studies.' Brush emphasizes that if all molecules had the same speed for a given temperature, the separation process envisaged by Maxwell would be impossible. A demon requires a non-uniform speed distribution, such as that bearing Maxwell's name.

1971   Chambadal, P., *Paradoxes of Physics*. The author finds fault with various aspects of both Szilard's model and Brillouin's solution to the Maxwell's demon puzzle, and he calls the attempts to exorcize the demon 'vain and unnecessary.' Some of his provocative views are out of the mainstream, but are interesting and worth reading.

1971   Rothstein, J., 'Informational Generalization of Entropy in Physics.'

Informational generalization of entropy provides a language appropriate to the operational viewpoint. In that language many paradoxes simply dissolve, for the ambiguities inherent in previous ways of talking about them are clearly revealed. Included are famous paradoxes of statistical and quantum mechanics. The crucial role of irreversible phenomena in measurement and for the physical foundation of biology is also clearly shown. The historical importance of operational and thermodynamic considerations for both relativity and quantum mechanics suggests that informationally generalized thermodynamics may play a key role in constructing a satisfactory relativistic quantum theory.

1971   Silver, R. S., *An Introduction to Thermodynamics*. Maxwell's demon is used to illustrate a contrast with normal engineering thermodynamics, which deals with interaction as a whole (e.g., in boilers) rather than with fluctuations.

1971   Tribus, M. and McIrvine, E. C., 'Energy and information.' Energy and entropy are scrutinized for a wide range of phenomena ranging from the hypothetical Maxwell's demon, to real computational, audio and pictorial record activities.

Maxwell's demon became an intellectual thorn in the side of thermodynamicists for almost a century. The challenge to the second law of thermodynamics was this: Is the principle of the increase of entropy in all spontaneous processes invalid where intelligence intervenes?

1972   Bekenstein, J. D., 'Baryon number, entropy and black hole thermodynamics.' A thought experiment of J. A. Wheeler envisages that a being drops entropy-bearing matter into a black hole, thereby destroying normal evidence of that entropy, in apparent violation of the second law. Bekenstein refers to the being who drops the matter into the black hole as 'Wheeler's demon.' He recalls that Brillouin generalized entropy, relating it to information to show that a Maxwell's demon cannot violate the second law. Then he shows that entropy can be generalized in a manner appropriate for black holes to show that Wheeler's demon also cannot transcend the second law.

1972   Jauch, J. M. and Báron, J. G., 'Entropy, information and Szilard's paradox.' Reprinted here as Article 3.7.

1972   Zernike, J., *Entropy: The Devil on the Pillion.*

... we might give (the demon) a torch, but then we are no longer dealing with a system at uniform temperature; and of course work can then be done ... Could the demon not set up signposts around his trapdoor, which warn him of the oncoming molecule? The whole thing might be automated; if the molecule passes two posts set in line with the door within a certain time, the door opens at the exact time of arrival. That indeed is possible in principle, but the transmission of a signal requires energy, more than a fast moving molecule could provide. We can surely think of as fast a molecule as we please with a correspondingly high amount of energy. But the signal has to be more rapid still, and by the same token would require more energy. The minute analysis of this case would lead us too far afield into the information theory ... So we have to restrict ourselves to writing down the conclusion: Maxwell's demon must remain incommunicado ... he cannot operate, because the necessary information cannot reach him.

1973   Bennett, C. H., 'Logical Reversibility of Computation.' Reprinted here as Article 4.2.

1973   Jammer, M., 'Entropy.' A comprehensive overview of entropy, with a section covering Maxwell's demon and other restrictions of the entropy concept.

1973   Jauch, J. M., *Are Quanta Real?* Written in the style of a Galilean dialogue, this book introduces Maxwell's demon in a dream involving a roulette table.

The demons cannot actually function because they are subject to the same fluctuations as the atoms which they are to control. The fact that

they can function in the dream means that they are creatures from an-
other level of reality than the dreamer, and thus carry the message of
the existence of deeper levels of consciousness . . .

1973   Kelly, D. C., *Thermodynamics and Statistical Physics.* The demon
            is discussed prior to Kelly's introduction of the entropy concept.

The demon sets out to pump heat from the cold reservoir to the hot
reservoir. . . . Unhappily, there is one minor problem—it will not work!
Why not? Because we forgot the demon. We did not include the demon
as part of the system. The demon cannot be regarded as part of the
surroundings since he must communicate with the molecules in order to
measure their speeds. The measurements made by the demon (or any
instrumentalized version of the demon) require that he exchange energy
with the molecules. Some of the energy being pumped uphill must be fed
to the demon—he does not work free. Once the system is enlarged to
include the demon one discovers the the heat pump has sprung a leak—a
large leak. The demon is so hungry that he eats himself out of a job. His
appetite completely wipes out the potential gain of his molecule-sorting
action.

1973   Lindblad, G., 'Entropy, information, and quantum measurements.'
            A formal mathematical treatment of the quantum measurement
            process, yielding a mathematical inequality that enables a compar-
            ison of entropy changes in an observed system and its measuring
            apparatus.

1974   Costa de Beauregard, O. and Tribus, M., 'Information theory and
            thermodynamics.' Reprinted here as Article 3.8.

1974   Davies, P. C. W., *The Physics of Time Asymmetry.*

Everyday experience indicates that information only increases with time.
Our own memories grow as we do, public libraries accumulate books, the
moon accumulates craters from meteoric impacts. There is no incompat-
ibility between the simultaneous growth of both entropy and information.
. . . The law of entropy increase refers to closed systems, the law of in-
formation increase to open systems.

1974   Gabor, D., 'Foreword.'

An interesting new approach, but one which must be used with great
caution is via the connection between thermodynamics and information
theory, pioneered in 1928 by Leo Szilard. Were it not for the Second
Principle, by asking questions and answering them by experiments, we
could reduce the object the laboratory and ourselves to any improbable
state. But in a time-reversed world, there would not be much point in
asking questions; the answer would always precede the question! . . . I be-
lieve that the Second Principle (like the Third) is meaningless in classical
physics and received a physical meaning only by quantum mechanics, be-
cause with classical electromagnetic theory one can construct Maxwell

Demons and Perpetuum Mobili of the second kind. It is a hunch only, but I am in good company. Max Born believed in it, and Einstein made a remark to this effect to my friend Leo Szilard, around 1925.

1974   Gasser, R. P. H. and Richards, W. G., *Entropy and Energy Levels.* Maxwell's demon is described, with quantitative connections for a crystal made up of independent two-state molecules.

1974   Grünbaum, A., 'Is the coarse-grained entropy of classical statistical mechanics an anthropomorphism?' The author argues that entropy depends on a human choice of cell size in phase space. He finds an invariance under cell size changes in the entropy behaviour of a majority of the systems in an ensemble, even though individual systems generally display no such property. His answer to the title question is negative.

1974   Jammer, M., *The Philosophy of Quantum Mechanics.* In a chapter on the theory of measurement, Jammer refers to von Neumann's views, which were influenced by Smoluchowski and Szilard.

1974   Kivel, B., 'A relation between the second law of thermodynamics and quantum mechanics.' This short discussion attributes the demon's failure to beat the second law to energy quantization

1974   Laing, R., 'Maxwell's demon and computation.' Reprinted here as Article 4.3.

1974   Lindblad, G., 'Measurements and information for thermodynamic quantities.' Lindblad shows that the reduction in entropy that an observer can obtain in a system described by a fluctuating thermodynamic parameter is less than the information possessed by the observer.

1974   Pekelis, V., *Cybernetics A to Z.* A lively, popularized account, where Maxwell's demon is used to impart an understanding of entropy. Relevant history from Clausius through Brillouin is covered qualitatively.

1974   Popper, K., *The Philosophy of Karl Popper.* Popper criticizes Szilard's 1929 paper, which establishes a link between entropy and information. He labels as 'spurious' Szilard's suggestion that knowledge and entropy are related. See the contrasting discussion in Section 1.5 herein.

*What I am **not** ready to accept is Szilard's more general argument by which he tries to establish the theorem that knowledge, or information, about the position of M (the molecule) can be converted into negentropy, and vice versa. This alleged theorem I regard, I am afraid, as sheer subjectivist nonsense. ... I assert, we do not need any knowledge regarding* *the location of M: all we need is to slide our piston into the cylinder. If M happens to be on the left, the piston will be driven to the right, and we can lift the weight. And if M is on the right, the piston will be driven to the left, and we can also lift a weight: nothing is easier than to fit the apparatus with some gear so that it lifts a weight in either case, without our having to know which of the two possible directions the impending movement will take. Thus no knowledge is needed here for the balancing of the entropy increase; and Szilard's analysis turns out to be a mistake: he has offered no valid argument whatever for the intrusion of knowledge into physics.*

1974   Rothstein, J., 'Loschmidt's and Zermelo's paradoxes do not exist.'

'Where reversal or recurrence are operationally realizable, no contradiction with the irreversible nature of macroscopic operations occurs. Paradox results either from neglecting irreversible phenomena in the means for preparing a reversed state, or from confusing elements or ensembles, which are meaningful in microstate language but meaningless operationally, with preparable macrostates, whose representation in microstate language is an ensemble whose very definition is incompatible with that of any paradox-generating element or ensemble.'

1974   Skagarstam, B., 'On the mathematical definition of entropy.'

1974   Sussman, M. V., 'Seeing entropy—the incompleat thermodynamics of the Maxwell demon bottle.' The Maxwell demon bottle is a demonstration device consisting of a long-necked, sealed flask with five black and five white spheres. The spheres can be mixed and unmixed, simulating the action of a Maxwell's demon. The author shows how the bottle can be used to 'see' entropy, and supports his discussion with calculations.

1975   Curzon, F. L. and Ahlborn, B., 'Efficiency of a Carnot Engine at Maximum Power Output.'

1975   Lerner, A. Y., *Fundamentals of Cybernetics.*

Another interesting feature is that in disproving the possibility of a Maxwell demon, we are led to establishing a direct physical relationship between information and energy. It proves possible to calculate the minimum quantity of negentropy necessary for obtaining each unit of information.

1975   Rosnay, J. de, *The Macroscope: A New World Scientific System.* The author proposes a total systemic approach to scientific knowledge and its applications to human life and society. His treatment of information theory provides a unique sociological perspective.

1975   Skagarstam, B., 'On the notions of entropy and information.' This review focuses on the history of the information-theoretic and thermodynamic entropy concepts.

1975   Trincher, K. S., 'Information and Biological Thermodynamics.'
            Maxwell's demon is addressed, but the article contains some ques-
            tionable statements.

1976   Bhandari, R., 'Entropy, information and Maxwell's demon after
            quantum mechanics.' The subjective nature of entropy and its
            relation to information and irreversibility is examined in light of
            the quantum measurement problem. Bhandari asserts that wave
            function collapse during a measurement and concomitant entropy
            increase of the universe is seen by observers who are only able to
            observe a restricted manifold of states determined by their levels
            of perception.

1976a   Brush, S. G., 'Irreversibility and indeterminism: Fourier to Heisen-
            berg.' 'Maxwell's immortal Demon proved that Victorian whimsy
            could relieve some of the gloom of the Germanic Heat Death.'
            Brush stresses that the demon 'gives us a new model for the funda-
            mental irreversible process: he translates heat flow into molecular
            mixing.'

1976b   Brush, S. G., *The Kind of Motion We Call Heat*. This detailed
            historical study of 'heat' contains discussions of Maxwell's demon
            in five different chapters.

            While Maxwell's demon is generally cited in connection with the possi-
            bility of violating the Second Law of Thermodynamics, it seems equally
            important to note that by making the mixing of different molecules the
            fundamental irreversible process, Maxwell has really strengthened the
            concept of irreversibility, especially for those who seek molecular expla-
            nations for all phenomena.

1976   Harney, R. C., 'Human perception and the uncertainty.' Order of
            magnitude calculations are given to illustrate the inability of hu-
            mans to directly observe Heisenberg's uncertainty principle. Even
            optically augmented vision is inadequate by three orders of magni-
            tude. The intent is to help reconcile the uncertainty principle with
            students' own experiences. Maxwell's demon is not addressed, but
            an extension of the arguments shown for humans to a demon's
            scale is inviting.

1976   Sherwood, M., *Maxwell's Demon*. The following quotation shows
            the role of Maxwell's demon in this novel.

            That would be a fine turn-out, a touch of cosmic irony. . . . That Max-
            well's demon should be out to cause chaos. Sorry, didn't you ever learn
            any thermodynamics? I'll explain. About a hundred years ago, . . .
            James Clerk Maxwell put forward an idea for getting around the second
            law of thermodynamics—you know, the one which Flanders and Swann
            explained as 'you can't pass heat from a colder to a hotter.' Maxwell
            postulated a two-part container . . . In the middle of the container was

a trapdoor joining the two sides, and an imp, which opened the trapdoor whenever he saw a hot molecule moving from the cold side towards the hot, to let it through. In this way, the imp, which became known as Maxwell's demon, created order out of chaos ... Until Leon Brillouin proved in the 1950s that even then you did not avoid the consequences of the second law of thermodynamics. Anyhow, that is why I liked your reverse Maxwell's demon—the one that creates chaos out of order ...

1976   Yu, F. T. S., *Optics and Information Theory.* An extensive treatment of Maxwell's demon, referring heavily to Brillouin's *Science and Information Theory* and Gabor's 'Light and Information.'

1977   Carnap, R., *Two Essays on Entropy.* See the quotation in Section 1.4

1978   Brush, S. G., *The Temperature of History. Phases of Science and Culture in the Nineteenth Century.* A brief discussion of the demon, with reference to a suggestion by Stewart and Tait that 'the Maxwell demon might operate in an "unseen universe", linked by human thought to this one, so that we could look forward to a future state untroubled by dissipation of energy.'

1978   Wehrl, A. 'General properties of entropy.' An advanced mathematical review article.

It is amusing to note that in practical applications of information theory ... the second law of thermodynamics has been adopted and there called the negentropy principle ... Thus we find a mutual interaction between physics and information theory rather than a perfect understanding of statistical mechanics on the grounds of information theory.

1979   Jaynes, E. T., 'Where Do We Stand on Maximum Entropy?' The principle of maximum entropy is examined from historical, present and potential future viewpoints.

1979   Penrose, O., 'Foundations of statistical mechanics.' An extensive review article that briefly covers various topics germane to Maxwell's demon. Discussing the non-uniqueness of entropy in non-equilibrium systems, he writes, 'Even in thermodynamics, where entropy is defined only for equilibrium states, the definition of entropy can depend on what problem we are interested in and on what experimental techniques are available ... '

1979   Poplavskii, R. P., 'Maxwell demon and the correspondence between information and entropy.' An entropic efficiency is defined, and is used to examine various order-producing control processes, including a traditional Maxwell's demon.

1979   Rothstein, J. 'Generalized Entropy, Boundary Conditions, and Biology.' Generalized entropy in the framework of a generalized thermodynamics is proposed to handle a wide variety of complex 'biotonic' laws.

1980   Bekenstein, J. D., 'Black-hole thermodynamics.' This is an update on ideas developed by the author in his Ph. D. dissertation (see Bekenstein, 1972).

1981   Denbigh, K., 'How subjective is entropy?' Reprinted here as Article 2.7.

1981   Denur, J., 'The Doppler demon.' See also Motz (1983) and Chardin (1984).

> *Equilibrium blackbody radiation, like all radiation, is, in general, Doppler shifted if it is emitted and/or reflected from a moving body. The relevance of this fact to the analysis of Maxwell's demon, which has been previously neglected, is revealed in this paper. In particular, we find that, by appropriately taking advantage of this fact, Maxwell's demon is, at least in principle, capable of operating, albeit very weakly, in violation of the Second Law of Thermodynamics.*

1981   El'yashevich, M. A. and Prot'ko, T. S., 'Maxwell's contribution to the development of molecular physics and statistical methods.' The authors examine Maxwell's contributions to molecular physics during 1859–1879, including his ideas on the limitations of the second law: 'Maxwell's demon was essentially the first important illustration of the difference between microscopic and macroscopic processes.'

1981   Gordon, L. G. M., 'Brownian movement and microscopic irreversibility.' A microengine model that appears to violate the second law of thermodynamics is proposed and discussed.

1981   Kosloff, R., 'Thermodynamic aspects of the quantum-mechanical measuring process.' An advanced treatment of quantum measurement theory that uses Maxwell's demon and the work of Szilard and Brillouin as a starting point.

1981a Rossis, G., 'La logique des expériences de pensée et l'expérience de Szilard.' This article supports criticisms of Popper and Feyerabend regarding Szilard's one-molecule heat engine. The author finds that the model 'does not demonstrate the necessity of the identity between negentropy and information.'

1981b Rossis, G., 'Sur la discussion par Brillouin de l'expérience de pensée de Maxwell.' Rossis argues that Brillouin's discussion of Maxwell's demon 'is limited to a mere examination of certain types of possible demons, which is methodologically incorrect.' He finds that 'Brillouin's discussion does not demonstrate in the least the necessity of the validity of the identity between entropy and information.'

1981   Zemansky, M. W. and Dittman, R. H., *Heat and Thermodynamics.* One of the surprisingly few texts that includes a good description of the function of the demon. Although the text follows his arguments, Brillouin's name is not mentioned; there is instead a reference to Rodd's 1964 analysis (Reprinted here as Article 3.5). Earlier, in the fourth edition (1957), Zemansky (sole author) alluded to Brillouin's work, stating 'information seems to be related to negative entropy or, as Brillouin puts it, "negentropy"—but use of a light source is not mentioned. In the Second edition (1943, prior to Brillouin's analysis), Zemansky presented the puzzle but did not attempt to solve it. He simply made Maxwell's point, 'If the trap door were left open and unattended by a Maxwell's demon, there would be a small probability of a separation of the fast from the slow molecules, but a much larger probability of an even distribution.'

1982   Benioff, P., 'Quantum mechanical models of Turing Machines that dissipate no energy.' This paper demonstrates non-dissipative Hamiltonian models of Turing machines, constructed on a finite lattice of spin-1/2 systems.

1982   Bennett, C. H., 'The thermodynamics of computation—a review.' Reprinted here as Article 4.4.

1982   Campbell, J., *Grammatical Man: Information, Entropy, Language, and Life.* An excellent book for a general audience, with a chapter on 'The Demon Deposed.' The following quotation by Claude Shannon in 1979 is given:

> *I think the connection between information theory and thermodynamics will hold up in the long run, but it has not been fully explored and understood. There is more there than we know at present. Scientists have been investigating the atom for about a hundred years and they are continually finding more and more depth, more and more understanding. It may be that the same will be true of the relationship we are speaking about.*

1982   Harman, P. M., *Energy, Force, and Matter: The Conceptual Development of Nineteenth-Century Physics.* An excellent discussion of the demon in the context of 19th century thermodynamics.

1982   Landauer, R., 'Uncertainty principle and minimal energy dissipation in the computer.' It is argued that Heisenberg's energy–time uncertainty principle, $\Delta E \Delta t \approx h/2\pi$, does not yield any information about dissipation in a computer system with switching time Δt.

1982   Landsberg, P. T., *The Enigma of Time.* Landsberg considers a pressure-demon, and observes that Maxwell, who predated quantum theory, assumed implicitly that the energy required for any observation can be made negligibly small, but quantum physics does not allow this.

1982   Likharev, K. K., 'Classical and quantum limitations on energy consumption in computation.' Using a model (parametric quantron) of a real physical device based on the Josephson effect in superconductors, Likharev argues that logical operations can be physically reversible. This kind of device can be an elementary cell in a logically reversible computer. Energy dissipation per logical operation in the classical and quantum limits, respectively, is found to be $< kT$ and $< h/(2\pi\tau)$ where τ is the process period.

1982   Pagels, H., *Cosmic Code.* This layman's book contains a readable account of statistical mechanics, including the statistical nature of the second law.

1982   Popper, K. R., *Quantum Theory and the Schism in Physics.*

> *There is a further very real difficulty which has contributed to make the subjectivist interpretation of entropy more acceptable. I have in mind the problem of Maxwell's demon: since 1905, the success of the exorcism of the demon has become dubious, and this fact has led to attempts to solve the problem by invoking subjective probabilities, and other measures of subjective knowledge (or 'information'). No doubt some interesting analogies have been unearthed, but the soundness of the edifice, and especially the part played by Maxwell's demon, seems to me highly questionable.*

1982   Schweber, S. 'Demons, angels, and probability: Some aspects of British science in the nineteenth century.' Maxwell's demon is compared with a species-sorting 'being' proposed in 1844 by Charles Darwin, and genealogies of both beings are conjectured. Influences of the nineteenth century philosophers Quetelet and Buckle on Darwin, Maxwell and Boltzmann are examined in detail.

1982   Silverman, M. P., 'The vortex tube: a violation of the second law?' The Hilsch vortex tube is considered and compared with Maxwell's demon. Analysis reveals that just as a Maxwell's demon cannot overthrow the second law, the vortex tube also fails to do so.

1982   Weinberg, A. M., 'On the relation between information and energy systems: A family of Maxwell's demons.' Reprinted here as Article 2.8.

1983   Davies, P. C. W., *God and the New Physics.* Davies asks: If a supreme being existed, constrained to act within the laws of physics, could it prevent the end of the universe? He concludes the answer is negative.

1983   Eigen, M. and Winkler, R., *Laws of the Game: How the Principles of Nature Govern Chance.* The authors examine an imagined cessation of irreversibility in nature, and discuss several thought-provoking hypothetical demons.

1983   Gordon, L. G. M., 'Maxwell's demon and detailed balancing.' Gordon analyzes an isothermal gas of molecules separated by a membrane, each pore of which is controlled by an independent molecular trap door that can exist in either of two states. Under certain conditions, this membrane acts like a Maxwell's demon, effecting a density and pressure gradient across the membrane, lowering the system's entropy—apparently violating the second law.

1983   Lindblad, G., *Non-equilibrium Entropy and Irreversibility.* The author gives a formal mathematical treatment of information and entropy, and applies it to the Maxwell's demon problem.

1983   Motz, H., 'The Doppler demon exorcised.' The author argues against the conclusion of Denur (1981) that a Doppler demon can defeat the second law. See also Chardin (1984).

1984   Robinson, A. L., 'Computing without dissipating energy.' A status report on the minimum energy needed for computation.

1984   Atkins, P. W., *The Second Law.* Atkins discusses 'Boltzmann's demon,' who constantly rearranges microscopic states without changing macroscopically observed phenomena. Though apparently inspired by the Maxwell's demon, it does not violate or threaten any laws, but its random actions trap it in the future by assuring that return to an initial state is overwhelmingly improbable.

1984   Chardin, G., 'No free lunch for the Doppler demon.' The author argues against the conclusion of Denur (1981) that a Doppler demon can defeat the second law. See also Motz (1983).

1984   Porod, W., Grondin, R. O., Ferry, D. K. and Porod, G., 'Dissipation in computation.' The authors object to the view that computation with dissipation $< kT \ln 2$ per bit operation is possible. This drew strong responses from Benioff, Bennett, Landauer and Toffoli, and a subsequent rejoinder from Porod *et al.*

> *The question of the energy dissipation in the computational process is considered. Contrary to previous studies, dissipation is found to be an integral part of computation. A complementarity is suggested between systems that are describable in thermodynamic terms and systems that can be used for computation.*

1984   Benioff, P., 'Comment on 'dissipation in computation'.' Benioff responds to Porod *et al* (1984).

> *... the construction of the quantum mechanical models ... is an idealized construction only. It is an open question whether such models can also be physically constructed in the laboratory. However, the idealized existence of such models demonstrates that one cannot use purely quantum mechanical arguments ... to deny the existence of models which dissipate no energy.*

1984   Bennett, C. H., 'Thermodynamically reversible computation.' Bennett responds to Porod *et al* (1984).

> *Although it is easy to imagine dissipative ways of reading or logically transforming information, there also exist, in general, thermodynamically reversible ways, whenever the intended logical transformation conserves phase space. In such a transformation, although the individual parts of the computer (e.g., the reading head) may indeed evolve in a many-to-one or one-to-many manner, the state of the whole computer evolves in a one-to-one manner. A simple example of reversible information transfer is the use of a classical mass spectrometer to transcribe mass information into positional information. Even in quantum mechanics, where some irreversibility may be needed to fix the result of a measurement by destroying the phase coherence between measured and measuring systems, a single irreversible step is enough to fix the result of a long chain of reversible premeasurements.*

1984a   Landauer, R., 'Dissipation in computation.' Landauer responds to Porod *et al* (1984).

> *(Porod et al) is confined to general arguments and does not explain, in detail, where the specific reversible computer proposals, e.g., that of Likharev, go astray. ...*

1984   Toffoli, R., 'Comment on 'Dissipation in computation'.' Toffoli responds to Porod *et al* (1984).

> *... the dissipation in a computer is bounded by the sum of **two terms**. Both are essentially proportional to kT; the first, through a coefficient $m \ln 2$, where m is no greater than the number of input/output lines; the second, through a coefficient nd, where n is no greater than the number of gates (each counted as many times as it is used ...), and d is a 'technological factor' that, as far as one knows, can be made as small as desired. Thus, the highest bound to the dissipation **per elementary operation** that is definitely known today is of the form $[(m/n)\ln 2 + d]kT$. For any T, this bound vanishes for computers that are designed to run long computations without displaying intermediate results (i.e., $n \gg m$), and in the limit of perfect technology $(d \to 0)$. This is what **virtually nondissipative computation** means.*

1984   Porod, W., Grondin, R. O., Ferry, D. K. and Porod, G., 'Porod *et al* respond.' This group defends its original position steadfastly,

stating : (1) physical and logical states of a system must be distinguished, and Landauer's 1961 paper fails to do so; (2) purely
mechanical models of computers are unrealistic because noise is
unavoidable for $T > 0$; (3) the zero speed limit is useless, for 'both
dissipation and computation disappear'; (4) information erasure
is a dissipative interaction with a heat bath, (rather than a non-
invertible process); and (5) if reading can be dissipationless, then
erasure can be too.

*Landauer is correct that merely coupling two systems together, especially
in a closed environment, does not induce dissipation.* **It also does not
constitute a measurement.** *Indeed, information initially in one of
the systems will oscillate back and forth between the two systems. Measurement of the information must arise from opening the closed environment at some particular time (and thus subjecting it to the background
heat bath). Erasure of information should be viewed not as a result of
non-invertibility, but as a result of interactions with the heat bath.*

1984b   Landauer, R., 'Fundamental physical limitations of the computa-
               tional process.'

*This study of ultimate computer limits is in its infancy; it is easier to
ask questions than answer them. To the extent that we have answers, the
limits are terribly far away from reality. Therefore, we cannot claim to
be guiding the technologist. Then why are the limits interesting? It is a
matter of basic science; we are starting a physical theory of mathematics.
Most mathematicians have little sympathy for the assertion that their
subject requires a basis in physics. Information, however, whether it is
in biological systems, in a digital computer, or handled by pencil and
paper, inevitably has a physical form. Information is represented by a
mark on a piece of paper, a hole in a punched card, a magnetic material
magnetized one way or the other, a charge that is present or absent, a
Josephson junction that is superconducting or not, etc. Information can
come on a much smaller scale, e.g., in the molecular configuration of
DNA or, conceivably, even through the spin of a single electron which
can be pointed up or down. It is impossible to get away from this sort
of physical embodiment. As a result, manipulation of information is
inevitably subject to the laws of physics.*

1984   Prigogine, I. and Stengers, I., *Order out of Chaos*. This well-known
               book describes recent progress in non-equilibrium thermodynam-
               ics.

*... in the subjective interpretation of irreversibility (further reinforced
by the ambiguous analogy with information theory), the observer is responsible for the temporal asymmetry characterizing the system's development. Since the observer cannot in a single glance determine the
positions and velocities of all the particles composing a complex system,
he cannot know the instantaneous state that simultaneously contains its
past and its future, nor can he grasp the reversible law that would allow
him to predict its developments from one moment to the next. Neither*

can he manipulate the system like the demon invented by Maxwell, who can separate fast- and slow-moving particles and impose on a system an anti-thermodynamic evolution toward an increasingly less uniform temperature distribution.

1984   Smorodinsky, Y. A., *Temperature*. In this semipopular book, the author devotes a section to 'Maxwell's Imp.' Although there are some interesting ideas here, the writing (or translation) is difficult to follow.

1984a Zurek, W. H., 'Maxwell's demon, Szilard's engine and quantum measurements.' Reprinted here as Article 4.5.

1984b Zurek, W. H., 'Reversibility and stability of information processing systems.'

Instabilities in the evolution of the classical 'billiard ball computer' are analyzed and shown to result in a one-bit increase of entropy per step of computation. 'Quantum spin computers,' on the other hand, are not only microscopically, but also operationally reversible. Readoff of the output of quantum computation is shown not to interfere with this reversibility. Dissipation, while avoidable in principle, can be used in practice along with redundancy to prevent errors.

1985   Bennett, C. H. and Landauer, R., 'The fundamental physical limits of computation.' A very readable article, intended for a sophisticated lay audience, on limiting factors in computation.

In physical systems without friction, information can never be destroyed; whenever information is destroyed, some amount of energy must be dissipated (converted into heat). As an example, imagine two easily distinguishable physical situations, such as a rubber ball held either one metre or two metres off the ground. If the ball is dropped, it will bounce. If there is no friction and the ball is perfectly elastic, an observer will always be able to tell what state the ball started out in (that is, what its initial height was) because a ball dropped from two meters will bounce higher than a ball dropped from one meter. If there is friction, however, the ball will dissipate a small amount of energy with each bounce, until it eventually stops bouncing and comes to rest on the ground. It will then be impossible to determine what the ball's initial state was; a ball dropped from two meters will be identical with a ball dropped from one meter. Information will have been lost as a result of energy dissipation.

1985   Denbigh, K. G. and Denbigh, J. S., *Entropy in Relation to Incomplete Knowledge*. This critical analysis of the notion that entropy is subjective is an outgrowth of Denbigh's 1981 paper.

Although information theory is more comprehensive than is statistical mechanics, this very comprehensiveness gives rise to objectionable consequences when it is applied in physics and chemistry. Since the subjective interpretation of probability, on which information theory has been based, is more general than is the objective interpretation, the language in which the theory is presented necessarily takes on a subjective character. A probability distribution is thus said to represent **our** *state of knowledge, whereas in physico-chemical contexts it is usually justifiable to go much further in an objective direction and to regard a probability distribution as being characteristic of the nature of the system in question and of the physical constraints upon it. It remains true, nevertheless, that information theory can be of value in an heuristic sense. This was seen to be so in the Maxwell Demon problem ...*

1985   Hastings, H. M. and Waner, S., 'Low dissipation computing in biological systems.'

1985a   Jaynes, E. T., 'Entropy and search theory.' The relation between entropy maximization and optimal strategy is explored for a model involving a search for a hidden target.

1985b   Jaynes, E. T., 'Generalized Scattering.' Inferential scattering is a process whereby inference is modified by added constraints based upon new knowledge. Remaximizing entropy using the new constraints, rather than using physical dynamics deductively, is examined, with emphasis on understanding why the MAXENT formalism works.

1985c   Jaynes, E. T., 'Macroscopic Prediction.' Given information about a set A of macroscopic quantities in space–time region 1, how one can best predict the values of a set B of macroscopic quantities in space–time region 2? Jaynes addresses this, focusing on inference based on information, rather than on logical deduction via physical law.

1985   Poundstone, W., *The Recursive Universe*. This readable book for a general audience contains a chapter on Maxwell's demon summarizing much of the work from Smoluchowski to Brillouin.

1985   Rosen, R., *Theoretical Biology and Complexity*.

     ... historically, the relation between theoretical physics and biology has never been close. None of the great names of physical science, from Newton to the present, have known or cared much about the properties of organisms, and therefore organic phenomena played no essential part in their science (leaving aside such diversions as Maxwell's demon, Schrödinger's informal essays, and the like).

1985   Waldram, J. R., *The Theory of Thermodynamics*.

     ... it is true in principle that we **can** *reduce the entropy of an isolated system ... by taking measurements of the system (though the number of measurements needed to produce even a tiny reduction in entropy is formidable). But we do not reduce the entropy of the whole world in*

this process, for there is a compensating increase of entropy associated
with the process of observation. There is therefore, alas, no prospect
of providing for the energy needs of mankind by suitably marshalling a
small horde of Maxwell demons.

1985   Watanabe, S., 'Wiener on cybernetics, information theory and en-
        tropy.' This contains commentary on six papers by Norbert Wiener
        on the title subjects, two of which (Wiener, 1950, 1952) are listed
        separately here.

Maxwell's demon is of course closely related to the possible decrease of
thermodynamical entropy. Indeed, Wiener's two major books ... start
with a chapter on the Bergsonian concept of time. Wiener was fascinated
by Bergson's idea that 'a living organism climbs the slope where the inert
objects go down', meaning that the former somehow behaves as if its
entropy were decreasing. Wiener probably wanted to suggest that the
cybernetical system somehow could reproduce such an entropy-decreasing
phenomenon without violating the second law of thermodynamics.

1986   Alekseev, G. N., *Energy and Entropy.* An interesting qualitative
        discourse concerned with the statistical nature of the second law,
        but with the following nonstandard view.

Despite the power of (Brillouin's) arguments, there may still be objec-
tions to it. The demon may be in form of a spring with a valve actu-
ated by fast molecules and closed after they enter. Another approach is
possible. Let us agree with Maxwell that a demon can really sort out
molecules, thereby creating a temperature difference and decreasing the
entropy of the gas. This would not violate the second law! This law is
statistical and only valid for macroscopic phenomena; it does not follow
the molecular level. If we consider only two molecules, they will settle in
one section of the vessel 50% of the time. If there are many molecules,
the probability that they all end up in one section is not excluded by the
second law, it is only reduced to its minimum value.

1986   Barrow, J. D. and Tipler, F. J., *The Anthropic Cosmological Prin-*
        ciple. This contains a well-written discussion of Maxwell's demon,
        emphasizing that the demon is the size of a molecule and sees
        things differently from macroscopic observers. The authors allude
        to existing controversies about Maxwell's demon, and side with the
        traditional view based largely on Brillouin's work.

1986   Davies, P. C. W., *The Ghost in the Atom.* This excellent book
        deals with the mysteries of quantum physics. Although there is
        no discussion of Maxwell's demon *per se*, there is a discussion of
        a single electron in a box into which an impenetrable screen is
        inserted. See the related discussion herein, in Section 1.6.1.

It is thought, prior to the observation, there are two nebulous electron
'ghosts' each inhabiting one chamber waiting for an observation to turn

one of them into a 'real' electron, and simultaneously to cause the other to vanish completely.

1986   Drogin, E. M., 'Maxwell's Demon Lives.'

According to Pierce you can feed a paper tape into a Turing machine and have it churn away madly for days and days, with no expenditure of energy required (provided that you don't have to know the initial state of the machine or reset it to get it going). But if a hammer comes out of the machine and hits you over the head to tell you the computation is complete, or if you use the teeniest, tiniest lit candle ... to read the scratches on the tape, you have broken the rules of the perpetual-motion machine game. Sorry about that.

1986   Feynman, R. P., 'Quantum Mechanical Computers.' Feynman examines idealized quantum mechanical computers, and gives support to the concept that logical operations can in principle be physically reversible.

... we are going to be even more ridiculous ... and consider bits written on one atom instead of the present 10^{11} atoms. Such nonsense is very entertaining to professors like me. I hope you will find it interesting and entertaining also. ... it seems that the laws of physics present no barrier to reducing the size of computers until bits are the size of atoms, and quantum behavior holds dominant sway.

1986   Fine, A., *The Shaky Game: Einstein, Realism, and the Quantum Theory.* Fine describes Einstein's thought experiment discussed herein in Section 1.6.1.

1986a   Landauer, R., 'Computation and physics: Wheeler's meaning circuit?'

Computation is a physical process, inevitably utilizing physical degrees of freedom. Computation, therefore, is restricted by the laws of physics and also by the construction materials and operating environments available in our actual universe. These restrictions have been investigated for a quarter century. ... Physical law, in turn, consists of algorithms for information processing. Therefore, the ultimate form of physical laws must be consistent with the restrictions on the physical executability of algorithms, which is in turn dependent on physical law.

1986b   Landauer, R., 'Reversible computation.'

Logically reversible functions can, of course, be carried out in ways which are very dissipative, e.g. via transistor circuitry. The logical reversibility, however, allows us to invent physical devices in which the process can actually be reversed, i.e., the information bearing degrees of freedom can be pushed back through the device to undo the operation. ... Energy dissipation, per step, and computing speed, are proportional to each other in these systems; if we are willing to compute slowly we have no minimal energy requirement per computer step. These are systems in which we allow friction, but we idealize and assume that the frictional forces, as in hydrodynamics and electricity, are proportional to velocity. We rule out static friction ...

1986   Porter, T. M., *The Rise of Statistical Thinking: 1820–1900.* An interesting historical study of how statistical ideas became used in the social sciences, biology, and physics. Maxwell's strong influence on the development of kinetic theory and statistical mechanics is well documented:

To Maxwell belongs the credit for first introducing the explicit consideration of probability distributions into physics. Indeed he was arguably the first to use distribution formulas in a significant and productive way in any science ... Maxwell first pointed out that his dynamical theory of gases implied the possibility of violating the second law in 1867, in a playful letter to P. G. Tait. There he introduced the 'very observant and neat-fingered being,' later dubbed by William Thomson Maxwell's 'demon,' whose mission was to 'pick a hole' in the second law ... Maxwell's invention implied that some physical principles, among them the second law, were really as much attributes of human perception as of nature itself.

1987   Bennett, C. H., 'Demons, engines and the Second law.' An excellent survey of Maxwell's demon history through Bennett's resolution of the puzzle via memory erasure.

Another source of confusion is that we do not generally think of information as a liability. We pay to have newspapers delivered, not taken away. Intuitively, the demon's record of past actions seems to be a valuable (or at worst a useless) commodity. But for the demon 'yesterday's newspaper' (the result of a previous measurement) takes up valuable space, and the cost of clearing that space neutralizes the benefit the demon derived from the newspaper when it was fresh. Perhaps the increasing awareness of environmental pollution and the information explosion brought on by computers have made the idea that information can have a negative value seem more natural now than it would have seemed earlier in this century.

1987   Hawking, S., 'The direction of time.' An expository article on the arrow of time. Hawking explicitly states that the process of writing to a computer memory is dissipative, putting him in conflict with proponents of the idea that in principle, computing can be done reversibly, and that only erasure of information is dissipative.

1987   Johnson, H. A., 'Thermal noise and biological information.' The steady loss of information due to thermal noise in information-handling biological systems is examined. The systems addressed include solutions, cell membranes and regulatory organs. Pointing out that the renal tubules of the kidney perform a sorting function like that of Maxwell's demon, the author estimates a kidney's energy requirement and efficiency when thermal noise is taken into account.

1987a   Landauer, R., 'Computation: A fundamental physical view.' Reprinted here as Article 4.6.

1987b   Landauer, R., 'Computation: A fundamental physical view.' Note that, despite the title similarity, this article is distinct from Landauer, 1987a. See the Alphabetical Bibliography for citation details.

1987c   Landauer, R., 'Energy requirements in communication.' This short paper uses physical transport of bistable systems as an example in which there is no minimal dissipation per transmitted bit of information, and in which dissipation occurs only when information is discarded.

1987d   Landauer, R., 'Fundamental physical limitations of the computational process; an informal commentary.'

1987a   Leff, H. S., 'Available work from a finite source and sink: how effective is a Maxwell's demon?' See Section 1.6.2 herein.

1987b   Leff, H. S., 'Thermal efficiency at maximum work output: New results for old heat engines.' See Section 1.6.2 herein.

1987   Lubkin, E., 'Keeping the entropy of measurement: Szilard revisited.' Reprinted here as Article 4.7.

1987   Obermayer, K., Mahler, G. and Haken, H., 'Multistable quantum systems: Information processing at microscopic levels.' The authors propose building a semiconductor device on a nanometre scale that will allow them to measure directly the energy dissipation involved in certain processes.

1987   Maddox, J., 'Quantum information storage.' A capsule summary of work by Obermayer, Mahler and Haken (1987).

1987   Rex, A. F., 'The operation of Maxwell's demon in a low entropy system.' Reprinted here as Article 3.9.

1987   Spielberg, N. and Anderson, B. D., *Seven Ideas that Shook the Universe.* In a chapter on entropy and probability, one of the seven areas that comprise this book, there is a section, 'Entropy and Order: Maxwell's Demon.' Described as famous and fanciful, the demon is dismissed because the 'second law of thermodynamics states that elves and demons exist only in fairy tales, and Maxwell's demon was only a figment of his imagination ... '

1987   Wicken, J. S., 'Entropy and information: Suggestions for a common language.' This paper clarifies the differences between thermodynamic and information theory entropies, and suggests 'semantic house-keeping', whereby information entropy is renamed 'complexity' and 'entropy' is reserved for thermodynamics.

> *There is no **real** information relevant to thermodynamics beyond that provided by the macroscopic state specification. Entropy is real in thermodynamics. And whereas microstates are probably real in some more-than-accounting sense, the concept of 'microscopic information' concerning their actual **occupancy** at any moment is an encumbering abstraction for thermodynamics. With information theory, on the other hand, entropy is the encumbering abstraction. Both abstractions are inimical to productive dialogue between thermodynamics and information theory.*

1988   Barrow, J. D., *The World within the World*. A good general interest book for the scientifically mature. Barrow gives credence to both the traditional (dissipative information acquisition) and modern (dissipative memory erasure) viewpoints, broadening the position in Barrow and Tipler's *The Anthropic Cosmological Principle* (1986).

> *The weak link in the demon's enterprise was discovered by Leo Szilard in 1929 ... The problem is that he has got to identify which are the fast and slow particles as they approach the trapdoor, trap them, liberate them into the other compartment, and then reset his apparatus into a state which can identify another molecule's speed as faster or slower than average ... The work he must perform in order to discriminate between the fast and slow particles and then destroy this information in order to repeat the operation from a clean start always outweighs the work that can be performed by exploiting the temperature difference created by the demonic activity. Maxwell's demon is exorcized. It is not possible for him to create a violation of the second law any more than it is possible to show a profit at roulette by always betting on all the numbers. The cost of implementing such a strategy always exceeds the possible winnings.*

1988   Bennett, C. H., 'Notes on the history of reversible computation.' Reprinted here as Article 4.8.

1988   Jaynes, E. T., 'Clearing up mysteries—The original goal.' The Bayesian inference viewpoint is used to understand three examples: diffusion, the EPR paradox, and the second law of thermodynamics in biology.

1988a   Landauer, R., 'Dissipation and noise immunity in computation and communication.'

> *... the word measurement is ambiguous, and remains so even in some sophisticated discussions of the concept. Some believe that involvement of a human observer is an essential ingredient. I believe that James*

Watt's invention of the centrifugal governor showed that the human mind did not have to participate. The thermostat in your home makes a measurement, even when you are not there. Other authors, although not arguing for human involvement do invoke the necessity of recording or registry in a macroscopic piece of apparatus, which I interpret as at least more reasonable. Nevertheless, at a time when we can manipulate and observe individual atoms and when we know how, in principle, to use apparatus modelled on the genetic code to do computation, it is not clear that macroscopic apparatus is essential.

1988   Lindgren, K., 'Microscopic and macroscopic entropy.' Seeking a microscopic counterpart to entropy, Lindgren examines a 'measure entropy' for physical systems in which microstates can be represented as symbol sequences. In the thermodynamic limit, the ensemble average of the measure entropy equals the thermodynamic entropy if correlations decrease sufficiently fast with distance.

1988   Porod, W., 'Comment on "Energy requirements in communication." A critical letter, reacting to Landauer's "Energy requirements in communication" ' (1987c).

... the flaw in Landauer's argument is the failure to distinguish between physical reversibility and logical reversibility. While physical irreversibility implies dissipation of energy, logical irreversibility (contrary to Landauer) does not, by itself, imply dissipation of energy. By the same token, logical reversibility does not imply physical reversibility. (This latter argument voids the basic premise on which all reversible computing schemes are based.) We emphasize that logical reversibility (or irreversibility) is irrelevant for the energy dissipation encountered in a process, be it computation or communication.

1988b   Landauer, R., 'Response.' A response to Porod's 1988 letter.

Porod is not the only one who has voiced some disagreement with reversible computation. Porod, however is the only one to claim: 'There is, however, no reason to assume that, in general, logical irreversibility implies physical irreversibility.' Porod asserts this without providing examples of logical irreversibility unaccompanied by physical irreversibility. Enough has been published on this subject, including rebuttals to similar earlier arguments by Porod and collaborators, so that a further detailed rebuttal is not needed. A number of of investigators ... have expanded our understanding of the energy requirements in computation ... We note that all of the critics invoke their perception of general principles supposedly violated by the discussions of reversible computation. The critics never point to flaws in the specific methods which are invoked to achieve low dissipation.

1988   Layzer, D., 'Growth of order in the universe,' Layzer imagines a Maxwell's demon substitute, programmed to open and close the trap door according to the results of a calculation that predicts the positions and velocities of all molecules for times after an initial moment. Sometimes called 'Loschmidt's non-demon' (see Rothstein, 1959), this shows that the second law can fail if sufficient microscopic information about the initial state is present.

1988   Peres, A., 'Schrödinger's immortal cat.' A review of the quantum measurement problem with a brief reference to Szilard's 1929 paper and a section on the physical limitations of computing.

1988a   Rothstein, J., 'Entropy and the evolution of complexity and individuality.' A broad-based discussion of the concept of generalized entropy and its relevance to quantum theory, biology and thermodynamics.

1988b   Rothstein, J., 'On ultimate thermodynamic limitations in communication and computation.'

> *Our attitude to reversible computing is thus much like that to Maxwell's demon—it is amusing, instructive, challenging and conceptually useful in helping to mark the boundary between what we would like to achieve and what can actually be achieved. We stress its value here to avoid misconstruing the intent of this paper. Though it obviously denies that reversible computers hold any hope of being 'practical' (in addition to all the foregoing they are too slow), it affirms the value and necessity of scrutinizing scientific foundations carefully. Thought experiments are not idle amusements. Good ones confront accepted concepts and techniques with paradoxes and new challenges, clarifying new advances and pointing out the limits of the old. Reversible computers are valuable additions to the library of thought experiments, and we hope they help in pushing computers to their ultimate thermodynamic limits.*

1988   Tansjö, L., 'Comment on the discovery of the second law.' A brief historical paper discussing the ideas of Carnot, Thomson, Maxwell and others.

1988a   Wright, R., *Three Scientists and Their Gods*. A popular account about three eccentric scientists concerned with information transfer in physics, computers, biology and in animal societies.

> *... the demon, all told, cannot reduce entropy. ... to create even the illusion of entropy reduction—to pile up lots of order in one place while sweeping disorder under the rug—the demon must process information. In the end, there is no escape from the second law, and it takes information even to buy time.*

1988b   Wright, R., 'Did the universe just happen?' This article, on computer scientist Edward Fredkin, contains similar material about Fredkin and Maxwell's demon to that in *Three Scientists and Their Gods* (1988).

1989   Costa de Beauregard, O., 'The computer and the heat engine.' A
              computer is viewed as an engine that delivers information. Both
              memory erasure and and message duplication are argued to be
              dissipative. The latter is in contrast with the findings of Landauer
              and Bennett.

1989a   Landauer, R., 'Response to "The computer and the heat engine".'

              *Our critics rely on their perception of general principles, which they
              believe we violate. They do not take one of the several detailed embod-
              iments of reversible computation ... and tell us what detailed mistake
              that author made. As a result of this omission, the critics can avoid
              confrontation of the details of the computational process ... They can
              stick to their own, possibly erroneous, perceptions about computation. It
              may be possible that one, or another, of the detailed reversible computer
              schemes has a flaw. The critics need to do more than find that; they
              need to show that a substantial proportion of the reversible computer
              proposals do not work.*

1989b   Landauer, R., 'Computation, measurement, communication and
              energy dissipation.'

              *... if we assume that we can characterize our initial system completely,
              can calculate its subsequent time evolution to any required degree of ac-
              curacy, and can build the equipment needed to extract the energy, then
              energy put into a finite Hamiltonian system can always be extracted, and
              there is not dissipation. All of the assumptions we have made, however,
              are open to question, if the system has a good many degrees of freedom
              and particularly if we have let a lot of time elapse since the energy was
              put into the system. ... We have, in a limited way come full circle.
              First we learned that discarding information requires energy dissipation.
              Now we are suggesting that energy dissipation is the consequence (in
              part) of insufficient information to allow energy retrieval. Thus, there
              is almost an equivalence between dissipation and an information loss.*

1989   Landsberg, P. T. and Leff, H. S., 'Thermodynamic cycles with
              nearly-universal maximum-work efficiencies.'   See Section 1.6.2
              herein.

1989   Leff, H. S., 'Maxwell's demon, power, and time.' See Section 1.6.2
              herein.

1989   Smith, C. and Wise, M. N., *Energy and Empire: A Biographical
              Study of Lord Kelvin.* A thoughtful account of the early history of
              Maxwell's demon, with emphasis on William Thomson's contribu-
              tions.

              *So long as the demon had to employ material tools—cricket bats, valves,
              arms, trap doors, or switches—in order to direct molecules, any descrip-
              tion of his action within abstract dynamics would require the transfer of*

finite amounts of energy from mind to the finite molecules of the directing material. The demon's action, therefore, could serve at best as a mere analogy for free will, limited to an idealized action that did not require mind to store energy. A number of authors in Thomson's circle employed Maxwell's analogy in this sense ...

1989?   Zurek, W. H., 'Algorithmic randomness and physical entropy. I.' An ambitious study of physical entropy, using ideas of algorithmic information theory. Physical entropy is viewed as a sum of missing Shannon information and the algorithmic information content. This enables a reformulation of the first law of thermodynamics for engines operated by entities capable of information acquisition and processing.

The definition of the physical entropy proposed here is made possible by the algorithmic definition of randomness. It is made necessary by the desire to discuss the function of the Maxwell's demon from its own perspective. Moreover, the demon's role can be successfully played by an automaton capable of (1) acquiring information through reversible measurements, (2) processing it in a manner analogous to the universal computer, and (3) adopting strategies which aim to optimize its behavior so that—for example—it can economically extract useful energy from the available sources.

1989b   Zurek, W. H., 'Thermodynamic cost of computation, algorithmic complexity and the information metric.' Algorithmic complexity is adopted as a measure of randomness. This sets limits on the thermodynamic cost of computation and casts new light on the limitations of Maxwell's demon.

I have demonstrated that the second law is safe even in the presence of 'intelligent beings', as long as their abilities to process information are subject to the same laws as those of universal Turing machines.

1990   Leff, H. S. and Rex, A. F., 'Resource Letter MD-1: Maxwell's Demon.' This contains more than 200 annotated references to Maxwell's demon and related subjects.

Alphabetical Bibliography

Alekseev, G. N., *Energy and Entropy* (Mir Publishers, Moscow, 1986), pp. 180–183.

Allen, H. S. and Maxwell, R. S., *A Text-Book of Heat* (Macmillan and Co., Ltd., London, 1939), p. 629, 815.

Angrist, S. W. and Hepler, L. G., *Order & Chaos* (Basic Books, Inc., New York, 1967), pp. 193–199.

Asimov, I., *Life and Energy* (Bantam Books, New York, 1965), pp. 65–76.

Atkins, P. W., *The Second Law* (Scientific American Books, New York, 1984), pp. 67–79.

Balazs, N. L., 'Les relations d'incertitude d'Heisenberg empechent-elle le démon de Maxwell d'opérer?,' *Comptes Rendus* **236**, 998–1000 (1953).

Balazs, N. L., 'L'effet des statistiques sur le démon de Maxwell,' *Comptes Rendus* **236**, 2385–2386 (1953).

Barrow, J. D. and Tipler, F. J., *The Anthropic Cosmological Principle* (Oxford University Press, New York, 1986), p. 174, 179, 669.

Barrow, J. D., *The World within the World* (Oxford University Press, Oxford, 1988), pp. 127–130.

Bekenstein, J. D., 'Baryon number, entropy, and black hole thermodynamics,' *Ph. D. Dissertation*, Princeton University (May 1972).

Bekenstein, J. D., 'Black-hole thermodynamics,' *Physics Today* **33**, 24–31 (1980).

Bell, D. A., *Intelligent Machines: An Introduction to Cybernetics* (Blaisdell Pub. Co., New York, 1962), pp. 7–10.

Bell, D. A., *Information Theory* (Sir Isaac Pitman & Sons, Ltd., London, 1968), pp. 20–21; 212–219.

Benioff, P., 'Quantum mechanical models of Turing Machines that dissipate no energy,' *Phys. Rev. Lett.* **48**, 1581–1585 (1982).

Benioff, P., 'Comment on "dissipation in computation",' *Phys. Rev. Lett.* **53**, 1203 (1984).

Bennett, C. H., 'Logical Reversibility of Computation,' *IBM J. Res. Dev.* **17**, 525–532 (1973).

Bennett, C. H., 'The thermodynamics of computation—a review,' *Int. J. Theor. Phys.* **21**, 905–940 (1982).

Bennett, C. H., 'Thermodynamically reversible computation,' *Phys. Rev. Lett.* **53**, 1202 (1984).

Bennett, C. H. and Landauer, R., 'The fundamental physical limits of computation,' *Sci. Am.* **253**, 48–56 (July 1985).

Bennett, C. H., 'Demons, engines and the second law,' *Sci. Am.* **257**, 108–116 (1987).

Bennett, C. H., 'Notes on the history of reversible computation,' *IBM J. Res. Dev.* **32**, 16–23 (1988).

Bent, H. A., *The Second Law* (Oxford University Press, New York, 1965), pp. 72–76.

Bhandari, R., 'Entropy, information and Maxwell's demon after quantum mechanics,' *Pramana* **6**, 135–145 (1976).

Bohm, D., *Quantum Theory* (Prentice-Hall, Inc., Englewood Cliffs, New Jersey, 1951), pp. 608–609.

Born, M., 'Die Quantenmchanik und der Zweite Hauptsatz der Thermodynamik,' Annalen der Physik **3**, 107 (1948a).

Born, M. and Green, H. S., 'The kinetic basis of thermodynamics,' *Proc. R. Soc. London* A **192**, 166–180 (1948b).

Boynton, W. P., *Applications of The Kinetic Theory* (Macmillan Co., New York, 1904), pp. 53–54.

Bridgman, P. W., *The Nature of Thermodynamics* (Harper & Brothers, New York, 1961), pp. 155–159.

Brillouin, L., 'Life, thermodynamics, and cybernetics,' *Am. Sci.* **37**, 554–568 (1949).

Brillouin, L., 'Can the rectifier become a thermodynamical demon?,' *Phys. Rev.* **78**, 627–628 (1950a).

Brillouin, L., 'Thermodynamics and information theory,' *Am. Sci.* **38**, 594–599 (1950b).

Brillouin, L., 'Maxwell's demon cannot operate: Information and entropy. I,' *J. Appl. Phys.* **22**, 334–337 (1951a).

Brillouin, L., 'Physical entropy and information. II,' *J. Appl. Phys.* **22**, 338–343 (1951b).

Brillouin, L., *Science and Information Theory* (Academic Press Inc., New York, 1956), Ch. 13.

Brush, S. G., 'James Clerk Maxwell and the kinetic theory of gases: A review based on recent historical studies,' *Am. J. Phys.* **39**, 631–640 (1971).

Brush, S. G., *The Kind of Motion We Call Heat* (North-Holland Publishing Co., New York, 1976a), Ch. 1, 4, 8, 14, 15.

Brush, S. G., 'Irreversibility and indeterminism: Fourier to Heisenberg,' *J. Hist. Ideas* **37**, 603–630 (1976b).

Brush, S. G., *The Temperature of History. Phases of Science and Culture in the Nineteenth Century* (Burt Franklin & Co., Inc., New York, 1978), pp. 65–67.

Campbell, J., *Grammatical Man: Information, Entropy, Language, and Life* (Simon & Schuster, Inc., New York, 1982), Ch. 3.

Carnap, R., *Two Essays on Entropy* (University of California Press, Berkeley, 1977), pp. 72–73.

Chambadal, P., *Paradoxes of Physics* (Transworld Publishers, London, 1971), Ch. IV and V, pp. 80–115.

Chardin, G., 'No free lunch for the Doppler demon,' *Am. J. Phys.* **52**, 252–253 (1984).

Clausing, P., 'Über die Entropieverminderung in einem thermodynamischen System bei Eingriffen intelligenter Wesen,' *Z. f. Physik* **56**, 671–672 (1929).

Costa, J. L., Smyth, H. D. and Compton, K. T., 'A mechanical Maxwell demon,' *Phys. Rev.* **30**, 349–353 (1927).

Costa de Beauregard, O., 'The computer and the heat engine,' *Found. Phys.* **19**, 725–727 (1989).

Costa de Beauregard, O. and Tribus, M., 'Information theory and thermodynamics,' *Helv. Phys. Acta* **47**, 238–247 (1974).

Curzon, F. L. and Ahlborn, B., 'Efficiency of a Carnot Engine at Maximum Power Output,' *Am. J. Phys.* **43**, 22–24 (1975).

Darling, L. and Hulburt, E. O., 'On Maxwell's demon,' *Am. J. Phys.* **23**, 470–471 (1955).

Darrow, K. K., 'The concept of entropy,' *Am. J. Phys.* **12**, 183–196 (1944).

Daub, E. E., 'Maxwell's demon,' *Studies Hist. & Phil. Sci.* **1**, 213–227 (1970).

Davies, P. C. W., *The Physics of Time Asymmetry* (University of California Press, Berkeley, 1974), pp. 53–54; 77.

Davies, P. C. W., *God and the New Physics* (Simon & Schuster, New York, 1983), pp. 211–213.

Davies, P. C. W., *The Ghost in the Atom* (Cambridge University Press, Cambridge, 1986), pp. 20–22.

Demers, P., 'Les demons de Maxwell et le second principe de la thermodynamique,' *Can. J. Research* **22**, 27–51 (1944).

Demers, P., 'Le second principe et la theorie des quanta,' *Can. J. Research* **23**, 47–55 (1945).

Denbigh, K., 'How subjective is entropy?,' *Chem. Brit.* **17**, 168–185 (1981).

Denbigh, K. G. and Denbigh, J. S., *Entropy in Relation to Incomplete Knowledge* (Cambridge University Press, London, 1985), pp. 1–5; 108–112.

Denur, J., 'The Doppler demon,' *Am. J. Phys.* **49**, 352–355 (1981).

Dodge, B. F., *Chemical Engineering Thermodynamics* (McGraw-Hill Book Co., Inc., New York, 1944), pp. 48–49.

Drogin, E. M., 'Maxwell's Demon Lives,' *Defense Electronics*, 31 (March 1986).

Dugdale, J. S., *Entropy and Low Temperature Physics* (Hutchinson University Library, London, 1966), pp. 151–153.

Dutta, M., 'A hundred years of entropy,' *Physics Today* **21**, 75–79 (1968).

Ehrenberg, W., 'Maxwell's demon,' *Sci. Am.* **217**, 103–110 (1967).

Eigen, M. and Winkler, R., *Laws of the Game: How the Principles of Nature Govern Chance* (Harper & Row, Publishers, New York, 1983), pp. 157–160.

El'yashevich, M. A. and Prot'ko, T. S., 'Maxwell's contribution to the development of molecular physics and statistical methods,' *Sov. Phys. – Usp.* **24**, 876–903 (1981).

Elsasser, W. M., *The Physical Foundation of Biology* (Pergamon Press, New York, 1958), pp. 203–214.

Feyerabend, P. K., 'On the possibility of a perpetuum mobile of the second kind.' In P. K. Feyerabend & G. Maxwell, *Mind, Matter, and Method: Essays in Philosophy and Science in Honor of Herbert Feigl*, (University of Minnesota Press, Minneapolis, 1966), pp. 409–412.

Feynman, R. P., 'Quantum Mechanical Computers,' *Found. Phys.* **16**, 507–531 (1986).

Feynman, R. P., Leighton, R. B. and Sands, M., *The Feynman Lectures on Physics – Vol. 1* (Addison-Wesley, Reading, Massachusetts, 1963), pp. 46.1–46.9.

Fine, A., *The Shaky Game: Einstein, Realism, and the Quantum Theory* (University of Chicago Press, Chicago, 1986), pp. 26–39.

Finfgeld, C. and Machlup, S., 'Well-informed heat engine: efficiency and maximum power,' *Am. J. Phys.* **28**, 324–326 (1960).

Frisch, D. H., 'The microscopic interpretation of entropy,' *Am. J. Phys.* **34**, 1171–1173 (1966).

Gabor, D., 'Light and Information,' *Progress in Optics* **1**, 111–153 (1964). Based upon lectures delivered in 1951.

Gabor, D., 'Foreword.' In B. Gal-or, Editor, *Modern Developments in Thermodynamics*, (John Wiley, New York, 1974), p. x.

Gamow, G., *Mr. Tompkins in Paperback* (Cambridge University Press, London, 1971), pp. 95–111. Originally published in *Mr. Tompkins Explores the Atom*, 1944.

Gasser, R. P. H. and Richards, W. G., *Entropy and Energy Levels* (Clarendon Press, Oxford, 1974), pp. 116–119.

Gordon, L. G. M., 'Brownian movement and microscopic irreversibility,' *Found. Phys.* **11**, 103–113 (1981).

Gordon, L. G. M., 'Maxwell's demon and detailed balancing,' *Found. Phys.* **13**, 989–997 (1983).

Grad, H., 'The many faces of entropy,' *Comm. Pure & Appl. Math.* **14**, 323–354 (1961).

Grünbaum, A., 'Is the coarse-grained entropy of classical statistical mechanics an anthropomorphism?' In B. Gal-or, Editor, *Modern Developments in Thermodynamics* (John Wiley, New York, 1974), pp. 413–428.

Haar, D. t., *Elements of Statistical Mechanics* (Rinehart & Co., Inc., New York, 1958), pp. 160–162.

Harman, P. M., *Energy, Force, and Matter: The Conceptual Development of Nineteenth-Century Physics* (Cambridge University Press, London, 1982), p. 8; pp. 139–143.

Harney, R. C., 'Human perception and the uncertainty principle,' *Am. J. Phys.* **44**, 790–792 (1976).

Hartley, R. V. L., 'Transmission of information,' *Bell System Tech. J.* **7**, 535–563 (July 1928).

Hastings, H. M. and Waner, S., 'Low dissipation computing in biological systems,' *BioSystems* **17**, 241–244 (1985).

Hatsopoulos, G. N. and Keenan, J. H., *Principles of General Thermodynamics* (John Wiley & Sons, Inc., New York, 1965), pp. xxxv-xl; 356–362.

Hawking, S., 'The direction of time,' *New Sci.* **115**, No. 1568, 46–49 (1987 – July 9).

Heimann, P. M., 'Molecular forces, statistical representation and Maxwell's demon,' *Studies Hist. & Phil. Sci.* **1**, 189–211 (1970).

Holman, J. P., *Thermodynamics* (McGraw-Hill Book Co., New York, 1969), pp.144–145.

Jacobson, H., 'The role of information theory in the inactivation of Maxwell's demon,' *Trans. N. Y. Acad. Sci.* **14**, 6–10 (1951).

Jammer, M., 'Entropy.' In P. Wiener, Editor, *Dictionary of the History of Ideas, Vol. 2*, (Charles Scribner's Sons, New York, 1973), pp. 112–120.

Jammer, M., *The Philosophy of Quantum Mechanics* (John Wiley, New York, 1974), pp. 479–480.

Jauch, J. M., *Are Quanta Real?* (Indiana University Press, Bloomington, 1973), pp. 103–104.

Jauch, J. M. and Báron, J. G., 'Entropy, information and Szilard's paradox,' *Helv. Phys. Acta* **45**, 220–232 (1972).

Jaynes, E. T., 'Information theory and statistical mechanics,' *Phys. Rev.* **106**, 620–630 (1957a).

Jaynes, E. T., 'Information theory and statistical mechanics. II,' *Phys. Rev.* **108**, 171–190 (1957b).

Jaynes, E. T., 'Information Theory and Statistical Mechanics.' In K. Ford, *Statistical Physics—1962 Brandeis Summer Institute Lectures in Theoretical Physics Vol. 3*, (W. A. Benjamin, Inc., New York, 1963), pp. 181–218.

Jaynes, E. T., 'Gibbs vs. Boltzmann entropies,' *Am. J. Phys.* **33**, 391–398 (1965).

Jaynes, E. T., 'Where Do We Stand on Maximum Entropy?' In R. D. Levine & M. Tribus, *The Maximum Entropy Formalism*, (The MIT Press, Cambridge, Mass., 1979), pp. 15–118.

Jaynes, E. T., 'Entropy and search theory.' In C. Ray Smith and W. T. Grandy, Jr., Editors, *Maximum-Entropy and Bayesian Methods in Inverse Problems*, (D. Reidel Publishing Co., Dordrecht, Holland, 1985a), pp. 443–454.

Jaynes, E. T., 'Generalized Scattering.' In C. Ray Smith and W. T. Grandy, Jr., Editors, *Maximum-Entropy and Bayesian Methods in Inverse Problems*, (D. Reidel Publishing Co., Dordrecht, Holland, 1985b), pp. 377–398.

Jaynes, E. T., 'Macroscopic Prediction.' In H. Haken, Editor, *Complex Systems—Operational Approaches*, (Springer-Verlag, Berlin, 1985c), pp. 254–269.

Jaynes, E. T., 'Clearing up mysteries—The original goal.' In J. Skilling, *Maximum Entropy and Bayesian Methods, Cambridge 1988*, (Kluwer Academic Publishers, Dordrecht, Holland, 1989), pp. 1–27.

Jeans, J. H., *Dynamical Theory of Gases* (Dover Publications, Inc., New York 4th edition, 1925), p. 183.

Jeans, J. H., *An Introduction to the Kinetic Theory of Gases* (Macmillan Co., New York, 1940), p. 271.

Johnson, H. A., 'Thermal noise and biological information,' *Q. Rev. Biol.* **62**, 141–152 (1987).

Jordan, P., 'On the process of measurement in quantum mechanics,' *Phil. Sci.* **16**, 269–278 (1949).

Kauzmann, W., *Thermal Properties of Matter Vol. II Thermodynamics and Statistics: With Applications to Gases* (W. A. Benjamin, Inc., New York, 1967), pp. 209–211.

Kelly, D. C., *Thermodynamics and Statistical Physics* (Academic Press, New York, 1973), pp. 97–101.

Kivel, B., 'A relation between the second law of thermodynamics and quantum mechanics,' *Am J. Phys.* **42**, 606–608 (1974).

Klein, M. J., 'Order, Organisation, and Entropy,' *Brit. J. Phil. Sci.* **4**, 158–160 (1953).

Klein, M. J., 'Maxwell, his demon, and the second law of thermodynamics,' *Am. Sci.* **58**, 84–97 (1970).

Knott, C. G., *Life and Scientific Work of Peter Guthrie Tait* (Cambridge University Press, London, 1911).

Kosloff, R., 'Thermodynamic aspects of the quantum-mechanical measuring process,' *Adv. Chem. Phys.* **46**, 153–193 (1981).

Kubo, R., *Statistical Mechanics* (North-Holland Publishing Co., Amsterdam, 1965), p. 13.

Laing, R., 'Maxwell's demon and computation,' *Phil. Sci.* **41**, 171–178 (1974).

Landauer, R., 'Irreversibility and heat generation in the computing process,' *IBM J. Res. Dev.* **5**, 183–191 (1961).

Landauer, R., 'Uncertainty principle and minimal energy dissipation in the computer,' *Int. J. Theor. Phys.* **21**, 283–297 (1982).

Landauer, R., 'Dissipation in computation,' *Phys. Rev. Lett.* **53**, 1205 (1984a).

Landauer, R., 'Fundamental physical limitations of the computational process.' *Computer Culture: The Scientific, Intellectual, and Social Impact of the Computer, Ann. New York Acad. Sci, 426,* 1984b), pp. 161–171.

Landauer, R., 'Computation and physics: Wheeler's meaning circuit?,' *Found. Phys.* **16**, 551–564 (1986a).

Landauer, R., 'Reversible computation.' In O. G. Folberth & C. Hackl, *Der Informationsbegriff in Technik un Wissenschaft,* (R. Oldenbourg, München, 1986b), pp. 139–158.

Landauer, R., 'Computation: A fundamental physical view,' *Phys. Scr.* **35**, 88–95 (1987a).

Landauer, R., 'Computation: A fundamental physical view,' *Speculations in Science and Technology* **10**, 292–302 (1987b). (Note: Despite the title similarity, this article is distinct from Landauer, 1987a.)

Landauer, R., 'Energy requirements in communication,' *Appl. Phys. Lett.* **51**, 2056–2058 (1987c).

Landauer, R., 'Fundamental physical limitations of the computational process; an informal commentary,' *Cybernetics Machine Group Newsheet (1/1/87)*, (1987d).

Landauer, R., 'Dissipation and noise immunity in computation and communication,' *Nature* **335**, 779–784 (1988a).

Landauer, R., 'Response,' *Appl. Phys. Lett.* **52**, 2191–2192 (1988b).

Landauer, R., 'Response to "The computer and the heat engine",' *Found. Phys.* **19**, 729–732 (1989a).

Landauer, R., 'Computation, measurement, communication and energy dissipation.' In S. Haykin, ed., *Signal Processing,* (Prentice-Hall, Englewood Cliffs, New Jersey, 1989b), pp. 18–47. (Note: Some figures have been printed incorrectly, rotated 90 or 180 degrees.)

Landsberg, P. T., *The Enigma of Time* (Adam Hilger Ltd., Bristol, G.B., 1982), p. 15, 78, 81.

Landsberg, P. T. and Leff, H. S., 'Thermodynamic cycles with nearly-universal maximum-work efficiencies,' *J. Phys. A: Math. Gen.* **22**, 4019–4026 (1989).

Layzer, D., 'Growth of order in the universe,' In Weber, B. H., et al, *Entropy, Information, and Evolution: New Perspectives on Physical & Biological Evolution*, (MIT Press, Cambridge, 1988), pp. 23–39.

Leff, H. S., 'Thermal efficiency at maximum work output: New results for old heat engines,' *Am. J. Phys.* **55**, 602–610 (1987a).

Leff, H. S., 'Available work from a finite source and sink: How effective is a Maxwell's demon?,' *Am. J. Phys.* **55**, 701–705 (1987b).

Leff, H. S., 'Maxwell's demon, power, and time,' *Am. J. Phys.* **58**, 135–142 (1990).

Leff, H. S. and Rex, A. F., 'Resource Letter MD-1: Maxwell's demon,' *Am. J. Phys.* **58**, 201–209 (1990).

Lehninger, A. L., *Bioenergetics: The Molecular Basis of Biological Energy Transformations* (W. A. Benjamin, Inc., New York, 1965), pp. 225–227.

Lerner, A. Y., *Fundamentals of Cybernetics* (Plenum Pub. Corp., New York, 1975), pp. 256–258.

Lewis, G. N. and Randall, M., *Thermodynamics and The Free Energy of Chemical Substances* (McGraw-Hill Book Co., Inc., New York, 1923), pp. 120–121.

Lewis, G. N., 'The symmetry of time in physics,' *Science* **71**, 569–577 (1930).

Likharev, K. K., 'Classical and quantum limitations on energy consumption in computation,' *Int. J. Theor. Phys.* **21**, 311–326 (1982).

Lindblad, G., 'Entropy, information, and quantum measurements,' *Commun. Math. Phys.* **33**, 305–322 (1973).

Lindblad, G., 'Measurements and information for thermodynamic quantities,' *J. Stat. Phys.* **11**, 231–255 (1974).

Lindblad, G., *Non-equilibrium Entropy and Irreversibility* (D. Reidel Publishing Co, Dordrecht, Holland, 1983), pp. 113–122.

Lindgren, K. 'Microscopic and macroscopic entropy,' *Phys. Rev. A* **38**, 4794–4798 (1988).

Loschmidt, J., 'Über den Zustand des Wärmegleichgewichtes eines System von Körpern mit Rücksicht auf die Schwerkraft,' *Sitzungsberichte der Akademie der Wissenschaften, Wien* **73**, 128–142 (1876).

Lotka, A. J., *Elements of Mathematical Biology (Originally published as Elements of Physical Biology)* (Dover Publications, Inc., New York, 1956), pp. 35–40; 121.

Lubkin, E., 'Keeping the entropy of measurement: Szilard revisited,' *Int J. Theor. Phys.* **26**, 523–535 (1987).

Maddox, J., 'Quantum information storage,' *Nature* **327**, 97 (1987).

Maxwell, J. C., Letter to P. G. Tait, 11 December 1867. In C. G. Knott, *Life and Scientific Work of Peter Guthrie Tait* (Cambridge University Press, London, 1911), pp. 213–215.

Maxwell, J. C., 'Letter to J. W. Strutt, 6 December 1870.' In R. J. Strutt, *Life of John William Strutt, Third Baron Rayleigh*, (E. Arnold, London, 1924), pp. 47–48.

Maxwell, J. C., *Theory of Heat* (Longmans, Green, and Co., London, 1871), Ch. 12.

Maxwell, J. C., 'Diffusion,' *Encyclopedia Britannica*, 9th Edition, (New York, 1878), pp. 214–221.

Maxwell, J. C., 'Tait's thermodynamics,' *Nature* **17**, 250 ff (1878). In J. C. Maxwell, *The Scientific Papers of James Clerk Maxwell, Vol. 2*, (Cambridge University Press, London, 1890), pp. 660–671.

Morowitz, H. J., *Energy Flow in Biology* (Academic Press, Inc., New York, 1968), pp. 124–133.

Morowitz, H. J., *Entropy for Biologists* (Academic Press, New York, 1970), pp. 108–111.

Motz, H., 'The Doppler demon exorcised,' *Am. J. Phys.* **51**, 72–73 (1983).

Neumann, J. von. See von Neumann.

Nyquist, H., 'Certain factors affecting telegraph speed,' *Bell System Tech. J.* **3**, 324–346 (April 1924).

Obermayer, K., Mahler, G. and Haken, H., 'Multistable quantum systems: Information processing at microscopic levels,' *Phys. Rev. Lett.* **58**, 1792–1795 (1987).

Pagels, H., *Cosmic Code* (Simon & Schuster, New York, 1982), Part I, Sec. 8.

Pekelis, V., *Cybernetics A to Z* (Mir Publishers, Moscow, 1974), pp. 104–110.

Penrose, O., *Foundations of Statistical Mechanics* (Pergamon Press, Oxford, 1970), pp. 221–238.

Penrose, O., 'Foundations of statistical mechanics,' *Rep. Prog. Phys.* **42**, 1937–2006 (1979).

Peres, A., 'Schrödinger's immortal cat,' *Found. Phys.* **18**, 57–76 (1988).

Pierce, J. R., *Symbols, Signals and Noise* (Harper & Brothers, New York, 1961), pp. 198–207.

Planck, M., *Treatise on Thermodynamics* (Dover Publications, Inc., New York, 1922 (translated from the 7th German edition)), pp. 105–107.

Poincaré, H., 'Mechanism and experience,' *Revue de Metaphysique et de Morale* **1**, 534–537 (1893). Reprinted in S. G. Brush, *Kinetic Theory, Vol. 2. – Irreversible Processes*, (Pergamon Press, Oxford, 1966), pp. 203–207.

Poplavskii, R. P., 'Maxwell demon and the correspondence between information and entropy,' *Sov. Phys. – Usp.* **22**, 371–380 (1979).

Popper, K., 'Irreversibility; or, entropy since 1905,' *Brit. J. Phil. Sci.* **8**, 151–155 (1957).

Popper, K., *The Philosophy of Karl Popper* (Open Court Publishing Co., LaSalle, Illinois, 1974), pp. 129–133; 178–179.

Popper, K. R., *Quantum Theory and the Schism in Physics* (Roman & Littlefield, Totowa, New Jersey, 1982), p. 114.

Porod, W., 'Comment on "Energy requirements in communication",' *Appl. Phys. Lett.* **52**, 2191 (1988).

Porod, W., Grondin, R. O., Ferry, D. K. and Porod, G., 'Dissipation in computation,' *Phys. Rev. Lett.* **52**, 232–235 (1984).

Porod, W., Grondin, R. O., Ferry, D. K. and Porod, G., 'Porod *et al.* respond,' *Phys. Rev. Lett.* **52**, 1206 (1984).

Porter, T. M., *The Rise of Statistical Thinking: 1820–1900* (Princeton University Press, Princeton, 1986), pp. 11–128; 194–219.

Poundstone, W., *The Recursive Universe* (W. Morrow & Co., Inc., New York, 1985), Ch. 3, 5.

Preston, T., *The Theory of Heat* (Macmillan and Co., Ltd., London, 1929), pp. 679–680.

Prigogine, I. and Stengers, I., *Order out of Chaos* (Bantam Books, New York, 1984), p. 175, 239.

Raymond, R. C., 'The well-informed heat engine,' *Am. J. Phys.* **19**, 109–112 (1951).

Raymond, R. C., 'Communication, entropy, and life,' *Am. Sci.* **38**, 273–278 (1950).

Rex, A. F., 'The operation of Maxwell's demon in a low entropy system,' *Am. J. Phys.* **55**, 359–362 (1987).

Robinson, A. L., 'Computing without dissipating energy,' *Science* **223**, 1164–1166 (1984 (16 March)).

Rodd, P., 'Some comments on entropy and information,' *Am. J. Phys.* **32**, 333–335 (1964).

Rosen, R., *Theoretical Biology and Complexity* (Academic Press, Inc., New York, 1985), p. 167.

Rosnay, J. d., *The Macroscope: A New World Scientific System* (Harper & Row, New York, 1975), pp. 130–167.

Rossis, G., 'La logique des expériences de pensée et l'expérience de Szilard,' *Fundamenta Scientiae* **2**, 151–162 (1981a).

Rossis, G., 'Sur la discussion par Brillouin de l'expérience de pensée de Maxwell,' *Fundamenta Scientiae* **2**, 37–44 (1981b).

Rothstein, J., 'Information, measurement, and quantum mechanics,' *Science* **114**, 171–175 (1951).

Rothstein, J., 'Information and Thermodynamics,' *Phys. Rev* **85**, 135 (1952a).

Rothstein, J., 'Organization and entropy,' *J. Appl. Phys.* **23**, 1281–82 (1952b).

Rothstein, J., 'A phenomenological uncertainty principle,' *Phys. Rev.* **86**, 640 (1952c).

Rothstein, J., 'Nuclear spin echo experiments and the foundations of statistical mechanics,' *Am. J. Phys.* **25**, 510–518 (1957).

Rothstein, J., 'Physical demonology,' *Methodos* **42**, 94–117 (1959).

Rothstein, J., 'Discussion: Information and organization as the language of the operational viewpoint,' *Phil. Sci.* **29**, 406–411 (1962).

Rothstein, J., 'Informational Generalization of Entropy in Physics.' In T. Bastin, Editor, *Quantum Theory and Beyond*, (Cambridge University Press, London, 1971), pp. 291-305.

Rothstein, J., 'Loschmidt's and Zermelo's paradoxes do not exist,' *Found. Phys.* **4**, 83–89 (1974).

Rothstein, J., 'Generalized Entropy, Boundary Conditions, and Biology.' In R. D. Levine & M. Tribus, *The Maximum Entropy Formalism*, (The MIT Press, Cambridge, Mass., 1979), pp. 423–468.

Rothstein, J., 'Entropy and the evolution of complexity and individuality,' Ohio State University Report OSU-CISRC-8/88-TR27 1–51 (1988a). Published also in C. Ponnamperuma and F. Eirich, Editors, *Conference Proceedings of the Eighth College Park Colloquium on Chemical Evolution: Prebiological Organization* (A. Deepak Publishing, Hampton, VA, 1990).

Rothstein, J., 'On ultimate thermodynamic limitations in communication and computation.' In F. K. Skwirzynski, Editor, *NATO ASI Series E, Vol. 142: Performance Limits in Communication Theory and Practice*, (Kluwer Academic Publishers, Dordrecht, 1988b), pp. 43–58.

Saha, M. N. and Srivastava, B. N., A *Treatise on Heat* (The Indian Press, Calcutta, 1958), p. 320.

Schrödinger, E., *What is Life?* (Cambridge University Press, London, 1967; published originally in 1944), Ch. 1, 6.

Schweber, S., 'Demons, angels, and probability: Some aspects of British science in the nineteenth century.' In A. Shimony & H. Feshbach, Editors, *Physics as Natural Philosophy: Essays in Honor of Lazlo Tisza on His 75th Birthday* (MIT Press, Cambridge, 1982), pp. 319–363.

Shannon, C. E. and Weaver, W., *The Mathematical Theory of Communication* (University of Illinois Press, Urbana, 1949).

Sherwood, M., *Maxwell's Demon* (New English Library, London, 1976), pp. 93–94.

Silver, R. S., *An Introduction to Thermodynamics* (Cambridge University Press, London, 1971), p. 42, 125.

Silverman, M. P., 'The vortex tube: a violation of the second law?,' *Eur. J. Phys.* **3**, 88–92 (1982).

Singh, J., *Great Ideas in Information Theory, Language and Cybernetics* (Dover Publications, Inc., New York, 1966), Ch. VII.

Skagarstam, B., 'On the mathematical definition of entropy,' *Z. Naturforsch.* **29** a, 1239–1243 (1974).

Skagarstam, B., 'On the notions of entropy and information,' *J. Stat. Phys.* **12**, 449–462 (1975).

Slater, J. C., *Introduction to Chemical Physics* (McGraw-Hill Book Co., Inc., New York, 1939), pp. 9–12; 43–46.

Smith, C. and Wise, M. N., *Energy and Empire: A Biographical Study of Lord Kelvin* (Cambridge University Press, Cambridge, 1989), pp. 620–628.

Smoluchowski, M. v., 'Experimentell nachweisbare der üblichen Thermodynamik widersprechende Molekularphänomene,' *Physik. Z.* **13**, 1069–1080 (1912).

Smoluchowski, M. v., 'Gültigkeitsgrenzen des zweiten Hauptsatzes der Wärmtheorie.' *Vorträge über die Kinetische Theorie der Materie und der Elektrizität,* (Teubner, Leipzig, 1914), pp. 89–121.

Smorodinsky, Y. A., *Temperature* (Mir Publishers, Moscow, 1984), pp. 241–245.

Spielberg, N. and Anderson, B. D., *Seven Ideas that Shook the Universe* (John Wiley & Sons, Inc., New York, 1987), pp. 134–135.

Steiner, L. E., *Introduction to Chemical Thermodynamics* (McGraw-Hill Book Co., Inc., New York, 1941), p. 166.

Sussman, M. V., 'Seeing entropy—the incompleat thermodynamics of the Maxwell demon bottle,' *Chem. Eng. Ed.*, 149–156 (1974)(Summer).

Szilard, L., 'On the extension of phenomenological thermodynamics to fluctuation phenomena,' *Z. f. Physik* **32**, 753–788 (1925). English translation is in B. T. Feld and G. Weiss Szilard, *The Collected Works of Leo Szilard: Scientific Papers,* (MIT Press, Cambridge, 1972), pp. 34–102.

Szilard, L., 'On the decrease of entropy in a thermodynamic system by the intervention of intelligent beings,' *Z. f. Physik* **53**, 840–856 (1929). English translations: *Behavioral Science* **9**, 301–310 (1964); B. T. Feld and G. Weiss Szilard, *The Collected Works of Leo Szilard: Scientific Papers,* (MIT Press, Cambridge, 1972), pp. 103–129; and J. A. Wheeler and W. H. Zurek, *Quantum Theory and Measurement* (Princeton University Press) pp. 539–548.

Tansjö, L., 'Comment on the discovery of the second law,' *Am. J. Phys.* **56**, 179 (1988).

Thomson, W., 'The Kinetic Theory of the Dissipation of Energy,' *Nature* **9**, 441–444 (1874). Reprinted in *Lord Kelvin's Mathematical and Physical Papers – V.5,* (Cambridge University Press, London, 1911), pp. 11–20; and also in Brush, S. G., *Kinetic Theory, Vol. 2 – Irreversible Processes* (Pergamon Press, Oxford, 1966), pp. 176–187.

Thomson, W., 'The Sorting Demon of Maxwell,' *R. Soc. Proc.* **9**, 113–114 (1879). *Lord Kelvin's Mathematical and Physical Papers – V.5,* (Cambridge University Press, London, 1911), pp. 21–23.

Toffoli, R., 'Comment on "Dissipation in computation",' *Phys. Rev. Lett.* **53**, 1204 (1984).

Tribus, M. and McIrvine, E. C., 'Energy and information,' *Sci. Am.* **225**, 179–188 (1971).

Trincher, K. S., 'Information and Biological Thermodynamics.' In L. Kubat and J. Zeman, Editors, *Entropy and Information in Science and Philosophy,* (Elsevier Scientific Pub. Co., New York, 1975), pp. 105–123.

von Neumann, J., *Mathematical Foundations of Quantum Mechanics* (Princeton University Press, Princeton, 1955; published originally in German in 1932), Ch. V.

von Neumann, J., 'Probabilistic logics from unreliable components.' Published originally in C. E. Shannon & J. Mc Carthy, Editors, *Automata Studies* Vol. V, No. 10 (Princeton University Press, Princeton, 1956), pp. 43–98. Reprinted in A. H. Taub, Editor, *J. von Neumann's Collected Works, Vol. V,* 1963). See pp. 341–342.

Waldram, J. R., *The theory of thermodynamics* (Cambridge University Press, London, 1985), pp. 306–308.

Watanabe, S., *Knowing and Guessing: A Quantitative Study of Inference and Information* (John Wiley & Sons, Inc., New York, 1969), pp. 245–254.

Watanabe, S., 'Wiener on cybernetics, information theory, and entropy.' In P. Masani, Editor, *Norbert Wiener: Collected Works with Commentaries*, (MIT Press, Cambridge, 1985), pp. 215–218.

Weber, H. C., *Thermodynamics for Chemical Engineers* (John Wiley & Sons, Inc., New York, 1939), pp. 127–128.

Wehrl, A., 'General properties of entropy,' *Rev. Mod. Phys.* **50**, 221–260 (1978).

Weinberg, A. M., 'On the relation between information and energy systems: A family of Maxwell's demons,' *Interdisciplinary Sci. Rev.* **7**, 47–52 (1982).

Whiting, H., 'Maxwell's demons,' *Science* **6**, 83 (1885).

Wicken, J. S., 'Entropy and information: Suggestions for a common language,' *Phil. Sci.* **54**, 176–193 (1987).

Wiener, N., 'Entropy and information,' *Proc. Symp. Appl. Math. Amer. Math. Soc.* **2**, 89 (1950). In P. Masani, Editor, *Norbert Wiener: Collected Works with Commentaries*, (MIT Press, Cambridge,1985), p. 202.

Wiener, N., 'Cybernetics,' *Scientia* (Italy) **87**, 233–235 (1952). In P. Masani, Editor, *Norbert Wiener: Collected Works with Commentaries*, (MIT Press, Cambridge,1985), pp. 203–205.

Wiener, N., *Cybernetics* (M.I.T. Press, Cambridge, 1961), pp. 57–59.

Wright, P. G., 'Entropy and Disorder,' *Contemp. Phys.* **11**, 581–588 (1970).

Wright, R., *Three Scientists and Their Gods* (Times Books, New York, 1988a), pp. 91–93.

Wright, R., 'Did the universe just happen?,' *The Atlantic Monthly*, pp. 29–44 (1988b) April.

Yockey, H. P., Platzman, R. L. and Quastler, H., *Symposium on Information Theory in Biology* (Pergamon Press, New York, 1958), p. 196.

Yu, F. T. S., *Optics and Information Theory* (John Wiley & Sons, Inc., New York, 1976), Ch. 4, 5, 6.

Zemansky, M. W. and Dittman, R. H., *Heat and Thermodynamics* (McGraw-Hill Book Co., Inc., Sixth Edition, New York, 1981), pp. 297–299.

Zernike, J., *Entropy: The Devil on the Pillion* (Kluwer-Deventer, 1972), Ch. 4.

Zurek, W. H., 'Maxwell's demon, Szilard's engine and quantum measurements.' In G. T. Moore and M. O. Scully, *Frontiers of Nonequilibrium Statistical Physics*, (Plenum Press, New York, 1984a), pp. 151–161.

Zurek, W. H., 'Reversibility and stability of information processing systems,' *Phys. Rev. Lett.* **53**, 391–394 (1984b).

Zurek, W. H., 'Algorithmic randomness and physical entropy. I,' *Phys. Rev. A* **40**, 4731–4751 (1989a).

Zurek, W. H., 'Thermodynamic cost of computation, algorithmic complexity and the information metric,' *Nature* **341** (6238), 119–124 (1989b).

Index

absolute continuity, 166
Adams, Henry, 37, 39
Ahlborn, B, 312
Alekseev, G N, 323
algorithmic entropy, 31, 244–247
Allen, H S, 294
Anderson, B D, 326
Angrist, S W, 7, 306
anthropic principle, 323, 327
Asimov, Isaac, 304
Atkins, P W, 318

Balazs, N L, 298–299
Baron, J G, 16, 25, 27, 115, 160, 173, 179–181,
  249–250, 252, 255, 258
Barrow, J D, 323, 327
Bayes, R T, 173–174
Beckenstein, J D, 115, 309, 315
Bell, D A, 303, 306
Benioff, Paul, 218, 287, 316, 318–319
Bennett, Charles H, 2–3, 8–9, 21–22, 24, 28,
  31, 197, 213, 215, 223, 230, 234, 244, 258,
  261–263, 265, 281, 309, 316, 318–319, 321,
  325, 327, 330
Bent, Henry, 20, 304
Bergson, Henri, 323
Bhandari, R, 313
binomial distribution, 35–36
bistable device, 188–190, 193–194, 238–241,
  326
bit, 2, 13, 15, 18, 28, 117, 143, 192, 227, 235,
  238–239, 243, 249, 275–276, 282–285, 318,
  324, 326
blackbody radiation, 11, 18, 20, 114, 134–135,
  143, 146, 148, 153, 295, 304, 315
black hole, 31, 115, 309, 315
Bohm, D, 297
Bohr, Neils, 107, 271

Boltzmann error, 195
Boltzmann, Ludwig, 20, 22, 44–46, 76, 80–84,
  94, 102, 104–105, 109–115, 151, 162–165,
  271, 290, 294, 300, 305, 317–318
Boltzmann partition function, 252
Boltzmann's mechanical explanation of the
  second law, 78–79
Boole, George, 54
Born, Max, 109, 155, 183, 295–296, 311
Boscovitch, R J, 60–61
Boynton, W P, 291
Bridgman, P W, 98–99, 103, 302
Brillouin, L, 2–3, 7–8, 18–21, 28, 89, 105, 109,
  119–123, 134, 143, 145–146, 160, 173–174,
  181, 183–184, 188, 281, 283, 286, 296–297,
  299, 303–308, 311, 314–316, 322–323
Brownian computer, 219–220, 284–287
Brownian motion, 11, 84, 136, 138, 189, 213,
  219–220, 229, 282, 294, 300, 304
Brush, S G, 308, 313–314
Bumstead, Henry A, 37

Campbell, J, 316
Carnap, Rudolph, 20, 314
Carnot engine, 31, 37, 171, 312
Carnot, Sadi, 76, 80, 85–86, 329
catalysis, 96–98, 103
Chaitin, G, 244–245
Challis, James, 60–61
Chalmers, Thomas, 66
Chambadal, P, 16, 25, 27, 308
Chardin, G, 8, 315, 318
Clapeyron, Emile, 85–86
Clausing, P, 293
Clausius, Rudolph, 6–7, 38, 42–45, 53–58, 60,
  75–84, 109, 115, 162, 173, 175, 177, 291, 311
completeness, 29, 30
Compton effect, 297